THE CALCULUS OF FINITE DIFFERENCES

THE CALCULUS
OF
FINITE DIFFERENCES

BY

L. M. MILNE-THOMSON, C.B.E.

MATHEMATICS RESEARCH CENTER UNITED STATES ARMY,
UNIVERSITY OF WISCONSIN
EMERITUS PROFESSOR OF MATHEMATICS IN THE ROYAL
NAVAL COLLEGE, GREENWICH

LONDON
MACMILLAN & CO LTD
NEW YORK · ST MARTIN'S PRESS
1960

First Edition . . . *1933*
Reprinted . . . *1951*
Reprinted . . . *1960*

MACMILLAN AND COMPANY LIMITED
London Bombay Calcutta Madras Melbourne

THE MACMILLAN COMPANY OF CANADA LIMITED
Toronto

ST MARTIN'S PRESS INC
New York

PRINTED IN GREAT BRITAIN BY
MORRISON AND GIBB LIMITED, LONDON AND EDINBURGH

PREFACE

THE object of this book is to provide a simple and connected account of the subject of Finite Differences and to present the theory in a form which can be readily applied.

Two distinct reasons impelled me to undertake this work. First, in my lectures at Greenwich to junior members of the Royal Corps of Naval Constructors I have occasion to treat certain aspects of difference equations; secondly, the calculation of tables of elliptic functions and integrals, on which I have been recently engaged, gave rise to several interesting practical difficulties which had to be overcome. For both these causes my attention has been directed towards the subject and the lack of a suitable text-book upon which to draw was brought to my notice. The only comprehensive English treatise, namely Boole's *Finite Differences*, is long since out of print, and in most respects out of date. My first idea was to revise Boole's book, but on looking into the matter it appeared that such a course would be unsatisfactory, if not impracticable. I therefore decided to write a completely new work in which not only the useful material of Boole should find a place, but in which room should also be found for the more modern developments of the finite calculus.

My aim throughout has been to keep in mind the needs of the beginner, so that the book may be regarded as suitable for a first course as well as for more advanced reading. I do not, however, believe that the needs of the beginner in a mathematical subject are best served by eschewing all but the most elementary mathematical apparatus. Rather, his interest in the subject may well form an adequate opportunity for enlarging his outlook on the science of mathematics, so that he may the better be enabled to distinguish and appreciate the connection of the whole system and the relative dependency of its several parts. Consequently I have not hesitated to use the mathematical process or terminology which has appeared to me most appropriate to the immediate object in view. On the other hand whenever this course seems to lead beyond the elementary matters, with which all who embark on the reading of a mathematical book must be presumed to be acquainted, I have included the necessary definitions or proofs as part of the text or have given accessible references to treatises which can ordinarily be found in any mathematical library. In this way it has been possible to treat the subject in a simple yet rigorous manner.

The subject-matter falls naturally into two main divisions which may be subsumed under the headings *Interpolation* and *Difference Equations*. The pioneer in interpolation was undoubtedly Briggs, whose work was largely of an arithmetical character. Newton was the originator of the systematic theory and his divided difference formula is really the fundamental basis of all the usual methods of polynomial interpolation. Gregory was probably an independent discoverer in the same field.*

The present work therefore starts with divided differences in Chapter I; and in a general sense Chapters III, IV and VII may be regarded as elaborations of Newton's work. Chapter V on reciprocal differences, describes a method of interpolation, due to Thiele, by means of rational functions, which is more general than polynomial interpolation, and which will possibly be new to many English readers. Chapter VI introduces the generalisations, due to Nörlund, of Bernoulli's polynomials, but here they are treated by a symbolic method, which seemed to me to be as efficacious and in many ways more suitable than Nörlund's method, which is founded upon a different principle. By means of these generalisations the subject of numerical differentiation and integration assumes a unified aspect which hardly seems to be attainable without them. Chapters I to VII therefore form a suitable introductory course and will make very little demand on the reader's previous mathematical knowledge. I have tried to meet the requirements of those who wish to make numerical applications by giving the formulae in a manner suited to direct use with a table of data. The numerical illustrations scattered through these chapters are mainly of a simple kind which can be easily worked, for it is not my purpose to obscure principles by unnecessary arithmetic. The subject-matter of some of these examples is perhaps

---

* See H. W. Turnbull, p. 101, footnote.

of an unusual nature, but this is intentional in order to lend variety to the applications. In the chapters on Interpolation I have followed Steffensen's excellent example in laying much stress on the remainder term, which measures the error committed in using an interpolation formula. Indeed, no formula has been given which is unaccompanied by a means of estimating the remainder.

The part of the book which deals with difference equations begins with Chapter VIII, which expounds Nörlund's method of treating the summation problem. Chapter IX applies these methods to elaborating the theory of the Gamma function. In Chapter X, I have attempted to give a consecutive account of the salient properties of factorial series, which, I hope, will prove interesting in itself. The object of this chapter is to develop the properties of the series in which the solutions of difference equations find their natural expression. Chapter XI discusses the difference equation of the first order ; the linear case is completely elucidated, and certain amenable non-linear forms are treated. This chapter includes an investigation of the exact difference equation of the first order. The methods of this, and of succeeding chapters, are illustrated by simple worked examples in the text. Chapter XII considers the properties of the general linear equation, including the application of generalised continued fractions treated by matrix methods. Chapter XIII deals with the important case of constant coefficients. Here the theory is complete, in the sense that the solution can be explicitly obtained. I have dealt with this equation at some length both by Boole's method and by a method of my own, which seems well adapted to applications of a geometrical or physical nature, and which is analogous to Heaviside's method for differential equations. The linear equation with constant coefficients has recently come into prominence in connection with various physical and mechanical problems ; for example in the theory of Structures. Chapters XIV and XVI develop the solution of linear difference equations with variable coefficients by means of Boole's operators, which I have generalised in order to render the treatment more complete. Chapter XV gives an alternative treatment founded on Nörlund's use of Laplace's transformation. Chapter XVII gives two fundamental theorems of Poincaré and Perron on the asymptotic properties of the solutions of a certain type of linear difference equation. The proof of Perron's theorem is made to depend upon the properties of a certain class of simultaneous linear equations in infinitely many unknowns. The theory is so interesting and so closely connected with finite differences that it has seemed worth while to give Perron's treatment *in extenso*.

Operational and symbolic methods have been freely used throughout the book, and it is hoped that the manner of presentation here given will be found free from the objections often associated with their use. Indeed it has always seemed to me that symbolic methods constitute the essence of the finite calculus. My choice of notations has therefore been made with a view to facilitating the statement and application of operational methods, and to stressing the analogies with the infinitesimal calculus.

In stating theorems I have as far as possible associated the name of the discoverer as sufficient indication of the origin, but it must not be assumed that the method of presentation is in every case that in which the theorem was originally given. Indeed in the case of the work of the older analysts it would be easy, but unprofitable, to point out defects and lack of rigour in many of their proofs.

My labour in correcting the proof sheets has been greatly lightened by Professor H. W. Turnbull, F.R.S., who has read the first proof and made many valuable suggestions both mathematical and historical; and by Dr. A. C. Aitken, F.R.S.E., who has performed the same kindly office, has supplied many original examples, and has verified the numerical work. To both these friends I wish to express my lively thanks for assistance which has helped me to remove many imperfections both of expression and demonstration. For any blemishes which may remain I am solely responsible, but I am led to express the hope that the work will be found to be free from important errors. I take this opportunity of expressing my thanks to the officials of the Glasgow University Press for the ready way in which they have met my somewhat exacting requirements.

L. M. MILNE-THOMSON.

MATHEMATICS DEPARTMENT,
ROYAL NAVAL COLLEGE,
GREENWICH,
July 1933.

CONTENTS

CHAPTER III

INTERPOLATION

CHAPTER IV

NUMERICAL APPLICATIONS OF DIFFERENCES

CHAPTER V

RECIPROCAL DIFFERENCES

CHAPTER VI

THE POLYNOMIALS OF BERNOULLI AND EULER

CHAPTER VII

NUMERICAL DIFFERENTIATION AND INTEGRATION

CHAPTER VIII

THE SUMMATION PROBLEM

CHAPTER IX

THE PSI FUNCTION AND THE GAMMA FUNCTION

CHAPTER X

FACTORIAL SERIES

CHAPTER XI

THE DIFFERENCE EQUATION OF THE FIRST ORDER

CHAPTER XII

GENERAL PROPERTIES OF THE LINEAR DIFFERENCE EQUATION

CHAPTER XIII

THE LINEAR DIFFERENCE EQUATION WITH CONSTANT COEFFICIENTS

CHAPTER XIV

THE LINEAR DIFFERENCE EQUATION WITH RATIONAL COEFFICIENTS. OPERATIONAL METHODS

CHAPTER XV

THE LINEAR DIFFERENCE EQUATION WITH RATIONAL COEFFICIENTS. LAPLACE'S TRANSFORMATION

CHAPTER XVI

EQUATIONS WHOSE COEFFICIENTS ARE EXPRESSIBLE BY FACTORIAL SERIES

CHAPTER XVII

THE THEOREMS OF POINCARÉ AND PERRON

INTRODUCTION

LET $f(x)$ be a given function of the variable x. The Differential Calculus is concerned with the properties of

$$f'(x) = Df(x) = \lim_{\omega \to 0} \frac{f(x+\omega) - f(x)}{\omega},$$

which is still a function of the single variable x. On the other hand the Calculus of Differences is concerned with the properties of

$$\underset{\omega}{\Delta} f(x) = \frac{f(x+\omega) - f(x)}{\omega},$$

which is a function of the two variables x and ω.

More generally, in contrast with the Infinitesimal Calculus, the Finite Calculus is concerned with the values of a function at a set of isolated points and with such properties as may be derivable therefrom.

Suppose then that we are given the numbers $f(x_1), f(x_2), f(x_3), \dots$, and an argument x different from $x_1, x_2, x_3, \dots$. Among the subjects of enquiry which naturally present themselves are the following.

(i) The determination of $f(x)$ from the given functional values. This is the Interpolation problem.

(ii) The determination of

$$f'(x), \quad \int_a^b f(x)dx.$$

These are the problems of Numerical Differentiation and Integration.

Extending our enquiries in another direction we are led to consider the properties of the functions $f(x)$ defined by the equation

$$\frac{f(x+\omega) - f(x)}{\omega} = g(x),$$

where $g(x)$ is a given function. This constitutes the Summation problem, which is analogous to the problem of integration in the Integral Calculus.

On the theory of summation we are able to found in a satisfactory manner the theory of the Gamma function which plays such an important part in the Calculus of Differences.

Consideration of more general relations between $f(x), f(x+\omega), \dots,$ $f(x+n\omega)$ brings us to the study of difference equations, which are analogous to the differential equations of the Infinitesimal Calculus.

NOTATIONS

The following list, which is intended only for reference, contains the symbols, operators, and functions which occur most frequently in this book. The numbers refer to the sections where explanations are given.

Symbols

$\binom{m}{n} = \dfrac{m(m-1)\dots(m-n+1)}{n!}.$

$\phi^{(n)}(x) = \dfrac{d^n}{dx^n}\phi(x).$

$\lim\limits_{x\to a} f(x)$, the limit of $f(x)$ when x tends to a.

$\limsup\limits_{n\to\infty} x_n$, Upper limit, 10·08.

$f(x) \sim g(x)$, 8·22.

$\doteqdot$, symbolic equivalence, 2·41.

$R(x)$, the real part of x, 8·4.

$R_n(x)$, R_n, Remainder Terms, 1·1, 7·11.

$|x|$, arg x, 8·4.

ϖ, Arbitrary Periodic Function, 11·1.

$[x_1 x_2 \dots x_n]$, Divided Difference, 1·0.

$x^{(m\omega)}$
$= x(x-\omega)(x-2\omega)\dots(x-m\omega+\omega)$, 2·11.

$x^{(-m\omega)}$
$= (x+\omega)^{-1}(x+2\omega)^{-1}\dots(x+m\omega)^{-1}$, 2·11.

$\overset{n}{\underset{\omega}{\Delta}} 0^m$, Difference Quotient of Zero, 2·53.

$B_\nu^{(n)}$, Bernoulli's Numbers of order n, 6·1.

$E_\nu^{(n)}$, Euler's Numbers of order n, 6·7.

B_ν, Bernoulli's Numbers, 6·5.

E_ν, Euler's Numbers, 6·8.

$O(z_n)$, 9·8.

Operators

Δ, Difference Operator, 2·0.

δ, $\mu\delta$, Central Difference Operators, 2·01.

$\underset{\omega}{\Delta}$, Difference Quotient Operator, 2·1.

D, Differentiation Operator, 2·1.

$\underset{\omega}{\Delta_x}$, Partial Difference Quotient, 2·105.

$\underset{\omega}{\nabla}$, 2·3.

E^{ω}, 2·4.

P^{-1}, Summation Operator, 2·6.

ρ, ρ_n, Reciprocal Difference, 5·1.

r, r_n, Reciprocal Derivate, 5·8.

$\mathcal{S}$, Sum Operator, 8·0.

π, ρ, 14·01, 14·0.

π_1, ρ_1, 14·03.

Functions

e^x, $\exp x$, Exponential Function.

$B_\nu^{(n)}(x)$, Bernoulli's Polynomial of order n, 6·1.

$B_\nu(x \mid \omega)$, Generalised Bernoulli's Polynomial, 8·16.

$E_\nu^{(n)}(x)$, Euler's Polynomial of order n, 6·7.

$B_\nu(x)$, Bernoulli's Polynomial, 6·5.

$E_\nu(x)$, Euler's Polynomial, 6·8.

$P_m(x)$, Periodic Bernoulli Function, 7·5.

$\mathrm{B}(x, y)$, Beta Function, 9·84.

$\Gamma(x)$, Gamma Function, 9·5.

$\Gamma_1(x)$, Complementary Gamma Function, 9·72.

$\Gamma(x \mid \omega)$, Generalised Gamma Function, 9·66.

$\Psi(x \mid \omega)$, Psi Function, 9·0.

$\Psi(x)$, Psi Function, 9·0.

$F(x \mid \omega)$, Sum Function, 8·0.

$F(a, b\,;\, c\,;\, x)$, Hypergeometric Function, 9·8.

$\Omega(x)$, Factorial Series Sum Function, 10·1.

CHAPTER I

DIVIDED DIFFERENCES

1·0. Definitions. Consider a function $f(x)$ whose values are given for the values $x_0, x_1, x_2, \dots, x_n$ of the variable x. These latter values we suppose to be all different.

The divided difference of $f(x)$ for the arguments x_0, x_1 is denoted by $[x_0x_1]$ and is defined by the relation

$$[x_0x_1] = \frac{f(x_0)-f(x_1)}{x_0-x_1} = \frac{f(x_1)-f(x_0)}{x_1-x_0} = [x_1x_0].$$

Similarly we define the divided difference of arguments x_1, x_2 by

$$[x_1x_2] = \frac{f(x_1)-f(x_2)}{x_1-x_2},$$

and so on.

Two divided differences of two arguments having a common argument can be used to define a divided difference of three arguments. Thus the divided difference $[x_0x_1x_2]$ of the three arguments x_0, x_1, x_2 is defined by

$$[x_0x_1x_2] = \frac{[x_0x_1]-[x_1x_2]}{x_0-x_2} = \frac{[x_0x_1]-[x_2x_1]}{x_0-x_2}.$$

Proceeding in this way we can form divided differences of $n+1$ arguments when we have defined the divided differences of n arguments. Thus *

$$[x_0x_1 \dots x_n] = \frac{[x_0x_1 \dots x_{n-1}]-[x_1x_2 \dots x_n]}{x_0-x_n}.$$

* Other notations are $\delta^n(x_0x_1 \dots x_n)$, $\delta^n f(x)$, $f_n(x_0, x_1, \dots, x_n)$. It will be proved in 1·3 that divided differences are symmetric functions of their arguments so that the order of symbols within the bracket is immaterial.

These results may be exhibited in a scheme of divided differences as follows:

$$
\begin{array}{llllll}
x_0 & f(x_0) & & & & \\
 & & [x_0x_1] & & & \\
x_1 & f(x_1) & & [x_0x_1x_2] & & \\
 & & [x_1x_2] & & [x_0x_1x_2x_3] & \\
x_2 & f(x_2) & & [x_1x_2x_3] & & [x_0x_1x_2x_3x_4] \\
 & & [x_2x_3] & & [x_1x_2x_3x_4] & . \\
x_3 & f(x_3) & & [x_2x_3x_4] & . & . \\
 & & [x_3x_4] & . & . & . \\
x_4 & f(x_4) & . & . & . & \\
. & . & . & . & [x_{n-3}x_{n-2}x_{n-1}x_n] & \\
. & . & . & [x_{n-2}x_{n-1}x_n] & & \\
. & . & [x_{n-1}x_n] & & & \\
x_n & f(x_n) & & & &
\end{array}
$$

1·1. Newton's Interpolation Formula with Divided Differences. Writing x for x_0 we have by definition

$$[xx_1x_2 \dots x_n] = -\frac{[x_1x_2 \dots x_n]}{x - x_n} + \frac{[xx_1 \dots x_{n-1}]}{x - x_n},$$

$$[xx_1 \dots x_{n-1}] = -\frac{[x_1x_2 \dots x_{n-1}]}{x - x_{n-1}} + \frac{[xx_1 \dots x_{n-2}]}{x - x_{n-1}},$$

$$[xx_1 \dots x_{n-2}] = -\frac{[x_1x_2 \dots x_{n-2}]}{x - x_{n-2}} + \frac{[xx_1 \dots x_{n-3}]}{x - x_{n-2}},$$

$$\dots \dots \dots \dots \dots \dots \dots$$

$$[xx_1x_2] = -\frac{[x_1x_2]}{x - x_2} + \frac{[xx_1]}{x - x_2},$$

$$[xx_1] = -\frac{f(x_1)}{x - x_1} + \frac{f(x)}{x - x_1}.$$

By repeatedly substituting for the second member on the right of each identity its value as given by the succeeding identity, we have

$$[xx_1x_2 \dots x_n] = -\frac{[x_1x_2 \dots x_n]}{x - x_n} - \frac{[x_1x_2 \dots x_{n-1}]}{(x - x_n)(x - x_{n-1})}$$

$$-\frac{[x_1x_2 \dots x_{n-2}]}{(x - x_n)(x - x_{n-1})(x - x_{n-2})} - \dots - \frac{[x_1x_2]}{(x - x_n)(x - x_{n-1}) \dots (x - x_2)}$$

$$-\frac{f(x_1)}{(x - x_n) \dots (x - x_2)(x - x_1)} + \frac{f(x)}{(x - x_n) \dots (x - x_1)},$$

or

$$f(x) = f(x_1) + (x - x_1)[x_1x_2] + (x - x_1)(x - x_2)[x_1x_2x_3] + \dots$$
$$+ (x - x_1)(x - x_2) \dots (x - x_{s-1})[x_1x_2 \dots x_s] + \dots$$
$$+ (x - x_1)(x - x_2) \dots (x - x_{n-1})[x_1x_2 \dots x_n]$$
$$+ (x - x_1)(x - x_2) \dots (x - x_n)[xx_1x_2 \dots x_n],$$

or

(1) $$f(x) = f(x_1) + \sum_{s=1}^{n-1} (x - x_1)(x - x_2) \dots (x - x_s)[x_1x_2 \dots x_{s+1}] + R_n(x),$$

(2) where $$R_n(x) = (x - x_1)(x - x_2) \dots (x - x_n)[xx_1x_2 \dots x_n].$$

This is Newton's general interpolation formula with the remainder term $R_n(x)$. The formula is of course a pure identity and is therefore true without any restriction on the form of $f(x)$.

By means of this formula the evaluation of a function $f(x)$ whose value is known for the values $x_1, x_2, \dots, x_n$ of the variable is reduced to the problem of evaluating the remainder term $R_n(x)$. Should this term be known or negligible, the required value $f(x)$ can be calculated from Newton's formula.

It should be observed that no particular rule is laid down for the sequence of the arguments $x, x_1, x_2, \dots, x_n$, which need not be in ascending or descending order of magnitude.

If $f(x)$ be a polynomial of degree $n-1$ in x, then

$$[xx_1] = \frac{f(x) - f(x_1)}{x - x_1}$$

is of degree $n-2$ in x. Hence the operation of taking the divided difference of a polynomial lowers the degree by unity. Consequently the divided difference of the $(n-1)$th order of a polynomial of degree $n-1$ is constant, and therefore the divided difference of the nth order is zero, that is, $[xx_1 \dots x_n] = 0$.

In this case $R_n(x) \equiv 0$, so that the value of $f(x)$ given by the formula

(3) $$f(x) = f(x_1) + \sum_{s=1}^{n-1} (x - x_1) \dots (x - x_s)[x_1x_2 \dots x_{s+1}]$$

is exact.

If $f(x)$ be not a polynomial, we see that

$$R_n(x) = 0, \text{ for } x = x_1, x_2, \dots, x_n,$$

so that the right-hand member of (3) yields the polynomial of degree $n-1$ whose value coincides with the value of $f(x)$ for

$$x = x_1, x_2, \dots, x_n.$$

Example. Find approximately the real root of the equation

$$y^3 - 2y - 5 = 0.$$

Let $$x = y^3 - 2y - 5.$$

This relation defines a function $y=f(x)$. We want the value of $f(0)$. Attributing suitable values to y we obtain the following table of divided differences.

x	$f(x)$			
$-1{\cdot}941$	$1{\cdot}9$			
		$+{\cdot}10627$		
$-1{\cdot}000$	**2·0**		$-{\cdot}0060$	
		+·09425		$+{\cdot}0005$
$+0{\cdot}061$	$2{\cdot}1$		**−·0044**	
		$+{\cdot}08425$		**+·0003**
$+1{\cdot}248$	$2{\cdot}2$		$-{\cdot}0034$	
		$+{\cdot}07582$		
$+2{\cdot}567$	$2{\cdot}3$			

Thus approximately, using (3) above, we have

$$\begin{aligned} y &= 2{\cdot}0 + 1 \times {\cdot}09425 + 1 \times {\cdot}061 \times {\cdot}0044 + 1 \times {\cdot}061 \times 1{\cdot}248 \times {\cdot}0003 \\ &= 2{\cdot}09454. \end{aligned}$$

The corresponding value of x is $-0{\cdot}00013$ and the above value of y is in error by about one unit in the last digit.

1·15. Rolle's Theorem. In order to discuss the form of the remainder term in Newton's formula we need the following theorem known as Rolle's theorem.

If the function $f(x)$ be continuous and differentiable in the interval $a \leqslant x \leqslant b$, where a, b are two roots of the equation $f(x) = 0$, then the equation $f'(x) = 0$ has at least one root interior to the interval (a, b).

Proof. If $f(x)$ have the constant value zero, the theorem is evident. If $f(x)$ be not constantly zero, it will take positive values or negative values. Suppose that $f(x)$ takes positive values. Then

$f(x)$ being continuous will attain a maximum value M for some point ξ such that $a < \xi < b$. Thus, if h be positive,

$$\frac{f(\xi+h)-f(\xi)}{h}$$

is negative or zero and hence the limit when $h \to 0$, namely $f'(\xi)$, cannot be a positive number, that is,

$$f'(\xi) \leqslant 0.$$

Similarly, by considering the ratio

$$\frac{f(\xi-h)-f(\xi)}{-h},$$

we prove that

$$f'(\xi) \geqslant 0.$$

Thus we have $f'(\xi) = 0$ and the theorem is proved. In the same way we prove the theorem for the case when $f(x)$ takes negative values.

1·2. The Remainder Term. From 1·1 (2), we have

$$R_n(x) = f(x) - P_{n-1}(x)$$

where $$P_{n-1}(x) = f(x_1) + \sum_{s=1}^{n-1} (x-x_1) \dots (x-x_s)\,[x_1 x_2 \dots x_{s+1}],$$

so that $P_{n-1}(x)$ is a polynomial of degree $n-1$, and its $(n-1)$th derivate is

(1) $$P_{n-1}^{(n-1)}(x) = (n-1)!\,[x_1 x_2 \dots x_n].$$

Hitherto $f(x)$ has been unrestricted. We now suppose that in the interval (a, b) bounded by the greatest and least of $x, x_1, x_2, \dots, x_n$ the function $f(t)$ of the real variable t, and its first $n-1$ derivates are finite and continuous and that $f^{(n)}(t)$ exists.

Then since $R_n(t)$ vanishes when $t = x_1, x_2, \dots, x_n$, by Rolle's theorem it follows that $R_n'(t)$ vanishes at $n-1$ points of (a, b) and therefore by a second application of the theorem that $R_n''(t)$ vanishes at $n-2$ points of (a, b). Proceeding in this way we see that $R_n^{(n-1)}(\eta) = 0$ where η is some point of (a, b).

Thus $$f^{(n-1)}(\eta) - P_{n-1}^{(n-1)}(\eta) = 0,$$

so that

$$(2) \qquad [x_1 x_2 \ldots x_n] = \frac{f^{(n-1)}(\eta)}{(n-1)!},$$

which is a formula expressing the divided difference of order $n-1$ in terms of the $(n-1)$th derivate of $f(x)$ at some point of (a, b). Hence we have

$$[x x_1 x_2 \ldots x_n] = \frac{f^{(n)}(\xi)}{n!},$$

where ξ is some point of (a, b). We have therefore

$$(3) \qquad R_n(x) = (x-x_1)(x-x_2)\ldots(x-x_n)\frac{f^{(n)}(\xi)}{n!},$$

where ξ is some point of (a, b).

This important result enables us to find an upper limit to the error committed in omitting the remainder term, provided that we can find an upper limit for the nth derivate of $f(t)$ in the interval bounded by the greatest and least of $x, x_1, x_2, \ldots, x_n$.

Example. Find an approximate value of $\log_{10} 4·01$ from the following table :

x	$\log_{10} x$		
4·0002	**0·6020 817**		
		+·108431	
4·0104	·6031 877		**−·0136**
		+·108116	
4·0233	·6045 824		−·0130
		+·107869	
4·0294	·6052 404		

The divided differences are as shewn. Thus approximately

$$\log 4·01 = ·6020817 + ·0098 \times ·108431 + ·0098 \times ·0004 \times ·0136$$
$$= ·6031444,$$

which is correct to seven places.

The error due to the remainder term is of order

$$\frac{·0098 \times ·0004 \times ·0133 \times ·4343 \times 2}{x^3 \times 3!},$$

where x varies between 4·0002 and 4·0294, which is less than 2 in the 10th decimal place. The above value could therefore be affected only by errors of rounding in the seventh place.

1·3. The Divided Differences are Symmetric Functions of the Arguments. By definition

$$[xx_1] = \frac{f(x)}{x-x_1} + \frac{f(x_1)}{x_1-x},$$

so that we obtain without difficulty

$$[xx_1x_2] = \frac{f(x)}{(x-x_1)(x-x_2)} + \frac{f(x_1)}{(x_1-x)(x_1-x_2)} + \frac{f(x_2)}{(x_2-x)(x_2-x_1)}.$$

It is now very easily proved by induction that

(1) $$[xx_1x_2 \dots x_n] = \frac{f(x)}{(x-x_1)(x-x_2)\dots(x-x_n)} + \frac{f(x_1)}{(x_1-x)(x_1-x_2)\dots(x_1-x_n)} + \dots + \frac{f(x_n)}{(x_n-x)(x_n-x_1)\dots(x_n-x_{n-1})}.$$

Clearly the interchange of any two of the arguments does not alter the value of the divided difference, which is therefore a symmetric function of its n arguments.

For example $[xx_1x_2] = [x_1xx_2] = [x_2xx_1]$.

Again $[x_1x_2x_3 \dots x_{n-1}x_nx_{n+1}] = [x_nx_2x_3 \dots x_{n-1}x_1x_{n+1}]$,

so that

(2) $$\frac{[x_1x_2x_3 \dots x_n] - [x_2x_3 \dots x_nx_{n+1}]}{x_1 - x_{n+1}} = \frac{[x_nx_2x_3 \dots x_{n-1}x_1] - [x_2x_3 \dots x_{n-1}x_1x_{n+1}]}{x_n - x_{n+1}} = \frac{[x_1x_2x_3 \dots x_{n-1}x_n] - [x_1x_2x_3 \dots x_{n-1}x_{n+1}]}{x_n - x_{n+1}}.$$

1·31. The divided differences of x^n can be obtained as follows :

from 1·3 (1),

$$[x_1x_2 \dots x_{p+1}] = \sum_{s=1}^{p+1} \frac{x_s^{\,n}}{(x_s-x_1)(x_s-x_2)\dots(x_s-x_{p+1})}.$$

This last is the coefficient of t^{n-p} in the expansion of

$$\sum_{s=1}^{p+1} \frac{x_s^p}{(x_s - x_1)\dots(x_s - x_{s-1})(1 - x_s t)(x_s - x_{s+1})\dots(x_s - x_{p+1})}.$$

But this expression is evidently the result of putting into partial fractions the function

$$(1 - x_1 t)^{-1}(1 - x_2 t)^{-1}\dots(1 - x_{p+1} t)^{-1},$$

and hence * the coefficient of t^{n-p} is the sum of the homogeneous products of degree $n-p$ of $x_1, x_2, \dots, x_{p+1}$.

Thus $$[x_1 x_2 \dots x_{p+1}] = \Sigma\, x_1^{a_1} x_2^{a_2} \dots x_{p+1}^{a_{p+1}},$$

where the summation is extended to all positive integers including zero which satisfy the relation $a_1 + a_2 + \dots + a_{p+1} = n - p$.

For the divided differences of $\frac{1}{x}$ we have

$$[x_1 x_2 \dots x_{p+1}] = \sum_{s=1}^{p+1} \frac{1}{(x_s - x_1)\dots(x_s - x_{s-1})\, x_s (x_s - x_{s+1})\dots(x_s - x_{p+1})},$$

and this is the value when $t = 0$ of

$$-\sum_{s=1}^{p+1} \frac{1}{(x_s - x_1)\dots(x_s - x_{s-1})(t - x_s)(x_s - x_{s+1})\dots(x_s - x_{p+1})},$$

which is obtained by putting into partial fractions

$$\frac{-1}{(t - x_1)(t - x_2)\dots(t - x_{p+1})};$$

so that

$$[x_1 x_2 \dots x_{p+1}] = \frac{(-1)^p}{x_1 x_2 \dots x_{p+1}}.$$

1·4. Lagrange's Interpolation Formula. From 1·3 (1) we have

$$\text{(1)} \qquad f(x) = f(x_1)\frac{(x - x_2)(x - x_3)\dots(x - x_n)}{(x_1 - x_2)(x_1 - x_3)\dots(x_1 - x_n)}$$
$$+ f(x_2)\frac{(x - x_1)(x - x_3)\dots(x - x_n)}{(x_2 - x_1)(x_2 - x_3)\dots(x_2 - x_n)} + \dots$$
$$+ f(x_n)\frac{(x - x_1)\dots(x - x_{n-1})}{(x_n - x_1)\dots(x_n - x_{n-1})} + R_n(x),$$

where $$R_n(x) = (x - x_1)(x - x_2)\dots(x - x_n)[x x_1 x_2 \dots x_n].$$

---

* G. Chrystal, *Algebra*, 2nd edition, (London, 1919), 205.

This is Lagrange's Interpolation Formula with the remainder term $R_n(x)$. Comparing with 1·1 (2) we see that this remainder term is the same as the remainder term in Newton's Formula. It follows that Lagrange's Formula has exactly the same range of application as Newton's and yields identical results.

The formula may also be written in a slightly different form. Write

(2) $$\phi(x) = (x-x_1)(x-x_2)\dots(x-x_n).$$

(3) Then $$f(x) = \sum_{s=1}^{n} \frac{f(x_s)}{x-x_s}\,\frac{\phi(x)}{\phi'(x_s)} + R_n(x).$$

1·5. Expression of Divided Differences by means of Determinants. By a well-known theorem in determinants originally due to Vandermonde and generalised by Cauchy, we have

(1) $$\begin{vmatrix} 1 & 1 & 1 & \dots & 1 \\ a_1 & a_2 & a_3 & \dots & a_n \\ a_1^2 & a_2^2 & a_3^2 & \dots & a_n^2 \\ \cdot & \cdot & \cdot & \dots & \cdot \\ a_1^{n-1} & a_2^{n-1} & a_3^{n-1} & \dots & a_n^{n-1} \end{vmatrix} = \prod_{j>i} (a_j - a_i),$$

where the product expression has $\frac{1}{2}n(n-1)$ factors. This important determinant is usually called an *alternant*.

Now from 1·3 (1),

$$[x_1x_2x_3\dots x_n] = \sum_{s=1}^{n} \frac{f(x_s)}{(x_s-x_1)(x_s-x_2)\dots(x_s-x_{s-1})(x_s-x_{s+1})\dots(x_s-x_n)}$$

$$= \sum_{s=1}^{n} \Big[(-1)^{n-s} f(x_s) \prod_{j>i}{}'(x_j-x_i)\Big] \Big/ \prod_{j>i}(x_j-x_i),$$

where $\Pi'(x_j-x_i)$ means that the value s is not to be ascribed to the suffixes i, j. Now

$$\sum_{s=1}^{n} (-1)^{n-s} f(x_s)\,\Pi'(x_j-x_i)$$

$$= (-1)^{n-1} \begin{vmatrix} f(x_1) & f(x_2) & \dots & f(x_n) \\ 1 & 1 & \dots & 1 \\ x_1 & x_2 & \dots & x_n \\ \cdot & \cdot & \dots & \cdot \\ x_1^{n-2} & x_2^{n-2} & \dots & x_n^{n-2} \end{vmatrix},$$

as is evident when the determinant is expanded by its top row.

Hence rearranging the order of the rows and thereby removing the factor $(-1)^{n-1}$, we get

(2) $[x_1 x_2 x_3 \ldots x_n]$

$$= \begin{vmatrix} f(x_1) & f(x_2) & \ldots & f(x_n) \\ x_1^{n-2} & x_2^{n-2} & \ldots & x_n^{n-2} \\ x_1^{n-3} & x_2^{n-3} & \ldots & x_n^{n-3} \\ \cdot & \cdot & \ldots & \cdot \\ x_1 & x_2 & \ldots & x_n \\ 1 & 1 & \ldots & 1 \end{vmatrix} \div \begin{vmatrix} x_1^{n-1} & x_2^{n-1} & \ldots & x_n^{n-1} \\ x_1^{n-2} & x_2^{n-2} & \ldots & x_n^{n-2} \\ x_1^{n-3} & x_2^{n-3} & \ldots & x_3^{n-3} \\ \cdot & \cdot & \ldots & \cdot \\ x_1 & x_2 & \ldots & x_n \\ 1 & 1 & \ldots & 1 \end{vmatrix}.$$

1·6. Divided Differences expressed by Definite Integrals. We shall prove by induction the following formula, which is due to Hermite :

(1) $$[x_1 x_2 \ldots x_n] = \int_0^1 dt_1 \int_0^{t_1} dt_2 \ldots \int_0^{t_{n-2}} f^{(n-1)}(u_n)\, dt_{n-1}$$

where $$u_n = (1-t_1)\,x_1 + (t_1 - t_2)\,x_2 + \ldots + (t_{n-2} - t_{n-1})\,x_{n-1} + t_{n-1} x_n,$$

and $t_1, t_2, \ldots, t_{n-1}$ are to be treated as $(n-1)$ independent variables, which of course disappear when the repeated definite integral is evaluated.

Proof. When $n = 2$, the right-hand member of (1) becomes

$$\int_0^1 f'((1-t_1)\,x_1 + t_1 x_2)\, dt_1 = \frac{f(x_2) - f(x_1)}{x_2 - x_1} = [x_1 x_2],$$

so that the formula is true when $n = 2$. We assume it to be true for n arguments, and proceed to employ a new x_{n+1} and a further parameter t_n.

Now

$$\int_0^{t_{n-1}} f^{(n)}(u_{n+1})\, dt_n = \frac{f^{(n-1)}((1-t_1)\,x_1 + \ldots + (t_{n-2} - t_{n-1})\,x_{n-1} + t_{n-1} x_n)}{x_n - x_{n+1}}$$
$$- \frac{f^{(n-1)}((1-t_1)\,x_1 + \ldots + (t_{n-2} - t_{n-1})\,x_{n-1} + t_{n-1} x_{n+1})}{x_n - x_{n+1}}.$$

Hence $$\int_0^1 dt_1 \int_0^{t_1} dt_2 \ldots \int_0^{t_{n-1}} f^{(n)}(u_{n+1})\, dt_n$$
$$= \frac{[x_1 x_2 \ldots x_n] - [x_1 x_2 \ldots x_{n-1} x_{n+1}]}{x_n - x_{n+1}}$$

$$= \frac{[x_1x_2 \dots x_n] - [x_2x_3 \dots x_nx_{n+1}]}{x_1 - x_{n+1}} \text{ by 1·3 (2)}$$

$$= [x_1x_2 \dots x_{n+1}],$$

so that the result follows by induction from the case $n = 2$.

1·7. Divided Differences expressed by Contour Integrals. Consider a simple closed contour C enclosing a simply connected region of the complex variable t in which are situated the points $z_1, z_2, \dots, z_n$. Then by Cauchy's Residue Theorem,* if $f(t)$ be holomorphic * throughout this region and on the contour C,

$$f(z) = \frac{1}{2\pi i}\int_C \frac{f(t)}{t-z}\,dt.$$

Again, the residue at $t = z_s$ of the function

$$\frac{f(t)}{(t-z_1)(t-z_2)\dots(t-z_n)} \text{ is } \frac{f(z_s)}{(z_s-z_1)\dots(z_s-z_{s-1})(z_s-z_{s+1})\dots(z_s-z_n)}.$$

Hence †

(1) $$\frac{1}{2\pi i}\int_C \frac{f(t)}{(t-z_1)(t-z_2)\dots(t-z_n)}\,dt = \sum_{s=1}^{n}{}' \frac{f(z_s)}{(z_s-z_1)\dots(z_s-z_n)}$$

$$= [z_1z_2 \dots z_n], \text{ by 1·3 (1)},$$

which is the required expression by a contour integral of the divided difference of order $n-1$ of $f(z)$.

We can use this result to obtain another proof of Newton's general interpolation formula, but with the remainder term now expressed as a contour integral. We have

$$\frac{1}{t-z} = \frac{1}{t-z_1} + \frac{z-z_1}{t-z_1}\,\frac{1}{t-z},$$

$$\frac{1}{t-z} = \frac{1}{t-z_2} + \frac{z-z_2}{t-z_2}\,\frac{1}{t-z},$$

. . . .

* See 8·4 and Whittaker and Watson, *Modern Analysis*, 4th edition, (Cambridge, 1927), 5·2, 6·1, 5·12. This work will be cited in later footnotes as *Modern Analysis*.

† The notation $\sum'$ means that the factor $z_s - z_s$ is excluded from the denominator for $s = 1, 2, \dots, n$.

so that by repeated substitution for $\dfrac{1}{t-z}$ we get the identity

$$\frac{1}{t-z}=\frac{1}{t-z_1}+\frac{z-z_1}{t-z_1}\frac{1}{t-z_2}+\frac{(z-z_1)(z-z_2)}{(t-z_1)(t-z_2)}\frac{1}{t-z_3}+\dots$$
$$+\frac{(z-z_1)(z-z_2)\dots(z-z_n)}{(t-z_1)(t-z_2)\dots(t-z_n)}\frac{1}{t-z},$$

so that

$$\frac{1}{2\pi i}\int_C\frac{f(t)}{t-z}dt=\frac{1}{2\pi i}\int_C\frac{f(t)}{t-z_1}dt+(z-z_1)\frac{1}{2\pi i}\int_C\frac{f(t)}{(t-z_1)(t-z_2)}dt+\dots$$
$$+(z-z_1)(z-z_2)\dots(z-z_n)\frac{1}{2\pi i}\int_C\frac{f(t)}{(t-z_1)\dots(t-z_n)(t-z)}dt,$$

that is

(2) $$f(z)=f(z_1)+(z-z_1)[z_1z_2]+(z-z_1)(z-z_2)[z_1z_2z_3]+\dots$$
$$+(z-z_1)(z-z_2)\dots(z-z_{n-1})[z_1z_2\dots z_n]+R_n(z),$$

where

(3) $$R_n(z)=(z-z_1)(z-z_2)\dots(z-z_n)\frac{1}{2\pi i}\int_C\frac{f(t)}{(t-z_1)\dots(t-z_n)}\frac{dt}{t-z},$$

which is again Newton's general formula. But it should be observed that, while in 1·1 (2) $f(x)$ is unrestricted, in the present case $f(t)$ is an analytic function holomorphic in a certain simply connected region.

1·8. Divided Differences with Repeated Arguments: the Confluent Case. The identities which define the divided differences in 1·0 become indeterminate if two of the arguments coincide. By 1·2 (2) we have

(1) $$[x_1x_2\dots x_n]=\frac{f^{(n-1)}(\eta)}{(n-1)!},$$

where η lies in the interval bounded by the greatest and least of $x_1, x_2, \dots, x_n$. If all these variables coincide with x_1 we take, as the definition of $[x_1x_1\dots x_1]$, the value of the right-hand member, so that for n coincident arguments x_1

(2) $$[x_1x_1\dots x_1]=\frac{f^{(n-1)}(x_1)}{(n-1)!}.$$

The limiting value of a divided difference, which arises when two or more of the arguments coincide, may, with propriety, be called a *confluent divided difference* arising from the *confluence* of the arguments in question.*

Provided that we write the difference scheme in such a way that all the arguments coincident with a given value occur in a single group, we can form a complete scheme of divided differences by the use of (2) above and the definitions of 1·0 without encountering indeterminate forms. Thus

$$\begin{array}{lllll}
x_1 & f(x_1) & & & \\
 & & f'(x_1) & & \\
x_1 & f(x_1) & & \tfrac{1}{2}f''(x_1) & \\
 & & f'(x_1) & & \tfrac{1}{6}f'''(x_1) \\
x_1 & f(x_1) & & \tfrac{1}{2}f''(x_1) & \\
 & & f'(x_1) & & [x_1x_1x_1x_2] \\
x_1 & f(x_1) & & [x_1x_1x_2] & \\
 & & [x_1x_2] & & [x_1x_1x_2x_2] \\
x_2 & f(x_2) & & [x_1x_2x_2] & \\
 & & f'(x_2) & & [x_1x_2x_2x_2] \\
x_2 & f(x_2) & & \tfrac{1}{2}f''(x_2) & \\
 & & f'(x_2) & & [x_2x_2x_2x_3] \\
x_2 & f(x_2) & & [x_2x_2x_3] & \\
 & & [x_2x_3] & & \\
x_3 & f(x_3) & & &
\end{array}$$

In this scheme, for example,

$$[x_1x_1x_2] = \frac{f'(x_1) - [x_1x_2]}{x_1 - x_2},$$

which is perfectly determinate.

In the case where all the arguments $x_1, x_2, \ldots, x_n$ coincide with x_1, Newton's formula 1·1 (1) yields Taylor's expansion, namely,

$$f(x) = f(x_1) + (x - x_1) f'(x_1) + \frac{(x-x_1)^2}{2!} f''(x_1) + \ldots$$

$$+ \frac{(x-x_1)^{n-1}}{(n-1)!} f^{(n-1)}(x_1) + R_n(x),$$

* cf. *Modern Analysis*, 10·5.

$$R_n(x) = \frac{(x-x_1)^n}{n!} f^{(n)}(\xi),$$

where ξ lies in the interval (x, x_1).

It should be noted that confluent divided differences can only be formed if $f(x)$ possess the necessary derivates.

To obtain a formula for $[x_1 \dots x_n]$ when n_1 arguments are equal to x_1, n_2 arguments are equal to x_2, ..., n_p arguments are equal to x_p, we use 1·7 (1), which gives the interpretation

$$[x_1 x_1 \dots x_p x_p] = \frac{1}{2\pi i}\int_C \frac{f(t)\,dt}{(t-x_1)^{n_1} \dots (t-x_p)^{n_p}} =$$

$$\frac{1}{(n_1-1)!}\frac{1}{(n_2-1)!}\cdots\frac{1}{(n_p-1)!}\frac{1}{2\pi i}\frac{\partial^{n_1-1}}{\partial x_1^{n_1-1}}\cdots\frac{\partial^{n_p-1}}{\partial x_p^{n_p-1}}\int_C \frac{f(t)\,dt}{(t-x_1)\dots(t-x_p)}$$

$$(3) \quad = \frac{1}{(n_1-1)!}\frac{1}{(n_2-1)!}\cdots\frac{1}{(n_p-1)!}\frac{\partial^{n_1+n_2+\dots+n_p-p}}{\partial x_1^{n_1-1}\dots\partial x_p^{n_p-1}}[x_1 x_2 \dots x_p].$$

If all the n arguments coincide with x_1, we have

$$[x_1 x_1 \dots x_1] = \frac{1}{2\pi i}\int_C \frac{f(t)}{(t-x_1)^n}\,dt = \frac{f^{n-1}(x_1)}{(n-1)!}$$

in agreement with (2) above.

1·9. Interpolation Polynomials. A polynomial of degree $n-1$ at most, whose values at the points $x_1, x_2, \dots, x_n$ are the same as the values of given function $f(x)$ at these points is called an interpolation polynomial of $f(x)$. If $I_{n-1}(x)$ denote such a polynomial, we have at once from Lagrange's interpolation formula 1·4 (3),

$$(1) \qquad I_{n-1}(x) = \sum_{s=1}^{n} \frac{I_{n-1}(x_s)}{x-x_s}\frac{\phi(x)}{\phi'(x_s)} = \sum_{s=1}^{n}\frac{f(x_s)}{x-x_s}\frac{\phi(x)}{\phi'(x_s)}$$

where $\qquad \phi(x) = (x-x_1)\dots(x-x_n).$

It is clear from this result that the degree of $I_{n-1}(x)$ is at most $n-1$.

Only one such polynomial with given agreement can exist, for if $J_{n-1}(x)$ denote a second polynomial with the same agreement, the polynomial $I_{n-1}(x) - J_{n-1}(x)$, which is of degree $n-1$ at most, has n zeros $x_1, x_2, \dots, x_n$ and therefore must vanish identically.

To recover the interpolation formula from which (1) was derived we have simply to add the remainder term

$$R_n(x) = (x-x_1)(x-x_2)\dots(x-x_n)\,[x x_1 x_2 \dots x_n].$$

Thus we have

$$f(x) = I_{n-1}(x) + R_n(x).$$

Since Newton's interpolation formula has the same remainder term as the formula of Lagrange, we have, from 1·1 (1), the alternative expression

(2) $$I_{n-1}(x) = f(x_1) + \sum_{s=1}^{n-1} (x-x_1)(x-x_2)\dots(x-x_s)[x_1x_2\dots x_{s+1}].$$

For example, if $n = 3$,

$$I_2(x) = f(x_1) + (x-x_1)[x_1x_2] + (x-x_1)(x-x_2)[x_1x_2x_3].$$

It should be observed that an interpolation polynomial, being fixed by the values of the function at the given points, does not depend on the order in which these points are considered. Thus if we take the four points x_{-1}, x_0, x_1, x_2 in turn in the orders

$$x_0, x_1, x_{-1}, x_2 \quad \text{and} \quad x_1, x_0, x_2, x_{-1}$$

we have the two expressions

$$I_3(x) = f(x_0) + (x-x_0)[x_0x_1] + (x-x_0)(x-x_1)[x_0x_1x_{-1}]$$
$$+ (x-x_0)(x-x_1)(x-x_{-1})[x_0x_1x_{-1}x_2],$$

$$I_3(x) = f(x_1) + (x-x_1)[x_1x_0] + (x-x_1)(x-x_0)[x_1x_0x_2]$$
$$+ (x-x_1)(x-x_0)(x-x_2)[x_1x_0x_2x_{-1}].$$

Adding these expressions and dividing by 2, we have

(3) $$I_3(x) = \tfrac{1}{2}\{f(x_0)+f(x_1)\} + (x-\tfrac{1}{2}x_0-\tfrac{1}{2}x_1)[x_0x_1]$$
$$+ (x-x_0)(x-x_1)\tfrac{1}{2}\{[x_{-1}x_0x_1]+[x_0x_1x_2]\}$$
$$+ (x-x_0)(x-x_1)(x-\tfrac{1}{2}x_{-1}-\tfrac{1}{2}x_2)[x_{-1}x_0x_1x_2],$$

which employs the divided differences shown in the scheme

x_{-1}				
x_0	$f(x_0)$		$[x_{-1}x_0x_1]$	
		$[x_0x_1]$		$[x_{-1}x_0x_1x_2]$
x_1	$f(x_1)$		$[x_0x_1x_2]$	
x_2				

From $I_3(x)$ we could obtain an interpolation formula by adding the remainder term

$$R_4(x) = (x-x_{-1})(x-x_0)(x-x_1)(x-x_2)[xx_{-1}x_0x_1x_2].$$

Again by taking five points $x_{-2}, x_{-1}, x_0, x_1, x_2$ in each of the orders $x_0, x_{-1}, x_1, x_{-2}, x_2$ and $x_0, x_1, x_{-1}, x_2, x_{-2}$ we obtain two expressions for $I_4(x)$ whose arithmetic mean gives

$$(4) \qquad \begin{aligned} I_4(x) = f(x_0) &+ (x-x_0)\tfrac{1}{2}\{[x_{-1}x_0]+[x_0x_1]\} \\ &+ (x-x_0)(x-\tfrac{1}{2}x_{-1}-\tfrac{1}{2}x_1)[x_{-1}x_0x_1] \\ &+ (x-x_{-1})(x-x_0)(x-x_1)\tfrac{1}{2}\{[x_{-2}x_{-1}x_0x_1]+[x_{-1}x_0x_1x_2]\} \\ &+ (x-x_{-1})(x-x_0)(x-x_1)(x-\tfrac{1}{2}x_{-2}-\tfrac{1}{2}x_2)[x_{-2}x_{-1}x_0x_1x_2], \end{aligned}$$

which employs the divided differences in the scheme

x_{-2}	•				
		•			
x_{-1}	•		•		
		$[x_{-1}x_0]$		$[x_{-2}x_{-1}x_0x_1]$	
x_0	$f(x_0)$		$[x_{-1}x_0x_1]$		$[x_{-2}x_{-1}x_0x_1x_2]$
		$[x_0x_1]$		$[x_{-1}x_0x_1x_2]$	
x_1	•				
		•			
x_2	•				

From $I_4(x)$ we could obtain an interpolation formula by adding $R_5(x)$.

The above results, (3) and (4), are also due to Newton. They can easily be extended to include divided differences of any order, the form (3) being taken if n be even and the form (4) if n be odd.

Returning to (2), if two or more of the arguments coincide we obtain a *confluent* interpolation polynomial. Thus if $n = 4$, with the arguments x_1, x_1, x_2, x_3, we obtain

$$\begin{aligned} I_3(x) &= f(x_1)+(x-x_1)[x_1x_1]+(x-x_1)^2[x_1x_1x_2] \\ &\qquad +(x-x_1)^2(x-x_2)[x_1x_1x_2x_3] \\ &= f(x_1)+(x-x_1)f'(x_1)+(x-x_1)^2\frac{\partial}{\partial x_1}[x_1x_2] \\ &\qquad +(x-x_1)^2(x-x_2)\frac{\partial}{\partial x_1}[x_1x_2x_3], \end{aligned}$$

so that, in this case,

$$I_3(x_1) = f(x_1), \quad I_3'(x_1) = f'(x_1).$$

It is easily seen, in the same way, that if ν arguments coincide with x_1, then

$$(5) \qquad f^{(s)}(x_1) = I_n^{(s)}(x_1), \quad s = 0, 1, \dots, \nu - 1,$$

and the polynomial may be said to have agreement of order ν with the function $f(x)$ at the point x_1. In this way we can construct polynomials having arbitrarily assigned orders of agreement with the function at given points. Thus the confluent interpolation polynomial of degree 4, which has agreement of order 3 at x_1 and of order 2 at x_2, is

$$\begin{aligned} I_4(x) &= f(x_1) + (x - x_1)[x_1x_1] + (x - x_1)^2 [x_1x_1x_1] \\ &\qquad + (x - x_1)^3 [x_1x_1x_1x_2] + (x - x_1)^3 (x - x_2)[x_1x_1x_1x_2x_2] \\ &= f(x_1) + (x - x_1) f'(x_1) + (x - x_1)^2 \frac{1}{2!} f''(x_1) \\ &\qquad + (x - x_1)^3 \frac{1}{2!} \frac{\partial^2}{\partial x_1^2} [x_1x_2] + (x - x_1)^3 (x - x_2) \frac{1}{2!} \frac{\partial^3}{\partial x_1^2 \partial x_2} [x_1x_2]. \end{aligned}$$

That this polynomial has agreement of order 3 at x_1 is obvious. That the agreement is of order 2 at x_2 is equally obvious if we observe that the polynomial could have been written down in an alternative form with the arguments taken in the order $x_2x_2x_1x_1x_1$.

EXAMPLES I

1. Shew that the divided differences of $f(x) + \phi(x)$ are the sums of the corresponding divided differences of $f(x)$ and of $\phi(x)$.

2. Shew that the divided differences of $c\,f(x)$ where c is a constant are c times the corresponding divided differences of $f(x)$.

3. If the arguments be each multiplied by the same constant c, while the tabular values remain unchanged, shew that the divided difference $[x_1x_2 \dots x_{n+1}]$ is multiplied by c^{-n}.

4. Shew that the divided differences of $f(x)$ are unaltered if the arguments be each increased by the same constant c, while the corresponding tabular values are left unchanged.

5. Form the divided differences of the polynomial

$$a_0 x^n + a_1 x^{n-1} + \dots + a_n.$$

6. Prove that

$$[x_1 x_2 \dots x_n] = \int \dots \int f^{(n-1)}(t_1 x_1 + t_2 x_2 + \dots + t_n x_n)\, dt_1\, dt_2 \dots dt_n,$$

where the integration is extended to all positive values, including zero, which satisfy $t_1 + t_2 + \dots + t_n = 1$. [Genocchi.]

7. With the notation of 1·8 (3) shew that

$$[x_1 x_1 \dots x_p x_p] = \int_0^1 dt_1 \int_0^{t_1} dt_2 \dots \int_0^{t_{p-2}} \phi(t)\, f^{(n-1)}(y)\, dt_{p-1},$$

where

$$y = (1 - t_1)\, x_1 + (t_1 - t_2)\, x_2 + \dots + (t_{p-2} - t_{p-1})\, x_{p-1} + t_{p-1}\, x_p,$$

$$\phi(t) = \frac{(1-t_1)^{n_1-1}(t_1-t_2)^{n_2-1} \dots (t_{p-2}-t_{p-1})^{n_{p-1}-1}\, t_{p-1}^{n_p-1}}{(n_1-1)!\,(n_2-1)! \dots (n_p-1)!}.$$

8. If

$$L_r(x) = \frac{(x-x_1)(x-x_2)\dots(x-x_{r-1})(x-x_{r+1})\dots(x-x_n)}{(x_r-x_1)(x_r-x_2)\dots(x_r-x_{r-1})(x_r-x_{r+1})\dots(x_r-x_n)},$$

$$r = 1, 2, \dots, n,$$

prove that

$$L_1(x) + L_2(x) + \dots + L_n(x) = 1,$$

$$(x_1 - x)^{\nu} L_1(x) + (x_2 - x)^{\nu} L_2(x) + \dots + (x_n - x)^{\nu} L_n(x) = 0,$$

$$\nu = 1, 2, 3, \dots, n-1.$$

9. Prove that the function

$$1 + \frac{t-a}{a-b} + \frac{(t-a)(t-b)}{(a-b)(a-c)} + \dots$$

becomes unity when $t = a$, and zero when $t = b, c, \dots$.

Hence with the notation of example 8, prove that

$$L_1(x) = 1 + \frac{x-x_1}{x_1-x_2} + \frac{(x-x_1)(x-x_2)}{(x_1-x_2)(x_1-x_3)} + \dots + \frac{(x-x_1)\dots(x-x_{n-1})}{(x_1-x_2)\dots(x_1-x_n)},$$

with similar expressions for $L_2(x)$, $L_3(x)$, ...

10. Deduce Lagrange's form of the interpolation polynomial from the rule for resolving

$$\frac{f(x)}{(x-x_1)(x-x_2)\dots(x-x_n)}$$

into partial fractions.

11. Find the polynomial of the lowest possible degree which assumes the values 3, 12, 15, -21 when x has the values 3, 2, 1, -1 respectively.

12. Three observations u_a, u_b, u_c of a quantity u_x are taken near a maximum or minimum. Shew that the value of x at the maximum or minimum is approximately

$$\frac{(b^2-c^2)\,u_a+(c^2-a^2)\,u_b+(a^2-b^2)\,u_c}{2\{(b-c)\,u_a+(c-a)\,u_b+(a-b)\,u_c\}}.$$

13. The values of a function at $m+n$ points are given. Prove that a rational function, whose numerator is of degree $m-1$ and whose denominator is of degree n, may be found, which assumes the $m+n$ given values at the given points. [Cauchy.]

14. If $m=2$, $n=1$, prove that the rational function of example 13, which assumes the values u_a, u_b, u_c at the points a, b, c, is

$$\frac{-u_bu_c(b-c)(x-a)-u_cu_a(c-a)(x-b)-u_au_b(a-b)(x-c)}{u_a(b-c)(x-a)+u_b(c-a)(x-b)+u_c(a-b)(x-c)}.$$

15. If the function

$$u(x)=A_0+(A_1\cos x+B_1\sin x)+\dots+(A_n\cos nx+B_n\sin nx)$$

assume the values $u_1, u_2, \dots, u_{2n+1}$ when $x=x_1, x_2, \dots, x_{2n+1}$, prove that

$$u(x)=\sum_{s=1}^{2n+1}\frac{\sin\frac{1}{2}(x-x_1)\sin\frac{1}{2}(x-x_2)\dots\sin\frac{1}{2}(x-x_{2n+1})}{\sin\frac{1}{2}(x_s-x_1)\sin\frac{1}{2}(x_s-x_2)\dots\sin\frac{1}{2}(x_s-x_{2n+1})}\,u_s,$$

the factor which becomes indeterminate when $x=x_s$ being omitted in each term of the sum. [Gauss.]

16. By means of 1·5 (2) express the confluent divided difference $[aabc]$ in the form

$$\begin{vmatrix} f(a) & f'(a) & f(b) & f(c) \\ a^2 & 2a & b^2 & c^2 \\ a & 1 & b & c \\ 1 & 0 & 1 & 1 \end{vmatrix} \div \begin{vmatrix} a^3 & 3a^2 & b^3 & c^3 \\ a^2 & 2a & b^2 & c^2 \\ a & 1 & b & c \\ 1 & 0 & 1 & 1 \end{vmatrix}.$$

17. Express the confluent divided difference $[aaabbc]$ as the quotient of two six row determinants.

18. From the confluence of the n arguments in 1·5 (2) deduce the formula 1·8 (2).

CHAPTER II

DIFFERENCE OPERATORS

2·0. Difference Notation. Let Δx be an increment of the variable x. The corresponding increment of a function * $u(x)$ is then given by

$$\Delta u(x) = u(x+\Delta x) - u(x).$$

This increment $\Delta u(x)$ is called the *first difference* of $u(x)$ with respect to the increment Δx. The most important case arises when the increment Δx is constant. Denoting this constant by ω we have for the first difference of $u(x)$

$$(1) \qquad \Delta u(x) = u(x+\omega) - u(x).$$

The result of performing the operation denoted by the operator Δ is still a function of x on which the operation may be repeated. We thus obtain the *second difference*

$$\Delta^2 u(x) = \Delta[\Delta u(x)] = [u(x+2\omega) - u(x+\omega)] - [u(x+\omega) - u(x)]$$

$$(2) \quad \Delta^2 u(x) = u(x+2\omega) - 2u(x+\omega) + u(x).$$

Proceeding in this way we can form the third, fourth, ..., nth differences, namely,

$$\Delta^3 u(x), \quad \Delta^4 u(x), \dots, \quad \Delta^n u(x),$$

by means of the relation

$$\Delta^s u(x) = \Delta[\Delta^{s-1} u(x)].$$

We find, for example, that

$$\Delta x^3 = 3x^2\omega + 3x\omega^2 + \omega^3,$$

$$\Delta^2 x^3 = 6x\omega^2 + 6\omega^3,$$

$$\Delta^3 x^3 = 6\omega^3,$$

$$\Delta^4 x^3 = 0.$$

---

* We shall denote a function of x by $u(x)$ or by u_x according to convenience.

The successive differences of a tabulated function are easily formed by simple subtraction. Thus for the function x^3 we have

x	x^3	Δ	Δ^2	Δ^3	Δ^4
0	0				
		1			
1	1		6		
		7		6	
2	8		12		0
		19		6	
3	27		18		0
		37		6	
4	64		24		
		61			
5	125				

More generally, if we denote the functional value $u(a+s\omega)$ by u_s, we have the scheme

Argument	Function					
$a-2\omega$	u_{-2}					
		Δu_{-2}				
$a-\omega$	u_{-1}		$\Delta^2 u_{-2}$			
		Δu_{-1}		$\Delta^3 u_{-2}$		
a	u_0		$\Delta^2 u_{-1}$		$\Delta^4 u_{-2}$	
		Δu_0		$\Delta^3 u_{-1}$		$\Delta^5 u_{-2}$
$a+\omega$	u_1		$\Delta^2 u_0$		$\Delta^4 u_{-1}$	
		Δu_1		$\Delta^3 u_0$		
$a+2\omega$	u_2		$\Delta^2 u_1$			
		Δu_2				
$a+3\omega$	u_3					

where each entry in a vertical difference column is obtained by subtracting the upper entry immediately to the left from the lower entry immediately to the left.

By adjoining further functional values we can extend the scheme as far as desired. Inspection of the scheme shews that to form a fifth difference six consecutive tabular entries are required. Similarly, to form a difference of the nth order, $n+1$ consecutive tabular entries are necessary. In the above scheme the differences Δu_0, $\Delta^2 u_0$, $\Delta^3 u_0, \ldots$, which lie on a line sloping diagonally downwards from u_0, are called descending, or forward, differences of u_0. The differences Δu_{-1}, $\Delta^2 u_{-2}, \ldots$, which lie on a line sloping diagonally upwards from u_0 are called ascending, or backward, differences of u_0.

2·01. Central Difference Notation. If we introduce the operator δ defined by

$$\delta^{2n} u_k = \Delta^{2n} u_{k-n},$$

$$\delta^{2n+1} u_{k+\frac{1}{2}} = \Delta^{2n+1} u_{k-n},$$

the difference scheme of the last section becomes

$a-2\omega$	u_{-2}					
		$\delta u_{-\frac{3}{2}}$				
$a-\omega$	u_{-1}		$\delta^2 u_{-1}$			
		$\delta u_{-\frac{1}{2}}$		$\delta^3 u_{-\frac{1}{2}}$		
a	u_0		$\delta^2 u_0$		$\delta^4 u_0$	
		$\delta u_{\frac{1}{2}}$		$\delta^3 u_{\frac{1}{2}}$		$\delta^5 u_{\frac{1}{2}}$
$a+\omega$	u_1		$\delta^2 u_1$		$\delta^4 u_1$	
		$\delta u_{\frac{3}{2}}$		$\delta^3 u_{\frac{3}{2}}$		
$a+2\omega$	u_2		$\delta^2 u_2$			
		$\delta u_{\frac{5}{2}}$				
$a+3\omega$	u_3					

The operator * δ is the *central difference operator* and the differences in the above table are known as *central differences.* It should be carefully observed that the numbers in the above difference scheme are the same as the numbers in the corresponding *positions* in the scheme of 2·0. The two schemes differ only in the *notations.* It will be seen that $\delta u_{\frac{1}{2}} = u_1 - u_0$, $\delta^2 u_0 = \delta u_{\frac{1}{2}} - \delta u_{-\frac{1}{2}}$, and so on. The differences in the same horizontal line with u_k are labelled with the suffix k. Those on the horizontal line between u_k and u_{k+1} are labelled with the suffix $k+\frac{1}{2}$. The notation of central differences is useful for the compact description of certain interpolation and other formulae. The arithmetic mean of successive

* This notation is due to W. F. Sheppard, *Proc. Lond. Math. Soc.* 31 (1899), 459.

differences in the same vertical column is denoted by $\mu\delta^r$ and is labelled with the arithmetic mean of the suffixes of the entries from which this expression arises.

Thus

$$\tfrac{1}{2}(\delta u_{-\frac{1}{2}}+\delta u_{\frac{1}{2}}) = \mu\delta u_0,$$

$$\tfrac{1}{2}(\delta^2 u_0+\delta^2 u_1) = \mu\delta^2 u_{\frac{1}{2}}.$$

When these are entered in the difference table the lines a, $a+\omega$, and the line between, will have the following appearance.

a	u_0	$\mu\delta u_0$	$\delta^2 u_0$	$\mu\delta^3 u_0$	$\delta^4 u_0$		$\dots,$
	$\mu u_{\frac{1}{2}}$	$\delta u_{\frac{1}{2}}$	$\mu\delta^2 u_{\frac{1}{2}}$	$\delta^3 u_{\frac{1}{2}}$	$\mu\delta^4 u_{\frac{1}{2}}$		$\dots,$
$a+\omega$	u_1	$\mu\delta u_1$	$\delta^2 u_1$	$\mu\delta^3 u_1$	$\delta^4 u_1$		$\dots,$

where $\mu u_{\frac{1}{2}}$ denotes $\frac{1}{2}(u_0+u_1)$.

Another notation, originally due to Gauss, for central differences is (m, n) where m denotes the row, and n the order, thus

$$\delta^2 u_0 = (0, 2), \quad \delta^5 u_{\frac{1}{2}} = (\tfrac{1}{2}, 5).$$

2·1. Difference Quotients. The notations of differences explained in the preceding sections, while of the greatest practical utility, do not sufficiently unmask the close analogy between the finite and the infinitesimal calculus. We now introduce Nörlund's operator $\underset{\omega}{\Delta}$, which is defined by the relation

(1) $$\underset{\omega}{\Delta} u(x) = \frac{u(x+\omega)-u(x)}{\omega}.$$

We call $\underset{\omega}{\Delta} u(x)$, which is evidently a divided difference, the *first difference quotient* of $u(x)$. This symbol has the advantage that

(2) $$\lim_{\omega\to 0} \underset{\omega}{\Delta} u(x) = D\,u(x),$$

where D denotes the operator of differentiation, in this case d/dx.

The operation can be repeated, thus

(3) $$\overset{2}{\underset{\omega}{\Delta}} u(x) = \underset{\omega}{\Delta}[\underset{\omega}{\Delta} u(x)] = \frac{\underset{\omega}{\Delta} u(x+\omega)-\underset{\omega}{\Delta} u(x)}{\omega}$$

$$= \frac{u(x+2\omega)-2u(x+\omega)+u(x)}{\omega^2},$$

and generally for the nth difference quotient

$$\overset{n}{\underset{\omega}{\Delta}} u(x) = \underset{\omega}{\Delta}\left[\overset{n-1}{\underset{\omega}{\Delta}} u(x)\right].$$

From this we infer the useful relation

$$\overset{n}{\underset{\omega}{\Delta}} u(x+\omega) = \omega \overset{n+1}{\underset{\omega}{\Delta}} u(x) + \overset{n}{\underset{\omega}{\Delta}} u(x).$$

We have also

(4) $$\lim_{\omega \to 0} \overset{n}{\underset{\omega}{\Delta}} u(x) = D^n u(x).$$

From the definitions it is clear that the operators $\varDelta$ and $\underset{\omega}{\Delta}$ are related by the formula

(5) $$\varDelta^n u(x) = \omega^n \overset{n}{\underset{\omega}{\Delta}} u(x),$$

and in the special case where $\omega = 1$ the two operators have precisely the same meaning.

If $\omega = 1$, we shall write Δ instead of $\underset{1}{\Delta}$.

2·105. Partial Difference Quotients. Consider $f(x, u)$ where x and u are regarded as independent variables. Let x be given the increment ω, and u the increment h. We then define *partial difference quotients* with respect to x and u by

$$\underset{\omega}{\Delta_x} f(x, u) = [f(x+\omega, u) - f(x, u)] / \omega,$$

$$\underset{h}{\Delta_u} f(x, u) = [f(x, u+h) - f(x, u)] / h.$$

The *difference* of $f(x, u)$ is defined by

$$\begin{aligned} \varDelta f(x, u) &= f(x+\omega, u+h) - f(x, u) \\ &= f(x+\omega, u+h) - f(x, u+h) + f(x, u+h) - f(x, u) \\ &= f(x+\omega, u+h) - f(x+\omega, u) + f(x+\omega, u) - f(x, u). \end{aligned}$$

Thus we have the two equivalent relations

(1) $$\varDelta f(x, u) = \omega \underset{\omega}{\Delta_x} f(x, u+h) + h \underset{h}{\Delta_u} f(x, u),$$

(2) $$\varDelta f(x, u) = \omega \underset{\omega}{\Delta_x} f(x, u) + h \underset{h}{\Delta_u} f(x+\omega, u).$$

Again

$$\underset{\omega}{\Delta_x} \underset{h}{\Delta_u} f(x, u) = \left[\underset{h}{\Delta_u} f(x+\omega, u) - \underset{h}{\Delta_u} f(x, u)\right] / \omega$$

$$= [f(x+\omega, u+h) - f(x+\omega, u) - f(x, u+h) + f(x, u)] / h\omega.$$

The symmetry of this result in h and ω shews that

(3) $$\underset{\omega}{\Delta_x} \underset{h}{\Delta_u} f(x, u) = \underset{h}{\Delta_u} \underset{\omega}{\Delta_x} f(x, u).$$

2·11. The Difference Quotients of Factorial Expressions. Products of the forms

(1) $$u(x) \,.\, u(x-\omega) \,.\, u(x-2\omega) \,\ldots\, u(x-m\omega+\omega),$$

(2) $$u(x+\omega) \,.\, u(x+2\omega) \,.\, u(x+3\omega) \,\ldots\, u(x+m\omega),$$

where m is a positive integer, are called *factorial expressions*, the first being a *descending* factorial, the second an *ascending* factorial expression.

Of expressions of these types the two simplest and also the two most important are

(3) $$x^{(m\omega)} = x(x-\omega)(x-2\omega) \ldots (x-m\omega+\omega),$$

(4) $$x^{(-m\omega)} = (x+\omega)^{-1}(x+2\omega)^{-1}(x+3\omega)^{-1} \ldots (x+m\omega)^{-1}.$$

If $m = 0$ we interpret each of these expressions as unity, that is

$$x^{(0 \,.\, \omega)} = 1;$$

and if $\omega \to 0$, we have also

$$\lim_{\omega \to 0} x^{(m\omega)} = x^m,$$

$$\lim_{\omega \to 0} x^{(-m\omega)} = x^{-m}.$$

To form the difference quotients of $x^{(m\omega)}$ we have

$$\omega \underset{\omega}{\Delta} x^{(m\omega)} = (x+\omega-x+m\omega-\omega)\, x(x-\omega) \ldots (x-m\omega+2\omega),$$

$$\underset{\omega}{\Delta} x^{(m\omega)} = m x^{(m\omega-\omega)}.$$

Hence, if $n \leqslant m$,

$$\underset{\omega}{\overset{n}{\Delta}} x^{(m\omega)} = m(m-1) \ldots (m-n+1)\, x^{(m\omega-n\omega)},$$

which can also be written, after dividing by $m\,!$, in the form

$$(5)\qquad \mathop{\Delta}_{\omega}^{n} \frac{x^{(m\omega)}}{m!} = \frac{x^{(m\omega-n\omega)}}{(m-n)!}, \quad n \leqslant m.$$

If $n = m$, we have

$$\mathop{\Delta}_{\omega}^{m} \frac{x^{(m\omega)}}{m!} = 1,$$

while if $n > m$ the result is zero.

If $\omega = 1$, we have

$$\frac{x^{(m)}}{m!} = \frac{x(x-1)\dots(x-m+1)}{m!} = \binom{x}{m}$$

in the usual notation for Binomial coefficients, so that (5) yields the important formula

$$(6)\qquad \overset{n}{\Delta}\binom{x}{m} = \binom{x}{m-n}, \quad n \leqslant m.$$

Again from (5), if $\omega \to 0$, we have by 2·1 (4)

$$D^n \frac{x^m}{m!} = \frac{x^{m-n}}{(m-n)!}.$$

These results shew the analogy between $x^{(m\omega)}$ in the finite calculus and x^m in the infinitesimal calculus.

For the difference quotients of $x^{(-m\omega)}$, we have

$$\omega \mathop{\Delta}_{\omega} x^{(-m\omega)} = \frac{x+\omega-x-m\omega-\omega}{(x+\omega)(x+2\omega)\dots(x+m\omega+\omega)},$$

$$\mathop{\Delta}_{\omega} x^{(-m\omega)} = -mx^{(-m\omega-\omega)},$$

so that

$$(7)\qquad \mathop{\Delta}_{\omega}^{n} x^{(-m\omega)} = (-m)(-m-1)\dots(-m-n+1)\,x^{(-m\omega-n\omega)},$$

which can be written

$$\mathop{\Delta}_{\omega}^{n}(m-1)!\,x^{(-m\omega)} = (-1)^n(m+n-1)!\,x^{(-m\omega-n\omega)}.$$

When $\omega \to 0$, we have

$$D^n(m-1)!\,x^{-m} = (-1)^n(m+n-1)!\,x^{-m-n}.$$

For more general forms of the types (1) and (2), we easily obtain

$$\omega \mathop{\Delta}_{\omega} u_x u_{x-\omega} \dots u_{x-m\omega+\omega}$$
$$= (u_{x+\omega} - u_{x-m\omega+\omega}) u_x u_{x-\omega} \dots u_{x-m\omega+2\omega}$$

$$\omega \mathop{\Delta}_{\omega} \frac{1}{v_{x+\omega} v_{x+2\omega} \dots v_{x+m\omega}} = \frac{v_{x+\omega} - v_{x+m\omega+\omega}}{v_{x+\omega} v_{x+2\omega} \dots v_{x+m\omega+\omega}}.$$

In particular for $u_x = v_x = ax+b$,
we can write

(8) $$u_x u_{x-\omega} \dots u_{x-m\omega+\omega} = (ax+b)^{(m\omega)},$$

(9) $$\frac{1}{v_{x+\omega} v_{x+2\omega} \dots v_{x+m\omega}} = (ax+b)^{(-m\omega)},$$

and we have

(10) $$\mathop{\Delta}_{\omega} (ax+b)^{(m\omega)} = am(ax+b)^{(m\omega-\omega)},$$

(11) $$\mathop{\Delta}_{\omega} (ax+b)^{(-m\omega)} = -am(ax+b)^{(-m\omega-\omega)}.$$

2·12. Expansion of a Polynomial in Factorials. Let $\phi(x)$ be a given polynomial of degree m. Assume that

(1) $$\phi(x) \equiv a_0 + a_1 \frac{x^{(\omega)}}{1!} + a_2 \frac{x^{(2\omega)}}{2!} + \dots + a_m \frac{x^{(m\omega)}}{m!},$$

which is evidently a legitimate assumption since the right-hand member is a polynomial of degree m with $m+1$ arbitrary coefficients. Forming the successive difference quotients, we have by 2·11 (5),

$$\mathop{\Delta}_{\omega} \phi(x) = a_1 + a_2 \frac{x^{(\omega)}}{1!} + \dots + a_m \frac{x^{(m\omega-\omega)}}{(m-1)!},$$

$$\mathop{\Delta}_{\omega}^{2} \phi(x) = a_2 + a_3 \frac{x^{(\omega)}}{1!} + \dots + a_m \frac{x^{(m\omega-2\omega)}}{(m-2)!},$$

. . . .

$$\mathop{\Delta}_{\omega}^{m} \phi(x) = a_m.$$

If in these results we put $x = 0$, we have expressions for the coefficients in the form

$$a_s = \mathop{\Delta}_{\omega}^{s} \phi(0), \qquad s = 0, 1, 2, \dots, m.$$

Thus

$$(2)\qquad \phi(x) = \phi(0) + \frac{x^{(\omega)}}{1!}\underset{\omega}{\Delta}\phi(0) + \frac{x^{(2\omega)}}{2!}\underset{\omega}{\overset{2}{\Delta}}\phi(0) + \dots + \frac{x^{(m\omega)}}{m!}\underset{\omega}{\overset{m}{\Delta}}\phi(0).$$

The coefficients in this expansion can be obtained by writing down the values of $\phi(x)$ for $x = 0, \omega, 2\omega, \dots, m\omega$ and then forming the successive difference quotients. Thus for

$$\phi(x) = x^3 + 3\omega^2 x + \omega^3,$$

we have

x	$\phi(x)$	$\underset{\omega}{\Delta}\phi(x)$	$\underset{\omega}{\overset{2}{\Delta}}\phi(x)$	$\underset{\omega}{\overset{3}{\Delta}}\phi(x)$
0	ω^3			
		$4\omega^2$		
ω	$5\omega^3$		6ω	
		$10\omega^2$		6
2ω	$15\omega^3$		12ω	
		$22\omega^2$		
3ω	$37\omega^3$			

so that

$$x^3 + 3\omega^2 . x + \omega^3 = \omega^3 + 4\omega^2\, x^{(\omega)} + 3\omega\, x^{(2\omega)} + x^{(3\omega)}.$$

Another method follows from observing that the coefficients $a_0, \frac{a_1}{1!}, \frac{a_2}{2!}, \dots$, are the successive remainders when we divide $\phi(x)$ by x, the quotient of this division by $(x-\omega)$, the new quotient by $(x-2\omega)$, and so on.

Thus with $\phi(x) = x^3 + 3\omega^2 x + \omega^3$, we have

x	$x^3 + 3\omega^2 x + \omega^3$	
$x-\omega$	$x^2 + 3\omega^2$	remainder ω^3
$x-2\omega$	$x+\omega$	remainder $4\omega^2$
	1	remainder 3ω

which gives the same expression for $\phi(x)$ as that obtained by the first method.

2·13. The Successive Difference Quotients of a Polynomial. To obtain the successive difference quotients we can express the polynomial in factorials by the method of the preceding paragraph and then apply 2·11 (5). Since each application of the operator $\underset{\omega}{\Delta}$ to a polynomial lowers the degree by unity we have the following important theorem :

The m*th difference quotients, and also the* m*th differences, of a polynomial of degree* m *are constant. The differences of order higher than the* m*th are zero.*

Thus with the polynomial

$$\begin{aligned}\phi(x) &= x^3+3\omega^2 x+\omega^3\\ &= x^{(3\omega)}+3\omega x^{(2\omega)}+4\omega^2 x^{(\omega)}+\omega^3,\end{aligned}$$

we have

$$\underset{\omega}{\Delta}\,\phi(x) = 3x^{(2\omega)}+6\omega x^{(\omega)}+4\omega^2 = 3x^2+3\omega x+4\omega^2,$$

$$\underset{\omega}{\overset{2}{\Delta}}\,\phi(x) = 6x^{(\omega)}+6\omega = 6x+6\omega,$$

$$\underset{\omega}{\overset{3}{\Delta}}\,\phi(x) = 6,$$

$$\underset{\omega}{\overset{4}{\Delta}}\,\phi(x) = 0.$$

2·14. The Difference Quotients of a^x.

We have

$$\underset{\omega}{\Delta}\,a^x = \frac{a^{x+\omega}-a^x}{\omega} = a^x\cdot\frac{a^\omega-1}{\omega}.$$

Thus

(1) $$\underset{\omega}{\overset{n}{\Delta}}\,a^x = a^x\left(\frac{a^\omega-1}{\omega}\right)^n.$$

Writing

$$a = (1+b\omega)^{\frac{1}{\omega}},$$

we have

(2) $$\underset{\omega}{\overset{n}{\Delta}}(1+b\omega)^{\frac{x}{\omega}} = b^n(1+b\omega)^{\frac{x}{\omega}}.$$

Since

$$\lim_{\omega\to 0}\,(1+b\omega)^{\frac{x}{\omega}} = e^{bx},$$

we have as a limiting case of (2)

$$D^n\,e^{bx} = b^n e^{bx}.$$

Thus in the finite calculus $(1+\omega)^{\frac{x}{\omega}}$ plays the part of e^x.

2·2. Properties of the Operator $\underset{\omega}{\Delta}$. From the definition it is evident that $\underset{\omega}{\Delta}$ obeys the following three laws:

(i) *The distributive law*

$$\underset{\omega}{\Delta}\,[u(x)+v(x)] = \underset{\omega}{\Delta}\,u(x)+\underset{\omega}{\Delta}\,v(x).$$

(ii) *The index law*

$$\overset{m}{\underset{\omega}{\Delta}}\left[\overset{n}{\underset{\omega}{\Delta}}\,u(x)\right] = \overset{m+n}{\underset{\omega}{\Delta}}\,u(x) = \overset{n}{\underset{\omega}{\Delta}}\left[\overset{m}{\underset{\omega}{\Delta}}\,u(x)\right],$$

where m and n are positive integers.

(iii) *The commutative law with regard to constants*

$$\underset{\omega}{\Delta}\,c\,u(x) = c\,\underset{\omega}{\Delta}\,u(x),$$

where c is independent of x. This result is also true if c be replaced by $\varpi(x)$, where $\varpi(x)$ is a periodic function of x with period ω; for

$$\begin{aligned}\omega\,\underset{\omega}{\Delta}\,\varpi(x)\,u(x) &= \varpi(x+\omega)\,u(x+\omega)-\varpi(x)\,u(x)\\ &= \varpi(x)\,u(x+\omega)-\varpi(x)\,u(x)\\ &= \omega\varpi(x)\,\underset{\omega}{\Delta}\,u(x).\end{aligned}$$

If then $\phi_1(\lambda) = a_0\lambda^n+a_1\lambda^{n-1}+\dots+a_n$ be a polynomial in λ whose coefficients are independent of x, we can associate with $\phi_1(\lambda)$ an operator $\phi_1(\underset{\omega}{\Delta})$, such that

$$\phi_1(\underset{\omega}{\Delta})\,u(x) = a_0\,\overset{n}{\underset{\omega}{\Delta}}\,u(x)+a_1\,\overset{n-1}{\underset{\omega}{\Delta}}\,u(x)+\dots+a_n u(x).$$

If $\phi_2(\lambda) = b_0\lambda^m+b_1\lambda^{m-1}+\dots+b_m$ be a second polynomial, and if we expand their product in the form

$$\phi_1(\lambda)\,\phi_2(\lambda) = c_0\lambda^{m+n}+c_1\lambda^{m+n-1}+\dots+c_{m+n},$$

we have, on account of the above laws,

$$\begin{aligned}\phi_1(\underset{\omega}{\Delta})\phi_2(\underset{\omega}{\Delta})u(x) &= \phi_2(\underset{\omega}{\Delta})\phi_1(\underset{\omega}{\Delta})u(x)\\ &= c_0\,\overset{m+n}{\underset{\omega}{\Delta}}\,u(x)+c_1\,\overset{m+n-1}{\underset{\omega}{\Delta}}\,u(x)+\dots+c_{m+n}u(x).\end{aligned}$$

We may also note that the above results are still true if the coefficients of the polynomials be replaced by periodic functions of x with period ω.

2·3. The Operator $\underset{\omega}{\nabla}$. The definition of this operator is given by

$$\underset{\omega}{\nabla} u(x) = \tfrac{1}{2}\left[u(x)+u(x+\omega)\right],$$

which may be compared with the definition of the central difference averaging operator μ of 2·01.

Repeating the operation, we have

$$\underset{\omega}{\overset{2}{\nabla}} u(x) = \tfrac{1}{4}\left[u(x)+2u(x+\omega)+u(x+2\omega)\right],$$

and generally, as is easily proved by induction,

$$\underset{\omega}{\overset{n}{\nabla}} u(x) = \frac{1}{2^n}\left[u(x)+\binom{n}{1}u(x+\omega)+\binom{n}{2}u(x+2\omega)+\dots\right.$$
$$\left.+\binom{n}{n}u(x+n\omega)\right].$$

As an example,

$$\underset{\omega}{\nabla} a^x = \tfrac{1}{2}a^x(a^\omega+1),$$

$$\underset{\omega}{\overset{n}{\nabla}} a^x = \frac{1}{2^n}a^x(a^\omega+1)^n.$$

2·4. The Operator E^ω. This operator is defined by the relation

(1) $$\mathsf{E}^\omega u(x) = u(x+\omega).$$

The operation may be repeated any number of times. Thus

$$(\mathsf{E}^\omega)^n u(x) = \mathsf{E}^{n\omega} u(x) = u(x+n\omega).$$

The operator E^ω clearly obeys the same laws of combination as $\underset{\omega}{\Delta}$. In particular, if $\phi_1(\lambda)$, $\phi_2(\lambda)$ be the polynomials of section 2·2 above, we have

$$\phi_1(\mathsf{E}^\omega)\phi_2(\mathsf{E}^\omega)u(x) = \phi_2(\mathsf{E}^\omega)\phi_1(\mathsf{E}^\omega)u(x)$$
$$= c_0\mathsf{E}^{m\omega+n\omega}u(x)+c_1\mathsf{E}^{m\omega+n\omega-\omega}u(x)+\dots+c_{m+n}u(x)$$
$$= c_0u(x+m\omega+n\omega)+c_1u(x+m\omega+n\omega-\omega)+\dots+c_{m+n}u(x).$$

2·41. Herschel's Theorem. *If $\phi(\lambda)$ be a polynomial with constant coefficients and if $\mathsf{E}^{n\omega}\, 0^m = [\mathsf{E}^{n\omega}\, x^m]_{x=0} = n^m\, \omega^m$, then*

$$\phi(e^{\omega t}) = \phi(1) + t\,\phi(\mathsf{E}^{\omega})\,0 + \frac{t^2}{2!}\phi(\mathsf{E}^{\omega})\,0^2 + \dots,$$

or symbolically

$$\phi(e^{\omega t}) \doteqdot \phi(\mathsf{E}^{\omega})e^{0\cdot t}.$$

The sign $\doteqdot$ is used to denote symbolic equivalence.

We have $\phi(e^{\omega t}) = \Sigma\, A_n\, e^{n\omega t}$ and it is therefore sufficient to prove the theorem for $\phi(e^{\omega t}) = e^{n\omega t}$, for the result will then follow by addition of constant multiples of terms of this type. Now

$$e^{(x+n\omega)t} = 1 + t(x+n\omega) + \frac{t^2}{2!}(x+n\omega)^2 + \dots$$

$$= 1 + t\,\mathsf{E}^{n\omega}\, x + \frac{t^2}{2!}\,\mathsf{E}^{n\omega}\, x^2 + \dots .$$

Putting $x = 0$, we have

$$e^{n\omega t} = 1 + t\,\mathsf{E}^{n\omega}\, 0 + \frac{t^2}{2!}\,\mathsf{E}^{n\omega}\, 0^2 + \dots$$

which proves the theorem.

2·42. From the definition of E^{ω}, we have

$$\mathsf{E}^{n\omega}\, a^x = a^{x+n\omega} = a^x\,.\,a^{n\omega}.$$

Thus if $\phi(\lambda) = \Sigma\, A_n\, \lambda^n$ be a polynomial in λ, we have

$$\phi(\mathsf{E}^{\omega})\, a^x = \Sigma\, A_n\, a^x a^{n\omega} = a^x\, \phi(a^{\omega}).$$

More generally, if the power series

$$\phi(\lambda) = \sum_{n=0}^{\infty} A_n\, \lambda^n$$

be convergent for $\lambda = a^{\omega}$, we have

$$\phi(\mathsf{E}^{\omega})\, a^x = a^x\, \phi(a^{\omega}).$$

2·43. Theorem. *If $\phi(\lambda)$ be a polynomial whose coefficients are independent of x, then*

(1) $$\phi(\mathsf{E}^{\omega})\, a^x\, u(x) = a^x\, \phi(a^{\omega}\mathsf{E}^{\omega})\, u(x).$$

(2) $$\phi(\mathsf{E}^{\omega})\, u(x) = a^x\, \phi(a^{\omega}\mathsf{E}^{\omega})\, a^{-x}\, u(x).$$

Let $\phi(\lambda) = \Sigma\, A_n\, \lambda^n$.

Then

$$\begin{aligned}\phi(\mathsf{E}^{\omega})\, a^x\, u(x) &= \Sigma A_n \mathsf{E}^{n\omega}\, a^x\, u(x)\\ &= \Sigma A_n\, a^{x+n\omega}\, u(x+n\omega)\\ &= a^x \Sigma A_n\, a^{n\omega} \mathsf{E}^{n\omega}\, u(x)\\ &= a^x\, \phi(a^{\omega}\mathsf{E}^{\omega})\, u(x),\end{aligned}$$

which proves (1), and (2) follows by replacing $u(x)$ by $a^{-x}\, u(x)$.

2·5. The Relations between $\underset{\omega}{\Delta}$, E^{ω} and D. We have from the definitions

$$\mathsf{E}^{\omega}\, u(x) = u(x+\omega) = u(x) + \omega \underset{\omega}{\Delta}\, u(x).$$

Thus

$$\mathsf{E}^{\omega} \doteqdot 1 + \omega \underset{\omega}{\Delta},$$

$$\omega \underset{\omega}{\Delta} \doteqdot \mathsf{E}^{\omega} - 1.$$

As deductions from these relations, we have Gregory's Theorem, namely,

(1) $$u(x+n\omega) = \mathsf{E}^{n\omega}\, u(x) = (1+\omega \underset{\omega}{\Delta})^n\, u(x)$$
$$= u(x) + \binom{n}{1}\omega \underset{\omega}{\Delta}\, u(x) + \binom{n}{2}\omega^2 \underset{\omega}{\overset{2}{\Delta}}\, u(x) + \dots$$
$$+ \binom{n}{n}\omega^n \underset{\omega}{\overset{n}{\Delta}}\, u(x),$$

n being a positive integer. This formula expresses $u(x+n\omega)$ in terms of $u(x)$ and its successive differences.

Again, we have

(2) $$\omega^n \underset{\omega}{\overset{n}{\Delta}}\, u(x) = (\mathsf{E}^{\omega} - 1)^n\, u(x)$$
$$= u(x+n\omega) - \binom{n}{1} u(x+\overline{n-1}\,\omega) + \binom{n}{2} u(x+\overline{n-2}\,\omega) - \dots$$
$$+ (-1)^n \binom{n}{n} u(x),$$

which expresses the nth difference in terms of functional values.

Again, assuming that $u(x+\omega)$ can be expanded by Taylor's Theorem, we have

$$\mathsf{E}^{\omega}\, u(x) = u(x+\omega) = u(x) + \omega D\, u(x) + \frac{\omega^2}{2!} D^2\, u(x) + \dots$$
$$\doteqdot e^{\omega D}\, u(x).$$

Thus we have the relations of operational equivalence

$$\mathsf{E}^{\omega} \doteqdot e^{\omega D},$$

$$1+\omega \underset{\omega}{\Delta} \doteqdot e^{\omega D},$$

$$\underset{\omega}{\Delta} \doteqdot \omega^{-1}(e^{\omega D}-1),$$

so that

$$\underset{\omega}{\overset{n}{\Delta}} u(x) \doteqdot \omega^{-n}(e^{\omega D}-1)^{n} u(x).$$

2·51. The Analogue of Leibniz' Theorem. The theorem of Leibniz in the differential calculus, namely,

$$D^{n}(uv) = (D^{n} u)\, v + \binom{n}{1}(D^{n-1} u) D v + \binom{n}{2}(D^{n-2} u) D^{2} v + \dots,$$

where D denotes the operation of differentiation, has an analogue in the finite calculus, which we proceed to obtain. We have

$$\begin{aligned}\omega \underset{\omega}{\Delta}(u_x v_x) &= u_{x+\omega} v_{x+\omega} - u_x v_x \\ &= \mathsf{E}^{\omega} u_x \mathsf{E}_1^{\omega} v_x - u_x v_x \\ &= \{(\mathsf{E}\mathsf{E}_1)^{\omega} - 1\} u_x v_x,\end{aligned}$$

where the operator E acts upon u_x alone and the operator E_1 acts upon v_x alone. Thus we have

(1) $$\omega^{n} \underset{\omega}{\overset{n}{\Delta}}(u_x v_x) = \{(\mathsf{E}\mathsf{E}_1)^{\omega} - 1\}^{n} u_x v_x.$$

In the expressions of E and E_1 let us suppose that $\underset{\omega}{\Delta}$ acts on u_x alone, while $\underset{\omega}{\Delta_1}$ acts on v_x alone, so that

$$\mathsf{E}^{\omega} \doteqdot 1+\omega \underset{\omega}{\Delta}, \qquad \mathsf{E}_1^{\omega} \doteqdot 1+\omega \underset{\omega}{\Delta_1}.$$

Then we have

$$(\mathsf{E}\mathsf{E}_1)^{\omega} - 1 \doteqdot \mathsf{E}^{\omega}(1+\omega \underset{\omega}{\Delta_1}) - 1 \doteqdot \omega(\underset{\omega}{\Delta} + \mathsf{E}^{\omega} \underset{\omega}{\Delta_1}).$$

Thus

$$\begin{aligned}\underset{\omega}{\overset{n}{\Delta}}(u_x v_x) &= (\underset{\omega}{\Delta} + \mathsf{E}^{\omega} \underset{\omega}{\Delta_1})^{n}(u_x v_x) \\ &= \left\{\underset{\omega}{\overset{n}{\Delta}} + \binom{n}{1} \underset{\omega}{\overset{n-1}{\Delta}} \mathsf{E}^{\omega} \underset{\omega}{\Delta_1} + \binom{n}{2} \underset{\omega}{\overset{n-2}{\Delta}} \mathsf{E}^{2\omega} \underset{\omega}{\overset{2}{\Delta_1}} + \dots\right\}(u_x v_x).\end{aligned}$$

Remembering that $\underset{\omega}{\Delta}$ and E operate only on u_x, we may drop the suffix and write

(2) $$\overset{n}{\underset{\omega}{\Delta}}(u_x v_x) = \left(\overset{n}{\underset{\omega}{\Delta}} u_x\right) v_x + \binom{n}{1}\left(\overset{n-1}{\underset{\omega}{\Delta}} u_{x+\omega}\right)\underset{\omega}{\Delta} v_x + \binom{n}{2}\left(\overset{n-2}{\underset{\omega}{\Delta}} u_{x+2\omega}\right)\overset{2}{\underset{\omega}{\Delta}} v_x + \dots,$$

which is the required theorem. Since

$$\lim_{\omega\to 0} \overset{s}{\underset{\omega}{\Delta}} u_x = D^s u_x,$$

we see that Leibniz' theorem may be regarded as a limiting case of this result.

The theorem may be expressed in other forms. If in (1) we expand the right-hand member directly, we have

$$\omega^n \overset{n}{\underset{\omega}{\Delta}}(u_x v_x) = \left(\mathsf{E}^{n\omega}\mathsf{E}_1^{n\omega} - \binom{n}{1}\mathsf{E}^{(n-1)\omega}\mathsf{E}_1^{(n-1)\omega} + \dots\right)(u_x v_x)$$

(3) $$= u_{x+n\omega}v_{x+n\omega} - \binom{n}{1} u_{x+(n-1)\omega}v_{x+(n-1)\omega} + \binom{n}{2} u_{x+(n-2)\omega}v_{x+(n-2)\omega} - \dots,$$

which is in fact a case of 2·5 (2).

If the expansion be required in difference quotients of u_x and v_x, we write

$$(\mathsf{E}\,\mathsf{E}_1)^{\omega} - 1 \doteqdot \omega \underset{\omega}{\Delta} + \omega \underset{\omega}{\Delta_1} + \omega^2 \underset{\omega}{\Delta}\underset{\omega}{\Delta_1},$$

so that

$$\overset{n}{\underset{\omega}{\Delta}}(u_x v_x) = (\underset{\omega}{\Delta} + \underset{\omega}{\Delta_1} + \omega \underset{\omega}{\Delta}\underset{\omega}{\Delta_1})^n (u_x v_x).$$

The expansion of the right-hand member gives the required result, but it is hardly worth while to write down the general expansion.

2·52. The Difference Quotients of $a^x v_x$. By 2·14 we have

$$\overset{n-s}{\underset{\omega}{\Delta}} a^{x+s\omega} = a^{x+s\omega} b^{n-s},$$

where $$b = \omega^{-1}(a^{\omega} - 1).$$

If then in (2) of 2·51 we put $u_x = a^x$, we obtain

$$\overset{n}{\underset{\omega}{\Delta}} a^x v_x = a^x \left[b^n v_x + \binom{n}{1} b^{n-1} a^\omega \underset{\omega}{\Delta} v_x + \binom{n}{2} b^{n-2} a^{2\omega} \overset{2}{\underset{\omega}{\Delta}} v_x + \dots \right]$$

$$= a^x \left[\frac{a^\omega - 1}{\omega} + a^\omega \underset{\omega}{\Delta} \right]^n v_x .$$

Thus if $\phi(\lambda)$ be a polynomial, we have the operational theorem

$$\phi(\underset{\omega}{\Delta})\, a^x v_x = a^x \phi\left(a^\omega \underset{\omega}{\Delta} + \frac{a^\omega - 1}{\omega} \right) v_x .$$

If next we put $a^\omega = 1 + \alpha\omega$, we obtain

$$\phi[\underset{\omega}{\Delta}]\, (1+\alpha\omega)^{\frac{x}{\omega}} v_x = (1+\alpha\omega)^{\frac{x}{\omega}} \phi[(1+\alpha\omega)\, \underset{\omega}{\Delta} + \alpha]\, v_x.$$

If we now let $\omega \to 0$, we obtain the corresponding theorem for the operator D, namely

$$\phi(D)\, e^{\alpha x} v_x = e^{\alpha x} \phi(D+\alpha)\, v_x.$$

2·53. The Difference Quotients of Zero. The value of $\overset{n}{\underset{\omega}{\Delta}} x^m$ when $x = 0$ is written $\overset{n}{\underset{\omega}{\Delta}} 0^m$ and is called a difference quotient of zero. Clearly

(1) $$\overset{n}{\underset{\omega}{\Delta}} 0^m = 0 \text{ if } n > m, \qquad \overset{n}{\underset{\omega}{\Delta}} 0^n = n!.$$

If in 2·51 (2) we put $u_x = x^{m-1}$, $v_x = x$, we have

$$\overset{n}{\underset{\omega}{\Delta}} x^m = x \overset{n}{\underset{\omega}{\Delta}} x^{m-1} + n \overset{n-1}{\underset{\omega}{\Delta}} (x+\omega)^{m-1}$$

$$= x \overset{n}{\underset{\omega}{\Delta}} x^{m-1} + n [\omega \overset{n}{\underset{\omega}{\Delta}} x^{m-1} + \overset{n-1}{\underset{\omega}{\Delta}} x^{m-1}] .$$

Putting $x = 0$, we have the recurrence relation

(2) $$\overset{n}{\underset{\omega}{\Delta}} 0^m = n\omega \overset{n}{\underset{\omega}{\Delta}} 0^{m-1} + n \overset{n-1}{\underset{\omega}{\Delta}} 0^{m-1},$$

which in conjunction with (1) enables these numbers to be calculated successively. Thus

$$\underset{\omega}{\Delta} 0 = 1,$$

$$\underset{\omega}{\Delta} 0^2 = \omega \underset{\omega}{\Delta} 0 = \omega,$$

$$\overset{2}{\underset{\omega}{\Delta}} 0^2 = 2!,$$

$$\underset{\omega}{\Delta} 0^3 = \omega \underset{\omega}{\Delta} 0^2 = \omega^2,$$

$$\overset{2}{\underset{\omega}{\Delta}} 0^3 = 2\omega \overset{2}{\underset{\omega}{\Delta}} 0^2 + 2 \underset{\omega}{\Delta} 0^2 = 6\omega,$$

$$\overset{3}{\underset{\omega}{\Delta}} 0^3 = 3!,$$

and so on. Expressions for these numbers will be obtained in Chapter VI in terms of Bernoulli's numbers.

2·54. Expression of Difference Quotients in terms of Derivates. By Herschel's Theorem, 2·41, we have

$$(e^{\omega t}-1)^n = t(\mathsf{E}^{\omega}-1)^n 0 + \frac{t^2}{2!}(\mathsf{E}^{\omega}-1)^n 0^2 + \dots .$$

Since $\mathsf{E}^{\omega} - 1 \doteqdot \omega \underset{\omega}{\Delta}$, we obtain

$$\omega^{-n}(e^{\omega t}-1)^n = t \overset{n}{\underset{\omega}{\Delta}} 0 + \frac{t^2}{2!} \overset{n}{\underset{\omega}{\Delta}} 0^2 + \dots ,$$

where

$$\overset{n}{\underset{\omega}{\Delta}} 0^s = [\overset{n}{\underset{\omega}{\Delta}} x^s]_{x=0},$$

which is equal to zero if $s < n$, and to $n!$ if $s = n$.

Thus

$$\omega^{-n}(e^{\omega t}-1)^n = t^n + \frac{t^{n+1}}{(n+1)!} \overset{n}{\underset{\omega}{\Delta}} 0^{n+1} + \frac{t^{n+2}}{(n+2)!} \overset{n}{\underset{\omega}{\Delta}} 0^{n+2} + \dots .$$

Now from 2·5 we have

$$\overset{n}{\underset{\omega}{\Delta}} \doteqdot \omega^{-n}(e^{\omega D}-1)^n.$$

Thus

$$\overset{n}{\underset{\omega}{\Delta}} u_x = D^n u_x + \frac{\overset{n}{\underset{\omega}{\Delta}} 0^{n+1}}{(n+1)!} D^{n+1} u_x + \frac{\overset{n}{\underset{\omega}{\Delta}} 0^{n+2}}{(n+2)!} D^{n+2} u_x + \dots .$$

[See also 7·05.]

2·6. The Summation Operator P^{-1}. If x be a positive integer variable, capable of taking the values 0, 1, 2, 3, ..., we write

(1) $$\mathsf{P}_{(x)}^{-1} u_t = u_{x-1} + u_{x-2} + u_{x-3} + \dots + u_0 = \sum_{t=0}^{x-1} u_t,$$

where the notation $\mathbf{P}^{-1}$ is introduced for formal reasons † and indicates the inverse nature of the operation. Indeed it follows at once, if u_t be independent of x, that

$$\begin{aligned}\Delta \mathbf{P}_{(x)}^{-1} u_t &= \mathbf{P}_{(x+1)}^{-1} u_t - \mathbf{P}_{(x)}^{-1} u_t \\ &= (u_x + u_{x-1} + \dots + u_0) - (u_{x-1} + u_{x-2} + \dots + u_0) \\ &= u_x,\end{aligned}$$

so that the operator Δ neutralises the operator $\mathbf{P}^{-1}$, which is in this sense an operation inverse to Δ. With the above notation we have, for example,

$$\mathbf{P}_{(x)}^{-1} u_{t+1} = u_x + u_{x-1} + \dots + u_2 + u_1,$$

$$\mathbf{P}_{(n-m+1)}^{-1} u_{t+m} = u_n + u_{n-1} + \dots + u_m = \mathbf{P}_{n+1}^{-1} u_t - \mathbf{P}_{(m)}^{-1} u_t.$$

When there is no risk of ambiguity we may conveniently write

(2) $$\mathbf{P}^{-1} u_x = u_{x-1} + u_{x-2} + \dots + u_0.$$

These notations may be compared with

$$\int_0^x u_t\,dt \quad \text{and} \quad \int_0^x u_x\,dx.$$

We have at once from (1),

(3) $$\mathbf{P}_{(1)}^{-1} u_t = u_0, \quad \mathbf{P}_{(0)}^{-1} u_t = 0.$$

If, by affixing an asterisk, we now define a function u_x^* by the properties

(4) $$u_x^* = u_x \text{ if } x \geqslant 0, \quad u_x^* = 0 \text{ if } x < 0,$$

we have

$$\begin{aligned}\mathbf{P}_{(x)}^{-1} u_t &= u_{x-1}^* + u_{x-2}^* + \dots + u_0^* + u_{-1}^* + u_{-2}^* + \dots \\ &= (\mathbf{E}^{-1} + \mathbf{E}^{-2} + \dots + \mathbf{E}^{-x} + \mathbf{E}^{-x-1} + \mathbf{E}^{-x-2} + \dots) u_x^*\end{aligned}$$

(5) $$\doteqdot (\mathbf{E} - 1)^{-1} u_x^*.$$

The operation can be repeated any number of times, thus

$$\begin{aligned}\mathbf{P}_{(x)}^{-2} u_t \doteqdot \mathbf{P}_{(x)}^{-1}[(\mathbf{E}-1)^{-1} u_t^*] &\doteqdot (\mathbf{E}-1)^{-2} u_x^* \\ &= u_{x-2} + 2u_{x-3} + 3u_{x-4} + \dots + (x-1)\,u_0,\end{aligned}$$

and this result is seen to be in agreement with (1) and (3).

† L. M. Milne-Thomson, *Proc. Camb. Phil. Soc.*, xxvii (1931), 26-36.

More generally we have

$$\mathsf{P}_{(x)}^{-n} u_t = (\mathsf{E}-1)^{-n} u^*_{(x)} = u^*_{x-n} + \binom{n}{1} u^*_{x-n-1} + \binom{n+1}{2} u^*_{x-n-2} + \dots$$

$$(6) \qquad = \mathsf{P}^{-1}_{(x-n+1)} \binom{x-t-1}{n-1} u_t,$$

which expresses n successive operations with P^{-1} in terms of a single operation. Also, if u_t be independent of x, we have

$$(7) \qquad \Delta \mathsf{P}_{(x)}^{-n} u_t = \Delta \mathsf{P}_{(x)}^{-1} [\mathsf{P}_{(t)}^{-n+1} u_s] = \mathsf{P}_{(x)}^{-n+1} u_t.$$

2·61. Theorem. *If $f(x)$ be a function of the positive integral variable x such that $\Delta f(x) = u_x$, and if u_t be independent of x, then*

$$\mathsf{P}_{(x)}^{-1} u_t = f(x) - f(0) = \Big[f(t) \Big]_0^x .$$

We have

$$\Delta \{\mathsf{P}_{(x)}^{-1} u_t - f(x)\} = u_x - u_x = 0.$$

Hence

$$\mathsf{P}_{(x)}^{-1} u_t - f(x) = \text{constant} = -f(0),$$

since $\mathsf{P}_{(0)}^{-1} u_t = 0$. This is the required theorem.

2·62. The following table exhibits the relations between the sums $\mathsf{P}^{-n} u_x$ and the functional values $u_0, u_1, u_2, \dots$.

			u_0			
		$\mathsf{P}^{-1} u_1$		Δu_0		
	$\mathsf{P}^{-2} u_2$		u_1		$\Delta^2 u_0$	
$\mathsf{P}^{-3} u_3$		$\mathsf{P}^{-1} u_2$		Δu_1		$\Delta^3 u_0$
	$\mathsf{P}^{-2} u_3$		u_2		$\Delta^2 u_1$	
$\mathsf{P}^{-3} u_4$		$\mathsf{P}^{-1} u_3$		Δu_2		$\Delta^3 u_1$
	$\mathsf{P}^{-2} u_4$		u_3		$\Delta^2 u_2$	
$\mathsf{P}^{-3} u_5$		$\mathsf{P}^{-1} u_4$		Δu_3		$\Delta^3 u_2$
	$\mathsf{P}^{-2} u_5$		u_4		$\Delta^2 u_3$	
$\mathsf{P}^{-3} u_6$		$\mathsf{P}^{-1} u_5$		Δu_4		
	$\mathsf{P}^{-2} u_6$		u_5			
		$\mathsf{P}^{-1} u_6$				

Each sum is formed by adding the members of the column on the right, beginning with the member immediately above the required sum. Thus

$$\mathsf{P}^{-1} u_3 = u_2 + u_1 + u_0, \quad \mathsf{P}^{-3} u_5 = \mathsf{P}^{-2} u_4 + \mathsf{P}^{-2} u_3 + \mathsf{P}^{-2} u_2.$$

We note also that each column can be formed by differencing the column immediately to the left. It will also be noticed that if we change the origin, that is, label another entry with the suffix 0, the resulting sum table will have each of its members altered in value while the differences will be unaffected. Lastly, we note that all entries labelled with the same suffix lie on a diagonal line.

Obviously in analogy with central differences we could also form " central sums " by a mere change of notation.

2·63. Moments. Given a set of x tabular values, say,

$$u_0, u_1, u_2, \dots, u_{x-1},$$

their nth moment * about the point $x-1$ is defined by

$$(1) \qquad M_n = \sum_{t=0}^{x-1} (t-x+1)^n u_t = \mathsf{P}^{-1}_{(x)} (t-x+1)^n u_t .$$

If we express $(x-t-1)^n$ in factorials by the method of 2·12 we obtain

$$(-1)^n (t-x+1)^n = \sum_{s=0}^{n} \binom{x-t-1}{s} c_s ,$$

where

$$(2) \qquad c_s = \overset{s}{\Delta} 0^n,$$

a difference of zero (see 2·53). Thus

$$(-1)^n M_n = \sum_{t=0}^{x-1} \sum_{s=0}^{n} c_s \binom{x-t-1}{s} u_t$$

$$= \sum_{s=0}^{n} \sum_{t=0}^{x-s-1} c_s \binom{x-t-1}{s} u_t ,$$

since $\binom{x-t-1}{s}$ vanishes when $t > x-s-1$.

* See for example W. Palin Elderton, *Frequency Curves and Correlation*, (London, 1927), chap. iii.

Hence from 2·6 (6) we have

(3) $$(-1)^n M_n = \sum_{s=0}^{n} c_s \mathsf{P}_{(x)}^{-s-1} u_t = \sum_{s=0}^{n} c_s \mathsf{P}^{-s-1} u_x.$$

Using the differences of zero given in 2·53 and noting that $c_0 = 0$, we have

$$M_1 = -\mathsf{P}^{-2} u_x,$$
$$M_2 = \mathsf{P}^{-2} u_x + 2\mathsf{P}^{-3} u_x,$$
$$M_3 = -\mathsf{P}^{-2} u_x - 6\mathsf{P}^{-3} u_x - 6\mathsf{P}^{-4} u_x,$$

and so on. The terms $\mathsf{P}^{-s} u_x$ (which are also called *factorial* moments) can be obtained directly from the sum table of 2·62. If the moments be required about another point, say y, we have

$$M_{n,y} = \sum_{t=0}^{x-1} (t-y)^n u_t$$
$$= \sum_{t=0}^{x-1} [(t-x+1)+(x-1-y)]^n u_t$$
$$= \sum_{r=0}^{n} \binom{n}{r} (x-y-1)^{n-r} M_r,$$

which expresses the moment $M_{n,y}$ in terms of the moments M_r.

2·64. Partial Summation. We have

$$u_x \Delta v_x = \Delta(u_x v_x) - v_{x+1} \Delta u_x.$$

Operating with P^{-1}, we obtain

$$\mathsf{P}_{(n)}^{-1} u_x \Delta v_x = \Big[u_x v_x \Big]_0^n - \mathsf{P}_{(n)}^{-1} v_{x+1} \Delta u_x.$$

Example. To calculate $\mathsf{P}_{(n)}^{-1} x a^x$.

We have $\Delta a^x = (a-1) a^x$, and hence

$$\mathsf{P}_{(n)}^{-1} x a^x (a-1) = \Big[x a^x \Big]_0^n - \mathsf{P}_{(n)}^{-1} a^{x+1}.$$

Now

$$\mathsf{P}_{(n)}^{-1} a^{x+1} = a^n + a^{n-1} + \dots + a = \frac{a^{n+1}-a}{a-1},$$

so that

$$\mathsf{P}_{(n)}^{-1} x a^x = \frac{n a^n}{a-1} - \frac{a^{n+1}-a.}{(a-1)^2}.$$

The analogy of the formula for partial summation with the formula for integration by parts should be noted. In fact if, taking $n\omega^{-1}$ to be an integer, we make the extended definition

$$\mathsf{P}_{(n)\omega}^{-1} u_x = \omega(u_{n-\omega} + u_{n-2\omega} + \dots + u_0),$$

the formula for summation by parts becomes

$$\mathsf{P}_{(n)\omega}^{-1} u_x \underset{\omega}{\Delta} v_x = \Big[u_x v_x\Big]_0^n - \mathsf{P}_{(n)\omega}^{-1} v_{x+\omega} \underset{\omega}{\Delta} u_x,$$

which when $\omega \to 0$ becomes

$$\int_0^n u_x\, dv_x = \Big[u_x v_x\Big]_0^n - \int_0^n v_x\, du_x.$$

2·7. The Summation of Finite Series. If we denote by u_x the xth term of a series, the sum of the first n terms is

$$\mathsf{P}_{(n)}^{-1} u_{x+1} = u_n + u_{n-1} + \dots + u_2 + u_1.$$

To evaluate this sum we see, from the theorem of 2·61, that it is sufficient to find a function $f(x)$ such that

$$\Delta f(x) = u_{x+1}.$$

The general problem of solving this equation constitutes the summation problem, which will be treated in Chapter VIII. For the present purpose we require only a particular solution, and we shall now shew how such a solution can be obtained for certain special forms of u_x.

2·71. Factorial Expressions of the form $x^{(m)}$. By 2·11 (5),

$$\Delta \frac{(x+1)^{(m+1)}}{m+1} = (x+1)^{(m)}.$$

Thus, by 2·61,

$$\mathsf{P}_{(n)}^{-1} (x+1)^{(m)} = \left[\frac{(x+1)^{(m+1)}}{m+1}\right]_0^n = \frac{(n+1)^{(m+1)}}{m+1}.$$

For example,

$$1\,.\,2\,.\,3 + 2\,.\,3\,.\,4 + \dots + (n-2)(n-1)\,n = \tfrac{1}{4}(n-2)(n-1)\,n\,(n+1).$$

Also

$$\begin{aligned} m(m+1)(m+2) &+ (m+1)(m+2)(m+3) + \dots + (n-2)(n-1)\,n \\ &= \mathsf{P}_{(n)}^{-1}(x+1)^{(3)} - \mathsf{P}_{(m+1)}^{-1}(x+1)^{(3)} \\ &= \tfrac{1}{4}(n-2)(n-1)\,n(n+1) - \tfrac{1}{4}(m-1)\,m(m+1)(m+2). \end{aligned}$$

Again, from 2·11 (10), we have

$$\Delta \frac{(ax+b)^{(m+1)}}{a(m+1)} = (ax+b)^{(m)},$$

whence we get

$$\mathbf{P}_{(n)}^{-1} \{a(x+1)+b\}^{(m)} = \left[\frac{\{a(x+1)+b\}^{(m+1)}}{a(m+1)}\right]_0^n.$$

Example. Sum to n terms the series

$$3\,.\,5\,.\,7+5\,.\,7\,.\,9+7\,.\,9\,.\,11+\dots .$$

The xth term is $(2x+5)(2x+3)(2x+1) = (2x+5)^{(3)}$ and the required sum is therefore

$$\mathbf{P}_{(n)}^{-1} (2x+7)^{(3)} = \left[\frac{(2x+7)^{(4)}}{8}\right]_0^n$$

$$= \tfrac{1}{8}(2n+7)(2n+5)(2n+3)(2n+1) - \tfrac{105}{8}.$$

2·72. Polynomials. If the xth term be a polynomial in x, we could use the method of 2·71, having first expressed u_x in factorials by the method of 2·12. But from 2·12 (2) we have

$$\phi(n) = \phi(0)+n\,\Delta\,\phi(0)+\frac{n(n-1)}{2!}\overset{2}{\Delta}\,\phi(0)+\dots .$$

Putting $\phi(n) = \mathbf{P}_{(n)}^{-1} u_{x+1}$, we obtain

$$\phi(0) = 0,\quad \Delta\,\phi(0) = u_1,\quad \overset{2}{\Delta}\,\phi(0) = \Delta\, u_1, \dots ,$$

so that we get the formula

$$\mathbf{P}_{(n)}^{-1} u_{x+1} = nu_1+\frac{n(n-1)}{2!}\Delta\, u_1+\frac{n(n-1)(n-2)}{3!}\overset{2}{\Delta}\, u_1+\dots .$$

Since u_x is a polynomial, the terms on the right vanish after a finite number of differences have been formed.

Example (i). Find the sum of n terms of the series

$$1^2+2^2+3^2+\dots .$$

Here $u_x = x^2$, $\Delta\, u_x = 2x+1$, $\overset{2}{\Delta}\, u_x = 2$ and the required sum is

$$n+\frac{3n(n-1)}{2}+\frac{n(n-1)(n-2)}{3} = \frac{n(n+1)(2n+1)}{6}.$$

Example (ii). Find the sum of n terms of the series whose nth term is n^3+7n.

We form the following table of differences:

$$\begin{array}{ccccccc} u_1 & & u_2 & & u_3 & & u_4 \\ 8 & & 22 & & 48 & & 92 \\ & 14 & & 26 & & 44 & \\ & & 12 & & 18 & & \\ & & & 6 & & & \end{array}$$

Hence the required sum is

$$8n+\frac{14n(n-1)}{2}+\frac{12n(n-1)(n-2)}{6}+\frac{6n(n-1)(n-2)(n-3)}{24}$$
$$=\tfrac{1}{4}n(n+1)(n^2+n+14).$$

Another method of summing series of this type by means of the Polynomials of Bernoulli will be explained in 6·501.

2·73. Factorial Expressions of the form $x^{(-m)}$. From 2·11 (7) and (9), we have

$$\Delta\frac{x^{(-m+1)}}{-m+1}=x^{(-m)}=\frac{1}{(x+1)(x+2)\ldots(x+m)},$$

$$\Delta\frac{(ax+b)^{(-m+1)}}{-a(m-1)}=(ax+b)^{(-m)}$$
$$=\frac{1}{[a(x+1)+b][a(x+2)+b]\ldots[a(x+m)+b]}.$$

Thus

$$\mathsf{P}_{(n)}^{-1}(x+1)^{(-m)}=\left[\frac{(x+1)^{(-m+1)}}{1-m}\right]_0^n,$$

$$\mathsf{P}_{(n)}^{-1}\{a(x+1)+b\}^{(-m)}=\left[\frac{\{a(x+1)+b\}^{(-m+1)}}{-a(m-1)}\right]_0^n.$$

Example. Find the sum of n terms of the series

$$\frac{1}{1\,.\,4\,.\,7}+\frac{1}{4\,.\,7\,.\,10}+\frac{1}{7\,.\,10\,.\,13}+\ldots.$$

Here the xth term is

$$\frac{1}{(3x-2)(3x+1)(3x+4)}=(3x-5)^{(-3)}.$$

Thus the required sum is

$$\mathsf{P}_{(n)}^{-1}[3(x+1)-5]^{(-3)} = \tfrac{1}{6}(3\,.\,1-5)^{(-2)} - \tfrac{1}{6}[3(n+1)-5]^{(-2)}$$

$$= \frac{1}{24} - \frac{1}{6(3n+1)(3n+4)}.$$

These results are analogous to the formula

$$\int_1^n (ax+b)^m\,dx = \frac{(an+b)^{m+1}}{a(m+1)} - \frac{(a+b)^{m+1}}{a(m+1)}.$$

2·74. A certain type of Rational Function. If

$$u_x = \frac{\phi(x)}{v_x v_{x+1} v_{x+2} \dots v_{x+m}},$$

where $$v_x = ax+b$$

and if $\phi(x)$ be a polynomial of degree lower by at least two unities than the degree of the denominator, then we can sum the series to n terms. We begin by expressing $\phi(x)$ in the form

$$\phi(x) = a_0 + a_1 v_x + a_2 v_x v_{x+1} + \dots + a_{m-1} v_x v_{x+1} v_{x+2} \dots v_{x+m-2}.$$

This can be done by an obvious extension of the methods of 2·12, or indeed by equating coefficients. It then follows that

$$u_x = \frac{a_0}{v_x v_{x+1} \dots v_{x+m}} + \frac{a_1}{v_{x+1} v_{x+2} \dots v_{x+m}} + \dots + \frac{a_{m-1}}{v_{x+m-1} v_{x+m}},$$

so that the sum can be obtained by the method of 2·73.

Again, supposing the numerator of a rational fraction to be of degree less by at least two unities than the degree of the denominator but intermediate factors alone to be wanting in the denominator to give it the factorial character described above, then, these factors being supplied to both numerator and denominator, we can obtain the sum. Thus, for example,

$$\mathsf{P}^{-1} \frac{x}{v_x v_{x+2} v_{x+3}} = \mathsf{P}^{-1} \frac{x\, v_{x+1}}{v_x v_{x+1} v_{x+2} v_{x+3}}.$$

Example. Find the sum of n terms of the series

$$\frac{2}{1\,.\,3\,.\,4} + \frac{3}{2\,.\,4\,.\,5} + \frac{4}{3\,.\,5\,.\,6} + \dots.$$

Here

$$u_x = \frac{x+1}{x(x+2)(x+3)} = \frac{x(x+1)+x+1}{x(x+1)(x+2)(x+3)},$$

$$u_{x+1} = (x+2)^{(-2)} + (x+1)^{(-3)} + x^{(-4)},$$

$$\mathsf{P}_{(n)}^{-1} u_{x+1} = 2^{(-1)} + \tfrac{1}{2}\,1^{(-2)} + \tfrac{1}{3}\,.\,0^{(-3)} - (n+2)^{(-1)} - \tfrac{1}{2}(n+1)^{(-2)} - \tfrac{1}{3}\,n^{(-3}$$

$$= \frac{1}{3} + \frac{1}{12} + \frac{1}{18} - \frac{1}{n+3} - \frac{1}{2(n+2)(n+3)} - \frac{1}{3(n+1)(n+2)(n+3)}.$$

2·75. The form $a^x\phi(x)$, $\phi(x)$ a Polynomial. We have

$$\Delta\, a^x v_x = a^x(a-1+a\,\Delta)\,v_x = a^x(a-1)(1+b\,\Delta)\,v_x,$$

where $$b = a\,/\,(a-1).$$

If $\phi(x)$ be a polynomial of degree ν, put

$$v_x = \frac{1}{a-1}\left\{1 - b\,\Delta + b^2 \overset{2}{\Delta} - \dots + (-1)^\nu b^\nu \overset{\nu}{\Delta}\right\}\phi(x).$$

Then

$$\Delta\, a^x v_x = a^x\{1 + (-1)^\nu b^{\nu+1} \overset{\nu+1}{\Delta}\}\,\phi(x) = a^x\,\phi(x).$$

We have therefore

(1) $$\mathsf{P}_{(n)}^{-1}\, a^{x+1}\phi(x+1)$$

$$= \frac{a^{n+1}}{a-1}[1 - b\,\Delta + b^2\overset{2}{\Delta} - \dots + (-1)^\nu b^\nu \overset{\nu}{\Delta}]\,\phi(n+1)$$

$$- \frac{a}{a-1}[1 - b\,\Delta + b^2\overset{2}{\Delta} - \dots + (-1)^\nu b^\nu \overset{\nu}{\Delta}]\,\phi(1).$$

Example. Find the sum to n terms of the series

$$1^2\,.\,2 + 2^2\,.\,2^2 + 3^2\,.\,2^3 + 4^2\,.\,2^4 + \dots\,.$$

Here $u_x = x^2\, 2^x$ and the required sum is

$$2^{n+1}\{1 - 2\Delta + 4\overset{2}{\Delta}\}(n+1)^2 - 2\{1 - 2\Delta + 4\overset{2}{\Delta}\}\,1^2$$

$$= 2^{n+1}\{(n+1)^2 - 2(2n+3) + 8\} - 2\{1 - 6 + 8\},$$

$$= 2^{n+1}(n^2 - 2n + 3) - 6.$$

2·76. The form $v_x\phi(x)$, $\phi(x)$ a Polynomial. Let $\phi(x)$ be a polynomial of degree ν. Consider the expression

$$f(x) = (\mathsf{P}^{-1} v_x)\,\phi(x-1) - (\mathsf{P}^{-2} v_x)\,\Delta\,\phi(x-2)$$

$$+ (\mathsf{P}^{-3} v_x)\,\overset{2}{\Delta}\,\phi(x-3) - \dots + (-1)^\nu (\mathsf{P}^{-\nu-1} v_x)\,\overset{\nu}{\Delta}\,\phi(x-\nu-1).$$

Since $$\Delta(s_x t_x) = t_{x+1}\Delta s_x + s_x \Delta t_x,$$
we have

$$\Delta f(x) = v_x \phi(x) + (\mathsf{P}^{-1} v_x)\Delta\phi(x-1)$$
$$-[(\mathsf{P}^{-1} v_x)\Delta\phi(x-1) + (\mathsf{P}^{-2} v_x)\overset{2}{\Delta}\phi(x-2)] + \dots$$
$$+(-1)^{\nu}[(\mathsf{P}^{-\nu} v_x)\overset{\nu}{\Delta}\phi(x-\nu) + (\mathsf{P}^{-\nu-1} v_x)\overset{\nu+1}{\Delta}\phi(x-\nu-1)]$$
$$= v_x\phi(x) + (-1)^{\nu}(\mathsf{P}^{-\nu-1} v_x)\overset{\nu+1}{\Delta}\phi(x-\nu-1) = v_x\phi(x),$$

since $$\overset{\nu+1}{\Delta}\phi(x-\nu-1) = 0.$$

Thus, by 2·61,

(1) $$\mathsf{P}_{(n)}^{-1} v_{x+1}\phi(x+1) = (\mathsf{P}_{(n)}^{-1} v_{x+1})\phi(n) - (\mathsf{P}_{(n)}^{-2} v_{x+1})\Delta\phi(n-1)$$
$$+(\mathsf{P}_{(n)}^{-3} v_{x+1})\overset{2}{\Delta}\phi(n-2) - \dots,$$

since $$\mathsf{P}_{(n)}^{-1} v_{x+1} = 0 \text{ when } n = 0.$$

This result enables us to sum the series whose xth term is $v_x\phi(x)$, where $\phi(x)$ is a polynomial of degree ν, provided that we can form the repeated sums

$$\mathsf{P}_{(n)}^{-s} v_{x+1}, \quad s = 1, 2, 3, \dots, \nu+1.$$

Example. Sum to n terms the series whose nth term is

$$(n-c)\sin(2an+b).$$

Here $\phi(x) = x - c$, $v_x = \sin(2ax+b)$, and the required sum is

$$\mathsf{P}_{(n)}^{-1}(x+1-c)\sin(2ax+2a+b)$$
$$= (n-c)\mathsf{P}_{(n)}^{-1}\sin(2ax+2a+b) - \mathsf{P}_{(n)}^{-2}\sin(2ax+2a+b).$$

Now* $$\Delta\sin(2ax+b) = \sin(2ax+2a+b) - \sin(2ax+b)$$
$$= 2\sin a \sin\left(2ax+b+a+\frac{\pi}{2}\right).$$

*It is interesting to note that, if we form the difference table for $\sin(ax+b)$ or more generally for e^{ax}, the terms in the same horizontal line are in Geometrical Progression. This fact was employed by Briggs and by Gregory.

Thus

$$\mathsf{P}_{(n)}^{-1}\sin(2ax+2a+b) = \frac{1}{2\sin a}\left[\sin\left(2ax+2a+b-a-\frac{\pi}{2}\right)\right]_0^n$$

$$= \frac{1}{2\sin a}\left[\sin\left(2an+b+a-\frac{\pi}{2}\right)+\cos(a+b)\right],$$

$$\mathsf{P}_{(n)}^{-2}\sin(2ax+2a+b) = \frac{1}{4\sin^2 a}\left[\sin(2ax+b-\pi)\right]_0^n+\frac{n\cos(a+b)}{2\sin a}.$$

Hence, after reduction, the required sum is

$$\frac{-c\sin na\sin(na+a+b)}{\sin a}-\frac{n\cos(2an+a+b)}{2\sin a}+\frac{\sin na\cos(an+b)}{2\sin^2 a}.$$

The repeated sums required for the method of this section can always be formed for the types $(ax+b)^{(m)}$, $\phi(x)$, $a^x\phi(x)$, where $\phi(x)$ is a polynomial, since the operation with P^{-1} in each case leads to a function of the same form. Repeated sums for $(ax+b)^{(-m)}$ can be formed, provided that the number of repetitions be not great enough to lead to the necessity of evaluating $\mathsf{P}^{-1}(ax+b)^{(-1)}$, for which no compact form exists in terms of the elementary functions here considered.

2·77. When the nth term of a series proposed for summation cannot be referred to any of the preceding forms it is often possible to conjecture the form of the sum from a general knowledge of the effects of the operator Δ, and hence to determine the sum by trial. For example, if $\phi(x)$ be a rational function, then

$$\Delta\, a^x\,\phi(x) = a^x\,\psi(x),$$

where $\psi(x)$ is likewise a rational function. Similarly

$$\Delta\tan^{-1}\phi(x) = \tan^{-1}\psi(x),$$

where $\psi(x)$ is rational if $\phi(x)$ be rational.

Example. To sum to n terms, when possible, the series

$$\frac{1^2\,.\,\lambda}{2\,.\,3}+\frac{2^2\,.\,\lambda^2}{3\,.\,4}+\frac{3^2\,.\,\lambda^3}{4\,.\,5}+\dots.$$

The xth term u_x is given by

$$u_x = \frac{x^2\,\lambda^x}{(x+1)(x+2)}.$$

Here we should evidently assume that

$$\mathsf{P}_{(n)}^{-1} u_{x+1} = \frac{an+b}{n+2}\lambda^{n+1} + \text{constant}.$$

Operating with Δ, we have

$$\frac{(n+1)^2\lambda^{n+1}}{(n+2)(n+3)} = \lambda^{n+1}\left\{\frac{(a(n+1)+b)\lambda}{n+3} - \frac{an+b}{n+2}\right\}.$$

Equating coefficients, we must have

$$(\lambda-1)a = 1, \quad 3a(\lambda-1)+b(\lambda-1) = 2, \quad 2(a+b)\lambda - 3b = 1,$$

From the first two, $(\lambda-1)(a+b) = 0$, whence from the third $b = -\frac{1}{3}$, so that $a = \frac{1}{3}$, $\lambda = 4$.

Thus the series can be summed if $\lambda = 4$, and we have for the sum

$$\left[\frac{(x-1)\,4^{x+1}}{3(x+2)}\right]_0^n = \frac{4^{n+1}(n-1)}{3(n+2)} + \frac{2}{3}.$$

This example is due to Boole, who explains the peculiarity as follows :

$$u_n = \lambda^n - \frac{4\lambda^n}{n+2} + \frac{\lambda^n}{n+1},$$

so that unless $\lambda = 4$, in which case the term $\dfrac{\lambda^n}{n+1}$ destroys the corresponding term $\dfrac{-4\lambda^{n-1}}{n+1}$ in u_{n-1}, we should require the sum of a series whose nth term is $\dfrac{\lambda^n}{n+1}$. Such a sum cannot be obtained in terms of the elementary functions considered here (but see Chapter IX).

EXAMPLES II

1. Prove that

$$\text{(i)}\quad \Delta \log u(x) = \log\left(1+\frac{\Delta u(x)}{u(x)}\right);$$

$$\text{(ii)}\quad \Delta \log(u_x u_{x-1} \dots u_{x-m+1}) = \log \frac{u_{x+1}}{u_{x-m+1}}.$$

2. Prove that

$$\overset{n}{\Delta} \sin(ax+b) = (2\sin\tfrac{1}{2}a)^n \sin\{ax+b+\tfrac{1}{2}n(a+\pi)\},$$

$$\overset{n}{\Delta} \cos(ax+b) = (2\sin\tfrac{1}{2}a)^n \cos\{ax+b+\tfrac{1}{2}n(a+\pi)\}.$$

Obtain corresponding results for the operator $\overset{n}{\underset{\omega}{\Delta}}$, and deduce the results for the operator D^n.

3. Prove that

$$\Delta \tan ax = \frac{\sin a}{\cos ax \cos a(x+1)},$$

$$\Delta \tan^{-1} ax = \tan^{-1} \frac{a}{1+a^2x+a^2x^2}.$$

4. Evaluate $\Delta \tan u_x$, $\Delta \tan^{-1} u_x$.

5. Find the first differences of

$$2^x \sin \frac{a}{2^x}, \quad \tan \frac{a}{2^x}, \quad \cot(a \,.\, 2^x).$$

6. Shew that

$$\underset{\omega}{\Delta} \frac{u_x}{v_x} = \frac{v_x \underset{\omega}{\Delta} u_x - u_x \underset{\omega}{\Delta} v_x}{v_x v_{x+\omega}}.$$

7. Prove that

$$\overset{n}{\Delta} 0^m = n^m - \binom{n}{1}(n-1)^m + \binom{n}{2}(n-2)^m - \dots,$$

$$n! = n^n - \binom{n}{1}(n-1)^n + \binom{n}{2}(n-2)^n - \dots.$$

8. If $\phi(\lambda)$ be a polynomial, shew that

$$\phi(\mathsf{E})\, 0^n = \mathsf{E}\, \phi'(\mathsf{E})\, 0^{n-1},$$

and deduce 2·53 (2).

9. From Herschel's Theorem, or otherwise, deduce the secondary form of Maclaurin's Theorem, namely,

$$\phi(t) = \phi(0) + t\,\phi(D)\,0 + \frac{t^2}{2!}\phi(D)\,0^2 + \frac{t^3}{3!}\phi(D)\,0^3 + \dots,$$

where $\phi(D)\,0^s$ is the value when $t = 0$ of $\phi(D)\,t^s$.

10. If $\mathsf{E}^n 0^x$ denote n^x, prove that

$$\phi(\mathsf{E}^n)\, 0^x = n^x \phi(\mathsf{E})\, 0^x.$$

11. Shew that the differences of zero

$$\overset{n}{\Delta} 0^n, \ \overset{n}{\Delta} 0^{n+1}, \ \overset{n}{\Delta} 0^{n+2}, \dots$$

form a recurring series and find the scale of relation.

12. If $C_x^n = \dfrac{1}{n!} \overset{n}{\Delta} 0^x$, shew that

$$C_x^n = C_{x-1}^{n-1} + n\, C_{x-1}^n.$$

13. Shew that

$$u_0+u_1x+\frac{u_2x^2}{2!}+\ldots=e^x\left\{u_0+x\Delta u_0+\frac{x^2}{2!}\overset{2}{\Delta}u_0+\ldots\right\},$$

where u_x is a polynomial.

14. If $S_n=\frac{1}{1\,.\,n}+\frac{1}{2(n-1)}+\ldots+\frac{1}{n\,.\,1}$, shew that, if $m>2$,

$$(S_1\overset{2}{\Delta}-S_2\overset{3}{\Delta}+\ldots)\,0^m=0.$$

15. Express $\overset{n}{\Delta}x^m$ in a series of terms, proceeding by powers of x, by means of the differences of zero.

Find a finite expression for the infinite series

$$1^m\,.\,x\;-\;3^m\,.\,\frac{x^3}{3!}+5^m\,.\,\frac{x^5}{5!}-\ldots,$$

where m is a positive integer. If $m=4$, shew that the result is

$$(x-6x^3)\cos x-(7x^2-x^4)\sin x.$$

16. Prove that

$$(x\Delta)^{(n)}u_x=(x+n-1)^{(n)}\overset{n}{\Delta}u_x,$$

$$f(x\Delta)(x\mathsf{E})^m u_x=(x\mathsf{E})^m f(x\Delta+m)u_x.$$

17. Find u_n from the relation

$$\sum_{n=0}^{\infty}t^n u_n=\frac{1-\sqrt{1-4t^2}}{2t}.$$

18. If $\sum_{n=0}^{\infty}t^n u_n=f(e^t)$, prove that

$$u_n=\frac{f(\mathsf{E})}{n!}\,0^n.$$

19. Find a symbolical expression for the nth difference of the product of any number of functions in terms of the differences of the separate functions, and deduce Leibniz' Theorem therefrom.

20. If the operator Δ act on n alone, prove that

$$\int_0^\infty\overset{m}{\Delta}\frac{x^{a+1}}{x^2+n^2}\,dx=\tfrac{1}{2}(-1)^{k+1}\frac{\pi}{\sin\frac{1}{2}a\pi}\overset{m}{\Delta}n^a,$$

m being a positive integer greater than a and $2k$ the even integer next greater than $a+1$.

21. Shew that

$$\overset{n-1}{\Delta}\, 2^p = \frac{\overset{n}{\Delta}\, 1^{p+1} + \overset{n-1}{\Delta}\, 1^p}{n+1}.$$

22. Prove that

$$\overset{n}{\Delta}\, 1^{p+1} = (n+1)\overset{n}{\Delta}\, 1^p + n\overset{n-1}{\Delta}\, 1^p,$$

and apply the formula to constructing a table of differences of powers of unity up to the fifth power.

23. Prove that

$$(-1)^n f(x+n\omega) = f(x) - 2\binom{n}{1}\underset{\omega}{\nabla} f(x) + 2^2\binom{n}{2}\overset{2}{\underset{\omega}{\nabla}} f(x) - \dots.$$

24. Prove that

$$\underset{\omega}{\Delta}\,\underset{\omega}{\nabla} f(x) = \underset{2\omega}{\Delta} f(x),$$

$$\overset{n}{\underset{\omega}{\Delta}}\,\overset{n}{\underset{\omega}{\nabla}} f(x) = \overset{n}{\underset{2\omega}{\Delta}} f(x).$$

25. Sum to n terms the following series

(i) $1.3.5.7+3.5.7.9+\dots.$

(ii) $\dfrac{1}{1.3.5.7}+\dfrac{1}{3.5.7.9}+\dots.$

(iii) $1.3.5.10+3.5.7.12+5.7.9.14+\dots.$

(iv) $\dfrac{10}{1.3.5}+\dfrac{12}{3.5.7}+\dfrac{14}{5.7.9}+\dots.$

(v) $1.3.5\cos\theta+3.5.7\cos 2\theta+5.7.9\cos 3\theta+\dots.$

(vi) $1+2a\cos\theta+3a^2\cos 2\theta+4a^3\cos 3\theta+\dots.$

26. The successive orders of figurate numbers are defined by this;—that the xth term of any order is equal to the sum of the first x terms of the order next preceding, while the terms of the first order are each equal to unity. Shew that the xth term of the nth order is

$$\frac{x(x+1)\dots(x+n-2)}{(n-1)!}.$$

27. Prove that $\mathsf{P}_{(x)}^{-1}\phi(t)\cos mt = f(x)-f(0)$, where $f(x)$ is equal to the expression

$$\frac{\sin\frac{m}{2}(2x-1)}{2\sin\frac{m}{2}}\phi(x)+\frac{\cos\frac{m}{2}(2x)}{\left(2\sin\frac{m}{2}\right)^2}\Delta\phi(x)-\frac{\sin\frac{m}{2}(2x+1)}{\left(2\sin\frac{m}{2}\right)^3}\overset{2}{\Delta}\phi(x)$$

$$-\frac{\cos\frac{m}{2}(2x+2)}{\left(2\sin\frac{m}{2}\right)^4}\overset{3}{\Delta}\phi(x)+\frac{\sin\frac{m}{2}(2x+3)}{\left(2\sin\frac{m}{2}\right)^5}\overset{4}{\Delta}\phi(x)+\dots .$$

28. Prove that

$$\mathsf{P}_{(x)}^{-n}a^t\phi(t)$$

$$=\frac{a^x}{(a-1)^n}\left\{\phi(x)-n\frac{a}{a-1}\Delta\phi(x)+\frac{n(n+1)}{2!}\left(\frac{a}{a-1}\right)^2\overset{2}{\Delta}\phi(x)-\dots\right\}$$

$$+C_0+C_1x+\dots+C_{n-1}x^{(n-1)},$$

and determine the constants $C_0, C_1, \dots, C_{n-1}$.

29. Use the result of Ex. 28 to discuss the summation of the series

$$u_1-u_2+u_3-u_4+\dots$$

to n terms. Consider the forms of u_x given in sections 2·71-2·76.

30. Prove that to n terms

(i) $$\frac{1}{\sin\theta}+\frac{1}{\sin 2\theta}+\frac{1}{\sin 4\theta}+\dots=\cot\tfrac{1}{2}\theta-\cot 2^{n-1}\theta\,;$$

(ii) $$\frac{1}{\cos\theta\cos 2\theta}+\frac{1}{\cos 2\theta\cos 3\theta}+\dots=\frac{2\sin n\theta}{\cos(n+1)\theta\sin 2\theta}.$$

31. Shew that $\mathsf{P}^{-1}\cot^{-1}(p+q+rx^2)$ can be evaluated in finite terms if $q^2-r^2=4(pr-1)$. Calculate:

$$\mathsf{P}_{(n)}^{-1}\tan^{-1}\frac{\lambda}{1+x(x-1)\lambda^2},\quad \mathsf{P}_{(n)}^{-1}\frac{\log\tan 2^x\alpha}{2^x},\quad \mathsf{P}_{(n)}^{-1}\frac{2^x(x-1)}{x(x+1)}.$$

32. It is always possible to assign such real or imaginary values to s that $\mathsf{P}^{-1}f(x)$ can be evaluated in finite terms, where

$$f(x)=\frac{(\alpha+\beta x+\gamma x^2+\dots+\nu x^n)\,s^x}{u_x u_{x+1}\dots u_{x+m-1}},$$

$\alpha, \beta, \dots, \nu$ being any constants, and $u_x = ax+b$. (Herschel.

33. Shew that

$$u_0+u_1\cos 2\theta+u_2\cos 4\theta+\dots$$

$$=\tfrac{1}{2}u_0-\frac{\Delta u_0}{4\sin^2\theta}+\frac{\overset{2}{\Delta} u_0}{8\sin^3\theta}\sin\theta+\frac{\overset{3}{\Delta} u_0}{16\sin^4\theta}\cos 2\theta-\frac{\overset{4}{\Delta} u_0}{32\sin^5\theta}\sin 3\theta-\dots.$$

34. If $\phi(x)=v_0+v_1x+v_2x^2+\dots,$ shew that

$$u_0v_0+u_1v_1x+u_2v_2x^2+\dots$$

$$=u_0\phi(x)+x\,\phi'(x)\,\Delta u_0+\frac{x^2}{2!}\phi''(x)\overset{2}{\Delta} u_0+\dots,$$

and if $\phi(x)=v_0+v_1x+v_2x^{(2)}+\dots,$ then

$$u_0v_0+u_1v_1x+u_2v_2x^{(2)}+\dots$$

$$=u_0\,\phi(x)+x\,\Delta\,\phi(x-1)\,.\,\Delta u_0+\binom{x}{2}\overset{2}{\Delta}\phi(x-2)\,.\,\overset{2}{\Delta} u_0+\dots.$$

(Gudermann.)

35. If $S_n=1^n+2^n+\dots+m^n$ and $p=m(m+1)$, shew that

$$S_n=p^2f(p)\quad\text{or}\quad(2m+1)\,pf(p),$$

according as n is odd or even, $f(p)$ being a polynomial.

36. Prove that the number of ways in which an integer which is the product of m prime numbers can be expressed as a product of factors relatively prime to each other is

$$S_m=\sum_{r=0}^{m}\overset{r}{\Delta}\,0^m/r!.$$

Prove also that S_m satisfies the recurrence relation

$$S_{m+1}=S_m+\binom{m}{1}S_{m-1}+\binom{m}{2}S_{m-2}+\dots+\binom{m}{m}.$$

37. Prove that

$$S_m=e^{-1}\sum_{r=0}^{\infty}r^m/r!,$$

and that, if m is a prime number, S_m-2 is divisible by m.

CHAPTER III

INTERPOLATION

In the practical applications of the finite calculus the problem of interpolation is the following: given the values of a function for a finite set of arguments, to determine the value of the function for some intermediate argument.

In the absence of further knowledge as to the nature of the function this problem is, in the general case, indeterminate, since the values for arguments other than those given can obviously be assigned arbitrarily.

If, however, certain analytic properties of the function be given, it is often possible to assign limits to the error committed in calculating the function from values given for a limited set of arguments. For example, when the function is known to be representable by a polynomial of degree n, the value for any argument is completely determinate when the values for $n+1$ distinct arguments are given. In the present chapter we propose to obtain certain formulae based on the successive differences of the function for the given arguments and to investigate the remainder term, the knowledge of which will enable us to decide as to what further information is necessary to ascertain limits within which the interpolated value represents the value sought. In actual calculations there is, of course, another source of error due to the fact that the known values are usually approximations obtained by curtailing at, let us say, the fifth figure a number which contains more than five figures. For an investigation of this error see papers by W. F. Sheppard.*

The basis of the interpolation formulae about to be obtained is the general formula of Newton for interpolation with divided differences.

* *Proc. London Math. Soc.* (2), 4 (1907), p. 320; 10 (1912), p. 139.

This formula with its remainder term has already been given. The formulae of Gauss, Stirling and Bessel were known to Newton, and if for brevity we do not attach his name to them, it does not detract from his credit in discovering them.

3·0. Divided Differences for Equidistant Arguments. If in the formula 1·3 (1), we put

$$x_s = x + s\omega, \quad s = 1, 2, 3, \dots, n,$$

we obtain for the divided difference the expression

$$[xx_1x_2 \dots x_n] = \frac{f(x+n\omega)}{n!\,\omega^n} - \frac{f(x+(n-1)\,\omega)}{(n-1)!\,1!\,\omega^n} + \frac{f(x+(n-2)\,\omega)}{(n-2)!\,2!\,\omega^n} - \dots$$

$$= \frac{1}{n!}\overset{n}{\underset{\omega}{\Delta}} f(x) \qquad \text{from 2·5 (2).}$$

Since the arguments in a divided difference can be written in any order we have thus proved the following theorem.

If the arguments $x_1, x_2, \dots, x_{n+1}$ taken in a certain order form an arithmetical progression whose first term is x_ν and whose common difference is ω, the divided difference of $f(x)$ formed with these arguments is given by the relations

$$(1) \qquad [x_1x_2x_3 \dots x_{n+1}] = \frac{1}{n!}\overset{n}{\underset{\omega}{\Delta}} f(x_\nu) = \frac{\omega^{-n}}{n!}\,\varDelta^n f(x_\nu).$$

Again by 1·2 (2), we have

$$[x_1x_2 \dots x_{n+1}] = \frac{1}{n!}\,f^{(n)}(\xi),$$

where ξ lies in the interval $(x_\nu, x_\nu+n\omega)$.

Thus we have

$$(2) \qquad \overset{n}{\underset{\omega}{\Delta}} f(x_\nu) = f^{(n)}(\xi),$$

where ξ is some point of the interval $(x_\nu, x_\nu+n\omega)$.

In the notation of differences this result can be written, using 2·1 (5),

$$(3) \qquad f^{(n)}(\xi) = \omega^{-n}\varDelta^n f(x_\nu).$$

This result shows that the nth column of differences formed from a table of functional values for equidistant arguments places before us a specimen set of values of the nth derivate of the function, each such derivate being multiplied by ω^n, which is a constant for the column in question.

3·1. Newton's Interpolation Formula (Forward Differences). Consider the following table of functional values and differences.

Argument	Function				
a	$f(a)$				
		$\Delta f(a)$			
$a+\omega$	$f(a+\omega)$		$\Delta^2 f(a)$		
		$\Delta f(a+\omega)$		$\Delta^3 f(a)$	
$a+2\omega$	$f(a+2\omega)$		$\Delta^2 f(a+\omega)$		.
		$\Delta f(a+2\omega)$		$\Delta^3 f(a+\omega)$	
$a+3\omega$	$f(a+3\omega)$		$\Delta^2 f(a+2\omega)$		.
		.		.	
.	.		.		.

If in Newton's general interpolation formula with divided differences, 1·1 (1), we write

$$x_s = a+(s-1)\,\omega, \quad s = 1, 2, 3, \dots, n,$$

we have by 3·0 and 1·2 (3)

$$[x_1 x_2 \dots x_{s+1}] = \frac{\omega^{-s}}{s!}\,\Delta^s f(a),$$

$$[x x_1 \dots x_n] = \frac{f^{(n)}(\xi)}{n!},$$

so that the formula gives

$$(1)\quad f(x) = f(a) + (x-a)\,\omega^{-1}\Delta f(a) + \frac{(x-a)(x-a-\omega)}{2!}\,\omega^{-2}\Delta^2 f(a) + \dots$$
$$+ \frac{(x-a)(x-a-\omega)\dots(x-a-n\omega+2\omega)}{(n-1)!}\,\omega^{-n+1}\Delta^{n-1} f(a) + R_n(x),$$

where

$$(2)\qquad R_n(x) = \frac{(x-a)(x-a-\omega)\dots(x-a-n\omega+\omega)}{n!}\,f^{(n)}(\xi),$$

and ξ lies somewhere in the interval bounded by the greatest and least of x, a, $a+n\omega-\omega$.

This is Newton's Interpolation formula with forward differences. The differences employed with this formula lie on a line sloping downwards from $f(a)$. The formula gives the value of $f(x)$ in terms of $f(a)$ and the differences of $f(a)$ provided that we can calculate the remainder term $R_n(x)$. The formula assumes a simpler form if we introduce the *phase* p, where

$$p = (x-a) / \omega, \tag{3}$$

which represents the ratio of the "distance" between the "points" x and a to the tabular interval of the argument. We then obtain

$$f(x) = f(a) + p\Delta f(a) + \binom{p}{2} \Delta^2 f(a) + \binom{p}{3} \Delta^3 f(a) + \dots \\ + \binom{p}{n-1} \Delta^{n-1} f(a) + \binom{p}{n} \omega^n f^{(n)}(\xi), \tag{4}$$

which is the most convenient form of Newton's formula with forward differences, the value of p being given by (3).

If in (4) we omit the remainder term, we obtain Newton's Interpolation polynomial (see 1·9)

$$I_{n-1}(x) = f(a) + p\Delta f(a) + \binom{p}{2} \Delta^2 f(a) + \dots + \binom{p}{n-1} \Delta^{n-1} f(a), \tag{5}$$

which assumes the values of $f(x)$ at the points

$$a,\ a+\omega,\ \dots,\ a+(n-1)\,\omega.$$

It follows that neglect of the remainder term is equivalent to replacing $f(x)$ by this interpolation polynomial. The degree of approximation attained by this process of polynomial interpolation of course depends on the magnitude of the neglected remainder term. This will be discussed in section 3·12.

We may here observe that the interpolation polynomial (5) can be written symbolically in the form

$$I_{n-1}(x) \doteqdot (1+\Delta)^p_{(n-1)} f(a), \tag{6}$$

where the suffix $n-1$ indicates that the expansion of the operator by the binomial theorem is to cease after the term in Δ^{n-1} has been obtained.

Newton's formula, or rather the series which arises from it when the number of terms is unlimited, is of great theoretical importance, as will be seen in Chapter X. For practical numerical interpolation the central difference formulae to be obtained later are preferred. Near the beginning of a table, however, when central differences are not given, Newton's forward formula is available.

In the above work we have written Newton's formula in the notation of differences, the form best suited to numerical applications. We can, however, use difference quotients. Using 2·1 (5), we see at once that (1) can be written

$$(7) \quad f(x) = f(a) + (x-a) \underset{\omega}{\Delta} f(a) + \frac{(x-a)(x-a-\omega)}{2!} \overset{2}{\underset{\omega}{\Delta}} f(a) + \dots$$
$$+ \frac{(x-a)(x-a-\omega)\dots(x-a-n\omega+2\omega)}{(n-1)!} \overset{n-1}{\underset{\omega}{\Delta}} f(a) + R_n(x).$$

Or in the factorial notation,

$$(8) \quad f(x) = f(a) + (x-a) \underset{\omega}{\Delta} f(a) + \frac{(x-a)^{(2\omega)}}{2!} \overset{2}{\underset{\omega}{\Delta}} f(a) + \dots$$
$$+ \frac{(x-a)^{(n\omega-\omega)}}{(n-1)!} \overset{n-1}{\underset{\omega}{\Delta}} f(a) + \frac{(x-a)^{(n\omega)}}{n!} f^{(n)}(\xi).$$

When $\omega \to 0$ we obtain Taylor's Theorem, namely,

$$f(x) = f(a) + (x-a) f'(a) + \frac{(x-a)^2}{2!} f''(a) + \dots$$
$$+ \frac{(x-a)^{n-1}}{(n-1)!} f^{(n-1)}(a) + \frac{(x-a)^n}{n!} f^{(n)}(\xi),$$

where ξ lies in the interval (a, x).

The formula of this section is often referred to as the Gregory-Newton formula, since it was actually discovered by James Gregory in 1670.*

3·11. Newton's Interpolation Formula (Backward Differences).

Here we consider the table

.	.		.		.
		.		.	
$a-3\omega$	$f(a-3\omega)$		$\Delta^2 f(a-4\omega)$		.
		$\Delta f(a-3\omega)$		$\Delta^3 f(a-4\omega)$	
$a-2\omega$	$f(a-2\omega)$		$\Delta^2 f(a-3\omega)$		.
		$\Delta f(a-2\omega)$		$\Delta^3 f(a-3\omega)$	
$a-\omega$	$f(a-\omega)$		$\Delta^2 f(a-2\omega)$		
		$\Delta f(a-\omega)$			
a	$f(a)$				

* The actual MS. letter from Gregory to Collins which gives this formula is dated 23 November 1670, and is preserved among other of its contemporary documents in the library of the Royal Society.

If in 1·1 (1) we write

$$x_s = a-(s-1)\omega, \quad s = 1, 2, \dots, n,$$

we have by the theorem of 3·0

$$[x_1 x_2 \dots x_{s+1}] = \frac{\omega^{-s}}{s!} \Delta^s f(a-s\omega).$$

Thus we have

$$f(x) = f(a) + (x-a)\omega^{-1}\Delta f(a-\omega)$$
$$+\frac{(x-a)(x-a+\omega)}{2!}\omega^{-2}\Delta^2 f(a-2\omega)+\dots,$$

or introducing again the phase $p = (x-a)/\omega$, this becomes

$$f(x) = f(a) + p\Delta f(a-\omega) + \frac{p(p+1)}{2!}\Delta^2 f(a-2\omega)+\dots,$$

which can be written

(1) $$f(x) = f(a) + p\Delta f(a-\omega) + \binom{p+1}{2}\Delta^2 f(a-2\omega)+\dots$$
$$+\binom{p+n-2}{n-1}\Delta^{n-1} f(a-n\omega+\omega) + \binom{p+n-1}{n}\omega^n f^{(n)}(\xi),$$

where ξ lies in the interval bounded by the greatest and least of x, a, $a-(n-1)\omega$. This result could also be obtained by writing the tabular values in the reversed order, differencing, and then applying the forward formula.

The differences employed with this formula lie on a line sloping upwards from $f(a)$. The corresponding interpolation polynomial obtained by omitting the remainder term may be written symbolically in the form

$$J_{n-1}(x) \doteqdot \Big[1 + p\Delta \mathsf{E}^{-\omega} + \binom{p+1}{2}\Delta^2 \mathsf{E}^{-2\omega} + \dots$$
$$+\binom{p+n-2}{n-1}\Delta^{n-1}\mathsf{E}^{n\omega-\omega}\Big] f(a)$$
$$\doteqdot (1-\Delta\mathsf{E}^{-\omega})^{-p}_{(n-1)} f(a),$$

where the suffix again indicates the index of the last term of the binomial expansion which is to be retained.

Newton's backward formula has its practical application to interpolation near the end of a table, when central differences are not given.

3·12. The Remainder Term. The process of interpolation applied to the values in a given table cannot of course give an accuracy greater than that of the values in the table, which are in themselves usually approximations. In attempting to attain the utmost accuracy which the table permits, when a given interpolation formula is used, it is common practice to omit from the interpolation formula the first term which ceases to influence the result obtained. The question then arises as to how far the result so obtained represents the desired approximation.

The error in the approximation arises from two sources: (i) errors of rounding, inherent in the tabular matter and the subsequent calculations; (ii) errors due to neglect of the remainder term. With regard to errors of the first category we shall content ourselves with the observation that, in so far as they arise from subsequent calculations, these errors can be minimised by using one or two extra figures which are subsequently discarded. As to the errors arising from (ii) we shall make some observations, with particular reference to Newton's forward formula, but which are of general application.

(*a*) In numerical work we naturally take x between a and $a+\omega$, so that the phase p is positive and less than unity. Consequently $\binom{p}{n}$ and $\binom{p}{n+1}$ are of opposite sign.

(*b*) If we can conveniently calculate $f^{(n)}(x)$ we can generally state upper and lower bounds to the value of this derivate in the interval $(a, a+(n-1)\omega)$ and thus delimit the error due to neglect of the remainder term.

(*c*) If $f^{(n)}(x)$ have a fixed sign in the interval $(a, a+(n-1)\omega)$ and $f^{(n+1)}(x)$ have the same fixed sign in the interval $(a, a+n\omega)$, then the inclusion of an extra term in the interpolation formula gives

$$R_n(x) = \binom{p}{n} \Delta^n f(a) + R_{n+1}(x).$$

Since, by (*a*), $\binom{p}{n}$ and $\binom{p}{n+1}$ have opposite signs, so also have $R_n(x)$ and $R_{n+1}(x)$: and consequently

$$\left|R_n(x)\right| < \left|\binom{p}{n} \Delta^n f(a)\right| :$$

that is, $R_n(x)$ is less than the first term omitted from the formula and has the same sign. This result is called by Steffensen the Error Test.* The test depends essentially on $R_n(x)$ and $R_{n+1}(x)$ having opposite signs.

(*d*) If nothing be known about the value or sign of $f^{(n)}(x)$, we can only regard the results of interpolation as a working hypothesis. This in particular would be the case if the tabular matter were empirical. In such cases we might be inclined to estimate the value of $f^{(n)}(x)$, on the grounds of the last part of section 3·0, by an examination of the nth column of differences. That such conjecture may be fallacious is seen from the following table :

x	$f(x)$		
0	0		
		1	
1	1		2
		3	
2	4		2
		5	
3	9		

We have

$$f(0{\cdot}5) = 0 + {\cdot}5 \times 1 - \frac{{\cdot}5 \times {\cdot}5}{2} \times 2 + \frac{{\cdot}5 \times {\cdot}5 \times 1{\cdot}5}{6} f^{(3)}(\xi)$$

$$= 0{\cdot}25 + \tfrac{1}{16} f^{(3)}(\xi).$$

The third difference is zero, so that an estimate of the error term would be zero and we would conclude that $f(0{\cdot}5) = 0{\cdot}25$.

This is correct if $f(x) = x^2$. If, however,

$$f(x) = x^2 + \sin \pi x, \quad f^{(3)}(x) = -\pi^3 \cos \pi x,$$

the maximum value of which is π^3, and the actual error is 1.

It might be contended that the instance is extremely artificial. To this we answer that a satisfactory mathematical theory must not exclude possibilities of such a nature, and, secondly, that if tabular matter be collected from observations made at equal intervals (say of time), a periodic term might quite well be masked in this manner.

---

* J. F. Steffensen, *Interpolation*, London (1927).

Example. From the following values * calculate

$$\sin 0{\cdot}1604, \quad \cos 0{\cdot}1616.$$

x	$\sin x$	$\underset{+}{\Delta}$	$\underset{-}{\Delta^2}$	$\cos x$	$\underset{-}{\Delta}$	$\underset{-}{\Delta^2}$
0·160	0·15931 82066			0·98722 72834		
		9871475			1598118	
·161	·16030 53541		1604	·98706 74716		9871
		9869871			1607989	
·162	·16129 23412			·98690 66727		

Using Newton's forward formula, we have for the sine

$$p = \frac{\cdot 0004}{\cdot 001} = \cdot 4.$$

The coefficient of the second difference is $\frac{1}{2} \times \cdot 4 \times - \cdot 6 = - \cdot 12$, while, since $\omega = \cdot 001$, the coefficient of the remainder term is

$$\tfrac{1}{6} \times \cdot 4 \times - \cdot 6 \times - 1{\cdot}6 \times (\cdot 001)^3 = 6{\cdot}4 \times 10^{-11}.$$

Since $f^{(3)}(x) = -\cos x$, the remainder term contributes

$$-6{\cdot}4 \times 10^{-11} \times \cdot 99,$$

that is, 6 in the eleventh decimal place. We have then, treating the tabular values as integers,

$$\sin \cdot 1604 = 1593182066 + 3948590{\cdot}0 + 192{\cdot}5 - \cdot 6 = 0{\cdot}1597130848.$$

For the cosine, using Newton's backward formula, we have $p = - \cdot 4$ and the coefficients $- \cdot 12$, $-6{\cdot}4 \times 10^{-11}$.

Here $f^{(3)}(x) = \sin x$, so that the remainder term contributes

$$-6{\cdot}4 \times 10^{-11} \times \cdot 16 = -1 \times 10^{-11}.$$

Thus

$$\cos \cdot 1616 = 9869066727 + 643195{\cdot}6 + 1184{\cdot}5 - \cdot 1 = 0{\cdot}9869711107.$$

In these values the only errors which can be present are those due to rounding.

3·2. The Interpolation Formulae of Gauss.

These are obtained from Newton's general divided difference formula, 1·1 (1), by means of a special distribution of the arguments $x_1, x_2, \ldots, x_n$.

* C. E. van Orstrand, *Nat. Academy of Sciences*, xiv, (1921), Part 5.

It is again convenient to introduce the phase

(1) $$p = (x-a)/\omega,$$

and to write

$$f(x) = f(a+p\omega) = u_p.$$

With the central difference notation of 2·01 we then have the table

(2)
$$\begin{array}{cccccccc} a & u_0 & & \delta^2 u_0 & & \delta^4 u_0 & & \\ & & \delta u_{\frac{1}{2}} & & \delta^3 u_{\frac{1}{2}} & & \delta^5 u_{\frac{1}{2}} & \\ a+\omega & u_1 & & & & & & \end{array}$$

If we put

(3) $$x_1 = a, \quad x_{2s} = a+s\omega, \quad x_{2s+1} = a-s\omega,$$

the theorem of 3·0 gives

$$[x_1x_2 \dots x_{2s+1}] = \frac{\omega^{-2s}}{(2s)!}\Delta^{2s}f(a-s\omega) = \frac{\omega^{-2s}}{(2s)!}\delta^{2s}u_0,$$

$$[x_1x_2 \dots x_{2s+2}] = \frac{\omega^{-2s-1}}{(2s+1)!}\Delta^{2s+1}f(a-s\omega) = \frac{\omega^{-2s-1}}{(2s+1)!}\delta^{2s+1}u_{\frac{1}{2}},$$

while

$$\begin{aligned}(x-x_1)(x-x_2)\dots(x-x_{2s}) \\ &= (x-x_{2s-1})(x-x_{2s-3})\dots(x-x_3)(x-x_1)(x-x_2)(x-x_4)\dots(x-x_{2s}) \\ &= (p+s-1)(p+s-2)\dots(p+1)p(p-1)(p-2)\dots(p-s)\,\omega^{2s} \\ &= \binom{p+s-1}{2s}(2s)!\,\omega^{2s}.\end{aligned}$$

Thus

$$(x-x_1)(x-x_2)\dots(x-x_{2s})[x_1x_2\dots x_{2s+1}] = \binom{p+s-1}{2s}\delta^{2s}u_0,$$

and similarly we can shew that

$$(x-x_1)(x-x_2)\dots(x-x_{2s+1})[x_1x_2\dots x_{2s+2}] = \binom{p+s}{2s+1}\delta^{2s+1}u_{\frac{1}{2}}.$$

If then we make in 1·1 (1) the substitutions given by (3), we obtain

$$f(x) = u_p = u_0 + \binom{p}{1}\delta u_{\frac{1}{2}} + \binom{p}{2}\delta^2 u_0 + \binom{p+1}{3}\delta^3 u_{\frac{1}{2}} + \binom{p+1}{4}\delta^4 u_0 + \dots + R_n(x).$$

This is Gauss' forward formula, and is used in conjunction with the zig-zag scheme of differences shewn in (2).

If $n = 2m$, we have

$$R_{2m}(x) = (x-x_1)(x-x_2)\ldots(x-x_{2m})f^{(2m)}(\xi)\,/\,(2m)!$$
$$= \binom{p+m-1}{2m}\omega^{2m}f^{(2m)}(\xi),$$

and Gauss' forward formula becomes

$$(4)\quad f(x) = u_p = u_0 + \sum_{s=0}^{m-1}\binom{p+s}{2s+1}\delta^{2s+1}u_{\frac{1}{2}} + \sum_{s=1}^{m-1}\binom{p+s-1}{2s}\delta^{2s}u_0$$
$$+\binom{p+m-1}{2m}\omega^{2m}f^{(2m)}(\xi),$$

where ξ lies in the interval $(a-(m-1)\omega,\ a+m\omega)$, when x lies in this interval.

If $n = 2m+1$, we have

$$(5)\quad f(x) = u_p = u_0 + \sum_{s=0}^{m-1}\binom{p+s}{2s+1}\delta^{2s+1}u_{\frac{1}{2}} + \sum_{s=1}^{m}\binom{p+s-1}{2s}\delta^{2s}u_0$$
$$+\binom{p+m}{2m+1}\omega^{2m+1}f^{(2m+1)}(\xi),$$

where ξ lies in the interval $(a-m\omega,\ a+m\omega)$, when x lies in this interval.

Gauss' backward formula is used in conjunction with the table

$$(6)\quad \begin{array}{llllllll} a-\omega & u_{-1} & & & & & & \\ & & \delta u_{-\frac{1}{2}} & & \delta^3 u_{-\frac{1}{2}} & & \delta^5 u_{-\frac{1}{2}} & \\ a & u_0 & & \delta^2 u_0 & & \delta^4 u_0 & & \end{array}$$

To obtain the formula we write

$$x_1 = a,\quad x_{2s} = a - s\omega,\quad x_{2s+1} = a + s\omega$$

in the formula 1·1 (1). We then obtain by the method described above

$$(x-x_1)(x-x_2)\ldots(x-x_{2s}) = \binom{p+s}{2s}\delta^{2s}u_0,$$

$$(x-x_1)(x-x_2)\ldots(x-x_{2s+1}) = \binom{p+s}{2s+1}\delta^{2s+1}u_{-\frac{1}{2}},$$

so that

$$f(x) = u_p = u_0 + \binom{p}{1}\delta u_{-\frac{1}{2}} + \binom{p+1}{2}\delta^2 u_0 + \binom{p+1}{3}\delta^3 u_{-\frac{1}{2}}$$

$$+\binom{p+2}{4}\delta^4 u_0 + \dots + R_n(x),$$

which is the required formula.

If $n = 2m$, we have

$$(7) \qquad f(x) = u_p = u_0 + \sum_{s=0}^{m-1}\binom{p+s}{2s+1}\delta^{2s+1}u_{-\frac{1}{2}} + \sum_{s=1}^{m-1}\binom{p+s}{2s}\delta^{2s}u_0$$

$$+\binom{p+m}{2m}\omega^{2m}f^{(2m)}(\xi),$$

where ξ, x lie in the interval $(a-m\omega, a+(m-1)\omega)$, while for $n = 2m+1$,

$$(8) \qquad f(x) = u_p = u_0 + \sum_{s=0}^{m-1}\binom{p+s}{2s+1}\delta^{2s+1}u_{-\frac{1}{2}} + \sum_{s=1}^{m}\binom{p+s}{2s}\delta^{2s}u_0$$

$$+\binom{p+m}{2m+1}\omega^{2m+1}f^{(2m+1)}(\xi),$$

where ξ, x lie in the interval $(a-m\omega, a+m\omega)$.

It should be noted that if in (5) and (8) we omit the remainder terms, the corresponding interpolation polynomials terminate at the same difference $\delta^{2m}u_0$, and therefore both agree with $f(x)$ at the same points, and consequently coincide. Thus Gauss' forward formula has the same remainder term as the backward formula if the last difference used in each be of the *same even order*, and both formulae give the same result.

Again, since

$$\binom{p+s}{2s} = \binom{-p+s-1}{2s}, \quad \binom{p+s}{2s+1} = -\binom{-p+s}{2s+1},$$

we see that, if in the forward formula the sign of p be changed, the coefficients of the even order differences coincide with the corresponding coefficients in the backward formula, while the coefficients of the odd order differences are equal in magnitude but opposite in sign to the corresponding coefficients in the backward formula.

3·3. Stirling's Interpolation Formula. Stirling's formula is obtained by taking the arithmetic mean of Gauss' forward and backward formulae.

We have

$$\binom{p+s}{2s+1} = \frac{(p+s)(p+s-1)\dots(p+1)\,p\,(p-1)\dots(p-s)}{(2s+1)!}$$

$$= \frac{p\,(p^2-1^2)(p^2-2^2)\dots(p^2-s^2)}{(2s+1)!},$$

$$\binom{p+s-1}{2s} + \binom{p+s}{2s} = \frac{2p\,(p+s-1)\dots(p-s+1)}{(2s)!}$$

$$= \frac{2p^2(p^2-1^2)(p^2-2^2)\dots(p^2-\overline{s-1}^2)}{(2s)!}.$$

Taking the arithmetic mean of 3·2 (5) and (8), we obtain

$$\text{(1)} \qquad f(x) = u_p = u_0 + \sum_{s=0}^{m-1} \frac{p\,(p^2-1^2)(p^2-2^2)\dots(p^2-s^2)}{(2s+1)!}\,\mu\delta^{2s+1}u_0$$

$$+ \sum_{s=1}^{m} \frac{p^2(p^2-1^2)(p^2-2^2)\dots(p^2-\overline{s-1}^2)}{(2s)!}\,\delta^{2s}u_0$$

$$+ \frac{p\,(p^2-1^2)\dots(p^2-m^2)}{(2m+1)!}\,\omega^{2m+1}f^{(2m+1)}(\xi),$$

where, as before,

$$p = (x-a)/\omega, \quad u_p = f(a+p\omega) = f(x).$$

This is Stirling's formula. The differences employed lie on a horizontal line through u_0 thus:

$$\text{(2)} \qquad a \quad u_0 \quad \mu\delta u_0 \quad \delta^2 u_0 \quad \mu\delta^3 u_0 \quad \delta^4 u_0 \quad \dots .$$

Stirling's formula is completely symmetrical about $p = 0$ and can therefore be used for either positive or negative values of p. In the form (1), which terminates with a difference of even order, the remainder term is the same as in the formulae of Gauss which terminate at the same difference. Hence from the point of view of numerical calculation the formula of Gauss is superior in that there is no necessity to form mean differences.

By taking the mean of 3·2 (4) and (7) we can obtain the remainder term of Stirling's formula when the last difference used is of odd order. It will be seen that this is not of a very simple form.

Stirling's formula written in full for $m = 2$ is

$$(3)\quad f(x) = u_p = u_0 + p\mu\delta u_0 + \frac{p^2}{2!}\delta^2 u_0 + \frac{p(p^2-1)}{3!}\mu\delta^3 u_0$$
$$+\frac{p^2(p^2-1)}{4!}\delta^4 u_0 + \frac{p(p^2-1)(p^2-4)}{5!}\omega^5 f^{(5)}(\xi),$$

where ξ, x lie in the interval $(a-2\omega, a+2\omega)$.

The corresponding interpolation polynomial obtained by omitting the remainder term in (3) agrees with 1·9 (4), which may be regarded as a generalisation of Stirling's formula for unequal intervals of the argument.

Example. Calculate exp (·0075) from the following table: *

x	e^x	Δ	Δ^2
0·006	1·00601 80361		
		10065212	
·007	1·00702 45573		10070
		10075282	
·008	1·00803 20855		

Here $p = \cdot 5$.

The coefficient of the second difference is ·125, and since $\omega = \cdot 001$ the remainder term is $-\cdot 0625 \times (\cdot 001)^3 e^x = -6 \times 10^{-11}$ approximately.

Thus, using Stirling's formula, we have

$$\exp(\cdot 0075) = 10070245573$$
$$+\tfrac{1}{4}(10065212 + 10075282) + \tfrac{1}{8}(10070) - \cdot 6$$
$$= 1\cdot 0075281955.$$

3·4. Bessel's Interpolation Formula. Bessel's formula is obtained by taking the arithmetic mean of Gauss' forward formula with initial argument a and the corresponding backward formula with initial argument $a+\omega$. We choose the forms which terminate with a difference of odd order, that is to say 3·2 (4) and (7).

* C. E. van Orstrand, *loc. cit.* p. 63.

With $p = (x-a)/\omega$, we have

$$f(x) = u_0 + \sum_{s=0}^{m-1} \binom{p+s}{2s+1} \delta^{2s+1} u_{\frac{1}{2}} + \sum_{s=1}^{m-1} \binom{p+s-1}{2s} \delta^{2s} u_0 + \binom{p+m-1}{2m} \omega^{2m} f^{(2m)}(\xi),$$

$$f(x) = u_1 + \sum_{s=0}^{m-1} \binom{p+s-1}{2s+1} \delta^{2s+1} u_{\frac{1}{2}} + \sum_{s=1}^{m-1} \binom{p+s-1}{2s} \delta^{2} u_1 + \binom{p+m-1}{2m} \omega^{2m} f^{(2m)}(\xi).$$

The second of these has been obtained by writing $p-1$ for p in 3·2 (7) since the initial argument is here $a+\omega$. The remainder term is the same in both since each terminates with the same difference, namely $\delta^{2m-1}u_{\frac{1}{2}}$. Taking the arithmetic mean, we obtain

$$f(x) = \mu u_{\frac{1}{2}} + \sum_{s=0}^{m-1} \frac{p-\frac{1}{2}}{2s+1} \binom{p+s-1}{2s} \delta^{2s+1} u_{\frac{1}{2}} + \sum_{s=1}^{m-1} \binom{p+s-1}{2s} \mu\delta^{2s} u_{\frac{1}{2}} + \binom{p+m-1}{2m} \omega^{2m} f^{(2m)}(\xi),$$

where ξ, x are in the interval $(a-(m-1)\omega,\ a+m\omega)$.

This is Bessel's formula. There is symmetry about the argument $a+\frac{1}{2}\omega$, for writing $-p+\frac{1}{2}$ for $p-\frac{1}{2}$, we have

$$\binom{p+s-1}{2s} = \binom{s-p}{2s},$$

so that the coefficients of the differences of even order are unaltered, while the other coefficients merely change sign.

It is convenient to replace $\mu u_{\frac{1}{2}} + (p-\frac{1}{2})\,\delta u_{\frac{1}{2}}$ by $u_0 + p\,\delta u_{\frac{1}{2}}$. The first summation above is then from $s = 1$ to $s = m-1$. Written in full for five differences, we have

$$f(x) = u_0 + p\,\delta u_{\frac{1}{2}} + \frac{p(p-1)}{2!} \mu\delta^2 u_{\frac{1}{2}} + \frac{p(p-\frac{1}{2})(p-1)}{3!} \delta^3 u_{\frac{1}{2}}$$
$$+ \frac{(p+1)p(p-1)(p-2)}{4!} \mu\delta^4 u_{\frac{1}{2}}$$
$$+ \frac{(p+1)p(p-\frac{1}{2})(p-1)(p-2)}{5!} \delta^5 u_{\frac{1}{2}}$$
$$+ \frac{(p+2)(p+1)p(p-1)(p-2)(p-3)}{6!} \omega^6 f^{(6)}(\xi).$$

The differences used with Bessel's formula are shewn in the scheme

a	u_0						
		$\delta u_{\frac{1}{2}}$	$\mu\delta^2 u_{\frac{1}{2}}$	$\delta^3 u_{\frac{1}{2}}$	$\mu\delta^4 u_{\frac{1}{2}}$	$\delta^5 u_{\frac{1}{2}}$	...
$a+\omega$	u_1						

The formula may be compared with 1·9 (3), which shows the more general form for arguments which are not equidistant.

If the last difference used be of even order the remainder term is not so simple.

Example. From the following table * of the Complete Elliptic Integral K, find the value of K when $m = 0{\cdot}032$ where $m(=k^2)$ is the squared modulus.

m	K	Δ	Δ^2	Δ^3	Δ^4
0·01	1·5747 45562				
		3994351			
·02	1·5787 39913		46078		
		4040429		999	
·03	1·5827 80342		47077		23
		4087506		1022	
·04	1·5868 67848		48099		42
		4135605		1064	
·05	1·5910 03453		49163		
		4184768			
·06	1·5951 88221				

Using Bessel's formula, the required value ($p = {\cdot}2$) is

$$1582780342 + {\cdot}2 \times 4087506 - {\cdot}08 \times 47588$$
$$+ {\cdot}008 \times 1022 + \text{remainder}.$$

In the absence of a convenient formula for the fourth order derivate we make the hypothesis that this is approximately represented by $\omega^{-4}\Delta^4$. Since $\omega = {\cdot}01$ we have for the remainder the hypothetical value $+10^{-9} \times {\cdot}0144 \times 33 = 5 \times 10^{-10}$ Thus we obtain $K = 1{\cdot}583594045$.

* L. M. Milne-Thomson, *Proc. London Math. Soc.*, (2), 33 (1932), p. 162.

3·41. Modified Bessel's Formula. Neglecting the remainder term, Bessel's formula correct to differences of the sixth order can be written in the form

$$f(x) = u_0 + p\,\delta u_{\frac{1}{2}} + \frac{p(p-1)}{2}\mu\delta^2 u_{\frac{1}{2}} + \frac{p(p-\frac{1}{2})(p-1)}{3!}[\delta^3 u_{\frac{1}{2}} - k\,\delta^5 u_{\frac{1}{2}}]$$

$$+\frac{(p+1)p(p-1)(p-2)}{4!}[\mu\delta^4 u_{\frac{1}{2}} - l\,\mu\delta^6 u_{\frac{1}{2}}] + A + B,$$

where

$$A = \frac{p(p-\frac{1}{2})(p-1)}{3!}\left[k + \frac{1}{20}(p+1)(p-2)\right]\delta^5 u_{\frac{1}{2}},$$

$$B = \frac{(p+1)p(p-1)(p-2)}{4!}\left[l + \frac{1}{30}(p+2)(p-3)\right]\mu\delta^6 u_{\frac{1}{2}}.$$

The mean value of A over the interval $p = 0$ to $p = \frac{1}{2}$ is

$$2\int_0^{\frac{1}{2}} A\,dp = \frac{2}{3!}\left[\frac{1}{64}k - \frac{13}{60\times 128}\right]\delta^5 u_{\frac{1}{2}},$$

and the mean value of B over the interval 0 to 1 is

$$\int_0^1 B\,dp = \frac{1}{4!}\left[\frac{11l}{30} - \frac{191}{2520}\right]\mu\delta^6 u_{\frac{1}{2}}.$$

These mean values vanish if we take

$$k = \frac{13}{120} = 0{\cdot}108, \quad l = \frac{191}{924} = 0{\cdot}207.$$

Putting

$$\delta_0{}^3 u_{\frac{1}{2}} = \delta^3 u_{\frac{1}{2}} - \frac{13}{120}\delta^5 u_{\frac{1}{2}}, \quad \mu\delta_0{}^4 u_{\frac{1}{2}} = \mu\delta^4 u_{\frac{1}{2}} - \frac{191}{924}\mu\delta^6 u_{\frac{1}{2}},$$

we have the modified form of Bessel's formula, namely,

$$f(x) = u_0 + p\,\delta u_{\frac{1}{2}} + \frac{p(p-1)}{2!}\mu\delta^2 u_{\frac{1}{2}} + \frac{p(p-\frac{1}{2})(p-1)}{3!}\delta_0{}^3 u_{\frac{1}{2}}$$

$$+\frac{(p+2)(p+1)p(p-1)}{4!}\mu\delta_0{}^4 u_{\frac{1}{2}},$$

which includes the effect of sixth order differences. The coefficients of the differences in A and B in the interval $0 \leqslant p \leqslant 1$ are of the orders 0·00002 and 0·00003 respectively, so that, if $\delta^5 u_{\frac{1}{2}}$ and $\mu\delta^6 u_{\frac{1}{2}}$ do not exceed 10,000, the maximum errors which would arise from the neglect of A and B would not exceed 0·2, 0·3 units of the last digit respectively. Actually we use rounded values so that the error may be greater.

The above method of modified differences can of course be extended to differences of higher order and to other interpolation formulae.

Example. Consider the following table* of $\vartheta_3^{-2}(0 \mid \tau)$, where $\vartheta_3(0 \mid \tau)$ is the value of the theta function $\vartheta_3(x \mid \tau)$, when $x = 0$, arranged according to values of m, the squared modulus.

m	$\vartheta_3^{-2}(0 \mid \tau)$	$\underline{\Delta}$	$\underline{\Delta}^2$	$\underline{\Delta}^3$	$\underline{\Delta}^4$	$\underline{\Delta}^5$	$\underline{\Delta}^6$
0·70	0·75687 78205		1161883		5889		109
		54346488		68293		788	
·71	·75144 31717		1230176		6677		145
		55576664		74970		933	
·72	·74588 55053		1305146		7610		166

Forming the reduced differences δ_0^3, $\mu\delta_0^4$, we have the following table for use with Bessel's modified formula.

m	$\vartheta_3^{-2}(0 \mid \tau)$				
0·70	0·75687 78205				
		54346488	1196030	68208	6257
·71	·75144 31717				
		55576664	1267661	74869	7111
·72	·74588 55053				

Calculating the function for $m = \cdot 706$, either by using all the differences or by using the modified formula, we get 0·7536313968.

3·5. Everett's Interpolation Formula. This formula uses even differences only on horizontal lines through u_0 and u_1 as in the scheme

a	u_0	$\delta^2 u_0$	$\delta^4 u_0$	$\delta^6 u_0$	. .
$a+\omega$	u_1	$\delta^2 u_1$	$\delta^4 u_1$	$\delta^6 u_1$	. .

* L. M. Milne-Thomson, *loc. cit.* p. 70.

Gauss' forward formula ending with an odd difference can be written

$$f(x) = u_0 + p\,\delta u_{\frac{1}{2}} + \sum_{s=1}^{m-1} \left\{ \binom{p+s-1}{2s} \delta^{2s} u_0 + \binom{p+s}{2s+1} \delta^{2s+1} u_{\frac{1}{2}} \right\}$$
$$+ \binom{p+m-1}{2m} \omega^{2m} f^{(2m)}(\xi).$$

The term in curled brackets is equal to

$$\frac{(p+s-1)(p+s-2)\dots(p-s)}{(2s+1)!} \left\{ (2s+1)\,\delta^{2s} u_0 + (p+s)\,\delta^{2s+1} u_{\frac{1}{2}} \right\}.$$

Now

$$(2s+1)\delta^{2s} u_0 + (p+s)\delta^{2s+1} u_{\frac{1}{2}} = (2s+1)\delta^{2s} u_0 + (p+s)(\delta^{2s} u_1 - \delta^{2s} u_0)$$
$$= (p+s)\delta^{2s} u_1 - (p-s-1)\delta^{2s} u_0 .$$

Hence we have one form of Everett's formula, namely,

$$f(x) = u_0 + p\,\delta u_{\frac{1}{2}} + \sum_{s=1}^{m-1} \left\{ \binom{p+s}{2s+1} \delta^{2s} u_1 - \binom{p+s-1}{2s+1} \delta^{2} u_0 \right\}$$
$$+ \binom{p+m-1}{2m} \omega^{2m} f^{(2m)}(\xi).$$

A more symmetrical way of writing the formula is obtained by observing that

$$\binom{p+s-1}{2s+1} = -\binom{1-p+s}{2s+1},$$

$$u_0 + p\,\delta u_{\frac{1}{2}} = u_0(1-p) + p\,u_1.$$

Hence introducing the complementary phase p', where

$$p' = 1 - p = (a + \omega - x)/\omega,$$

we have the symmetrical form

$$f(x) = pu_1 + \sum_{s=1}^{m-1} \binom{p+s}{2s+1} \delta^{2s} u_1$$
$$+ p'u_0 + \sum_{s=1}^{m-1} \binom{p'+s}{2s+1} \delta^{2s} u_0 + \binom{p+m-1}{2m} \omega^{2m} f^{(2m)}(\xi),$$

where ξ, x lie in the interval $(a-(m-1)\omega,\ a+m\omega)$.

Everett's formula is useful when employing tables which provide even differences only, a practice which saves space and printing cost but which offers little advantage to the user of the tables.

For numerical values of the coefficients in Everett's formula as well as the formula of Gauss the reader is referred to E. Chappell, *A Table to facilitate Interpolation by the Formulae of Gauss, Bessel and Everett* (1929). (Printed and published by the author, 41 Westcombe Park Road, London, S.E. 3.) The coefficients are given at interval 0·001 for the phase p and for differences up to the sixth order, and are so arranged that the coefficients in Everett's formula for p and the complementary phase p' each appear on the same page. Another table (of Everett's coefficients only) is that by A. J. Thompson, *Tracts for Computers No. V*, 1921, Cambridge University Press. The latter book gives many numerical examples of interpolation.

3·6. Steffensen's Interpolation Formula. Gauss' forward formula ending with an even order difference, 3·2 (5), can be written

$$f(x) = u_0 + \sum_{s=1}^{m} \left\{ \binom{p+s-1}{2s-1} \delta^{2s-1} u_{\frac{1}{2}} + \binom{p+s-1}{2s} \delta^{2s} u_0 \right\} + R_{2m+1}(x).$$

The term in brackets is equal to

$$\frac{1}{2s}\binom{p+s-1}{2s-1}\left\{(p+s)\,\delta^{2s-1}u_{\frac{1}{2}} - (p-s)\,\delta^{2s-1}u_{-\frac{1}{2}}\right\}$$

$$= \binom{p+s}{2s}\delta^{2s-1}u_{\frac{1}{2}} - \binom{p+s-1}{2s}\delta^{2s-1}u_{-\frac{1}{2}}.$$

Now
$$\binom{p+s-1}{2s} = \binom{-p+s}{2s},$$

so that we have

$$f(x) = u_0 - \sum_{s=1}^{m}\binom{-p+s}{2s}\delta^{2s-1}u_{-\frac{1}{2}} + \sum_{s=1}^{m}\binom{p+s}{2s}\delta^{2s-1}u_{\frac{1}{2}}$$
$$+ \binom{p+m}{2m+1}\omega^{2m+1} f^{(2m+1)}(\xi),$$

which is Steffensen's formula. The formula employs odd differences only according to the scheme

$a-\omega$	u_{-1}					
		$\delta u_{-\frac{1}{2}}$	$\delta^3 u_{-\frac{1}{2}}$	$\delta^5 u_{-\frac{1}{2}}$	.	.
a	u_0					
		$\delta u_{\frac{1}{2}}$	$\delta^3 u_{\frac{1}{2}}$	$\delta^5 u_{\frac{1}{2}}$	.	.
$a+\omega$	u_1					

3·7. Interpolation without Differences. The problem of interpolation without the use of differences is solved in principle by Lagrange's formula 1·4 (3), which gives

$$(1) \qquad f(x) = \sum_{s=1}^{n} \frac{f(x_s)}{x - x_s} \frac{\phi(x)}{\phi'(x_s)} + \phi(x) \frac{f^{(n)}(\xi)}{n!},$$

$$\phi(x) = (x - x_1)(x - x_2) \dots (x - x_n).$$

From this we can obtain a formula equivalent to Gauss' formula by substituting the proper distribution of arguments. Thus to obtain a formula completely equivalent to 3·2 (4), we put

$$x_{2s-1} = a - (s-1)\,\omega, \quad x_{2s} = a + s\omega, \quad s = 1, 2, 3, \dots, m.$$

Introducing the phase $p = (x - a)/\omega$, we have

$$\phi(x) = (p + m - 1)(p + m - 2) \dots (p - m)\,\omega^{2m},$$

$$\phi'(x_{2s-1}) = (m - s)!\,(m + s - 1)!\,(-1)^{m+s-1}\omega^{2m-1},$$

$$\phi'(x_{2s}) = (m + s - 1)!\,(m - s)!\,(-1)^{m-s}\omega^{2m-1},$$

so that (1) gives

$$f(x) = \sum_{s=1}^{m} \frac{(p + m - 1) \dots (p - m)}{(m + s - 1)!\,(m - s)!} (-1)^{m+s-1} \left\{ \frac{f(a - s\omega + \omega)}{p + s - 1} - \frac{f(a + s\omega)}{p - s} \right\}$$
$$+ \text{remainder}.$$

This can be written in the simpler form

$$f(x) = 2m \binom{p + m - 1}{2m} \sum_{s=1}^{m} (-1)^{m+s-1} \binom{2m - 1}{m - s}$$
$$\times \left\{ \frac{f(a - s\omega + \omega)}{p + s - 1} - \frac{f(a + s\omega)}{p - s} \right\} + \binom{p + m - 1}{2m} \omega^{2m} f^{(2m)}(\xi).$$

Other formulae of this nature can be obtained by varying the distribution of the arguments. The practical objection to the use of the Lagrangian formulae lies in the excessive labour of numerical calculation involved. In using interpolation formulae founded on differences the order of magnitude of the terms becomes progressively less. Moreover, if it be found desirable to include further differences it is only necessary to add more terms. In Lagrange's formula every term is of equal importance and when another functional value has to be included the calculation must be started *de novo*.

The first attempt to avoid forming differences when interpolating in a table not provided with them, and at the same time to escape the labour of Lagrange's formula, was due to C. Jordan,* who formed certain linear interpolates and operated upon these. We shall not describe Jordan's process, since an essential improvement thereon has been made by A. C. Aitken,† who realised that the practical advantage lay in the process of linear interpolation, and devised a method of interpolation by iterating this process.

3·81. Aitken's Linear Process of Interpolation by Iteration. Let $u_a, u_b, u_c, \ldots$, denote the values of a function corresponding to the arguments $a, b, c, \ldots$.

We denote as usual the divided differences by $[ab]$, $[abc]$, … . Let $f(x;\ a, b, c)$, for example, denote the interpolation polynomial which coincides in value with u_x at the points a, b, c. Then by 1·9 (2)

$$f(x;\ a, b) = u_a + (x-a)[ab],$$

$$f(x;\ a, b, c) = u_a + (x-a)[ab] + (x-a)(x-b)[abc],$$

$$f(x;\ a, b, c, d) = u_a + (x-a)[ab] + (x-a)(x-b)[abc] + (x-a)(x-b)(x-c)[abcd],$$

and so on. We have then, for example,

$$f(x;\ a, b, c, d) = f(x;\ a, b, c) + (x-a)(x-b)(x-c)[abcd].$$

Since the order of the arguments is immaterial we have also

$$f(x;\ a, b, c, d) = f(x;\ a, b, d) + (x-a)(x-b)(x-d)[abcd].$$

Eliminating $[abcd]$ we obtain

$$(1) \quad f(x;\ a, b, c, d) = \frac{(d-x)\,f(x;\ a, b, c) - (c-x)\,f(x;\ a, b, d)}{(d-x)-(c-x)}$$

$$= \begin{vmatrix} f(x;\ a, b, c) & c-x \\ f(x;\ a, b, d) & d-x \end{vmatrix} \div (d-c).$$

Thus $f(x;\ a, b, c, d)$ is obtained by the ordinary rule of proportional parts from the values of $f(x;\ a, b, y)$ for $y = c$, $y = d$. This argument is clearly general.

---

* (i) *Atti del Congresso Internaz. dei Matematici, Bologna*, (1928), vi, p. 157. (ii) *Metron*, vii (1928), p. 47.

† A. C. Aitken, *Proc. Edinburgh Math. Soc.* (2), iii (1932), p. 56.

Applying this rule we can now write down the following scheme:

Argument	Function	(1)	(2)	(3)	...	Parts
a	u_a					$a-x$
b	u_b	$f(x;\ a, b)$				$b-x$
c	u_c	$f(x;\ a, c)$	$f(x;\ a, b, c)$			$c-x$
d	u_d	$f(x;\ a, d)$	$f(x;\ a, b, d)$	$f(x, a, b, c, d)$		$d-x$
.	.	.	.	.		.

Each entry is formed by cross-multiplication and division, with the numbers in their actual positions, thus

$$f(x;\ a, b) = \begin{vmatrix} u_a & a-x \\ u_b & b-x \end{vmatrix} \div (b-a),$$

$$f(x;\ a, c) = \begin{vmatrix} u_a & a-x \\ u_c & c-x \end{vmatrix} \div (c-a),$$

$$f(x;\ a, d) = \begin{vmatrix} u_a & a-x \\ u_d & d-x \end{vmatrix} \div (d-a),$$

$$f(x;\ a, b, c) = \begin{vmatrix} f(x;\ a, b) & b-x \\ f(x;\ a, c) & c-x \end{vmatrix} \div (c-b),$$

and so on.

The above scheme constitutes Aitken's process.

The members of column (1) are linear interpolation polynomials, those of column (2) quadratic interpolation polynomials, those of column (3) cubic interpolation polynomials, and so on. If a numerical value be substituted for x, each member of the rth column is the value of an interpolation polynomial which coincides with u_x at $r+1$ points and gives the value of u_x within a degree of approximation measured by the remainder term at this stage. The process is therefore completely equivalent to interpolation with Newton's general divided difference formula. Thus, for example,

$$u_x = f(x;\ a, b, c, d) + (x-a)(x-b)(x-c)(x-d)\, u_\xi^{(iv)} / 4!,$$

where ξ lies in the smallest interval containing a, b, c, d, x. If then interpolation by Newton's formula be practicable, the numbers in later columns will tend to equality as the work proceeds. This leads to a simplification, since in the linear interpolation those figures at the beginning which are common to all the members of a column can be dropped. The process terminates when further interpolation would cease to influence the result. With regard to the column headed "Parts," we may replace the entries by any numbers proportional to them, as is obvious from (1). In particular, if the arguments be equidistant, we may divide each entry in this column by the argument interval ω. Moreover, when the arguments are equidistant, this division by ω will make them differ by integers. The method is eminently suited to use with an arithmometer and is independent of tables of interpolation coefficients. The process can also be used at the beginning or end of a table.

Example. From the given values of the elliptic function $\operatorname{sn}(x \mid 0{\cdot}2)$, find by interpolation the value of $\operatorname{sn}(0{\cdot}3 \mid 0{\cdot}2)$.

x	$\operatorname{sn}(x \mid 0{\cdot}2)$	(1)	(2)	(3)	(4)	(5)	Parts
0·0	0·00000						−3
·1	·09980	29940					−2
·2	·19841	29761·5	29583				−1
·4	·38752	29064	29356	... 469·5			+1
·5	·47595	28557	29248·5	... 471·5	... 467·5		+2
·6	·55912	27956	29146·4	... 473·85	... 467·3	... 7·9	+3

Here the "parts" are −·3, −·2, −·1, +·1, +·2, +·3, which we replace by integers. We also treat the tabular numbers as integers and carry extra figures as a guard. After column (2) we can drop the figures 29. We could likewise treat the entries of column (3) as 9·5, 11·5, 13·85. The following are examples shewing how the numbers are obtained.

$$29940 = \begin{vmatrix} 0 & -3 \\ 9980 & -2 \end{vmatrix} \div 1, \qquad 29064 = \begin{vmatrix} 0 & -3 \\ 38752 & +1 \end{vmatrix} \div 4,$$

$$469{\cdot}5 = \begin{vmatrix} 583 & -1 \\ 356 & +1 \end{vmatrix} \div 2, \qquad 7{\cdot}9 = \begin{vmatrix} 7{\cdot}5 & 2 \\ 7{\cdot}3 & 3 \end{vmatrix} \div 1.$$

The result is 0·29468, which is correct * to five places.

3·82. Aitken's Quadratic Process. Suppose given an even number of symmetrically placed data such as

$$u_{-a},\ u_{-b},\ u_{-c},\ u_a,\ u_b,\ u_c.$$

* Milne-Thomson, *Die elliptischen Funktionen von Jacobi*, Berlin (1931).

The expression

(1) $$\frac{(y+x)\,u_y+(y-x)\,u_{-y}}{2y}=f(x;\;y^2)=\begin{vmatrix} u_y & x-y \\ u_{-y} & x+y \end{vmatrix}\div(2y)$$

is an even function of y, since it remains unaltered when $-y$ is written for y. This justifies the notation. Also $f(x;\,x^2)=u_x$. With the given data we can form, by means of (1), the values of $f(x;\,a^2)$, $f(x;\,b^2)$, $f(x;\,c^2)$. If we apply the linear process of the last section to these new data, taking as variables a^2, b^2, c^2, we thereby obtain an interpolated value for $f(x;\,x^2)$ or u_x. Thus we can form by 3·81 (1)

(2) $$f(x;\;a^2,b^2)=\begin{vmatrix} f(x;\;a^2) & a^2-x^2 \\ f(x;\;b^2) & b^2-x^2 \end{vmatrix}\div(b^2-a^2),$$

$$f(x;\;a^2,b^2,c^2)=\begin{vmatrix} f(x;\;a^2,b^2) & b^2-x^2 \\ f(x;\;a^2,c^2) & c^2-x^2 \end{vmatrix}\div(c^2-b^2),$$

and so on until the data are exhausted.

Thus we form from (1)

$$f(x;\;a^2)=\begin{vmatrix} u_a & x-a \\ u_{-a} & x+a \end{vmatrix}\div(2a),\text{ etc.,}$$

and form by means of (2) the scheme

$$\begin{array}{llll} f(x;\;a^2) & & & a^2-x^2 \\ f(x;\;b^2) & f(x;\;a^2,b^2) & & b^2-x^2 \\ f(x;\;c^2) & f(x;\;a^2,c^2) & f(x;\;a^2,b^2,c^2) & c^2-x^2 \\ \cdot & \cdot & \cdot & \cdot \end{array}$$

which is essentially the same as that of the last section, but with squared variables.

Since we are in fact using 2, 4, 6, ... values of the function in successive columns, we are progressively taking account of the first, third, fifth, ... differences in an ordinary interpolation formula. If then $2n$ values be used, the remainder term is

$$R_{2n}(x)=(x^2-a^2)(x^2-b^2)\dots(x^2-k^2)\frac{u^{(2n)}(\xi)}{(2n)!}.$$

This process can also be worked at the end or beginning of a table.

In applying this method to equidistant data we first subtract from each argument the middle argument m about which they are symmetrical. After division by the interval ω the arguments become $\pm\frac{1}{2}$, $\pm 1\frac{1}{2}$, $\pm 2\frac{1}{2}$, ... and x is replaced by the phase $p = (x-m)/\omega$. The "parts" then become $(\frac{1}{2})^2 - p^2$, $(1\frac{1}{2})^2 - p^2$, $(2\frac{1}{2})^2 - p^2$, which are of the form θ, $2+\theta$, $6+\theta$, $12+\theta$, $20+\theta$, $30+\theta$, ..., where $\theta = (\frac{1}{2})^2 - p^2$. The advantage of this will be apparent from the following example.

Example. From the following values of Jacobi's Zeta function $Z(x \mid 0{\cdot}6)$, calculate by interpolation $Z(0{\cdot}11 \mid 0{\cdot}6)$.

x	$Z(x \mid 0{\cdot}6)$	(a)	(b)
0·00	0·0000 000	−2·5	2·75
·04	·0133 469	−1·5	1·75
·08	·0266 172	−0·5	0·75
·12	·0397 350	+0·5	−0·25
·16	·0526 262	+1·5	−1·25
·20	·0652 186	+2·5	−2·25

Here the middle argument is 0·10, column (a) shows the prepared arguments obtained by subtracting 0·10 and dividing by $\omega = 0{\cdot}04$. The phase is $(0{\cdot}11 - 0{\cdot}10) \div 0{\cdot}04 = 0{\cdot}25$.

Column (b) gives the numbers $x-a$, $x+a$, etc. for formula (1). Thus we have (treating the tabular values as integers),

364 555·50			0·1875
362 598·25	3647 38·99		2·1875
358 702·30	3647 38·41	... 9·31	6·1875

The first column is formed by formula (1) thus, for example,

$$364\ 555{\cdot}50 = \begin{vmatrix} 397\ 350 & -{\cdot}25 \\ 266\ 172 & {\cdot}75 \end{vmatrix} \div 1.$$

After this we use (2) thus,

$$364\ 738{\cdot}41 = \begin{vmatrix} 364\ 555{\cdot}50 & 0{\cdot}1875 \\ 358\ 702{\cdot}30 & 6{\cdot}1875 \end{vmatrix} \div 6.$$

Finally we obtain $Z(0{\cdot}11 \mid 0{\cdot}6) = 0{\cdot}0364\ 739$, which is correct to 7 places.*

* L. M. Milne-Thomson, Zeta Function of Jacobi, *Proc. Roy. Soc., Edinburgh*, 52 (1932), p. 236.

If the number of data be odd but symmetrical, Aitken has devised several methods founded on iteration, but it is actually simpler to retain one method and annex an extra tabular value. For details the reader is referred to Aitken's paper.*

3·83. Neville's Process of Iteration. A somewhat different technique has been developed by Neville,† which has the advantage of finding a place in the iteration scheme for those derivates of the function of which the values may be known.

The essential point of the process consists in interpolation between consecutive entries in the columns, beginning at the centre and working outwards, new functional values being adjoined as required. The clustering of the interpolates round a central value leads to greater equality between the members of a column as the work progresses and avoids the necessity of any preliminary estimate of the number of tabular values required.

With the notation of 3·81 the process is indicated by the following scheme :

Argument	Parts	Function				
a	$x-a$	u_a				
			$f(x;\ a, b)$			
b	$x-b$	u_b		$f(x;\ a, b, c)$		
			$f(x;\ b, c)$		$f(x;\ a, b, c, d)$	
c	$x-c$	u_c		$f(x;\ b, c, d)$		$f(x;\ a, b, c, d, e)$
			$f(x;\ c, d)$		$f(x;\ b, c, d, e)$	
d	$x-d$	u_d		$f(x;\ c, d, e)$		
			$f(x;\ d, e)$			
e	$x-e$	u_e				

Here it is convenient to write 3·81 (1) in the form

$$(1) \qquad f(x;\ a, b, c) = \begin{vmatrix} x-a & f(x;\ a, b) \\ x-c & f(x;\ b, c) \end{vmatrix} \div (c-a)$$

* *loc. cit.* p. 76.

† E. H. Neville, in a paper read at the International Congress of Mathematicians, Zürich, 1932. This paper will be published in a commemoration volume of the *Journal of the Indian Mathematical Society*. Prof. Neville has kindly allowed me to use his MS. and upon this the present section is based.

in order that the "parts" may be identified as lying at the base of a triangle of which the interpolate is the vertex.

The process of course leads to the same interpolation polynomial as Aitken's process when founded on the same arguments.

In the case of equal intervals the parts may be most conveniently treated by division with the tabular interval ω.

Example. Find sin 0·25 from the values given below.

0·1	1·5	0·0998			
			2481·5		
0·2	·5	·1987		... 73·6	
			2471		... 4·1
0·3	– ·5	·2955		... 74·6	
			2485·5		
0·4	– 1·5	·3894			

Here $x = 0{\cdot}25$, $\omega = 0{\cdot}1$; the parts are given in the second column.

$$2471 = \begin{vmatrix} \cdot 5 & 1987 \\ -\cdot 5 & 2955 \end{vmatrix}, \quad 74{\cdot}6 = \begin{vmatrix} \cdot 5 & 71 \\ -1{\cdot}5 & 85{\cdot}5 \end{vmatrix} \div 2,$$

$$\sin 0{\cdot}25 = 0{\cdot}2474.$$

In order to introduce derivates into the scheme, we first notice that the interpolation polynomial $f(x;\ a, b)$ is given by

$$f(x;\ a, b) = u_a + (x-a)\,[ab],$$

where $[ab]$ is the divided difference of u_a, u_b.

If $a = b$, we have $[aa] = u'_a$ (see 1·8 (2)), and we can write

$$(2) \qquad f(x;\ a, a) = u_a + (x-a)\,u'_a = f(x;\ a^2) \text{ say.}$$

Similarly, if $a = b = c$, we have

$$(3) \qquad f(x;\ a, a, a) = f(x;\ a^2) + (x-a)^2\,[aaa]$$
$$= f(x;\ a^2) + \tfrac{1}{2}(x-a)^2\,u''_a = f(x;\ a^3) \text{ say.}$$

These values can be calculated and introduced into Neville's scheme in the appropriate columns. Suppose, for example, that we are given u_a, u'_a, u''_a, u_b, u_c, u'_c. The scheme becomes, by repeating the arguments,

$$\begin{array}{llllllll}
a & x-a & u_a & & & & & \\
 & & & \mathbf{f(x;\ a^2)} & & & & \\
a & x-a & u_a & & \mathbf{f(x;\ a^3)} & & & \\
 & & & \mathbf{f(x;\ a^2)} & & f(x;\ a^3, b) & & \\
a & x-a & u_a & & f(x;\ a^2, b) & & f(x;\ a^3, b, c) & \\
 & & & f(x;\ a, b) & & f(x;\ a^2, b, c) & & f(x;\ a^3, b, c^2) \\
b & x-b & u_b & & f(x;\ a, b, c) & & f(x;\ a^2, b, c^2) & \\
 & & & f(x;\ b, c) & & f(x;\ a, b, c^2) & & \\
c & x-c & u_c & & f(x;\ b, c^2) & & & \\
 & & & \mathbf{f(x;\ c^2)} & & & & \\
c & x-c & u_c & & & & &
\end{array}$$

The entries in heavy type are calculated from (2) and (3) and the interpolation proceeds by formula (1). Thus, for example,

$$f(x;\ a^3, b) = \begin{vmatrix} x-a & f(x;\ a^3) \\ x-b & f(x;\ a^2, b) \end{vmatrix} \div (b-a),$$

$$f(x;\ a, b, c^2) = \begin{vmatrix} x-a & f(x;\ a, b, c) \\ x-c & f(x;\ b, c^2) \end{vmatrix} \div (c-a).$$

Example. Find sin 0·25 from the following table :

x	$\sin x$	$\cos x$
0·2	0·1987	0·9801
0·3	·2955	0·9553

We form $f(0\cdot 25;\ 0\cdot 2^2) = 2477\cdot 05$, $f(0\cdot 25;\ 0\cdot 3^2) = 2477\cdot 35$, then

$$\begin{array}{lllll}
0\cdot 2 & \cdot 5 & 1987 & & \\
 & & & \mathbf{2477\cdot 05} & \\
\cdot 2 & \cdot 5 & 1987 & & \ldots 4\cdot 0 \\
 & & & 2471 & \\
\cdot 3 & -\cdot 5 & 2955 & & \ldots 4\cdot 2 \\
 & & & \mathbf{2477\cdot 35} & \\
\cdot 3 & -\cdot 5 & 2955 & &
\end{array}$$

$$\sin 0\cdot 25 = 0\cdot 2474.$$

EXAMPLES III

1. Find approximately the value of antilog 0·9763 452 given the table:

x	antilog x
0·95	8·912 509
·96	9·120 108
·97	9·332 543
·98	9·549 926
·99	9·772 372

and discuss the limits of error. Calculate also antilog 0·9532 641, and antilog 0·9873 256 (*a*) by Newton's formula, (*b*) by Aitken's process.

2. The logarithms in Tables of n decimal places differ from the true values by $\pm 5 \times 10^{-n-1}$ at most. Hence shew that the errors of logarithms of n places obtained from the Tables by interpolating to first and second differences cannot exceed $\pm 10^{-n} + e$, and $\pm 10^{-n} \times (9/8) + e'$ respectively, e and e' being the errors due exclusively to interpolation.

[Smith's Prize.]

3. From the table

x	$\sqrt{x}$
530·1	23·02 3901
540·1	23·24 0052
550·1	23·45 4211
560·1	23·66 6432

form a scheme of differences and calculate $\sqrt{530{\cdot}67459}$, $\sqrt{540{\cdot}67459}$, $\sqrt{550{\cdot}67459}$, in each case determining the limits of error.

4. If $f(a) = u_0$, $f(a+\omega) = u_1$, prove the following formula for interpolation in the middle, or to "halves",

$$f(a+\tfrac{1}{2}\omega) = \mu u_{\frac{1}{2}} - \frac{1}{8}\mu\delta^2 u_{\frac{1}{2}} + \frac{3}{128}\mu\delta^4 u_{\frac{1}{2}} - \frac{5}{1024}\mu\delta^6 u_{\frac{1}{2}} + \frac{35}{2^{15}}\omega^8 f^{(8)}(\xi).$$

Obtain the general form of this result when the last difference used is $\mu\delta^{2n} u_{\frac{1}{2}}$.

5. Supply the values corresponding to $x = 0{\cdot}101$, $\cdot 103$, $\cdot 105$ in the following table :

x	$\sin x$
0·100	0·09983 3417
·102	·10182 3224
·104	·10381 2624
·106	·10580 1609

6. The following table gives values of the complete elliptic integral * E corresponding to values of $m(=k^2)$:

m	E
0·00	1·5707 96327
·02	1·5629 12645
·04	1·5549 68546
·06	1·5469 62456
·08	1·5388 92730

Insert the values corresponding to $m = 0{\cdot}01$, $\cdot 03$, $\cdot 05$, $\cdot 07$ and construct a corresponding table of E for $k = 0{\cdot}00, \cdot 01, \cdot 02, \ldots, \cdot 08$.

7. Find expressions for the remainder term in Stirling's formula when terminated with a difference of odd order, and in Bessel's formula when terminated with a difference of even order.

8. Taking $\omega = 1$, prove the central difference interpolation formula †

$$f(x) = f(0) + \sum_{s=1}^{n-1} \frac{x}{s} \binom{x+\frac{1}{2}s-1}{s-1} \delta^s f(0)$$

$$+ \frac{x}{n}\binom{x+\frac{1}{2}n-1}{n-1} f^{(n)}(\xi_0) + \frac{x}{n+1}\binom{x+\frac{1}{2}n-\frac{1}{2}}{n} f^{(n+1)}(\xi_1).$$

9. Taking $\omega = 1$, prove the equivalence of the following operations :

$$\mu\, u_x \doteq \frac{1}{2}\left(\mathsf{E}^{\frac{1}{2}} + \mathsf{E}^{-\frac{1}{2}}\right) u_x,$$

$$\delta\, u_x \doteq \left(\mathsf{E}^{\frac{1}{2}} - \mathsf{E}^{-\frac{1}{2}}\right) u_x,$$

* L. M. Milne-Thomson, *Proc. London Math. Soc.* (2), 33 (1932), p. 163.

† Steffensen, *Interpolation*, p. 32.

$$\mu^2 u_x \doteq \left(1+\frac{1}{4}\delta^2\right) u_x,$$

$$\mathsf{E}^{\frac{1}{2}} u_x \doteq \left(\mu+\frac{1}{2}\delta\right) u_x.$$

10. Use the result of the last example to prove that the terms of the central difference formula of example 8 are obtained by expanding in ascending powers of δ the expression

$$\left\{\frac{1}{2}\delta+\left(1+\frac{1}{4}\delta^2\right)^{\frac{1}{2}}\right\}^{2x} f(0).$$

11. Find from the following data an approximate value of log 212:

log 210 = 2·322 2193	log 213 = 2·328 3796
log 211 = 2·324 2825	log 214 = 2·330 4138

and discuss the error term.

12. From the following table of $\log \Gamma(n)$, determine approximately $\log \Gamma(\frac{1}{2})$:

n	$\log \Gamma(n)$	n	$\log \Gamma(n)$
$\frac{2}{12}$	0·74556	$\frac{7}{12}$	0·18432
$\frac{3}{12}$	·55938	$\frac{8}{12}$	·13165
$\frac{4}{12}$	·42796	$\frac{9}{12}$	·08828
$\frac{5}{12}$	·32788	$\frac{10}{12}$	·05261

13. If n radii vectores (n being an odd integer) be drawn from the pole dividing the four right angles into equal parts, shew that an approximate value of a radius vector u_θ, which makes an angle θ with the initial line is

$$u_\theta = \frac{1}{n}\sum \frac{\sin \frac{1}{2}n(\theta-\alpha)}{\sin \frac{1}{2}(\theta-\alpha)} u_\alpha,$$

where α, β, ..., are the angles which the n radii vectores make with the initial line.

CHAPTER IV

NUMERICAL APPLICATIONS OF DIFFERENCES

IN this chapter we consider a few important applications of differences and interpolation formulae, mostly of a numerical nature.

4·0. Differences when the Interval is Subdivided. Suppose that we have the difference scheme

$$\begin{array}{ccccc} u_0 & & \delta^2 u_0 & & \delta^4 u_0 \\ & \delta u_{\frac{1}{2}} & & \delta^3 u_{\frac{1}{2}} & \\ u_1 & & \delta^2 u_1 & & \delta^4 u_1 \end{array}$$

and that we wish to form the central differences corresponding to the table $u_0, u_{\cdot 1}, u_{\cdot 2}, u_{\cdot 3}, \dots, u_{\cdot 9}, u_1$, where the interval has been subdivided into 10 equal parts. The first two lines of the new scheme will then read

$$\begin{array}{ccccc} u_0 & & \partial^2 u_0 & & \partial^4 u_0 \\ & \partial u_{\cdot 05} & & \partial^3 u_{\cdot 05} & \\ u_{\cdot 1} & & \partial^2 u_{\cdot 1} & & \partial^4 u_{\cdot 1} \end{array}$$

We have $\partial u_{\cdot 05} = u_{\cdot 1} - u_0$, so that from Bessel's formula

$$(1) \qquad \partial u_{\cdot 05} = \tfrac{1}{10}\, \delta u_{\frac{1}{2}} - \tfrac{9}{200}\, \mu\delta^2 u_{\frac{1}{2}} + \tfrac{6}{1000}\, \delta^3 u_{\frac{1}{2}} + \tfrac{627}{8000}\, \mu\delta^4 u_{\frac{1}{2}} - \dots .$$

The remaining first differences can be found in the same way.

To form the second differences we have

$$\partial^2 u_0 = u_{-\cdot 1} - 2u_0 + u_{\cdot 1}.$$

Using Stirling's formula, this gives

(2) $$\partial^2 u_0 = \tfrac{1}{100}\delta^2 u_0 - \tfrac{33}{40000}\delta^4 u_0 + \dots .$$

Similarly from

$$\partial^3 u_{\cdot 05} = u_{\cdot 2} - 3u_{\cdot 1} + 3u_0 - u_{-\cdot 1},$$

we obtain

$$\partial^3 u_{\cdot 05} = \tfrac{1}{1000}\delta^3 u_{\frac{1}{2}} - \tfrac{9}{20000}\mu\delta^4 u_{\frac{1}{2}} - \dots ,$$

and in a like manner

$$\partial^4 u_0 = \tfrac{1}{10000}\delta^4 u_0 - \dots .$$

It will be noticed that division of the interval by 10 has the general effect of reducing the order of magnitude of the first, second, third, ... , differences in the ratios 10^{-1}, 10^{-2}, 10^{-3}, ...

More generally, if we subdivide * the interval into a parts, we shall reduce the differences approximately in the ratios

$$a^{-1},\quad a^{-2},\quad a^{-3}, \dots .$$

4·1. The Differences of a Numerical Table. The success of interpolation by the formulae of Chapter III in a numerical table of a function tabulated for equidistant values of the argument depends upon the remainder term becoming insignificant to the order of accuracy required. Since the remainder term is proportional to a value of the derivate of a certain order of the function, and the differences of this order are also proportional to values of this derivate, the practical conclusion is that the effect of the differences of a certain order shall become negligible. In the case of a polynomial of degree n, the $(n+1)$th order differences are zero; in the case of other functions, or even in the case of a polynomial when the values are curtailed to a fewer number of figures than the full value for the arguments, the differences never attain the constant value zero. In examining a table in which it is proposed to interpolate by differences it is therefore first requisite to ascertain at what stage

* For the application of the differences of the subdivided interval to interpolation, see the introductory article by A. J. Thompson in the *British Association Tables*, vol. i, (1931).

the effect of the differences become negligible, which can be done by actually forming the differences in question. Consider, for example, the following table of $\sqrt{x}$.

x	$\sqrt{x}$	Δ	Δ^2	Δ^3
1000	31·62 2777			
		15807		
1001	31·63 8584		−7	
		15800		−2
1002	31·65 4384		−9	
		15791		+2
1003	31·67 0175		−7	
		15784		−1
1004	31·68 5959		−8	
		15776		0
1005	31·70 1735		−8	
		15768		0
1006	31·71 7503		−8	
		15760		+1
1007	31·73 3263		−7	
		15753		−2
1008	31·74 9016		−9	
		15744		+2
1009	31·76 4760		−7	
		15737		−1
1010	31·78 0497		−8	

x	$\sqrt{x}$	Δ	Δ^2	Δ^3
1010	31·78 0497		−8	
		15729		0
1011	31·79 6226		−8	
		15721		+1
1012	31·81 1947		−7	
		15714		−1
1013	31·82 7661		−8	
		15706		0
1014	31·84 3367		−8	
		15698		0
1015	31·85 9065		−8	
		15690		0
1016	31·87 4755		−8	
		15682		+1
1017	31·89 0437		−7	
		15675		−1
1018	31·90 6112		−8	
		15667		+1
1019	31·92 1779		−7	
		15660		
1020	31·93 7439			

Here we see that the differences Δ^2 do not vary much, while Δ^3 alternates in sign. Since the third order derivate of $\sqrt{x}$ has a positive sign, the fluctuation in sign of Δ^3 must be attributed to the fact that the values here given are only approximations to $\sqrt{x}$. This suggests that we should investigate the nature of the fluctuations which will be introduced into the differences by an error in the tabulated function.

The effect of a single error x in an otherwise correct table is shewn in the following scheme:

Error	Δ	Δ^2	Δ^3	Δ^4	Δ^5	Δ^6
0						x
					x	
0				x		$-6x$
			x		$-5x$	
0		x		$-4x$		$+15x$
	x		$-3x$		$+10x$	
x		$-2x$		$+6x$		$-20x$
	$-x$		$+3x$		$-10x$	
0		x		$-4x$		$+15x$
			$-x$		$+5x$	
0				x		$-6x$
					$-x$	
0						x

It will be noticed that the coefficients of the errors in the column Δ^n are the coefficients in binomial expansion of $(1-z)^n$, as is indeed obvious from 2·5 (2).

If we replace the zeros in the above scheme by $x_1, x_2, x_3, x_5, x_6, x_7$, we have for the sixth order difference opposite to x the expression

$$\delta^6 x = x_1 - 6x_2 + 15x_3 - 20x + 15x_4 - 6x_5 + x_6.$$

In a table of approximations correct to a given number of figures the maximum error in a single tabular value is $\pm 0{\cdot}5$, the tabular values being regarded as integers. The corresponding maximum error in the sixth difference arises when the errors are alternately $+0{\cdot}5$ and $-0{\cdot}5$, the result then being $\delta^6 x = \pm 32$. When the differences fluctuate in a way which cannot be accounted for by these considerations the presumption is that the tabular values contain an error, the probable position of which is indicated approximately as that entry which stands on the horizontal line opposite to the largest anomalous difference of even order.

Returning to the above table of $\sqrt{x}$, we see that a knowledge of all the values in the column Δ^2, of the first entry in column Δ and the eight-figure value of $\sqrt{1000}$, would enable us to reconstruct the table, by first completing the column Δ and then the column $\sqrt{x}$. Moreover, a knowledge of the last digit in the column $\sqrt{x}$ enables us to infer the values in the column Δ^2 thus :

$\sqrt{x}$	Δ	Δ^2
7		
	7	
4		-7
	0	
4		-9
	1	
5		

provided that we subtract in the appropriate directions and have prior knowledge of the approximate magnitude of the numbers Δ^2. This fact is often useful in determining whether a printed table contains errors other than those in the last digit. For we can rapidly form the differences Δ^2 (or a higher order, if necessary) by differencing the end digits in the manner described. We can then build up the table again, preferably on an adding machine, and compare the result with the original table.

4·2. Subtabulation. The principle enunciated at the end of 4·1 can be employed in subtabulation. Suppose a function to have been calculated at equal intervals of the argument and let it be required to reduce the interval to 1 / 10 of the original interval. The problem here is to obtain new values of the function for the phases

$$\cdot 1,\ \cdot 2,\ \cdot 3,\ \cdot 4,\ \cdot 5,\ \cdot 6,\ 7,\ \cdot 8,\ \cdot 9.$$

Taking Bessel's formula, in the modified form if necessary (see 3·41), we have

(1) $$u_p = u_0 + p\,\delta u_{\frac{1}{2}} + \tfrac{1}{4}p(p-1)\,2\mu\delta^2 u_{\frac{1}{2}} + \tfrac{1}{6}p(p-\tfrac{1}{2})(p-1)\,\delta^3 u_{\frac{1}{2}}$$
$$\tfrac{1}{48}(p+1)\,p(p-1)(p-2)\,2\mu\delta^4 u_{\frac{1}{2}},$$

where the phase p has the above values and the remainder term is neglected. The formula has been written with the mean differences doubled in order to avoid divisions by 2. The values of the coefficients of the differences are shewn in the following table :

p	$\frac{1}{4}p(p-1)$	$\frac{1}{6}p(p-\frac{1}{2})(p-1)$	$\frac{1}{48}(p+1)p(p-1)(p-2)$
·1	−·0225	+·006	+·0039 1875
·2	−·0400	+·008	+·0072 0000
·3	−·0525	+·007	+·0096 6875
·4	−·0600	+·004	+·0112 0000
·5	−·0625	·000	+·0117 1875
·6	−·0600	−·004	+·0112 0000
·7	−·0525	−·007	+·0096 6875
·8	−·0400	−·008	+·0072 0000
·9	−·0225	−·006	+·0039 1875

As we only want the last digit of each interpolate we need only write down the two relevant figures of the products in (1), keeping one decimal as a guard. Those products which are negative can be made positive by the addition of 10·0. If we add the resulting products for each value of p, keeping only the last two figures in the sum and then round off, we get the required end digits of the interpolates. The differences can then be formed and the 9 interpolates built up by summation as described in 4·1, the initial first difference being obtained from 4·0 (1).

We shall illustrate the method by constructing the table of $\sqrt{x}$ given in 4·1 from the following data :

	x	$\sqrt{x}$	Δ	Δ^2	Δ^3
u_0	1000	31·62 2777		−792	
			157720	−1570	+14
u_1	1010	31·78 0497		−778	
			156942	−1546	+10
u_2	1020	31·93 7439		−768	

From (1) we have for the first interpolate, regarded as an integer,

$$(2) \qquad 3162\,277\,\mathbf{7{\cdot}0} + 1577\,\mathbf{2{\cdot}0} + 3\,\mathbf{5{\cdot}3} + \mathbf{0{\cdot}1}$$

$$= 3163\,858\,\mathbf{4{\cdot}4} = 3163\,858\,\mathbf{4}.$$

Writing down only the figures in large type we have the following scheme in which the figures just obtained are in the horizontal line opposite the argument 1001.

						E	Δ	Δ^2
1000	a	b	c	d	s	7		
							7	
1	7·0	2·0	5·3	0·1	4·4	4		−7
							0	
2	7·0	4·0	2·8	0·1	3·9	4		−9
							1	
3	7·0	6·0	2·4	0·1	5·5	5		−7
							4	
4	7·0	8·0	4·2	0·1	9·3	9		−8
							6	
5	7·0	0·0	8·1	0·0	5·1	5		−8
							8	
6	7·0	2·0	4·2	9·9	3·1	3		−8
							0	
7	7·0	4·0	2·4	9·9	3·3	3		−7
							3	
8	7·0	6·0	2·8	9·9	5·7	6		−9
							4	
9	7·0	8·0	5·3	9·9	0·2	0		−7
							7	
1010						7		−8

						E	Δ	Δ^2
1010	a_1	b_1	c_1	d_1	s	7		−8
							9	
1	7·0	4·2	4·8	0·1	6·1	6		−8
							1	
2	7·0	8·4	1·8	0·1	7·3	7		−7
							4	
3	7·0	2·6	1·2	0·1	0·9	1		−8
							6	
4	7·0	6·8	2·8	0·0	6·6	7		−8
							8	
5	7·0	1·0	6·6	0·0	4·6	5		−8
							0	
6	7·0	5·2	2·8	0·0	5·0	5		−8
							2	
7	7·0	9·4	1·2	9·9	7·5	7		−7
							5	
8	7·0	3·6	1·8	9·9	2·3	2		−8
							7	
9	7·0	7·8	4·8	9·9	9·5	9		−7
							0	
1020						9		

In the above scheme the numbers in the columns a, b, c, d represent the contributions of u_0, $\delta u_{\frac{1}{2}}$, $2\mu\delta^2 u_{\frac{1}{2}}$, $\delta^3 u_{\frac{1}{2}}$ to the last figure of the interpolate. The numbers under s are the sums of these contributions, two figures only, and the column E represents the rounded value of s. The columns a_1, b_1, c_1, d_1 refer in the same way to the initial value u_1. We then form the differences as shewn. To form the leading first difference we have, from 4·0 (1),

$$\partial u_{\cdot 05} = 15807{\cdot}4 = 15807.$$

We can therefore complete the required table in the manner described in 4·1. The theoretical value of the second difference opposite the argument 1010 is by 4·0 (2) equal to $-7\cdot78$ or -8, which agrees with the value in the scheme and serves as a check. It will be observed that the above process, if correctly performed, must reproduce the exact value of u_1.

If we had continually to reproduce calculations of the type (2) above, little would be gained by this procedure. It is, however, a simple matter to construct, once for all, tables which give the two-figure numbers used in this process, for all values of the differences which can arise. Such tables, with examples of their use, are to be found in the *Nautical Almanac*, 1931. We may remark that in practice it is more convenient to arrange the work so that the additions, here shewn horizontally for convenience of exposition, are performed vertically.* The decimal points are, of course, unnecessary, as in similar work of this kind.

Another method of subtabulation which has been widely used consists in calculating by the formulae of **4·0** the theoretical values of the differences of the interpolates in that difference column where the differences are small or constant. The practical objection to this method is that small errors in a high order difference rapidly accumulate large errors in the functional values, so that a large number of useless figures have to be carried through the work and subsequently discarded. If, however, the contribution of the third order difference in the original table be negligible, it is quite practical to assume a constant value for the second difference and reject the decimal figures of the interpolates, treating the original values as integers.

Thus in the example just considered for $\sqrt{x}$, starting with $x = 1000$, we have with the notations of 4·0, neglecting third differences entirely,

(3) $$\partial_{\cdot 05} = 15807\cdot325,$$

and if we take the constant value

(4) $$\partial^2_{\cdot 1} = \tfrac{1}{100}\,\mu\delta^2_{\frac{1}{2}} = 7\cdot850,$$

we can build up by summation the values already obtained. The

---

* For an example of extensive interpolation in this way, see L. M. Milne-Thomson, *Standard Table of Square Roots* (1929). This table was first formed as a ten-figure table and was afterwards reduced to eight figures.

value for $\sqrt{1010}$ will be reproduced exactly, since the value obtained with the above differences is

$$u_0+10(\cdot 1\delta u_{\frac{1}{2}}-\cdot 045\,\mu\delta^2 u_{\frac{1}{2}})+45\times\cdot 01\mu\delta u_{\frac{1}{2}}=u_0+\delta u_{\frac{1}{2}}=u_1.$$

We can then proceed to calculate $\partial_{1\cdot 05}$ and $\partial^2_{1\cdot 1}$ and start again. The work can, however, be made continuous by using a suitable second difference opposite u_1. Consider the scheme

$$\begin{array}{ccc} u_{\cdot 9} & & \partial^2_{\cdot 1} \\ & \partial_{\cdot 05}+9\,\partial^2_{\cdot 1} & \\ u_1 & & x \\ & \partial_{1\cdot 05} & \\ u_{1\cdot 1} & & \partial^2_{1\cdot 1} \end{array}$$

which shews the end of the first calculation, u_0 to u_1, and the beginning of the next, u_1 to u_2. If for x we put $\partial^2_{\cdot 1}$ we shall not in general produce the correct value of $\partial_{1\cdot 05}$ as given by the above method, for

$$\partial_{1\cdot 05}=\cdot 1\,\delta u_{\frac{3}{2}}-\cdot 045\,\mu\delta^2 u_{\frac{3}{2}}=\cdot 1\,\delta u_{\frac{3}{2}}-4\cdot 5\,\partial^2_{1\cdot 1},$$
$$\partial_{\cdot 05}=\cdot 1\,\delta u_{\frac{1}{2}}-\cdot 045\,\mu\delta^2 u_{\frac{1}{2}}=\cdot 1\,\delta u_{\frac{1}{2}}-4\cdot 5\,\partial^2_{\cdot 1}.$$

But if we put

$$x=\partial_{1\cdot 05}-\partial_{\cdot 05}-9\,\partial^2_{\cdot 1}=\tfrac{1}{2}(\partial^2_{\cdot 1}+\partial^2_{1\cdot 1})+\tfrac{1}{10}\{\delta^2 u_1-100\times\tfrac{1}{2}(\partial^2_{\cdot 1}+\partial^2_{1\cdot 1})\},$$

we obtain the correct value of $\partial_{1\cdot 05}$ and the work can then proceed with the second constant $\partial^2_{1\cdot 1}$ until we reach u_2, when the second difference opposite to u_2 is again adjusted. The decimal figures introduced in this way are discarded when the tabulation is completed.

4·3. Inverse Interpolation. The problem of interpolation briefly stated consists of finding, from a table of the function, the value of the function which corresponds to a given argument. The problem of inverse interpolation is that of finding from the same table the argument corresponding to a given value of the function. Thus if y be a function of the argument x, given the table

Argument	Function
x_1	y_1
x_2	y_2
.	.

we require the argument x corresponding to a given functional value y. A numerical table by its nature determines a single-valued function of the argument but the inverse function may very well be many-valued.

Thus, for example, a table of the function $y = x^2 - 4x + 3$ takes the form

x	0	1	2	3	4	...
y	3	0	-1	0	3	...

and there are two arguments corresponding to $y = 0$ (and in fact to every value of y). This simple example shows that care is needed in formulating a problem of the inverse type which may only become determinate when the range of variation of the argument is in some way restricted.

A practical way of obtaining such restriction is to form a rough estimate of the required result and to confine the arguments of the table to values in the neighbourhood of this estimate. Assuming then that a determinate problem has been formulated, we proceed to consider methods of obtaining the solution.

4·4. Inverse Interpolation by Divided Differences. The given table, by interchanging the rôles of the argument x and the function y, becomes

Argument	Function		
y_1	x_1		
		$[y_1 y_2]$	
y_2	x_2		$[y_1 y_2 y_3]$
		$[y_2 y_3]$	
y_3	x_3		.
		.	
.	.		

where we have formed the divided differences

$$[y_1 y_2] = (x_1 - x_2) \div (y_1 - y_2), \text{ etc.}$$

We then obtain

$$x = x_1 + (y - y_1)[y_1 y_2] + (y - y_1)(y - y_2)[y_1 y_2 y_3] + \dots,$$

where, if we stop at the divided difference $[y_1 y_2 \dots y_n]$, the remainder term is

$$(y-y_1)(y-y_2)\dots(y-y_n)[yy_1y_2\dots y_n].$$

This is a complete theoretical solution of the problem provided that we have some means of evaluating the remainder term or, in other words, of calculating the nth derivate of y with respect to x, or an equivalent process. In practice this may present difficulties. We can, however, estimate the suitability of the value of x by interpolating the original table and seeing how far the result agrees with the given value of y.

Example. Calculate

$$\int_{\cdot 37}^{1} \frac{dx}{\sqrt{(1-x^2)\left(\frac{3}{5}+\frac{2}{5}x^2\right)}}$$

from the following table * of $\mathrm{cn}\,(u\,|\,\frac{2}{5})$.

$\mathrm{cn}\,(u\,\|\,\frac{2}{5})$	u			
0·44122	1·2			
		−1·34048		
·36662	1·3		−·132	
		−1·32066		−·18
·29090	1·4		−·091	
		−1·30685		−·16
·21438	1·5		−·055	
		−1·29836		
·13736	1·6			

The required integral is the inverse function $\mathrm{cn}^{-1}(\cdot 37\,|\,\frac{2}{5})$. The divided differences regarding the left-hand column as the argument are shewn. We have, therefore, the value

$$1\cdot 2 + \cdot 07122 \times 1\cdot 34048 + \cdot 07122 \times \cdot 00338 \times \cdot 132$$
$$+ \cdot 07122 \times \cdot 00338 \times \cdot 07910 \times \cdot 18 = 1\cdot 29550.$$

4·5. Inverse Interpolation by Iterated Linear Interpolation. The iterative methods described in the last chapter

* Milne-Thomson, *Die elliptischen Funktionen von Jacobi*, Berlin (1931).

(3·81, 3·83) are very well adapted to inverse interpolation when several orders of differences have to be taken into account. These methods do not depend on the argument proceeding by equal steps, and hence we may interchange argument and function in the same way as before and so arrive at the required result by the general (linear) iterative process.

Neville * has shewn that known derivates, at least of the first two orders, can be conveniently employed by means of the formulae

$$\frac{dx}{dy} = 1 \Big/ \frac{dy}{dx}, \quad \frac{d^2 x}{dy^2} = -\frac{d^2 y}{dx^2} \Big/ \left(\frac{dy}{dx}\right)^3.$$

We give the following example as worked by Aitken.†

Example. Find the positive root of the equation

$$x^7 + 28x^4 - 480 = 0.$$

From a graph of $y = x^7 + 28x^4 - 480$ it is easily seen that the root is slightly beyond 1·9. We form the table given below and seek the value of x corresponding to $y = 0$.

y	x				
−25·7140261	1·90				
−14·6254167	1·91	2 3189586			
−3·3074639	1·92	2952228	28 82864		
+8·2439435	1·93	2716929	87312	84138	
+20·0329830	1·94	2483678	91702	17	53

Since $y = 0$ the left-hand column contains the "parts" used in the process. Thus

$$23189586 = \begin{vmatrix} 1{\cdot}90 & -257140261 \\ 1{\cdot}91 & -146254167 \end{vmatrix} \div 110886094,$$

and so on. We obtain

$$x = 1{\cdot}922884153,$$

which is correct to ten figures.

---

* *loc. cit.* p. 81.

† *loc. cit.* p. 76. The equation is due to W. B. Davies, *Educational Times*, 1867, p. 108. See also Whittaker and Robinson, *Calculus of Observations*, (1924), p. 61.

4·6. Inverse Interpolation by Successive Approximation. This widely employed method proceeds as follows. By linear interpolation a few figures of the argument are found, and the values of the function for this and one or two adjacent arguments are calculated. Using these functional values we find some more figures of the argument, and then repeat the process until it ceases to yield figures different from those already obtained.

Example. Find the value of m corresponding to $q = 0{\cdot}01$ from the following table,* which gives values of the nome q as a function of the squared modulus $k^2 = m$.

m	q	Δ	Δ^2	Δ^3	Δ^4
0·12	0·00798 89058				
		71 40944			
·13	·00870 30002		82195		
		72 23139		1887	
·14	·00942 53141		84082		68
		73 07221		1955	
·15	·01015 60362		86037		67
		73 93258		2022	
·16	·01089 53620		88509		
		74 81317			
·17	·01164 34937				

As a first approximation

$$m = {\cdot}14 + \frac{575}{7307} = {\cdot}14787.$$

Using Gauss' formula, we find

m	q
·14787	·00999 96780
·14788	·01000 04112

The interval is now 1 / 1000 of the original interval, so that by

* L. M. Milne-Thomson, *Journ. London Math. Soc.*, 5, (1930), p. 148.

4·0 the second difference is negligible and we have, dividing 3220 by the new first difference 7332,

$$m = \cdot 14787\ 4392.$$

4·7. Inverse Interpolation by Reversal of Series.

The relation between the function y and the argument x, which is obtained from an interpolation formula by neglect of the remainder term, can be written in the form

$$y - y_1 = a_1 p + a_2 p^2 + a_3 p^3 + \dots + a_n p^n,$$

where $p = (x - x_1) / \omega$ is the phase.

This (finite) power series can be reversed in the form

$$p = b_1 (y - y_1) + b_2 (y - y_1)^2 + b_3 (y - y_1)^3 + \dots,$$

where *

$$b_1 = \frac{1}{a_1}, \quad b_2 = -\frac{a_2}{a_1^{\,3}}, \quad b_3 = \frac{-a_1 a_3 + 2a_2^{\,2}}{a_1^{\,5}},$$

$$b_4 = \frac{-a_1^{\,2} a_4 + 5a_1 a_2 a_3 - 5a_2^{\,3}}{a_1^{\,7}}.$$

Thus we have

$$(1) \qquad p = \frac{y - y_1}{a_1} - \frac{a_2 (y - y_1)^2}{a_1^{\,3}} + \frac{(2a_2^{\,2} - a_1 a_3)(y - y_1)^3}{a_1^{\,5}} + \dots.$$

Taking for example Bessel's formula and neglecting fourth order differences, we have

$$y - y_1 = p\,\delta y_{\frac{3}{2}} + \tfrac{1}{2}(p^2 - p)\,\mu\delta^2 y_{\frac{3}{2}} + \tfrac{1}{6}(p^3 - \tfrac{3}{2}p^2 + \tfrac{1}{2}p)\,\delta^3 y_{\frac{3}{2}},$$

and we therefore take

$$a_1 = (\delta - \tfrac{1}{2}\mu\delta^2 + \tfrac{1}{12}\delta^3)\, y_{\frac{3}{2}},$$

$$a_2 = (\tfrac{1}{2}\mu\delta^2 - \tfrac{1}{4}\delta^3)\, y_{\frac{3}{2}}, \quad a_3 = \tfrac{1}{6}\delta^3 y_{\frac{3}{2}},$$

and we then obtain p from (1).

The method is of limited application since the convergence is often slow.

---

* For the first 12 coefficients, see C. E. van Orstrand, *Phil. Mag.*, May 1908. A simple determinantal expression for the general coefficient is given by M. Ward, *Rendiconti di Palermo*, liv (1930), p. 42. See also G. J. Lidstone, *J.I.A.*, 51 (1918), p. 43.

Example. Find an approximate value of coth 0·6 from the following table.*

x	$\coth^{-1} x$	Δ	Δ^2	Δ^3
1·85	0·6049 190			
		−40968		
1·86	·6008 222		+616	
		−40352		−16
1·87	·5967 870		+600	
		−39752		
1·88	·5928 118			

Taking $y_1 = \cdot 6008\ 222$, we have

$$y - y_1 = -8222, \quad a_1 = -40657, \quad a_2 = 308, \quad a_3 = -2\cdot 7.$$

Substituting in (1), we get $p = \cdot 20254$.

Since $\omega = \cdot 01$, we have therefore the approximation

$$\coth 0\cdot 6 = 1\cdot 862025.$$

EXAMPLES IV

1. If $\Delta_1 f(x) = f(x+1) - f(x)$, $\Delta f(x) = f(x+10) - f(x)$, shew that

$$(1+\Delta_1)^{10} f(x) \doteqdot (1+\Delta) f(x),$$

and by means of this formula express the forward differences† of $f(x)$ for unit intervals in terms of the forward differences for interval 10.

2. Obtain corresponding formulae connecting the differences for intervals ω and $m\omega$, where m is a positive integer.

3. Obtain the central differences corresponding to one-fifth of the tabular interval in terms of the central differences for the whole interval.

---

* L. M. Milne-Thomson, *Atti del Cong. Internaz. d. Matematici, Bologna*, (1928), t. 2. p. 357.

† This is essentially the problem of Briggs. See H. W. Turnbull, "James Gregory", *Proc. Edinburgh Math. Soc.*, (2) 3 (1933), p. 166.

4. Obtain the table of $\sqrt{x}$ in 4·1 from the values of $\sqrt{x}$ at interval 10 by first halving the interval and then interpolating to fifths.

5. Taking logarithms to seven figures at interval 10 in the neighbourhood of 350, find the logarithms at unit intervals from 350 to 370.

6. Find cosech 3·63 from the table of inverse values:

x	$\text{cosech}^{-1} x$	Δ^2
0·052	3·6503341	3704
·053	3·6313121	3566
·054	3·6126467	3435

7. From the following table of inverse secants calculate sec 0·17856:

x	$\sec^{-1} x$	Δ^2
1·015	0·1721329	1962
1·016	0·1777050	1782
1·017	0·1830989	1629

8. Calculate cosec 1·3957 from the following table of inverse cosecants:

x	$\text{cosec}^{-1} x$	Δ^2
1·015	1·3986634	1962
1·016	1·3930913	1782
1·017	1·3876974	1629
1·018	1·3824664	1497

9. Check the value of cosec^{-1} 1·016 in (8) from the table:

x	$\text{cosec}\, x$	Δ^2
1·393	1·0160 1666	109
1·394	1·0158 3463	108

10. Check the value of $\sec^{-1}$ 1·016 in (7) by means of the table:

x	$\sec x$	Δ^2
0·177	1·0158 7162	108
0·178	1·0160 5387	108

11. Calculate $\cot^{-1} 2{\cdot}9883$ from the table :

x	$\cot x$
0·320	3·0175980
·322	2·9975074
·323	2·9875522
·326	2·9580402

12. Prove that if the linear iterative process of 3·81 (p. 76) be applied to the divided differences

$$\frac{u_a - u_b}{a-b}, \quad \frac{u_a - u_c}{a-c}, \quad \frac{u_a - u_d}{a-d}, \ldots,$$

the multipliers being $b, c, d, \ldots$, the sequences obtained tend to the derivate $u'(a)$. Investigate the remainder after n steps.

[Aitken.]

13. Prove that if the quadratic process of 3·82 (p. 78) be applied to the central divided differences

$$\frac{u_a - u_{-a}}{2a}, \quad \frac{u_b - u_{-b}}{2b}, \quad \frac{u_c - u_{-c}}{2c}, \ldots,$$

the multipliers being $a^2, b^2, c^2, \ldots$, the sequences tend to $u'(0)$, and that if u_x be a polynomial of degree $2n+2$ the value obtained in n steps is exact. [Aitken.]

14. Prove that if the multipliers used in Example 13 be $a^2-\omega^2$, $b^2-\omega^2$, $c^2-\omega^2, \ldots$, the sequences tend to the subtabulated central divided difference $(u_\omega - u_{-\omega})/2\omega$.

15. By means of the methods of Examples 12 and 13 above compute the derivates at $x = 0{\cdot}00$, $0{\cdot}10$, of the function $Z(x \mid 0{\cdot}6)$ from the tabular values given on p. 80. [Aitken.]

CHAPTER V

RECIPROCAL DIFFERENCES

5·0. The interpolation methods hitherto considered are founded on the approximate representation of the function to be interpolated by a polynomial and the use of divided differences or the equivalent formula of Lagrange. Reciprocal differences, introduced by Thiele,* lead to the approximate representation of a function by a rational function and consequently to a more general method of interpolation. In this chapter we shall consider a few of the most important properties of Thiele's reciprocal differences.

5·1. Definition of Reciprocal Differences. Let the values of a function $f(x)$ be given for the values $x_0, x_1, x_2, \dots, x_n$ of the argument x. We shall for the present suppose that no two of these arguments are equal. The reciprocal difference of $f(x)$, of arguments x_0, x_1, is defined by †

$$\rho(x_0 x_1) = \frac{x_0 - x_1}{f(x_0) - f(x_1)}, \tag{1}$$

which is the reciprocal of the divided difference $[x_0 x_1]$. The reciprocal difference of three arguments x_0, x_1, x_2 is defined by

$$\rho_2(x_0 x_1 x_2) = \frac{x_0 - x_2}{\rho(x_0 x_1) - \rho(x_1 x_2)} + f(x_1). \tag{2}$$

* T. N. Thiele, *Interpolationsrechnung*, Leipzig, 1909. See also N. E. Nörlund, *Differenzenrechnung*, Berlin, 1924.

† The order of the arguments within the brackets is immaterial, for it will be shewn in 5·4 that reciprocal differences, like divided differences, are symmetrical in all their arguments.

We have here denoted the order by a suffix, since $\rho_2(x_0x_1x_2)$ is not formed by a repetition of the operation denoted by ρ. The operator ρ does not obey the index law, neither is the operator distributive, that is to say, the reciprocal difference of $f(x)+g(x)$ is not equal to the sum of the reciprocal differences of $f(x)$ and $g(x)$.

Proceeding to reciprocal differences of four arguments we define

$$\text{(3)} \qquad \rho_3(x_0x_1x_2x_3) = \frac{x_0-x_3}{\rho_2(x_0x_1x_2)-\rho_2(x_1x_2x_3)} + \rho(x_1x_2),$$

and generally when we have defined reciprocal differences of n arguments we define reciprocal differences of $n+1$ arguments by the relation

$$\text{(4)} \qquad \rho_n(x_0x_1x_2\ldots x_n) = \frac{x_0-x_n}{\rho_{n-1}(x_0x_1\ldots x_{n-1})-\rho_{n-1}(x_1x_2\ldots x_n)} + \rho_{n-2}(x_1x_2\ldots x_{n-1}).$$

Comparing this with (1), we see that

$$\text{(5)} \qquad \rho_n(x_0x_1x_2\ldots x_n) = \rho\,\rho_{n-1}(x_0x_1\ldots x_{n-1}) + \rho_{n-2}(x_1x_2\ldots x_{n-1}).$$

Reciprocal differences may be exhibited in a difference scheme as follows:

$$\begin{array}{llllll}
x_0 & f(x_0) & & & & \\
 & & \rho(x_0x_1) & & & \\
x_1 & f(x_1) & & \rho_2(x_0x_1x_2) & & \\
 & & \rho(x_1x_2) & & \rho_3(x_0x_1x_2x_3) & \\
x_2 & f(x_2) & & \rho_2(x_1x_2x_3) & & \rho_4(x_0x_1x_2x_3x_4) \\
 & & \rho(x_2x_3) & & \rho_3(x_1x_2x_3x_4) & \\
x_3 & f(x_3) & & \rho_2(x_2x_3x_4) & & \cdot \\
 & & \rho(x_3x_4) & & \cdot & \\
x_4 & f(x_4) & & & & \cdot \\
 & & \cdot & & \cdot &
\end{array}$$

As an example, the following table shews reciprocal differences of $1/(1+x^2)$:

x	$\dfrac{1}{1+x^2}$	ρ	ρ_2	ρ_3	ρ_4
0	1				
		-2			
1	$\frac{1}{2}$		-1		
		$-\frac{10}{3}$		0	
2	$\frac{1}{5}$		$-\frac{1}{10}$		0
		-10		40	
3	$\frac{1}{10}$		$-\frac{1}{25}$		0
		$-\frac{170}{7}$		140	
4	$\frac{1}{17}$		$-\frac{1}{46}$		
		$-\frac{442}{9}$			
5	$\frac{1}{26}$				

This table exemplifies the fact that the reciprocal differences of a certain order of any rational function are constant. In this case the differences of the fourth order have the constant value zero.

5·2. Thiele's Interpolation Formula.

If in the formulae of the last section we write x for x_0, we have successively,

$$f(x) = f(x_1) + \frac{x - x_1}{\rho(xx_1)},$$

$$\rho(xx_1) = \rho(x_1x_2) + \frac{x - x_2}{\rho_2(xx_1x_2) - f(x_1)},$$

$$\rho_2(xx_1x_2) = \rho_2(x_1x_2x_3) + \frac{x - x_3}{\rho_3(xx_1x_2x_3) - \rho(x_1x_2)},$$

$$\rho_3(xx_1x_2x_3) = \rho_3(x_1x_2x_3x_4) + \frac{x - x_4}{\rho_4(xx_1x_2x_3x_4) - \rho_2(x_1x_2x_3)},$$

$$\rho_4(xx_1x_2x_3x_4) = \rho_4(x_1x_2x_3x_4x_5) + \frac{x - x_5}{\rho_5(xx_1x_2x_3x_4x_5) - \rho_3(x_1x_2x_3x_4)}.$$

Thus we have for $f(x)$ the continued fraction

$$f(x_1) + \cfrac{x-x_1}{\rho(x_1x_2) + \cfrac{x-x_2}{\rho_2(x_1x_2x_3) - f(x_1) + \cfrac{x-x_3}{\rho_3(x_1x_2x_3x_4) - \rho(x_1x_2) + \cfrac{x-x_4}{\rho_4(x_1x_2x_3x_4x_5) - \rho_2(x_1x_2x_3) + \cfrac{x-x_5}{\rho_5(xx_1x_2x_3x_4x_5) - \rho_3(x_1x_2x_3x_4)}}}}}. \tag{1}$$

This continued fraction constitutes Thiele's interpolation formula for five interpolation points. Like Newton's divided difference formula, the relation is simply an identity. There is no difficulty in writing down the corresponding continued fraction for n interpolation points, the last two constituent partial fractions being in this case

$$\cfrac{x-x_{n-1}}{\rho_{n-1}(x_1x_2 \dots x_n) - \rho_{n-3}(x_1x_2 \dots x_{n-2}) + \cfrac{x-x_n}{\rho_n(xx_1 \dots x_n) - \rho_{n-2}(x_1x_2 \dots x_{n-1})}}$$

Now it is a known property of continued fractions, that if a numerator of one of the constituent partial fractions vanish, this and all the following constituents do not affect the value, and can be ignored.* If in the identity (1) we put in turn $x = x_1, x_2, x_3, x_4, x_5$, we obtain

$$f(x_1),\ f(x_2),\ \dots,\ f(x_5),$$

and in no case does the last constituent partial fraction affect the result. Thus if from (1) we delete the last constituent partial fraction, namely,

$$\frac{x-x_5}{\rho_5(xx_1x_2x_3x_4x_5) - \rho_3(x_1x_2x_3x_4)},$$

* O. Perron, *Die Lehre von den Kettenbrüchen*, Leipzig, 1929, § 42.

we obtain a rational function, expressed in the form of a partial fraction, which agrees in value with $f(x)$ at the points

$$x_1, x_2, x_3, x_4, x_5.$$

It follows that Thiele's formula gives us a method of obtaining a rational function which agrees in value with a given function at any finite number of prescribed points.

Example. Determine tan 1·5685 from the following table * :

x	$\tan x$	ρ_1	ρ_2
1·566	208·49128		
		0·000018208313	
1·567	263·41125		−0·00382
		10615733	
1·568	357·61106		·00276
		05023108	
1·569	556·69098		·00178
		01430462	
1·570	1255·76559		

The required value is

$$357{\cdot}61106 + \cfrac{{\cdot}0005}{{\cdot}000005023108 + \cfrac{-{\cdot}0005}{-357{\cdot}61106 - {\cdot}00178}}$$

$$= 357{\cdot}61106 + \frac{{\cdot}0005}{{\cdot}000006421268}$$

$$= 435{\cdot}47730.$$

According to Hayashi's table the last figure should be 2.

The principal part of $\tan x$ near $\frac{1}{2}\pi$ being

$$\frac{1}{\frac{1}{2}\pi - x},$$

Thiele's formula is suitable for interpolation, while the ordinary difference formulae are not.

5·3. The Matrix Notation for Continued Fractions. A convenient notation for defining continued fractions of any number of dimensions and for developing their properties has been

* K. Hayashi, *Sieben u. mehrstellige Tafeln*, Berlin (1926).

described by Milne-Thomson,* and is well adapted for ordinary two dimensional continued fractions of the form

(1) $$a_1 + \frac{b_2}{a_2+}\,\frac{b_3}{a_3+}\,\frac{b_4}{a_4+}\cdots.$$

It depends upon the rule for matrix multiplication,† namely,

(2) $$\begin{bmatrix} x_1 & x_2 \\ y_1 & y_2 \end{bmatrix}\begin{bmatrix} u_1 & v_1 \\ u_2 & v_2 \end{bmatrix} = \begin{bmatrix} x_1u_1+x_2u_2 & x_1v_1+x_2v_2 \\ y_1u_1+y_2u_2 & y_1v_1+y_2v_2 \end{bmatrix},$$

which is essentially the row by column rule for multiplying determinants. We also recall that equality of two matrices implies equality of their corresponding elements. Thus if

$$\begin{bmatrix} a & b \\ c & d \end{bmatrix} = \begin{bmatrix} p & q \\ r & s \end{bmatrix},$$

then $a = p$, $b = q$, $c = r$, $d = s$.

If p_n / q_n denote the nth convergent of (1), we have the known recurrence relations

(3) $$p_n = a_n p_{n-1} + b_n p_{n-2},$$
$$q_n = a_n q_{n-1} + b_n q_{n-2},$$

and hence from (2)

$$\begin{bmatrix} p_n & p_{n-1} \\ q_n & q_{n-1} \end{bmatrix} = \begin{bmatrix} p_{n-1} & p_{n-2} \\ q_{n-1} & q_{n-2} \end{bmatrix}\begin{bmatrix} a_n & 1 \\ b_n & 0 \end{bmatrix}.$$

If we write $p_0 = 1$, $q_0 = 0$, we have by repetition of the above operation

$$\begin{bmatrix} p_n & p_{n-1} \\ q_n & q_{n-1} \end{bmatrix} = \begin{bmatrix} a_1 & 1 \\ 1 & 0 \end{bmatrix}\begin{bmatrix} a_2 & 1 \\ b_2 & 0 \end{bmatrix}\begin{bmatrix} a_3 & 1 \\ b_3 & 0 \end{bmatrix}\cdots\begin{bmatrix} a_{n-1} & 1 \\ b_{n-1} & 0 \end{bmatrix}\begin{bmatrix} a_n & 1 \\ b_n & 0 \end{bmatrix}.$$

Thus we are led to define a continued fraction as the continued matrix product

(4) $$\begin{bmatrix} a_1 & 1 \\ 1 & 0 \end{bmatrix}\begin{bmatrix} a_2 & 1 \\ b_2 & 0 \end{bmatrix}\begin{bmatrix} a_3 & 1 \\ b_3 & 0 \end{bmatrix}\begin{bmatrix} a_4 & 1 \\ b_4 & 0 \end{bmatrix}\cdots,$$

and this definition leads at once to the recurrence relations (3) and is fully equivalent to (1).

---

* L. M. Milne-Thomson, in a paper at the International Congress of Mathematicians, Zürich, 1932. *Proc. Edinburgh Math. Soc.* (2), 3 (1933), p. 189.

† Turnbull and Aitken, *Theory of Canonical Matrices* (1932), p. 3.

In particular the components p_n, q_n of the nth convergent are given by

(5) $$\begin{bmatrix} p_n \\ q_n \end{bmatrix} = \begin{bmatrix} a_1 & 1 \\ 1 & 0 \end{bmatrix} \begin{bmatrix} a_2 & 1 \\ b_2 & 0 \end{bmatrix} \cdots \begin{bmatrix} a_{n-1} & 1 \\ b_{n-1} & 0 \end{bmatrix} \begin{bmatrix} a_n \\ b_n \end{bmatrix}.$$

5·4. Reciprocal Differences expressed by Determinants.

If we write for brevity

(1) $$y = f(x), \quad y_s = f(x_s), \quad \rho_s = \rho_s(x_1 x_2 \dots x_{s+1}),$$

the components of the nth convergent of Thiele's continued fraction are given, in the notation of the last section, by

$$\begin{bmatrix} p_n(x) \\ q_n(x) \end{bmatrix} = \begin{bmatrix} y_1 & 1 \\ 1 & 0 \end{bmatrix} \begin{bmatrix} \rho_1 & 1 \\ x - x_1 & 0 \end{bmatrix} \begin{bmatrix} \rho_2 - y_1 & 1 \\ x - x_2 & 0 \end{bmatrix} \begin{bmatrix} \rho_3 - \rho_1 & 1 \\ x - x_3 & 0 \end{bmatrix} \cdots$$
$$\times \begin{bmatrix} \rho_{n-1} - \rho_{n-3} & 1 \\ x - x_{n-1} & 0 \end{bmatrix} \begin{bmatrix} \rho_n - \rho_{n-2} \\ x - x_n \end{bmatrix}.$$

Consideration of this product shews at once that

$$p_{2n+1}(x), \quad q_{2n+1}(x), \quad p_{2n}(x)$$

are polynomials in x of degree n while $q_{2n}(x)$ is a polynomial of degree $n-1$, and that these polynomials are of the following forms:

(2) $$p_{2n}(x) = a_0 + a_1 x + a_2 x^2 + \dots + a_{n-1} x^{n-1} + x^n,$$

(3) $$q_{2n}(x) = b_0 + b_1 x + \dots + b_{n-2} x^{n-2} + x^{n-1} \rho_{2n-1},$$

(4) $$p_{2n+1}(x) = c_0 + c_1 x + c_2 x^2 + \dots + c_{n-1} x^{n-1} + x^n \rho_{2n},$$

(5) $$q_{2n+1}(x) = d_0 + d_1 x + d_2 x^2 + \dots + d_{n-1} x^{n-1} + x^n.$$

If we take the nth convergent of Thiele's continued fraction as an approximation to y, we have

$$y = \frac{p_n(x)}{q_n(x)} + R_n(x),$$

where $R_n(x)$ is the error of the approximation.

Now $R_n(x)$ vanishes when $x = x_1, x_2, \dots, x_n$, so that

(6) $$y_s = \frac{p_n(x_s)}{q_n(x_s)}, \quad s = 1, 2, \dots, n,$$

and hence

(7) $$p_n(x_s) - y_s q_n(x_s) = 0, \quad s = 1, 2, \dots, n.$$

Thus from (2) and (3), writing $2n$ for n in (7), we have

(8) $$a_0 + a_1 x_s + \dots + a_{n-1} x_s^{n-1} + x_s^n - b_0 y_s - b_1 x_s y_s - \dots \\ - b_{n-2} x_s^{n-2} y_s - x_s^{n-1} y_s \rho_{2n-1} = 0.$$

If in this relation we give s its values in turn, namely $1, 2, 3, \dots, 2n$, we have a set of $2n$ linear equations, which suffice to determine $a_0, a_1, \dots, a_{n-1}, b_0, b_1, \dots, b_{n-2}$ and ρ_{2n-1} and subsequently the value of $p_{2n}(x) / q_{2n}(x)$. The chief interest, however, lies in the determination of ρ_{2n-1}, which we obtain by direct solution as the quotient of two determinants. Rearranging (8), we have the equations

$$a_0 - b_0 y_s + a_1 x_s - b_1 x_s y_s + a_2 x_s^2 - b_2 x_s^2 y_s + \dots \\ + a_{n-1} x_s^{n-1} + x_s^n - x_s^{n-1} y_s \rho_{2n-1} = 0,$$

from which we obtain

(9) $\rho_{2n-1}(x_1 x_2 \dots x_{2n})$

$$= \frac{|\,1,\ y_s,\ x_s,\ x_s y_s,\ x_s^2,\ x_s^2 y_s,\ \dots,\ x_s^{n-2},\ x_s^{n-2} y_s,\ x_s^{n-1},\ x_s^n\,|}{|\,1,\ y_s,\ x_s,\ x_s y_s,\ \dots,\ x_s^{n-2},\ x_s^{n-2} y_s,\ x_s^{n-1},\ x_s^{n-1} y_s\,|},$$

where the determinants are contracted by writing only the sth row in each, $s = 1, 2, 3, \dots, 2n$. These determinants differ only the last column.

The above expression gives the important result that

$$\rho_{2n-1}(x_1, x_2, \dots, x_{2n})$$

is a *symmetric function of the arguments*: for an interchange of any two arguments merely interchanges two corresponding rows in the determinants and leaves the value of their ratio unaltered.

To obtain the value of ρ_{2n}, we have similarly from equations (4), (5), (7),

$$c_0 - d_0 y_s + c_1 x_s - d_1 x_s y_s + \dots + c_{n-1} x_s^{n-1} \\ - d_{n-1} x_s^{n-1} y_s - x_s^n y_s + x_s^n \rho_{2n} = 0,$$

which gives in the same way

(10) $\rho_{2n}(x_1 x_2 \dots x_{2n+1})$

$$= \frac{|\,1,\ y_s,\ x_s,\ x_s y_s,\ x_s^2,\ x_s^2 y_s,\ \dots,\ x_s^{n-1},\ x_s^{n-1} y_s,\ x_s^n y_s\,|}{|\,1,\ y_s,\ x_s,\ x_s y_s,\ \dots,\ x_s^{n-1},\ x_s^{n-1} y_s,\ x_s^n\,|},$$

whence we infer in the same way that $\rho_{2n}(x_1 x_2 \dots x_{2n+1})$ is a symmetric function of the arguments.

Thus we have proved that *the reciprocal differences of any order are symmetric functions of their arguments.*

It follows from this result that the arguments can be taken in any order which may happen to be convenient. In particular, we could write down interpolation continued fractions in which the reciprocal differences proceed across the difference scheme along a zig-zag line in complete analogy with the backward and forward formulae of Gauss. We shall not develop this here, but it is worthy of mention from the standpoint of practical interpolation.

5·5. The Reciprocal Differences of a Quotient. The determinantal forms for ρ_{2n-1}, ρ_{2n} furnish a means of obtaining expressions for reciprocal differences of a function which is expressed in the form of the quotient of one function divided by another, say $f(x) / g(x)$. If for brevity we write

$$y = f(x), \quad z = g(x), \quad y_s = f(x_s), \quad z_s = g(x_s),$$

we have from 5·4 (9), after multiplying top and bottom by $z_1 z_2 \dots z_{2n-1}$,

$$(1) \quad \rho_{2n-1}\left(\frac{y}{z}\right)$$

$$= \frac{| z_s, y_s, x_s z_s, x_s y_s, \dots, x_s^{n-2} z_s, x_s^{n-2} y_s, x_s^{n-1} z_s, x_s^{n} z_s |}{| z_s, y_s, x_s z_s, x_s y_s, \dots, x_s^{n-2} z_s, x_s^{n-2} y_s, x_s^{n-1} z_s, x_s^{n-1} y_s |}.$$

Similarly from 5·4 (10) we obtain

$$(2) \quad \rho_{2n}\left(\frac{y}{z}\right)$$

$$= \frac{| z_s, y_s, x_s z_s, x_s y_s, \dots, x_s^{n-1} z_s, x_s^{n-1} y_s, x_s^{n} y_s |}{| z_s, y_s, x_s z_s, x_s y_s, \dots, x_s^{n-1} z_s, x_s^{n-1} y_s, x_s^{n} z_s |}.$$

Thus we have the following particular relations for $n = 1, 2$:

$$\rho\left(\frac{y}{z}\right) = \begin{vmatrix} z_1 & x_1 z_1 \\ z_2 & x_2 z_2 \end{vmatrix} \div \begin{vmatrix} z_1 & y_1 \\ z_2 & y_2 \end{vmatrix},$$

$$\rho_2\left(\frac{y}{z}\right) = \begin{vmatrix} z_1 & y_1 & x_1 y_1 \\ z_2 & y_2 & x_2 y_2 \\ z_3 & y_3 & x_3 y_3 \end{vmatrix} \div \begin{vmatrix} z_1 & y_1 & x_1 z_1 \\ z_2 & y_2 & x_2 z_2 \\ z_3 & y_3 & x_3 z_3 \end{vmatrix},$$

$$\rho_3\left(\frac{y}{z}\right) = \begin{vmatrix} z_1 & y_1 & x_1 z_1 & x_1^2 z_1 \\ z_2 & y_2 & x_2 z_2 & x_2^2 z_2 \\ z_3 & y_3 & x_3 z_3 & x_2^2 z_3 \\ z_4 & y_4 & x_4 z_4 & x_4^2 z_4^2 \end{vmatrix} \div \begin{vmatrix} z_1 & y_1 & x_1 z_1 & x_1 y_1 \\ z_2 & y_2 & x_2 z_2 & x_2 y_2 \\ z_3 & y_3 & x_3 z_3 & x_3 y_3 \\ z_4 & y_4 & x_4 z_4 & x_4 y_4 \end{vmatrix},$$

$$\rho_4\left(\frac{y}{z}\right) = \begin{vmatrix} z_1 & y_1 & x_1 z_1 & x_1 y_1 & x_1^2 y_1 \\ z_2 & y_2 & x_2 z_2 & x_2 y_2 & x_2^2 y_2 \\ z_3 & y_3 & x_3 z_3 & x_3 y_3 & x_3^2 y_3 \\ z_4 & y_4 & x_4 z_4 & x_4 y_4 & x_4^2 y_4 \\ z_5 & y_5 & x_5 z_5 & x_5 y_5 & x_5^2 y_5 \end{vmatrix} \div \begin{vmatrix} z_1 & y_1 & x_1 z_1 & x_1 y_1 & x_1^2 z_1 \\ z_2 & y_2 & x_2 z_2 & x_2 y_2 & x_2^2 z_2 \\ z_3 & y_3 & x_3 z_3 & x_3 y_3 & x_3^2 z_3 \\ z_4 & y_4 & x_4 z_4 & x_4 y_4 & x_4^2 z_4 \\ z_5 & y_5 & x_5 z_5 & x_5 y_5 & x_5^2 z_5 \end{vmatrix}.$$

We can use these relations to prove that at a certain order the reciprocal differences of a rational function are constant..

To illustrate the reasoning, we take the function

$$\frac{a+bx+cx^2}{\alpha+\beta x+\gamma x^2} = \frac{y}{z}$$

and shew that the fourth order differences are constant.

The determinant in the numerator of ρ_4 is

$$N_4 = |\,\alpha+\beta x_s+\gamma x_s^2,\ a+bx_s+cx_s^2,\ \alpha x_s+\beta x_s^2+\gamma x_s^3,$$
$$ax_s+bx_s^2+cx_s^3,\ ax_s^2+bx_s^3+cx_s^4\,|.$$

If we denote the columns of a determinant by c_1, c_2, c_3, c_4, c_5 and the columns of the new determinant, derived by manipulation, by c_1', etc., we can form successively the following determinants each equivalent to N_4:

$$|\,\beta_1 x_s+\gamma_1 x_s^2, a+bx_s+cx_s^2, \alpha x_s+\beta x_s^2+\gamma x_s^3,$$
$$ax_s+bx_s^2+cx_s^3, ax_s^2+bx_s^3+cx_s^4\,|$$

by the operation $c_1' = c_1 - \dfrac{\alpha}{a} c_2$;

$$|\,\beta_1 x_s+\gamma_1 x_s^2, a+c_1 x_s^2, \beta_2 x_s^2+\gamma x_s^3, b_1 x_s^2+cx_s^3, ax_s^2+bx_s^3+cx_s^4\,|$$

by the operation $c_2' = c_2 - \dfrac{b}{\beta_1} c_1,\quad c_3' = c_3 - \dfrac{\alpha}{\beta_1} c_1,\quad c_4' = c_4 - \dfrac{a}{\beta_1} c_1$;

$$|\,\beta_1 x_s+\gamma_1 x_s^2,\ a+c_1 x_s^2,\ \beta_2 x_s^2+\gamma x_s^3,\ c_2 x_s^3,\ b_2 x_s^3+cx_s^4\,|$$

by the operation $c_4' = c_4 - \dfrac{b_1}{\beta_2} c_3,\quad c_5' = c_5 - \dfrac{a}{\beta_2} c_3$;

$$|\,\beta_1 x_s+\gamma_1 x_s^2,\ a+c_1 x_s^2,\ \beta_2 x_s^2,\ c_2 x_s^3,\ cx_s^4\,|$$

by the operation $c_3' = c_3 - \frac{\gamma}{c_2} c_4, \quad c_5' = c_5 - \frac{b_2}{c_2} c_4;$

$$| \beta_1 x_s, \ a, \ \beta_2 x_s^2, \ c_2 x_s^3, \ c x_s^4 |$$

by the operation $c_1' = c_1 - \frac{\gamma_1}{\beta_2} c_3, \quad c_2' = c_2 - \frac{c_1}{\beta_2} c_3;$

so that

$$N_4 = \beta_1 a \beta_2 c_2 c \, | x_s, \ 1, \ x_s^2, \ x_s^3, \ x_s^4 |.$$

Similarly for the denominator we obtain

$$\beta_1 a \beta_2 c_2 \gamma \, | x_s, \ 1, \ x_s^2, \ x_s^3, \ x_s^4 |.$$

Thus $\rho_4\left(\frac{y}{z}\right) = \frac{c}{\gamma}$, which is constant.

We have assumed in the above construction that none of

$$a, \ \beta_1, \ \beta_2, \ c_2, \ \gamma$$

vanish. These cases present no special difficulty, but we may note that if $\gamma = 0$, ρ_4 is infinite, so that ρ_3 must be constant.

5·6. Some Properties of Reciprocal Differences. If in 5·5 (2) we put $y = 1$, we have

$$\rho_{2n}\left(\frac{1}{z}\right) = \frac{| z_s, \ 1, \ x_s z_s, \ x_s, \ \dots, \ x_s^{n-1} z_s, \ x_s^{n-1}, \ x_s^n |}{| z_s, \ 1, \ x_s z_s, \ x_s, \ \dots, \ x_s^{n-1} z_s, \ x_s^{n-1}, \ x_s^n z_s |},$$

(1) $$\rho_{2n}\left(\frac{1}{z}\right) = \frac{1}{\rho_{2n}(z)},$$

by 5·4 (10). Thus the reciprocal differences of even order of a given function are equal to the reciprocals of the reciprocal differences of the same order of the reciprocal of the function.

Again, from 5·4 (10),

$$\rho_{2n}(y+c) = \frac{| 1, \ y_s + c, \ x_s, \ x_s y_s + c x_s, \ \dots, \ x_s^{n-1} y_s + x_s^{n-1} c, \ x_s^n y_s + x_s^n c |}{| 1, \ y_s + c, \ x_s, \ x_s y_s + c x_s, \ \dots, \ x_s^{n-1}, \ x_s^{n-1} y_s + x_s^{n-1} c, \ x_s^n |}$$

$$= \frac{| 1, \ y_s, \ x_s, \ x_s y_s, \ \dots, \ x_s^{n-1} y_s, \ x_s^n y_s + x_s^n c |}{| 1, \ y_s, \ x_s, \ x_s y_s, \ \dots, \ x_s^{n-1} y_s, \ x_s^n |}.$$

Thus

(2) $$\rho_{2n}(y+c) = \rho_{2n}(y) + c.$$

Similarly, from 5·4 (9),

(3) $$\rho_{2n-1}(y+c) = \rho_{2n-1}(y).$$

Again, from 5·4 (10),

$$\rho_{2n}(cy) = \frac{|\,1,\ c\,y_s,\ x_s,\ c\,x_s\,y_s, \ldots,\ x_s^{\,n-1},\ c\,x_s^{\,n-1}y_s,\ c\,x_s^{\,n}y_s\,|}{|\,1,\ c\,y_s,\ x_s,\ c\,x_s\,y_s, \ldots,\ x_s^{\,n-1},\ c\,x_s^{\,n-1}y_s,\ x_s^{\,n}\,|}$$

(4) $$= c\,\rho_{2n}(y),$$

since the numerator contains the factor c in one more column than the denominator.

Similarly, from 5·4 (9),

(5) $$\rho_{2n-1}(cy) = \frac{1}{c}\,\rho_{2n-1}(y).$$

Also, since

$$\frac{a+by}{c+dy} = \frac{b}{d} + \frac{(a-bc/d)}{c+dy},$$

we have

$$\rho_{2n}\left(\frac{a+by}{c+dy}\right) = \frac{b}{d} + \rho_{2n}\left(\frac{a-bc/d}{c+dy}\right), \quad \text{from (2)},$$

$$= \frac{b}{d} + \left(a - \frac{bc}{d}\right)\rho_{2n}\left(\frac{1}{c+dy}\right), \quad \text{from (4)},$$

$$= \frac{b}{d} + \left(a - \frac{bc}{d}\right)\frac{1}{\rho_{2n}(c+dy)}, \quad \text{from (1)},$$

$$= \frac{b}{d} + \left(a - \frac{bc}{d}\right)\frac{1}{c+d\,\rho_{2n}(y)},$$

from (2) and (4), so that

(6) $$\rho_{2n}\left(\frac{a+by}{c+dy}\right) = \frac{a+b\,\rho_{2n}(y)}{c+d\,\rho_{2n}(y)}.$$

This formula expresses the differences of even order, of a linear fraction of y, in terms of the differences of even order of y itself. If we take advantage of the symmetry in the arguments of the reciprocal differences we can also form the differences of odd order in Thiele's continued fraction by means of 5·1 (5).

Thus, for example,

$$\rho_5(x_1x_2x_3x_4x_5x_6) - \rho_3(x_1x_2x_3x_4) = \rho_5(x_5x_1x_2x_3x_4x_6) - \rho_3(x_1x_2x_3x_4)$$
$$= \rho\,\rho_4(x_5x_1x_2x_3x_4),$$

so that from a knowledge of the even order reciprocal differences of y we can expand

$$\frac{a+by}{c+dy}$$

in a continued fraction.

5·7. The Remainder in Thiele's Formula. If we take n interpolation points $x_1, x_2, \dots, x_n$ and form Thiele's continued fraction for a function $f(x)$, we can write

(1) $$f(x) = \frac{p_n(x)}{q_n(x)} + R_n(x),$$

where $p_n(x)$, $q_n(x)$ are the components of the nth convergent. $R_n(x)$ then measures the error committed if we replace $f(x)$ by the nth convergent. Let (a, b) be the smallest interval containing the real numbers $x, x_1, x_2, \dots, x_n$. Let us suppose that in the interval (a, b) of the real variable x the function $f(x)$ has poles at $\alpha_1, \alpha_2, \dots, \alpha_\nu$ of orders $r_1, r_2, \dots, r_\nu$, where $r_1+r_2+\dots+r_\nu = m$.

We shall suppose that none of these poles coincides with an interpolation point and that at all points of (a, b) except the poles $f(x)$ has a finite derivate of order n. If we write

(2) $$\phi(x) = (x-\alpha_1)^{r_1}(x-\alpha_2)^{r_2} \dots (x-\alpha_\nu)^{r_\nu},$$

the function $f(x)\,\phi(x)$ is finite at every point of (a, b).

We shall suppose n to be so large that the degree of $q_n(x)$ is greater than or equal to m.

Now let a polynomial $\psi(x)$ be chosen such that, if

(3) $$Q(x) = \phi(x)\,\psi(x),$$

$Q(x)$ and $q_n(x)$ have the same degree. Thus from 5·4,

if $n = 2h$, $Q(x)$ is of degree $h-1$,

if $n = 2h+1$, $Q(x)$ is of degree h.

Write

(4) $$R_n(x) = \chi(x)\frac{(x-x_1)(x-x_2)\dots(x-x_n)}{q_n(x)\,Q(x)};$$

and consider the function

$$f(t) - \frac{p_n(t)}{q_n(t)} - \chi(x)\frac{(t-x_1)\dots(t-x_n)}{q_n(t)\,Q(t)},$$

which vanishes when $t = x_1, x_2, \dots, x_n$ and also when $t = x$ by (4) and (1).

Then the function

(5) $$\omega(t) = f(t)\,q_n(t)\,Q(t) - p_n(t)\,Q(t) - \chi(x)(t-x_1)\dots(t-x_n)$$

also vanishes when $t = x, x_1, x_2, \dots, x_n$, all of which lie in the interval (a, b). Thus by Rolle's Theorem $\omega'(t)$ has at least n zeros in (a, b), $\omega''(t)$ has $(n-1)$ zeros in (a, b), and so on, until finally we conclude that $\omega^{(n)}(t)$ has at least one zero, say $t = \xi$, in (a, b). Now $p_n(t)$ is a polynomial of degree h, when $n = 2h$ or $2h+1$, and we have chosen $Q(t)$ so that the degree is $h-1$ or h, according as $n = 2h$ or $2h+1$. Thus $p_n(t)\,Q(t)$ is a polynomial of degree $n-1$ and hence the nth derivate vanishes identically. Hence from (5),

$$\chi(x) = \frac{1}{n!}\frac{d^n}{d\xi^n}\{f(\xi)q_n(\xi)\,Q(\xi)\},$$

whence we have the error term

$$(6) \qquad R_n(x) = \frac{(x-x_1)(x-x_2)\dots(x-x_n)}{n!\;q_n(x)\,Q(x)}\frac{d^n}{d\xi^n}\{f(\xi)\,q_n(\xi)\,Q(\xi)\}.$$

It should be observed that the above formula is only valid if n be sufficiently large.

If $f(x)$ have no infinities in the interval (a, b) we can take

$$Q(x) = q_n(x),$$

and the error term is then given by

$$(7) \qquad R_n(x) = \frac{(x-x_1)(x-x_2)\dots(x-x_n)}{n!\,[q_n(x)]^2}\frac{d^n}{d\xi^n}\{f(\xi)\,[q_n(\xi)]^2\}.$$

5·8. Reciprocal Derivates ; the Confluent Case. In the definition of reciprocal differences we supposed the arguments to be distinct. Just as in the corresponding case of divided differences, we can here suppose two or more arguments to coincide and so obtain *confluent* reciprocal differences. The simplest way to proceed is to consider the limiting forms assumed by the determinants (9) and (10) of 5·4. Thus, for example, we define

$$\rho_2(xxy) = \lim_{h\to 0}\rho_2(x, x+h, y)$$

$$= \lim_{h\to 0}\begin{vmatrix} 1 & f(x) & xf(x) \\ 1 & f(x+h) & (x+h)f(x+h) \\ 1 & f(y) & yf(y)\end{vmatrix} \div \begin{vmatrix} 1 & f(x) & x \\ 1 & f(x+h) & x+h \\ 1 & f(y) & y\end{vmatrix}.$$

Subtracting the first row from the second and dividing by h, we have

$$\rho_2(xxy) = \begin{vmatrix} 1 & f(x) & xf(x) \\ 0 & f'(x) & xf'(x)+f(x) \\ 1 & f(y) & yf(y) \end{vmatrix} \div \begin{vmatrix} 1 & f(x) & x \\ 0 & f'(x) & 1 \\ 1 & f(y) & y \end{vmatrix}.$$

If now we write $x+k$ for y, subtract the sum of the first row and k times the second row from the third row, divide by k^2 and then let $k \to 0$, we obtain

$$(1) \qquad \rho_2(xxx) = \begin{vmatrix} 1 & f(x) & xf(x) \\ 0 & f'(x) & xf'(x)+f(x) \\ 0 & \frac{1}{2}f''(x) & \frac{1}{2}xf''(x)+f'(x) \end{vmatrix} \div \begin{vmatrix} 1 & f(x) & x \\ 0 & f'(x) & 1 \\ 0 & \frac{1}{2}f''(x) & 0 \end{vmatrix}.$$

It is clear that in this way we can obtain confluent reciprocal differences of any order, since indeterminate forms can always be avoided by taking advantage of the symmetry of the differences with respect to their arguments. Particular interest attaches to the case in which all the arguments have a common value. This particular form of confluent reciprocal difference is called a *reciprocal derivate* and we write

$$2) \qquad r_n f(x) = \lim_{x_1, x_2, \ldots, x_{n+1} \to x} \rho_n(x_1 x_2 \ldots x_{n+1})$$
$$= \rho_n(xxx \ldots x).$$

In particular,

$$(3) \qquad rf(x) = \lim_{x_1, x_2, \to x} \frac{x_1 - x_2}{f(x_1) - f(x_2)} = \frac{1}{f'(x)},$$

so that the reciprocal derivate of the first order is the reciprocal of the ordinary derivate.

The successive reciprocal derivates can be calculated from a recurrence relation which may be obtained as follows:

from 5·1 (4), we have

$$\frac{\rho_2(xxx) - \rho_2(xxy)}{x-y} = \frac{1}{\rho_3(xxxy) - \rho(xx)},$$

$$\frac{\rho_2(xxy) - \rho_2(xyy)}{x-y} = \frac{1}{\rho_3(xxyy) - \rho(xy)},$$

$$\frac{\rho_2(xyy) - \rho_2(yyy)}{x-y} = \frac{1}{\rho_3(xyyy) - \rho(yy)};$$

adding, we have

$$\frac{\rho_2(xxx)-\rho_2(yyy)}{x-y}=\frac{1}{\rho_3(xxxy)-\rho(xx)}+\frac{1}{\rho_3(xxyy)-\rho(xy)}$$
$$+\frac{1}{\rho_3(xyyy)-\rho(yy)}.$$

If we now let $y\to x$, we obtain

$$\frac{1}{r\,r_2 f(x)}=\frac{3}{r_3 f(x)-rf(x)}.$$

Thus

$$r_3 f(x)=rf(x)+3r\,r_2 f(x).$$

This is a particular case of the general recurrence relation whose form is easily seen to be

$$(4)\qquad r_n f(x)=r_{n-2}f(x)+nr\,r_{n-1}f(x).$$

In particular,

$$r_2 f(x)=f(x)+2r\left(\frac{1}{f'(x)}\right)$$
$$=f(x)-\frac{2[f'(x)]^2}{f''(x)}$$

which agrees with (1).

Since the reciprocal differences of some order of a rational function are constant, the same must hold for reciprocal derivates.

For example,

$$r\,x^2=\frac{1}{2x},\quad r_2\,x^2=-3x^2,\quad r_3\,x^2=0.$$

$$r\left(\frac{ax+b}{cx+d}\right)=-\frac{(cx+d)^2}{bc-ad},\quad r_2\left(\frac{ax+b}{cx+d}\right)^2=\frac{a}{c}.$$

This last result can be obtained also from 5·6 (6) as follows :

$$r_2\left(\frac{ax+b}{cx+d}\right)=\frac{ar_2\,x+b}{cr_2\,x+d}=\frac{a}{c},$$

since $\qquad r_2\,x=\infty.$

5·9. Thiele's Theorem. We have seen that Taylor's Theorem, which gives the expansion of a function in a power series whose coëfficients are proportional to the successive derivates at a point, can be obtained from Newton's general interpolation formula with divided differences. In a similar way Thiele's interpolation formula gives rise to a remarkable development of a function as a continued fraction in which the reciprocal derivates at a point are employed.

In fact, when $x_1, x_2, \ldots, x_{n+1} \to x$, we have

$$\begin{aligned}\lim \{ \rho_n (x_1 x_2 \ldots x_{n+1}) - \rho_{n-2} (x_1 x_2 \ldots x_{n-1}) \} &= r_n f(x) - r_{n-2} f(x) \\ &= nr\, r_{n-1} f(x)\end{aligned}$$

by 5·8 (4). Thus Thiele's interpolation formula of 5·2 yields Thiele's Theorem, namely,

$$f(x+h) = f(x) + \cfrac{h}{rf(x) + \cfrac{h}{2r\,rf(x) + \cfrac{h}{3r\,r_2 f(x) + \ldots}}}, \tag{1}$$

in which, if we stop at the nth partial divisor, this will be

$$\lim_{x_1, \ldots, x_n \to x} \rho_n (x+h, x_1, x_2, \ldots, x_n) - r_{n-2} f(x).$$

The error term is given by 5·7 (6), where ξ lies in the interval $(x, x+h)$.

Just as Taylor's series terminates when the function is a polynomial, so Thiele's Continued Fraction terminates when the function is rational.

Thus, for example,

$$(x+h)^2 = x^2 + \cfrac{h}{\cfrac{1}{2x} + \cfrac{h}{-4x^2 + \cfrac{h}{-\cfrac{1}{2x}}}},$$

$$\frac{a(x+h)+b}{c(x+h)+d} = \frac{ax+b}{cx+d} + \cfrac{h}{\cfrac{(cx+d)^2}{ad-bc} + \cfrac{h}{\cfrac{ad-bc}{c(cx+d)}}},$$

$$\frac{ax+b}{cx+d} = \frac{b}{d} + \cfrac{x}{\cfrac{d^2}{ad-bc} + \cfrac{x}{(ad-bc)/(cd)}}.$$

Example. By means of Thiele's Theorem, find a continued fraction for e^x.

We have

$$re^x = e^{-x}, \qquad r_2 e^x = -e^x,$$
$$r_3 e^x = -2e^{-x}, \qquad r_4 e^x = e^x,$$
$$r_5 e^x = 3e^{-x}, \qquad r_6 e^x = -e^x.$$

These suggest the results

$$r_{2n} e^x = (-1)^n e^x, \quad r_{2n+1} e^x = (-1)^n (n+1) e^{-x}.$$

Assuming these for n, we have by 5·8 (4),

$$r_{2n+2} e^x = \left((-1)^n - \frac{2n+2}{(-1)^n (n+1)}\right) e^x = (-1)^{n+1} e^x,$$

$$r_{2n+3} e^x = \left((-1)^n (n+1) + \frac{2n+3}{(-1)^{n+1}}\right) e^{-x} = (-1)^{n+1} (n+2) e^{-x},$$

so that the results are established by induction.

Then

$$(2n+1)\, r\, r_{2n} e^x = r_{2n+1} e^x - r_{2n-1} e^x = (-1)^n (2n+1) e^{-x},$$
$$(2n+2)\, r\, r_{2n+1} e^x = r_{2n+2} e^x - r_{2n} e^x = 2(-1)^{n+1} e^x.$$

In Thiele's Theorem, writing 0 for x, and x for h, we have

$$e^x = 1 + \cfrac{x}{1 + \cfrac{x}{-2 + \cfrac{x}{-3 + \cfrac{x}{2 + \cfrac{x}{5 + \cfrac{x}{-2 + \dots}}}}}}.$$

We can write this so that the integers all have positive signs, and we then obtain *

$$e^x = 1 + \frac{x}{1-}\,\frac{x}{2+}\,\frac{x}{3-}\,\frac{x}{2+}\,\frac{x}{5-}\,\frac{x}{2+}\,\frac{x}{7-}\cdots.$$

* O. Perron, *loc. cit.* p. 107 (353, (20)).

EXAMPLES V

1. Form the reciprocal differences of x^3, x^{-3}, $x+x^{-1}$.

2. Form reciprocal differences for the following table:

x	0·010	·011	·012	·013	·014
coth x	100·00	90·91	83·34	76·93	71·43

and calculate coth 0·01257.

3. Form reciprocal differences of a^x and hence develop a^x in a continued fraction.

4. Prove that ρ_2, ρ_4 can be expressed in terms of divided differences as follows:

$$\rho_2(x_1x_2x_3) = \begin{vmatrix} f(x_2) & [x_1x_2] \\ [x_2x_3] & . \; [x_1x_2x_3] \end{vmatrix} \div [x_1x_2x_3],$$

$$\rho_4(x_1x_2x_3x_4x_5)$$

$$= \begin{vmatrix} f(x_3) & [x_2x_3] & [x_1x_2x_3] \\ [x_3x_4] & [x_2x_3x_4] & [x_1x_2x_3x_4] \\ [x_3x_4x_5] & [x_2x_3x_4x_5] & [x_1x_2x_3x_4x_5] \end{vmatrix} \div \begin{vmatrix} [x_2x_3x_4] & [x_1x_2x_3x_4] \\ [x_2x_3x_4x_5] & [x_1x_2x_3x_4x_5] \end{vmatrix}.$$

Obtain corresponding expressions for ρ_3, ρ_5, ρ_6.

5. Obtain determinants for $p_3(x)$, $q_3(x)$, $p_4(x)$, $q_4(x)$, the components of the third and fourth convergents of Thiele's interpolation formula.

6. Obtain Thiele's interpolation formula for five arguments in forms which utilise reciprocal differences in the same relative positions in the difference scheme as those employed in the forward and backward formulae of Gauss.

7. Prove that

$$\rho\,\rho_{2n}\left(\frac{1}{y}\right) = -(\rho_{2n}\,y)^2\,\rho\,\rho_{2n}\,y,$$

$$\rho\,\rho_{2n+1}\left(\frac{1}{y}\right) = \frac{-\rho\,\rho_{2n+1}\,y}{(\rho_{2n}\,y)(\rho_{2n+2}\,y)}.$$

8. Given the reciprocal differences of y for the arguments $x_1, x_2, x_3, \ldots$, develop $\dfrac{1}{y}$ in a continued fraction as far as reciprocal differences of order 6.

9. If we denote $\frac{dy}{dx}$ by y', $\frac{d^2y}{dx^2}$ by y'', and so on, prove that

$$r_3 y = \frac{y'''}{3!} \div \begin{vmatrix} y' & \frac{y''}{2!} \\ \frac{y''}{2!} & \frac{y'''}{3!} \end{vmatrix},$$

$$r_4 y = \begin{vmatrix} y & y' & \frac{y''}{2!} \\ y' & \frac{y''}{2!} & \frac{y'''}{3!} \\ \frac{y''}{2!} & \frac{y'''}{3!} & \frac{y^{\text{iv}}}{4!} \end{vmatrix} \div \begin{vmatrix} \frac{y''}{2!} & \frac{y'''}{3!} \\ \frac{y'''}{3!} & \frac{y^{\text{iv}}}{4!} \end{vmatrix}$$

and obtain analogous expressions for $r_5 y$, $r_6 y$.

10. Determine the order of constant reciprocal differences in the case of the rational function $f_m(x) / f_n(x)$ where $f_m(x), f_n(x)$ are polynomials of degrees m and n respectively.

11. Shew that in the case of a rational function Thiele's interpolation formula terminates and yields a continued fraction which is identically equal to the given function.

CHAPTER VI

THE POLYNOMIALS OF BERNOULLI AND EULER

IN this chapter we develop some properties of two classes of polynomials, which play an important part in the finite calculus, namely the polynomials of Bernoulli and the polynomials of Euler. These have been the object of much research and have been generalised in a very elegant manner by Nörlund.*

We shall here approach these polynomials by a symbolic method described by Milne-Thomson † by which they arise as generalisations of the simplest polynomials, namely, the powers of x. The method is applicable to whole classes of polynomials, including those of Hermite. Considerations of space must limit us to the discussion of only a few of the most interesting relations to which these polynomials give rise.

6·0. The φ Polynomials. We define ϕ polynomials $\phi_\nu^{(n)}(x)$ of *degree* ν and *order* n by the relation ‡

(1) $$f_n(t)\, e^{xt+g(t)} = \sum_{\nu=0}^{\infty} \frac{t^\nu}{\nu!} \phi_\nu^{(n)}(x),$$

where $f_n(t)$ and $g(t)$ are such that for a certain range of x the expansion on the right exists as a uniformly convergent series in t.

Putting $x = 0$, we have

(2) $$f_n(t)\, e^{g(t)} = \sum_{\nu=0}^{\infty} \frac{t^\nu}{\nu!} \phi_\nu^{(n)},$$

where $\phi_\nu^{(n)} = \phi_\nu^{(n)}(0)$ is called a ϕ number of order n.

* N. E. Nörlund, *Acta Math.*, 43 (1920), pp. 121-196.

† L. M. Milne-Thomson, *Proc. London Math. Soc.*, (2), 35 (1933).

‡ Observe that the notation $\phi_\nu^{(n)}(x)$ does not here denote the nth derivate of $\phi_\nu(x)$.

If in (1) we write $x+y$ for x, we obtain

$$\sum_{\nu=0}^{\infty} \frac{t^\nu}{\nu!} \phi_\nu^{(n)}(x+y) = e^{xt} \sum_{\nu=0}^{\infty} \frac{t^\nu}{\nu!} \phi_\nu^{(n)}(y).$$

Equating the coefficients of t^ν, we have

$$\phi_\nu^{(n)}(x+y)$$
$$= \phi_\nu^{(n)}(y) + x\binom{\nu}{1}\phi_{\nu-1}^{(n)}(y) + x^2\binom{\nu}{2}\phi_{\nu-2}^{(n)}(y) + \dots + x^\nu \binom{\nu}{\nu}\phi_0^{(n)}(y).$$

Putting $y=0$, we obtain

$$\phi_\nu^{(n)}(x) = \phi_\nu^{(n)} + x\binom{\nu}{1}\phi_{\nu-1}^{(n)} + x^2\binom{\nu}{2}\phi_{\nu-2}^{(n)} + \dots + x^\nu\binom{\nu}{\nu}\phi_0^{(n)},$$

which shews, unless $\phi_0^{(n)}=0$, that $\phi_\nu^{(n)}(x)$ is actually of degree ν.

Thus we have the symbolic equality

(3) $$\phi_\nu^{(n)}(x) \doteqdot (\phi^{(n)}+x)^\nu,$$

where, after expansion, each index of $\phi^{(n)}$ is to be replaced by the corresponding suffix.

The ϕ polynomials are thus completely characterised by (3), and by the ϕ numbers defined by (2).

From (3), we have

(4) $$\frac{d}{dx}\phi_\nu^{(n)}(x) \doteqdot \nu(\phi_\nu^{(n)}+x)^{\nu-1} = \nu\,\phi_{\nu-1}^{(n)}(x).$$

(5) $$\int_a^x \phi_\nu^{(n)}(t)\,dt = \frac{\phi_{\nu+1}^{(n)}(x) - \phi_{\nu+1}^{(n)}(a)}{\nu+1}.$$

Thus differentiation depresses the degree by one unit, integration raises the degree by one unit, but neither operation affects the order.

Operating on (1) with Δ, we have

(6) $$\sum_{\nu=0}^{\infty}\frac{t^\nu}{\nu!}\Delta\phi_\nu^{(n)}(x) = (e^t-1)f_n(t)\,e^{xt+g(t)}.$$

Operating on (1) with ∇, we have

(7) $$\sum_{\nu=0}^{\infty}\frac{t^\nu}{\nu!}\nabla\phi_\nu^{(n)}(x) = \frac{e^t+1}{2}f_n(t)\,e^{xt+g(t)}.$$

6·01. The β Polynomials. Formula 6·0 (6) suggests that a particularly simple class of ϕ polynomials should arise if we take in 6·0 (1)

$$f_n(t) = t^n (e^t - 1)^{-n},$$

where n is any integer positive, negative, or zero.

The polynomials which arise in this way we shall call β polynomials, and we write

$$\frac{t^n}{(e^t-1)^n} e^{xt+g(t)} = \sum_{\nu=0}^{\infty} \frac{t^\nu}{\nu!} \beta_\nu^{(n)}(x), \tag{1}$$

so that from 6·0 (6),

$$\sum_{\nu=0}^{\infty} \frac{t^\nu}{\nu!} \Delta\, \beta_\nu^{(n)}(x) = t \sum_{\nu=0}^{\infty} \frac{t^\nu}{\nu!} \beta_\nu^{(n-1)}(x),$$

whence we obtain

$$\Delta\, \beta_\nu^{(n)}(x) = \nu\, \beta_{\nu-1}^{(n-1)}(x). \tag{2}$$

Thus the operator Δ depresses both the order and the degree by one unit.

With the aid of 6·0 (3), (2) can be written in the form

$$(\beta^{(n)} + x + 1)^\nu - (\beta^{(n)} + x)^\nu \doteqdot \nu(\beta^{(n-1)} + x)^{\nu-1}. \tag{3}$$

Writing $x = 0$, we have the symbolic equation

$$(\beta^{(n)} + 1)^\nu - \beta_\nu^{(n)} \doteqdot \nu\, \beta_{\nu-1}^{(n-1)}, \tag{4}$$

which gives a recurrence relation between the β numbers of orders n and $n-1$.

6·1. Definition of Bernoulli's Polynomials. The β polynomials of order zero have the generating function $e^{xt+g(t)}$. The simplest polynomials of this type are obtained by putting $g(t) = 0$. The generating function then becomes e^{xt}, and the corresponding β polynomials of zero order are simply the successive powers of x. It is convenient to regard these simplest β polynomials as Bernoulli's polynomials of order zero. We therefore make the following definition:

Bernoulli's polynomial of order zero and degree ν *is given by the relation*

$$B_\nu^{(0)}(x) = x^\nu.$$

Thus we have

(1) $$e^{xt} = \sum_{\nu=0}^{\infty} \frac{t^\nu}{\nu!} B_\nu^{(0)}(x).$$

Then, in accordance with 6·01 (1), we have the further definition:

Bernoulli's polynomials of order n *are given by the identity*

(2) $$\frac{t^n e^{xt}}{(e^t-1)^n} = \sum_{\nu=0}^{\infty} \frac{t^\nu}{\nu!} B_\nu^{(n)}(x).$$

If we put $x = 0$, we have for Bernoulli's numbers of order n

(3) $$\frac{t^n}{(e^t-1)^n} = \sum_{\nu=0}^{\infty} \frac{t^\nu}{\nu!} B_\nu^{(n)}.$$

From this we obtain

$$B_0^{(n)} = 1,\quad B_1^{(n)} = -\tfrac{1}{2}n,\quad B_2^{(n)} = \tfrac{1}{12}n(3n-1),\quad B_3^{(n)} = -\tfrac{1}{8}n^2(n-1),$$

$$B_4^{(n)} = \tfrac{1}{240}n(15n^3-30n^2+5n+2),$$

$$B_5^{(n)} = -\tfrac{1}{96}n^2(n-1)(3n^2-7n-2),$$

$$B_6^{(n)} = \tfrac{1}{4032}n(63n^5-315n^4+315n^3+91n^2-42n-16).$$

6·11. Fundamental Properties of Bernoulli's Polynomials. Bernoulli's polynomials are β polynomials and therefore also ϕ polynomials. Hence we have

(1) $$B_\nu^{(n)}(x) \doteqdot (B^{(n)}+x)^\nu.$$

(2) $$\frac{d}{dx} B_\nu^{(n)}(x) = \nu B_{\nu-1}^{(n)}(x).$$

(3) $$\int_a^x B_\nu^{(n)}(t)\,dt = \frac{1}{\nu+1}\left[B_{\nu+1}^{(n)}(x) - B_{\nu+1}^{(n)}(a)\right].$$

(4) $$\Delta B_\nu^{(n)}(x) = \nu B_{\nu-1}^{(n-1)}(x).$$

(5) $$(B^{(n)}+1)^\nu - B_\nu^{(n)} \doteqdot \nu B_{\nu-1}^{(n-1)}.$$

The first three properties are shared by all ϕ polynomials, the last two by all β polynomials.

By repeated application of (4), we have, if $\nu \geqslant n$,

(6) $$\overset{n}{\Delta} B_\nu^{(n)}(x) = \nu(\nu-1)(\nu-2)\ldots(\nu-n+1)\,x^{\nu-n},$$

since $B_\nu^{(0)} = x^\nu$. If $\nu < n$, the right-hand member vanishes. Relations (4) and (5) form the point of departure of Nörlund's theory of these polynomials.

We also note the useful relations derived from (4),

(7) $$B_\nu^{(n)}(x+1) = B_\nu^{(n)}(x) + \nu B_{\nu-1}^{(n-1)}(x),$$

(8) $$B_\nu^{n}(1) = B_\nu^{(n)} + \nu B_{\nu-1}^{(n-1)}.$$

From (3) and (4), we have

(9) $$\int_x^{x+1} B_\nu^{(n)}(t)\,dt = \frac{1}{\nu+1}\Delta B_{\nu+1}^{(n)}(x) = B_\nu^{(n-1)}(x),$$

and in particular

(10) $$\int_0^1 B_\nu^{(n)}(t)\,dt = B_\nu^{(n-1)}.$$

6·2. The Complementary Argument Theorem. The arguments x and $n-x$ are called complementary. We shall now prove that

(1) $$B_\nu^{(n)}(n-x) = (-1)^\nu B_\nu^{(n)}(x).$$

We have, from 6·1 (2),

$$\sum_{\nu=0}^{\infty} \frac{t^\nu}{\nu!} B_\nu^{(n)}(n-x) = \frac{t^n e^{(n-x)t}}{(e^t-1)^n} = \frac{t^n e^{-xt}}{(1-e^{-t})^n}$$
$$= \frac{(-t)^n e^{-xt}}{(e^{-t}-1)^n} = \sum_{\nu=0}^{\infty} \frac{(-t)^\nu}{\nu!} B_\nu^{(n)}(x),$$

whence by equating coefficients of t^ν we have the required result. This is the complementary argument theorem. The theorem is true for any β polynomial in whose generating function, 6·01 (1), $g(t)$ is an even function.

If in (1) we put $x = 0$, $\nu = 2\mu$, we have

(2) $$B_{2\mu}^{(n)}(n) = B_{2\mu}^{(n)}.$$

Thus $B_{2\mu}^{(n)}(x) - B_{2\mu}^{(n)}$ has zeros at $x = n$, $x = 0$.

Again with $x = \frac{1}{2}n$, $\nu = 2\mu+1$, we have

$$B_{2\mu+1}^{(n)}(\tfrac{1}{2}n) = -B_{2\mu+1}^{(n)}(\tfrac{1}{2}n).$$

Thus

(3) $$B_{2\mu+1}^{(n)}(\tfrac{1}{2}n) = 0.$$

6·3. The Relation between Polynomials of Successive Orders. We have

$$\sum_{\nu=0}^{\infty} \frac{t^\nu}{\nu!} B_\nu^{(n)}(x) = \frac{t^n e^{xt}}{(e^t-1)^n}.$$

If we differentiate both sides with respect to t and then multiply by t, we have

$$\sum_{\nu=1}^{\infty} \frac{t^\nu}{(\nu-1)!} B_\nu^{(n)}(x) = \frac{nt^n e^{xt}}{(e^t-1)^n} + \frac{xt^{n+1} e^{xt}}{(e^t-1)^n} - \frac{nt^{n+1} e^{(x+1)t}}{(e^t-1)^{n+1}}$$

$$= n \sum_{\nu=0}^{\infty} \frac{t^\nu}{\nu!} B_\nu^{(n)}(x) + xt \sum_{\nu=0}^{\infty} \frac{t^\nu}{\nu!} B_\nu^{(n)}(x) - n \sum_{\nu=0}^{\infty} \frac{t^\nu}{\nu!} B_\nu^{(n+1)}(x+1).$$

Equate coefficients of t^ν. Then

(1) $$\nu B_\nu^{(n)}(x) = n B_\nu^{(n)}(x) + x\nu B_{\nu-1}^{(n)}(x) - n B_\nu^{(n+1)}(x+1).$$

From 6·11 (7),

$$B_\nu^{(n+1)}(x+1) = B_\nu^{(n+1)}(x) + \nu B_{\nu-1}^{(n)}(x).$$

Thus we have

(2) $$B_\nu^{(n+1)}(x) = \left(1-\frac{\nu}{n}\right) B_\nu^{(n)}(x) + \nu\left(\frac{x}{n}-1\right) B_{\nu-1}^{(n)}(x),$$

which is the required relation between Bernoulli's polynomials of orders n and $n+1$.

Putting $x = 0$, we have

(3) $$B_\nu^{(n+1)} = \left(1-\frac{\nu}{n}\right) B_\nu^{(n)} - \nu B_{\nu-1}^{(n)}.$$

Again from (1), putting $x = 0$, we obtain

$$B_\nu^{(n+1)}(1) = \left(1-\frac{\nu}{n}\right) B_\nu^{(n)},$$

or, writing $n+\nu$ for n,

(4) $$B_\nu^{(n+\nu+1)}(1) = \frac{n}{n+\nu} B_\nu^{(n+\nu)}.$$

6·4. Relation of Bernoulli's Polynomials to Factorials. In 6·3 (2) put $\nu = n$. Then

$$B_n^{(n+1)}(x) = (x-n) B_{n-1}^{(n)}(x) = (x-n)(x-n+1) B_{n-2}^{(n-1)}(x) = \dots$$

$$= (x-n)(x-n+1) \dots (x-2)(x-1) B_0^{(1)}(x).$$

Thus

(1) $$B_n^{(n+1)}(x) = (x-1)(x-2)\dots(x-n) = (x-1)^{(n)},$$

(2) $$B_n^{(n+1)}(x+1) = x(x-1)(x-2)\dots(x-n+1) = x^{(n)}.$$

Integrating these expressions from 0 to 1, we have from 6·11 (10),

(3) $$\int_0^1 (x-1)(x-2)\dots(x-n)\,dx = B_n^{(n)}.$$

(4) $$\int_0^1 x(x-1)(x-2)\dots(x-n+1)\,dx = B_n^{(n)}(1) = -\frac{1}{n-1}B_n^{(n-1)},$$

from 6·3 (4), putting $n = -1$.

If we differentiate (1) $n-\nu$ times ($n > \nu$), we have, using 6·11 (2),

$$n(n-1)\dots(n-n+\nu+1)\,B_\nu^{(n+1)}(x) = \frac{d^{n-\nu}}{dx^{n-\nu}}(x-1)^{(n)},$$

which gives an explicit expression for $B_\nu^{(n+1)}(x)$, namely,

(5) $$B_\nu^{(n+1)}(x) = \frac{\nu!}{n!}\frac{d^{n-\nu}}{dx^{n-\nu}}[(x-1)(x-2)\dots(x-n)].$$

The following coefficients appear in Stirling's and Bessel's interpolation formulae (3·3, 3·4),

$$a_{2s+1}(p) = \binom{p+s}{2s+1}, \qquad a_{2s}(p) = \frac{p}{2s}\binom{p+s-1}{2s-1},$$

$$b_{2s+1}(p) = \frac{p-\frac{1}{2}}{2s+1}\binom{p+s-1}{2s}, \quad b_{2s}(p) = \binom{p+s-1}{2s}.$$

From (1), we have

$$a_{2s+1}(p) = \frac{1}{(2s+1)!}B_{2s+1}^{(2s+2)}(p+s+1), \quad a_{2s}(p) = \frac{p}{(2s)!}B_{2s-1}^{(2s)}(p+s),$$

$$b_{2s+1}(p) = \frac{p-\frac{1}{2}}{(2s+1)!}B_{2s}^{(2s+1)}(p+s), \qquad b_{2s}(p) = \frac{1}{(2s)!}B_{2s}^{(2s+1)}(p+s).$$

If we differentiate each of these m times with respect to p and then put $p = 0$ in the first two and $p = \frac{1}{2}$ in the second two, we have

(6) $$D^m a_{2s+1}(0) = \frac{1}{(2s-m+1)!}B_{2s-m+1}^{(2s+2)}(s+1).$$

(7) $$D^m a_{2s}(0) = \frac{m}{2s(2s-m)!}B_{2s-m}^{(2s)}(s).$$

(8) $$D^m b_{2s+1}(\tfrac{1}{2}) = \frac{m}{(2s+1)(2s-m+1)!} B^{(2s+1)}_{2s-m+1}(s+\tfrac{1}{2}).$$

(9) $$D^m b_{2s}(\tfrac{1}{2}) = \frac{1}{(2s-m)!} B^{(2s+1)}_{2s-m}(s+\tfrac{1}{2}).$$

From these we have, with the aid of 6·2 (3),

(10) $$D^{2m} a_{2s+1}(0) = 0, \quad D^{2m+1} a_{2s}(0) = 0.$$

(11) $$D^{2m} b_{2s+1}(\tfrac{1}{2}) = 0, \quad D^{2m+1} b_{2s}(\tfrac{1}{2}) = 0.$$

6·401. The Integral of the Factorial. A function which is of importance in the theory of numerical integration is

(1) $$\chi(x) = \int_{1-k}^{x} (y-1)(y-2)\dots(y-2n+1)\,dy$$
$$= \frac{B^{(2n)}_{2n}(x) - B^{(2n)}_{2n}(1-k)}{2n},$$

where k is zero or unity. From the complementary argument theorem of 6·2 we have at once

(2) $$\chi(2n+k-1) = \chi(1-k) = 0.$$

From (2) we have, integrating by parts,

(3) $$\int_{1-k}^{2n+k-1} 1 \, . \, \chi(x)\,dx = -\int_{1-k}^{2n+k-1} x(x-1)\dots(x-2n+1)\,dx$$
$$= \frac{B^{(2n+1)}_{2n+1}(2-k) + B^{(2n+1)}_{2n+1}(1-k)}{2n+1},$$

because $B^{(2n+1)}_{2n+1}(2n+k) = -B^{(2n+1)}_{2n+1}(1-k)$ from the complementary argument theorem.

Again, $$B^{(2n-1)}_{2n-1} = \int_0^1 (y-1)(y-2)\dots(y-2n+1)\,dy,$$

and it is clear that the integrand is negative when $0 < y < 1$.

Thus $B^{(2n-1)}_{2n-1}$ is negative. Similarly

$$B^{(2n-1)}_{2n-1}(1) = \int_1^2 (y-1)(y-2)\dots(y-2n+1)\,dy,$$

and we have $B^{(2n-1)}_{2n-1}(1)$ positive. Proceeding in this way we see that if ν be an integer, $0 \leqslant \nu \leqslant 2n$,

(4) $$(-1)^{\nu+1} B^{(2n-1)}_{2n-1}(\nu) > 0.$$

We now prove that

$$(5)\qquad (-1)^{\nu} B_{2n-1}^{(2n-1)}(\nu-1) > (-1)^{\nu+1} B_{2n-1}^{(2n-1)}(\nu), \quad 1 \leqslant \nu \leqslant n-1.$$

We have, from 6·11 (9),

$$(6)\qquad B_{2n-1}^{(2n-1)}(\nu-1) = \int_{\nu-1}^{\nu} (y-1)(y-2)\dots(y-2n+1)\,dy,$$

$$B_{2n-1}^{2n-1}(\nu) = \int_{\nu}^{\nu+1} (y-1)\dots(y-2n+1)\,dy$$

$$= \int_{\nu-1}^{\nu} y(y-1)\dots(y-2n+2)\,dy.$$

$$(7)\qquad = -\int_{\nu-1}^{\nu} \frac{y}{2n-y-1}(y-1)(y-2)\dots(y-2n+1)\,dy.$$

Now $y/(2n-y-1)$ is positive and less than unity provided that $y < n-\frac{1}{2}$, which is satisfied since $\nu-1 < y < \nu$, and $\nu \leqslant n-1$. Comparing then the integrands of (6) and (7), we see that the integrand of (7) is less in absolute value than the absolute value of the integrand of (6). The result (5) therefore follows.

We can now prove that $\chi(x)$, defined by (1), has a fixed sign for

$$1-k < x < 2n+k-1.$$

Let x lie between the integers $\nu-1$, ν.

For $\nu-1 < y < \nu$ the integrand of (1) does not change sign and hence $\chi(x)$ lies between the following pair of integrals:

$$\int_{1-k}^{\nu-1} (y-1)\dots(y-2n+1)\,dy, \quad \int_{1-k}^{\nu} (y-1)\dots(y-2n+1)\,dy.$$

If we divide the ranges of integration into intervals

$$(1-k,\ 2-k), \quad (2-k,\ 3-k), \dots,$$

we see that $\chi(x)$ lies between the sums

$$B_{2n-1}^{(2n-1)}(1-k) + B_{2n-1}^{(2n-1)}(2-k) + \dots + B_{2n-1}^{(2n-1)}(\nu-2),$$

$$B_{2n-1}^{(2n-1)}(1-k) + B_{2n-1}^{(2n-1)}(2-k) + \dots + B_{2n-1}^{(2n-1)}(\nu-1).$$

Here we can suppose that $\nu < n$, for by the complementary argument theorem such terms as exist when $\nu > n$ cancel out. By (5) the terms in these sums are in descending order of absolute magnitude and alternate in sign.

Hence each sum has the sign of the first term, namely, the sign of $B_{2n-1}^{(2n-1)}(1-k)$.

Thus we have proved, in particular, that $B_{2n}^{(2n)}(x)-B_{2n}^{(2n)}$ has no zeros in the interval $0<x<2n$, and that

(8) $$\left|B_{2n-1}^{(2n-1)}(1-k)\right|>\left|B_{2n-1}^{(2n-1)}(2-k)\right|,\quad k=0 \text{ or } 1.$$

6·41. Expansion of $x^{(n)}$ in Powers of x. Differentiating 6·4 (2) p times, we have

$$\frac{d^p}{dx^p}x^{(n)}=n^{(p)}B_{n-p}^{(n+1)}(x+1).$$

Putting $x=0$, we have

$$\left[\frac{d^p}{dx^p}x^{(n)}\right]_{x=0}=\frac{n!}{(n-p)!}B_{n-p}^{(n+1)}(1)=\frac{n!}{(n-p)!}\frac{p}{n}B_{n-p}^{(n)},$$

from 6·3 (4).

Thus, developing $x^{(n)}$ by Maclaurin's Theorem, we have

$$x^{(n)}=\sum_{p=0}^{n}\frac{x^p}{p!}\frac{n!}{(n-p)!}\frac{p}{n}B_{n-p}^{(n)}=\sum_{p=0}^{n}\binom{n-1}{p-1}x^pB_{n-p}^{(n)}.$$

6·42. Expansion of x^ν in Factorials. We have by Newton's Interpolation formula 3·1 (4), since $B_\nu^{(n)}(x+h)$ is a polynomial of degree ν,

(1) $$B_\nu^{(n)}(x+h)=B_\nu^{(n)}(h)+\sum_{s=1}^{\nu}\frac{x^{(s)}}{s!}\overset{s}{\Delta}B_\nu^{(n)}(h)$$

$$=\sum_{s=0}^{\nu}\binom{\nu}{s}x^{(s)}B_{\nu-s}^{(n-s)}(h),$$

using 6·11 (4). Putting $h=0$, we have a factorial series for $B_\nu^{(n)}(x)$, namely,

(2) $$B_\nu^{(n)}(x)=\sum_{s=0}^{\nu}\binom{\nu}{s}x^{(s)}B_{\nu-s}^{(n-s)}.$$

Putting $n=0$, we have $B_\nu^{(0)}(x)=x^\nu$, so that

(3) $$x^\nu=\sum_{s=0}^{\nu}\binom{\nu}{s}x^{(s)}B_{\nu-s}^{(-s)}$$

which is the required expansion.

If we operate on (3) with $\overset{n}{\Delta}$, $(n \leqslant \nu)$ and then put $x = 0$, we obtain the differences of zero (see 2·53), namely,

$$\overset{n}{\Delta} 0^{\nu} = \frac{\nu!}{(\nu-n)!} B_{\nu-n}^{(-n)}.$$

If in (1) we put $n = \nu+1$, and $h+1$ for h, we have, using 6·4 (2),

$$(x+h)^{(\nu)} = \sum_{s=0}^{\nu} \binom{\nu}{s} x^{(s)} h^{(\nu-s)},$$

which is Vandermonde's theorem in factorials analogous to the Binomial Theorem

$$(x+h)^{\nu} = \sum_{s=0}^{\nu} \binom{\nu}{s} x^{s} h^{\nu-s}.$$

From (1) we have also, interchanging x and h,

$$\frac{B_{\nu}^{(n)}(x+h) - B_{\nu}^{(n)}(x)}{h} = \sum_{s=1}^{\nu} \binom{\nu}{s} (h-1)^{(s-1)} B_{\nu-s}^{(n-s)}(x).$$

If we let $h \to 0$, the left-hand side becomes the derivate of $B_{\nu}^{(n)}(x)$, that is, $\nu B_{\nu-1}^{(n)}(x)$. Thus

$$\nu B_{\nu-1}^{(n)}(x) = \sum_{s=1}^{\nu} \binom{\nu}{s} (-1)^{s-1} (s-1)!\, B_{\nu-s}^{(n-s)}(x).$$

In particular, for $x = 0$,

$$\nu B_{\nu-1}^{(n)} = \sum_{s=1}^{\nu} \binom{\nu}{s} (-1)^{s-1} (s-1)!\, B_{\nu-s}^{(n-s)}.$$

6·43. Generating Functions of Bernoulli's Numbers. We have, by the Binomial Theorem,

$$(1+t)^{x-1} = \sum_{\nu=0}^{\infty} \frac{(x-1)\dots(x-\nu)}{\nu!} t^{\nu} = \sum_{\nu=0}^{\infty} \frac{t^{\nu}}{\nu!} B_{\nu}^{(\nu+1)}(x).$$

Differentiate n times with respect to x and we obtain

$$(1+t)^{x-1} [\log(1+t)]^{n} = \sum_{\nu=n}^{\infty} \frac{t^{\nu}}{(\nu-n)!} B_{\nu-n}^{(\nu+1)}(x).$$

Putting $x = 1$ and dividing by t^n, we have

(1) $$\left[\frac{\log(1+t)}{t}\right]^n = \sum_{\nu=0}^{\infty} \frac{t^\nu}{\nu!} B_\nu^{(n+\nu+1)}(1)$$

$$= \sum_{\nu=0}^{\infty} \frac{t^\nu}{\nu!} \frac{n}{n+\nu} B_\nu^{(n+\nu)},$$

using 6·3 (4).

In particular, for $n = 1$,

(2) $$\frac{\log(1+t)}{t} = \sum_{\nu=0}^{\infty} \frac{t^\nu}{(\nu+1)!} B_\nu^{(\nu+1)}.$$

Again, integrating $(1+t)^{x-1}$ with respect to x from x to $x+1$, n times in succession, we have from 6·11 (9),

$$\frac{(1+t)^{x-1}t^n}{[\log(1+t)]^n} = \sum_{\nu=0}^{\infty} \frac{t^\nu}{\nu!} B_\nu^{(\nu-n+1)}(x).$$

Putting $x = 0$, we have

(3) $$\frac{t^n}{(1+t)[\log(1+t)]^n} = \sum_{\nu=0}^{\infty} \frac{t^\nu}{\nu!} B_\nu^{(\nu-n+1)},$$

and in particular, for $n = 1$,

(4) $$\frac{t}{(1+t)\log(1+t)} = \sum_{\nu=0}^{\infty} \frac{t^\nu}{\nu!} B_\nu^{(\nu)},$$

which is the generating function of the numbers $B_\nu^{(\nu)}$.

Again putting $x = 1$, we have

(5) $$\left[\frac{t}{\log(1+t)}\right]^n = \sum_{\nu=0}^{\infty} \frac{t^\nu}{\nu!} B_\nu^{(\nu-n+1)}(1),$$

which shews that (1) also holds when n is negative.

In particular, for $n = 1$,

(6) $$\frac{t}{\log(1+t)} = \sum_{\nu=0}^{\infty} \frac{t^\nu}{\nu!} B_\nu^{(\nu)}(1),$$

which is the generating function of the numbers $B_\nu^{(\nu)}(1)$.

Using 6·3 (4), we have from (6),

(7) $$\frac{t}{\log(1+t)} = 1+\tfrac{1}{2}t - \sum_{\nu=2}^{\infty} \frac{t^\nu}{\nu!} \frac{B_\nu^{(\nu-1)}}{\nu-1}.$$

We give a list of ten of the numbers $B_\nu^{(\nu)}$:

$$B_1^{(1)} = -\tfrac{1}{2}, \qquad B_6^{(6)} = \tfrac{19087}{84},$$
$$B_2^{(2)} = \tfrac{5}{6}, \qquad B_7^{(7)} = -\tfrac{36799}{24},$$
$$B_3^{(3)} = -\tfrac{9}{4}, \qquad B_8^{(8)} = \tfrac{1070017}{90},$$
$$B_4^{(4)} = \tfrac{251}{30}, \qquad B_9^{(9)} = -\tfrac{2082753}{20},$$
$$B_5^{(5)} = -\tfrac{475}{12}, \qquad B_{10}^{(10)} = \tfrac{134211265}{132}.$$

6·5. Bernoulli's Polynomials of the First Order. We shall write $B_\nu(x)$ instead of $B_\nu^{(1)}(x)$, the order unity being understood. Thus from 6·1 (2), we have

$$(1) \qquad \frac{t\,e^{xt}}{e^t-1} = \sum_{\nu=0}^{\infty} \frac{t^\nu}{\nu!} B_\nu(x),$$

as the generating function of the polynomials and

$$(2) \qquad \frac{t}{e^t-1} = \sum_{\nu=0}^{\infty} \frac{t^\nu}{\nu!} B_\nu,$$

as the generating function of Bernoulli's numbers, B_ν, of the first order.

From 6·11, we have the following properties:

$$(3) \qquad B_\nu(x) \doteqdot (B+x)^\nu.$$

$$(4) \qquad (B+1)^\nu - B_\nu \doteqdot 0, \quad \nu = 2, 3, 4, \ldots .$$

$$(5) \qquad \frac{d}{dx} B_\nu(x) = \nu\, B_{\nu-1}(x).$$

$$(6) \qquad \int_a^x B_\nu(t)\,dt = \frac{1}{\nu+1}\left[B_{\nu+1}(x) - B_{\nu+1}(a)\right].$$

$$(7) \qquad \Delta B_\nu(x) = \nu\, x^{\nu-1}.$$

$$(8) \qquad B_\nu(1-x) = (-1)^\nu B_\nu(x), \text{ from } 6{\cdot}2.$$

The first seven polynomials are given in the following list:

$$B_0(x) = 1,$$
$$B_1(x) = x - \tfrac{1}{2},$$
$$B_2(x) = x^2 - x + \tfrac{1}{6},$$

$$B_3(x) = x(x-1)(x-\tfrac{1}{2}) = x^3 - \tfrac{3}{2}x^2 + \tfrac{1}{2}x,$$

$$B_4(x) = x^4 - 2x^3 + x^2 - \tfrac{1}{30},$$

$$B_5(x) = x(x-1)(x-\tfrac{1}{2})(x^2 - x - \tfrac{1}{3}) = x^5 - \tfrac{5}{2}x^4 + \tfrac{5}{3}x^3 - \tfrac{1}{6}x,$$

$$B_6(x) = x^6 - 3x^5 + \tfrac{5}{2}x^4 - \tfrac{1}{2}x^2 + \tfrac{1}{42}.$$

We have also for the values of the first seven numbers:

B_0	B_1	B_2	B_3	B_4	B_5	B_6
1	$-\frac{1}{2}$	$\frac{1}{6}$	0	$-\frac{1}{30}$	0	$\frac{1}{42}$

6·501. A Summation Problem. To evaluate $\sum_{s=1}^{n} s^\nu$.

We have by 6·5 (6) and (7),

$$\int_s^{s+1} B_\nu(x)\,dx = \frac{1}{\nu+1}[B_{\nu+1}(s+1) - B_{\nu+1}(s)]$$
$$= s^\nu.$$

Thus

$$\sum_{s=1}^{n} s^\nu = \int_0^{n+1} B_\nu(x)\,dx = \frac{1}{\nu+1}[B_{\nu+1}(n+1) - B_{\nu+1}].$$

For example, if $\nu = 3$,

$$\sum_{s=1}^{n} s^3 = \tfrac{1}{4}[B_4(n+1) - B_4]$$
$$= \tfrac{1}{4}[(n+1)^4 - 2(n+1)^3 + (n+1)^2]$$
$$= [\tfrac{1}{2}n(n+1)]^2.$$

The method can clearly be applied if the sth term of a finite series be a polynomial in s.

6·51. Bernoulli's Numbers of the First Order. We have from 6·5 (2),

$$(1) \qquad \frac{t}{2} + \sum_{\nu=0}^{\infty} \frac{t^\nu}{\nu!} B_\nu = \frac{t}{2} \cdot \frac{e^t+1}{e^t-1}.$$

The function on the right is even, since the change of $-t$ for t leaves the function unaltered. It follows that the expansion contains no odd powers of t, and hence

$$B_{2\mu+1} = 0, \quad \mu > 0,$$

$$B_1 = -\tfrac{1}{2}.$$

If in (1) we write $2t$ for t, we obtain

$$t \coth t = 1 + \frac{2^2 t^2}{2!} B_2 + \frac{2^4 t^4}{4!} B_4 + \dots,$$

and writing it for t, we get

(2) $$t \cot t = 1 - \frac{2^2 t^2}{2!} B_2 + \frac{2^4 t^4}{4!} B_4 - \dots.$$

Expansions for cosec t and tan t are easily obtained by use of the identities

$$\operatorname{cosec} t = \cot \tfrac{1}{2}t - \cot t,$$

$$\tan t = \cot t - 2 \cot 2t$$

$$= \sum_{\nu=1}^{\infty} (-1)^{\nu-1} \frac{2^{2\nu}(2^{2\nu}-1)}{(2\nu)!} B_{2\nu} t^{2\nu-1}.$$

Again we have the expansion in partial fractions,*

(3) $$\pi t \cot \pi t = 1 + 2t^2 \sum_{\nu=1}^{\infty} \frac{1}{t^2 - \nu^2}.$$

This series may be rearranged and thus, comparing coefficients of t^{2p} in (3) and the series for $\pi t \cot \pi t$ derived from (2), we have

(4) $$(-1)^{p-1} \frac{(2\pi)^{2p} B_{2p}}{2\,(2p)!} = \sum_{n=1}^{\infty} \frac{1}{n^{2p}}.$$

The sum of the series on the right lies between 1 and 2. Thus we see that B_{2p} increases rapidly as p increases and that Bernoulli's numbers alternate in sign. Moreover, we have

$$(-1)^{p-1} B_{2p} > 0.$$

To express Bernoulli's numbers by determinants we have from 6·5 (4),

$$\frac{1}{2!} + \frac{B_1}{1!} = 0,$$

$$\frac{1}{3!} + \frac{1}{2!}\frac{B_1}{1!} + \frac{1}{1!}\frac{B_2}{2!} = 0,$$

. . . .

$$\frac{1}{(n+1)!} + \frac{1}{n!}\frac{B_1}{1!} + \frac{1}{(n-1)!}\frac{B_2}{2!} + \dots + \frac{1}{2!}\frac{B_{n-1}}{(n-1)!} + \frac{B_n}{n!} = 0,$$

---

* K. Knopp, *Theory of Infinite Series*, (London, 1928), § 117, 135.

whence, solving these equations, we have for $(-1)^n B_n / n!$ the determinant

$$\begin{vmatrix} \frac{1}{2!} & 1 & 0 & 0 & \dots & 0 \\ \frac{1}{3!} & \frac{1}{2!} & 1 & 0 & \dots & 0 \\ \frac{1}{4!} & \frac{1}{3!} & \frac{1}{2!} & 1 & \dots & 0 \\ \cdot & \cdot & \cdot & \cdot & \dots & \cdot \\ \frac{1}{(n+1)!} & \frac{1}{n!} & \frac{1}{(n-1)!} & \frac{1}{(n-2)!} & \dots & \frac{1}{2!} \end{vmatrix}.$$

Since $B_{2\mu+1} = 0$, $\mu > 0$, we have

$$B_\nu(x) + \tfrac{1}{2}\nu x^{\nu-1} \doteqdot (x+B)^\nu + \tfrac{1}{2}\nu x^{\nu-1}$$
$$= x^\nu + \binom{\nu}{2} x^{\nu-2} B_2 + \binom{\nu}{4} x^{\nu-4} B_4 + \dots,$$

so that
$$B_\nu(x) + \tfrac{1}{2}\nu x^{\nu-1}$$
is an even function when ν is even and an odd function when ν is odd.

6·511. The Euler-Maclaurin Theorem for Polynomials. Let $P(x)$ be a polynomial of degree n.

From 6·5 (7), (3), we have

$$\nu x^{\nu-1} \doteqdot (x+B+1)^\nu - (x+B)^\nu.$$

It follows from this result that

(1) $$P'(x) \doteqdot P(x+B+1) - P(x+B),$$

and consequently that

(2) $$P'(x+y) \doteqdot P(x+y+B+1) - P(x+y+B)$$
$$\doteqdot P(x+1+B(y)) - P(x+B(y)).$$

Now by Taylor's Theorem

$$P(x+B(y)) \doteqdot P(x) + B_1(y) P'(x) + \frac{1}{2!} B_2(y) P''(x) + \dots$$
$$+ \frac{1}{n!} B_n(y) P^{(n)}(x).$$

Thus substituting in (2), we have

$$(3)\quad P'(x+y) = \Delta P(x) + B_1(y)\,\Delta P'(x) + \frac{1}{2!}B_2(y)\,\Delta P''(x) + \dots + \frac{1}{n!}B_n(y)\,\Delta P^{(n)}(x).$$

This is the Euler-Maclaurin Theorem for a polynomial.

In particular, putting $y = 0$,

$$(4)\quad P'(x) = \Delta P(x) + B_1\,\Delta P'(x) + \frac{1}{2!}B_2\,\Delta P''(x) + \frac{1}{4!}B_4\,\Delta P^{(iv)}(x) + \frac{1}{6!}B_6\,\Delta P^{(vi)}(x) + \dots,$$

since B_3, B_5, B_7, ... all vanish.

If we now write

$$P(x) = \int_a^x \phi(t)\,dt,$$

we have

$$(5)\quad \phi(x) = \int_x^{x+1} \phi(t)\,dt + B_1\,\Delta\phi(x) + \frac{1}{2!}B_2\,\Delta\phi'(x) + \frac{1}{4!}B_4\,\Delta\phi'''(x) + \dots.$$

Since $B_1 = -\frac{1}{2}$, we can also write

$$(6)\quad \int_x^{x+1} \phi(t)\,dt = \tfrac{1}{2}[\phi(x+1) + \phi(x)] - \frac{1}{2!}B_2\,\Delta\phi'(x) - \frac{1}{4!}B_4\,\Delta\phi'''(x) - \dots,$$

where $\phi(x)$ is any polynomial. The series on the right of course terminates after a finite number of terms.

Again, (1) shews that the difference equation

$$\Delta u(x) = P'(x)$$

has the polynomial solution

$$u(x) \doteqdot P(x+B) \doteqdot P(B(x)).$$

Thus, for example,

$$\Delta u(x) = x^3 - 3x^2 + 1$$

has the solution

$$u(x) = \tfrac{1}{4}B_4(x) - B_3(x) + B_1(x) + c,$$

where c is an arbitrary constant. To obtain the general solution, we replace c by an arbitrary periodic function $\varpi(x)$, such that

$$\varpi(x+1) = \varpi(x).$$

6·52. The Multiplication Theorem. If m be a positive integer, we have from 6·5 (1)

$$\sum_{\nu=0}^{\infty} \frac{t^\nu}{\nu!} \sum_{s=0}^{m-1} B_\nu\left(x+\frac{s}{m}\right) = \sum_{s=0}^{m-1} \frac{te^{\left(x+\frac{s}{m}\right)t}}{e^t-1}$$

$$= \frac{te^{xt}(e^t-1)}{(e^t-1)(e^{\frac{t}{m}}-1)} = \frac{m\cdot\frac{t}{m}e^{mx\cdot\frac{t}{m}}}{e^{\frac{t}{m}}-1}$$

$$= \sum_{\nu=0}^{\infty} m\cdot\frac{t^\nu}{m^\nu\,\nu!} B_\nu(mx).$$

Thus

$$B_\nu(mx) = m^{\nu-1} \sum_{s=0}^{m-1} B_\nu\left(x+\frac{s}{m}\right).$$

This result is known as the multiplication theorem for Bernoulli's polynomials of order unity.

Putting $x = 0$, we have

$$\sum_{s=1}^{m-1} B_\nu\left(\frac{s}{m}\right) = -\left(1-\frac{1}{m^{\nu-1}}\right) B_\nu.$$

Hence, if $m = 2$,

$$B_\nu\left(\tfrac{1}{2}\right) = -\left(1-\frac{1}{2^{\nu-1}}\right) B_\nu, \quad \nu = 1, 2, \ldots .$$

6·53. Bernoulli's Polynomials in the Interval (0, 1). From 6·5 (8), we have

(1) $$B_{2\nu}(1-x) = B_{2\nu}(x).$$

(2) $$B_{2\nu+1}(1-x) = -B_{2\nu+1}(x).$$

Thus $B_{2\nu}(x) - B_{2\nu}$ has the zeros 0 and 1. We shall prove that these are the only zeros in the interval $0 \leqslant x \leqslant 1$.

Again, $B_{2\nu+1}(\frac{1}{2}) = -B_{2\nu+1}(\frac{1}{2})$, so that $B_{2\nu+1}(\frac{1}{2}) = 0$. $B_{2\nu+1}(x)$ is symmetrical about $x = \frac{1}{2}$ (from (2)), so that $B_{2\nu+1}(x)$, for $\nu < 0$, has the zeros 0, $\frac{1}{2}$, 1. We shall prove that these are the only zeros in the interval $0 \leqslant x \leqslant 1$.

For suppose that both these statements are true up to and including $\nu = \mu > 0$. Since

(3) $$D[B_{2\mu+2}(x) - B_{2\mu+2}] = (2\mu+2)\, B_{2\mu+1}(x)$$

$B_{2\mu+2}(x) - B_{2\mu+2}$, which vanishes at $x = 0$, $x = 1$, has its only maximum or minimum for $0 < x < 1$ at $x = \frac{1}{2}$, and consequently cannot vanish in this interval.

Again,

$$DB_{2\mu+3}(x) = (2\mu+3)\,[B_{2\mu+2}(x) - B_{2\mu+2}] + (2\mu+3)\, B_{2\mu+2},$$

and this expression can vanish at most once for $0 < x < \frac{1}{2}$.

Hence $B_{2\mu+3}(x)$ cannot vanish in $0 < x < \frac{1}{2}$ and therefore by (2) cannot vanish in $\frac{1}{2} < x < 1$.

By induction the properties therefore follow.

From 6·51 we have $(-1)^{\nu+1} B_{2\nu} > 0$. If x be sufficiently small and positive $(-1)^{\nu+1} B_{2\nu+1}(x)$ has the same sign as the derivate, that is, the same sign as $(-1)^{\nu+1} B_{2\nu}(x)$, which for x small and positive has the same sign as $(-1)^{\nu+1} B_{2\nu}$ which is positive. Thus

$$(-1)^{\nu+1} B_{2\nu+1}(x) > 0, \quad 0 < x < \tfrac{1}{2}.$$

Hence, from (3), $(-1)^{\mu+1}(B_{2\mu+2}(x) - B_{2\mu+2})$ increases from the value 0 as x increases from 0 to $\frac{1}{2}$ and is therefore positive. Hence

$$(-1)^{\mu}\,(B_{2\mu}(x) - B_{2\mu}) > 0, \quad 0 < x < 1,$$

since the expression only vanishes at 0 and 1.

6·6. The η Polynomials. A second method of generalising polynomials is suggested by 6·0 (7). If we write $f_n(t) = 2^n (e^t + 1)^{-n}$ we have a class of polynomials, which we call η polynomials, given by

(1) $$\frac{2^n e^{xt+g(t)}}{(e^t+1)^n} = \sum_{\nu=0}^{\infty} \frac{t^\nu}{\nu!}\, \eta_\nu^{(n)}(x),$$

so that

$$\sum_{\nu=0}^{\infty} \frac{t^\nu}{\nu!}\, \nabla\, \eta_\nu^{(n)}(x) = \sum_{\nu=0}^{\infty} \frac{t^\nu}{\nu!}\, \eta_\nu^{(n-1)}(x),$$

whence we obtain

(2) $$\nabla \eta_\nu^{(n)}(x) = \eta_\nu^{(n-1)}(x).$$

Thus the operator ∇ depresses the order by one unit but leaves the degree unchanged.

Using 6·0 (3), we have

(3) $$(\eta^{(n)}+x+1)^\nu + (\eta^{(n)}+x)^\nu \doteqdot 2(\eta^{(n-1)}+x)^\nu,$$

so that the η numbers satisfy the recurrence-relation

(4) $$(\eta^{(n)}+1)^\nu + \eta_\nu^{(n)} \doteqdot 2\eta_\nu^{(n-1)}.$$

6·7. Definition of Euler's Polynomials. The simplest η polynomials, obtained by putting $g(t) = 0$, $n = 0$ in the generating function, are the powers of x, whose generating function is e^{xt}. We shall now regard these simplest η polynomials as Euler's polynomials of order zero. Thus

$$E_\nu^{(0)}(x) = x^\nu, \quad e^{xt} = \sum_{\nu=0}^{\infty} \frac{t^\nu}{\nu!} E_\nu^{(0)}(x),$$

where $E_\nu^{(0)}(x)$ denotes Euler's polynomial of order zero and degree ν. Then in accordance with 6·6 (1) we define Euler's polynomials of order n by the relation

(1) $$\frac{2^n e^{xt}}{(e^t+1)^n} = \sum_{\nu=0}^{\infty} \frac{t^\nu}{\nu!} E_\nu^{(n)}(x).$$

In accordance with our general theory we should call Euler's numbers the values of $E_\nu^{(n)}(0)$. This would, however, run counter to the notation of Nörlund, who discovered these generalised polynomials. In order therefore to avoid confusion with the accepted notation we shall follow Nörlund and write

(2) $$E_\nu^{(n)}(0) = 2^{-\nu} C_\nu^{(n)}.$$

The generating function for the C numbers is therefore

(3) $$\frac{2^n}{(e^t+1)^n} = \sum_{\nu=0}^{\infty} \frac{t^\nu}{\nu!} \frac{1}{2^\nu} C_\nu^{(n)}.$$

The values of $2^\nu E_\nu^{(n)}(x)$ for $x = \frac{1}{2}n$ are called Euler's numbers $E_\nu^{(n)}$, of order n. Thus

(4) $$E_\nu^{(n)} = 2^\nu E_\nu^{(n)}(\tfrac{1}{2}n).$$

We shall prove in 6·72 that Euler's numbers with an odd suffix all vanish.

6·71. Fundamental Properties of Euler's Polynomials. Euler's polynomials are η polynomials and therefore also ϕ polynomials. Hence we have

(1) $$E_\nu^{(n)}(x) \doteq (\tfrac{1}{2}C^{(n)}+x)^\nu.$$

(2) $$\frac{d}{dx}E_\nu^{(n)}(x) = \nu\, E_{\nu-1}^{(n)}(x).$$

(3) $$\int_a^x E_\nu^{(n)}(t)\,dt = \frac{1}{\nu+1}\left[E_{\nu+1}^{(n)}(x) - E_{\nu+1}^{(n)}(a)\right].$$

(4) $$\nabla E_\nu^{(n)}(x) = E_\nu^{(n-1)}(x),$$

$$(\tfrac{1}{2}C^{(n)}+1)^\nu + \frac{1}{2^\nu}C_\nu^{(n)} \doteq \frac{2}{2^\nu}C_\nu^{(n-1)},$$

from 6·6 (4) and 6·7 (2). Thus

(5) $$(C^n+2)^\nu + C_\nu^{(n)} \doteq 2C_\nu^{(n-1)}.$$

By repeated application of (4), we have

(6) $$\overset{n}{\nabla} E_\nu^{(n)}(x) = x^\nu,$$

since $$E_\nu^{(0)}(x) = x^\nu.$$

We have also from (4),

(7) $$E_\nu^{(n)}(x+1) = 2E_\nu^{(n-1)}(x) - E_\nu^{(n)}(x).$$

Since $$E_\nu^{(n)} = 2^\nu E_\nu^{(n)}\left(\frac{n}{2}\right) \doteq \left(\tfrac{1}{2}C^{(n)}+\frac{n}{2}\right)^\nu . 2^\nu \quad \text{from (1),}$$

we have

$$E^{(n)} \doteq n + C^{(n)}.$$

Hence we have

(8) $$E_\nu^{(n)}(x) \doteq (x-\tfrac{1}{2}n+\tfrac{1}{2}E^{(n)})^\nu,$$

$$E_\nu^{(n)}\left(\frac{n+x}{2}\right) \doteq \left(\frac{x+E^{(n)}}{2}\right)^\nu.$$

Thus we have, by putting in turn $x=1$, $x=-1$, and adding

$$(E^{(n)}+1)^\nu + (E^{(n)}-1)^\nu \doteq 2^\nu E_\nu^{(n)}\left(\frac{n+1}{2}\right) + 2^\nu E_\nu^{(n)}\left(\frac{n-1}{2}\right)$$

$$\doteq 2^{\nu+1}\nabla E_\nu^{(n)}\left(\frac{n-1}{2}\right)$$

$$\doteq 2^{\nu+1}E_\nu^{(n-1)}\left(\frac{n-1}{2}\right) \quad \text{from (4)}$$

(9) $$\doteq 2E_\nu^{(n-1)}.$$

6·72. The Complementary Argument Theorem. The arguments x and $n-x$ are called complementary. We shall now prove that

(1) $$E_\nu^{(n)}(n-x) = (-1)^\nu E_\nu^{(n)}(x).$$

We have from 6·7 (1),

$$\sum_{\nu=0}^{\infty} \frac{t^\nu}{\nu!} E_\nu^{(n)}(n-x) = \frac{2^n e^{(n-x)t}}{(e^t+1)^n} = \frac{2^n e^{-xt}}{(e^{-t}+1)^n}$$

$$= \sum_{\nu=0}^{\infty} \frac{(-t)^\nu}{\nu!} E_\nu^{(n)}(x),$$

whence by equating coefficients of t^ν we have the required result. This is the complementary argument theorem. The theorem is true for any η polynomial in whose generating function $g(t)$ is an even function.

If in (1) we put $x=0$, we have, for $\nu = 2\mu$,

$$E_{2\mu}^{(n)}(n) = E_{2\mu}^{(n)}(0) = 2^{-2\mu} C_{2\mu}^{(n)}.$$

Thus $E_{2\mu}^{(n)}(x) - 2^{-2\mu} C_{2\mu}^{(n)}$ has zeros at $x=0$, $x=n$.

Again, putting $x = \frac{1}{2}n$, $\nu = 2\mu+1$, in (1), we have

$$E_{2\mu+1}^{(n)} = -E_{2\mu+1}^{(n)}.$$

Thus $E_{2\mu+1}^{(n)} = 0$, that is, Euler's numbers with an odd suffix are all zero.

6·73. Euler's Polynomials of Successive Orders. We have

$$\sum_{\nu=0}^{\infty} \frac{t^\nu}{\nu!} E_\nu^{(n)}(x) = \frac{2^n e^{xt}}{(e^t+1)^n}.$$

Differentiate both sides with respect to t and then multiply by t. We then have

$$\sum_{\nu=1}^{\infty} \frac{t^\nu}{(\nu-1)!} E_\nu^{(n)}(x) = \frac{2^n x\, t e^{xt}}{(e^t+1)^n} - \frac{2^n n\, t e^{(x+1)t}}{(e^t+1)^{n+1}}$$

$$= x\sum_{\nu=1}^{\infty} \frac{t^\nu}{(\nu-1)!} E_{\nu-1}^{(n)}(x) - \tfrac{1}{2}n \sum_{\nu=1}^{\infty} \frac{t^\nu}{(\nu-1)!} E_{\nu-1}^{(n+1)}(x+1).$$

Equate coefficients of $t^{\nu+1}$. Then

$$E_{\nu+1}^{(n)}(x) = x\, E_\nu^{(n)}(x) - \tfrac{1}{2}n\, E_\nu^{(n+1)}(x+1).$$

Now by 6·71 (7),

$$E_\nu^{(n+1)}(x+1) = 2\,E_\nu^{(n)}(x) - E_\nu^{(n+1)}(x).$$

Therefore we have the recurrence relation

$$E_\nu^{(n+1)}(x) = \frac{2}{n}\,E_{\nu+1}^{(n)}(x) + \frac{2}{n}(n-x)\,E_\nu^{(n)}(x).$$

Writing $x = 0$, we obtain

$$C_\nu^{(n+1)} = \frac{1}{n}\,C_{\nu+1}^{(n)} + 2\,C_\nu^{(n)}.$$

6·8. Euler's Polynomials of the First Order. We shall write $E_\nu(x)$ for $E_\nu^{(1)}(x)$, the order unity being understood. We have then from 6·7, 6·71

(1) $$\frac{2e^{xt}}{e^t+1} = \sum_{\nu=0}^{\infty} \frac{t^\nu}{\nu!} E_\nu(x), \quad \frac{2}{e^t+1} = \sum_{\nu=0}^{\infty} \frac{t^\nu}{\nu!}\frac{1}{2^\nu} C_\nu,$$

(2) $$\frac{2e^{\frac{1}{2}t}}{e^t+1} = \sum_{\nu=0}^{\infty} \frac{t^\nu}{\nu!}\frac{E_\nu}{2^\nu}.$$

(3) $$E_\nu(x) \doteq (\tfrac{1}{2}C+x)^\nu, \quad (C+2)^\nu + C_\nu \doteq 0, \quad \nu > 0.$$

(4) $$\nabla E_\nu(x) = x^\nu, \quad DE_\nu(x) = \nu E_{\nu-1}(x).$$

(5) $$E_\nu(1-x) = (-1)^\nu E_\nu(x), \quad \text{from 6·72.}$$

The first seven polynomials are given in the following list :

$$E_0(x) = 1,$$
$$E_1(x) = x - \tfrac{1}{2},$$
$$E_2(x) = x(x-1),$$
$$E_3(x) = (x-\tfrac{1}{2})(x^2-x-\tfrac{1}{2}),$$
$$E_4(x) = x(x-1)(x^2-x-1),$$
$$E_5(x) = (x-\tfrac{1}{2})(x^4-2x^3-x^2+2x+1),$$
$$E_6(x) = x(x-1)(x^4-2x^3-2x^2+3x+3),$$

E_0	E_2	E_4	E_6	E_8	E_{10}	E_{12}
1	−1	5	−61	1385	−50521	2702765

Example. Evaluate $\sum_{s=1}^{n}(-1)^s s^\nu$.

We have by (4),

$$\sum_{s=1}^{n}(-1)^s s^\nu = \sum_{s=1}^{n}(-1)^s \nabla E_\nu(s)$$

$$= \frac{1}{2}\sum_{s=1}^{n}(-1)^s \Big[E_\nu(s+1)+E_\nu(s)\Big]$$

$$= \tfrac{1}{2}(-1)^n E_\nu(n+1) - \tfrac{1}{2}E_\nu(1).$$

6·81. Euler's Numbers of the First Order. From 6·8 (2), writing $2t$ for t, we have

$$\frac{2}{e^t+e^{-t}} = \sum_{\nu=0}^{\infty}\frac{t^\nu}{\nu!}E_\nu.$$

Thus

$$\operatorname{sech} t = \sum_{\nu=0}^{\infty}\frac{t^\nu}{\nu!}E_\nu = 1+\frac{t^2}{2!}E_2+\frac{t^4}{4!}E_4+\dots,$$

and writing it for t,

$$\text{(1)} \qquad \sec t = 1-\frac{t^2}{2!}E_2+\frac{t^4}{4!}E_4-\dots.$$

Again, by rearranging the expansion,*

$$\frac{\pi}{4\cos\dfrac{\pi x}{2}} = \sum_{\nu=0}^{\infty}\frac{(-1)^\nu(2\nu+1)}{(2\nu+1)^2-x^2},$$

and equating the coefficient of x^{2p} to the coefficient of x^{2p} in the series for $\frac{1}{4}\pi\sec\dfrac{\pi x}{2}$ obtained from (1), we have

$$(-1)^p\frac{E_{2p}}{2^{2p+2}(2p)!}\pi^{2p+1} = 1-\frac{1}{3^{2p+1}}+\frac{1}{5^{2p+1}}-\frac{1}{7^{2p+1}}+\dots,$$

which shews how Euler's numbers increase and that they alternate in sign.

---

* See K. Knopp, *loc. cit.* p. 138.

By the method used in 6·51 we obtain from the recurrence relation a determinant for $(-1)^n E_{2n}/(2n)!$, namely,

$$\begin{vmatrix} \frac{1}{2!} & 1 & 0 & 0 & \cdots & 0 \\ \frac{1}{4!} & \frac{1}{2!} & 1 & 0 & \cdots & 0 \\ \frac{1}{6!} & \frac{1}{4!} & \frac{1}{2!} & 1 & \cdots & 0 \\ \cdot & \cdot & \cdot & \cdot & \cdots & \cdot \\ \frac{1}{(2n)!} & \frac{1}{(2n-2)!} & \frac{1}{(2n-4)!} & \frac{1}{(2n-6)!} & \cdots & \frac{1}{2!} \end{vmatrix}.$$

With regard to the numbers C_ν, we have from 6·8 (1)

$$\sum_{\nu=0}^{\infty} \frac{t^\nu}{\nu!}\frac{C_\nu}{2^\nu} - 1 = -\frac{e^t-1}{e^t+1} = -\tanh \tfrac{1}{2}t,$$

which is an odd function, so that all the numbers $C_{2\mu}$, $\mu > 0$, vanish. Writing $2t$ for t, we have

$$\tanh t = t - \frac{t^3}{3!}C_3 - \frac{t^5}{5!}C_5 - \frac{t^7}{7!}C_7 - \dots,$$

whence with it for t, we get

$$\tan t = t + \frac{t^3}{3!}C_3 - \frac{t^5}{5!}C_5 + \frac{t^7}{7!}C_7 - \dots .$$

If we equate corresponding coefficients in this series and the series for $\tan t$ in 6·51, we have

$$C_{2\nu-1} = -\frac{2^{2\nu}(2^{2\nu}-1)}{2\nu}B_{2\nu}.$$

Since the numbers $C_{2\mu}$, $\mu > 0$, all vanish, we note that

$$E_\nu(x) - x^\nu \doteqdot (x + \tfrac{1}{2}C)^\nu - x^\nu$$
$$= \binom{\nu}{1}\frac{x^{\nu-1}}{2}C_1 + \binom{\nu}{3}\frac{x^{\nu-3}}{2^3}C_3 + \dots,$$

so that $E_\nu(x) - x^\nu$ is an odd function when ν is even, and an even function when ν is odd.

6·82. Boole's Theorem for Polynomials. From 6·71 (8), when $n = 1$, we have

$$E_\nu(x) \doteqdot (x+\tfrac{1}{2}E-\tfrac{1}{2})^\nu.$$

Hence

$$2x^\nu = 2\nabla E_\nu(x) \doteqdot (x+1+\tfrac{1}{2}E-\tfrac{1}{2})^\nu + (x+\tfrac{1}{2}E-\tfrac{1}{2})^\nu,$$

and if $P(x)$ be a polynomial,

$$(1) \qquad 2P(x) \doteqdot P(x+1+\tfrac{1}{2}E-\tfrac{1}{2}) + P(x+\tfrac{1}{2}E-\tfrac{1}{2}).$$

Writing $x+y$ for x,

$$2P(x+y) \doteqdot P(x+y+1+\tfrac{1}{2}E-\tfrac{1}{2}) + P(x+y+\tfrac{1}{2}E-\tfrac{1}{2})$$
$$\doteqdot P(x+1+E(y)) + P(x+E(y)).$$

Now, by Taylor's Theorem,

$$P(x+E(y)) \doteqdot P(x) + E_1(y)P'(x) + \frac{1}{2!}E_2(y)P''(x) + \dots,$$

Thus we have

$$(2) \quad P(x+y) = \nabla P(x) + E_1(y)\nabla P'(x) + \frac{1}{2!}E_2(y)\nabla P''(x) + \dots,$$

which is Boole's Theorem. If we put $x = 0$, we have the expansion of $P(y)$ in terms of Euler's polynomials.

From 6·72, we have

$$E_{2s}(1) = E_{2s}(0) = 2^{-2s}C_{2s} = 0,$$
$$E_{2s+1}(1) = -E_{2s+1}(0) = -2^{-2s-1}C_{2s+1}.$$

Hence putting $y = 1$ in (2), we have

$$(3) \quad P(x+1) - P(x) = -C_1\nabla P'(x) - \frac{1}{3!\,2^2}C_3\nabla P'''(x)$$
$$- \frac{1}{5!\,2^4}C_5\nabla P^{(v)}(x) - \dots.$$

Again from (1), we see that the difference equation

$$\nabla u(x) = P(x)$$

has the solution

$$u(x) \doteqdot P(x+\tfrac{1}{2}E-\tfrac{1}{2}) \doteqdot P(E(x)).$$

Thus, for example, the equation

$$\nabla u(x) = x^3 + 2x^2 + 1$$

has the solution

$$u(x) = E_3(x) + 2E_2(x) + 1.$$

The general solution may be obtained by adding to this an arbitrary periodic function $\pi(x)$ of period 2, and such that

$$\pi(x+1) = -\pi(x).$$

EXAMPLES VI

1. Prove that

(i) $$B_\nu^{(m+n)}(x+y) \doteqdot [B^{(m)}(x) + B^{(n)}(y)]^\nu ;$$

(ii) $$B_\nu^{(n)}(x+y) = \sum_{p=0}^{\nu} \binom{\nu}{p} B_p^{(n)}(x)\, y^{\nu-p} ;$$

(iii) $$B_\nu^{(n)}(x) = \sum_{p=0}^{\nu} \binom{\nu}{p} B_p\, B_{\nu-p}^{(n-1)}(x).$$

2. Obtain the formulae

(i) $$(x+y)^\nu = \sum_{p=0}^{\nu} \binom{\nu}{p} B_p^{(n)}(x)\, B_{\nu-p}^{(-n)}(y) ;$$

(ii) $$(x+y)^\nu = \sum_{p=0}^{\nu} \binom{\nu}{p} E_p^{(n)}(x)\, E_{\nu-p}^{(-n)}(y) ;$$

(iii) $$\sum_{p=0}^{\nu} \binom{\nu}{p} B_p^{(n)}\, B_{\nu-p}^{(-n)} = 0, \quad \nu > 0.$$

3. Prove that

$$1 + \frac{1}{2} + \frac{1}{3} + \dots + \frac{1}{n} = \frac{(-1)^{n-1}}{(n-1)!} B_{n-1}^{(n+1)}.$$

4. Prove that

$$E_\nu^{(n)}(x) = \sum_{p=0}^{\nu} \frac{E_p^{(n)}}{2^p} \binom{\nu}{p} (x - \tfrac{1}{2}n)^{\nu-p}.$$

5. Prove that

$$E_\nu^{(m+n)}(x+y) \doteqdot [E^{(m)}(x) + E^{(n)}(y)]^\nu$$

6. If $P(x)$ be a polynomial, prove that

$$P(B^{(n)}(x)+1) - P(B^{(n)}(x)) \doteqdot P'(B^{(n-1)}(x)),$$

and hence shew that the difference equation

$$\overset{n}{\Delta} u(x) = \frac{d^n}{dx^n} P(x)$$

is satisfied by

$$u(x) \doteqdot P(B^{(n)}(x)).$$

7. Prove that

$$B_1^{(2)}(x) = x - 1, \quad B_2^{(2)}(x) = x^2 - 2x + \tfrac{5}{6}.$$

8. Draw graphs showing the forms in the interval $0 \leqslant x \leqslant 1$ of $(-1)^\nu B_{2\nu-1}(x)$, $(-1)^\nu (B_{2\nu}(x) - B_{2\nu})$, $(-1)^\nu E_{2\nu-1}(x)$, $(-1)^\nu E_{2\nu}(x)$.

9. Prove that

$$B_{2n} = \frac{\Delta\, 0^{2n+1}}{1^2} - \frac{\overset{2}{\Delta}\, 0^{2n+1}}{2^2} + \dots + \frac{\overset{2n+1}{\Delta}\, 0^{2n+1}}{(2n+1)^2}.$$

10. If n be an odd integer, prove that, taking $\frac{1}{2}(n-1)$ terms,

$$\tfrac{1}{2} = n B_2 + \binom{n}{3} B_4 + \binom{n}{5} B_6 + \dots .$$

11. Shew that

$$(-1)^{n-1} B_{2n} = (\tfrac{1}{2} - \tfrac{1}{3}\Delta + \tfrac{1}{4}\overset{2}{\Delta} - \dots)\, 1^{2n-1}.$$

12. Prove the relation

$$\frac{2^{2n-1}}{(4n)!\, 2!} B_{4n} - \frac{2^{2n-3}}{(4n-4)!\, 6!} B_{4n-4} + \dots + \frac{(-1)^{n-1} n}{(4n+2)!} = 0.$$

13. Obtain B_{2n} as a definite integral from the identity

$$\frac{e^x+1}{e^x-1} - \frac{2}{x} = 4\int_0^\infty \frac{\sin xt}{e^{2\pi t}-1}\, dt.$$

14. Prove that the coefficient of θ^{2n} in the expansion of $(\theta \operatorname{cosec} \theta)^2$ is $2^{2n}(2n-1)(-1)^{n-1} B_{2n} / (2n)!$.

15. Shew that the coefficient of $z^n / n!$ in

$$\int_0^z \log(1-e^{-t})\, dt - z \log z \quad \text{is numerically equal to} \quad \frac{B_{n-1}}{n-1}.$$

16. By means of Bernoulli's numbers or otherwise, prove that

$$\frac{1^2}{1^2+1} \cdot \frac{2^2}{2^2+1} \cdot \frac{3^2}{3^2+1} \dots = \frac{2\pi}{e^\pi - e^{-\pi}}.$$

17. Prove that

$$1-\frac{\pi^2}{2!}B_2+\frac{\pi^4}{4!}B_4-\ldots=0.$$

18. Express the sums of the powers of numbers less than n and prime to it in series involving Bernoulli's numbers.

19. Shew that

$$1-\frac{1}{3^3}+\frac{1}{5^3}-\ldots=\frac{\pi^3}{32},$$

$$1-\frac{1}{3^5}+\frac{1}{5^5}-\ldots=\frac{5\pi^5}{1536}.$$

20. If $S_x^n=1^n+2^n+3^n+\ldots+x^n$, shew that

$$S_x^n=x\,S_x^{n-1}-\sum_{r=1}^{x-1}S_r^{n-1}.$$

21. If $F(x)=1^n+2^n+3^n+\ldots+(x-1)^n$, shew that $F(x)$ is a polynomial in $(x-\frac{1}{2})$ and cannot contain both odd and even powers of the same.

22. Prove that $\frac{1}{r!}\overset{r}{\Delta}\{0+(n-r)\}^{s+r}$ expresses the sum of all the homogeneous products of s dimensions which can be formed of the $r+1$ consecutive numbers $n, n-1, \ldots, n-r$.

23. Express $x^{(m)}\times x^{(n)}$ in factorials.

24. If K_r^m denote the number of combinations of m things r together with repetitions, and if C_r^m denote the number of combinations of m things r together without repetitions, then

$$K_r^m=\frac{1}{m!}\overset{m}{\Delta}\,0^{m+r}$$

and C_r^m is obtained by writing $-(m+1)$ for m in the expanded expression for K_r^m.

25. Prove that

$$B_{n-1}^{(n)}+\binom{n-1}{1}B_{n-2}^{(n)}+\binom{n-1}{2}B_{n-3}^{(n)}+\ldots=0,$$

$$\binom{n-1}{1}B_2B_{n-2}^{(n)}+\binom{n-1}{3}B_4B_{n-4}^{(n)}+\ldots=\frac{(-1)^n(n-1)!}{2}\cdot\frac{n-1}{n+1}.$$

26. Expand $(x-1)^{(-n)}$ in powers of x^{-1}.

27. Expand x^{-n} in factorials of the form $(x-1)^{(-s)}$.

28. Prove that

$$B_n^{(n+1)}(x+1) = \frac{2\,n!}{\pi}\int_0^{\pi} 2\,(\cos(\tfrac{1}{2}z))^x \cos(\tfrac{1}{2}xz)\cos mz\,dz.$$

29. If $D_1 \equiv x\dfrac{d}{dx}$, shew that

$$D_1^{n+1} f(x) = xf'(x) + \frac{\Delta 1^n}{1!}x^2 f''(x) + \frac{\overset{2}{\Delta} 1^n}{2!} x^3 f'''(x) + \dots,$$

$f(x)$ being a polynomial.

30. Prove that $\qquad B_n = \sum_{m=0}^{n} \dfrac{(-1)^m}{m+1} \overset{m}{\Delta}\, 0^n.$

31. Prove Staudt's Theorem, namely, that every Bernoulli number B_{2n} is equal to an integer diminished by the sum of the reciprocals of all and only those prime numbers which, when diminished by unity, are divisors of $2n$.

32. Prove that $\qquad \sum_{s=0}^{n} \dfrac{(-1)^s}{n-s+1} \dfrac{B_s^{(s)}}{s!} = 1.$

33. Prove that

$$B_\nu^{(n+\nu+2)}(1) = \sum_{s=0}^{\nu} \binom{\nu}{s} B_{\nu-s}^{(n+1)}(1)\, B_s^{(\nu+1)}(1).$$

CHAPTER VII

NUMERICAL DIFFERENTIATION AND INTEGRATION

THE problem of numerical differentiation consists in finding an approximate value of the derivate of a given order from the values of the function at given isolated arguments. The problem of numerical integration consists in finding approximately, from the same data, the integral of the given function between definite limits. In this chapter we shall investigate a few of the many formulae which have been proposed for this purpose. It will be found that the generalised numbers of Bernoulli enable us to obtain general expressions for the coefficients of most of the formulae. It may be observed that some of the methods of numerical integration (often called mechanical quadrature) lead to corresponding methods of summation when the integral is known.

7·0. The First Order Derivate. We have from Newton's formula 3·1 (4),

$$f(x+y) = f(x) + p\Delta f(x) + \dots + \binom{p}{n-1}\Delta^{n-1} f(x) + \binom{p}{n} f^{(n)}(\xi)\,\omega^n,$$

where ω denotes the tabular interval and $p = y/\omega$.

Thus

$$\omega\frac{f(x+y)-f(x)}{y} = \Delta f(x) + \frac{(p-1)}{2!}\Delta^2 f(x) + \frac{(p-1)(p-2)}{3!}\Delta^3 f(x)$$

$$+ \dots + \frac{(p-1)(p-2)\dots(p-n+2)}{(n-1)!}\Delta^{n-1} f(x)$$

$$+ \frac{(p-1)\dots(p-n+1)}{n!} f^{(n)}(\xi)\,\omega^n.$$

If we let $y \to 0$, then $p \to 0$, and

$$(1) \quad \omega f'(x) = \Delta f(x) - \tfrac{1}{2}\Delta^2 f(x) + \tfrac{1}{3}\Delta^3 f(x) - \dots + \frac{(-1)^{n-2}}{n-1}\Delta^{n-1} f(x) + \frac{(-1)^{n-1}}{n} f^{(n)}(\xi)\omega^n,$$

which expresses $f'(x)$ in terms of the differences of $f(x)$.

To use the formula we have therefore to form a difference table in which x figures as one of the arguments.

The above method can of course be applied to any of the interpolation formulae of Chapter III. .Thus, from Newton's backward formula,

$$\omega f'(x) = \Delta f(x-\omega) + \tfrac{1}{2}\Delta^2 f(x-2\omega) + \tfrac{1}{3}\Delta^3 f(x-3\omega) + \dots + \frac{1}{n-1}\Delta^{n-1} f(x-(n-1)\omega) + \frac{\omega^n}{n} f^{(n)}(\xi).$$

Again, if we use Stirling's formula we note that the coefficients of the even differences vanish when $p \to 0$, so that from 3·3 (3), for example, we have

$$\omega f'(x) = \mu\delta\, u_0 - \tfrac{1}{6}\mu\delta^3\, u_0 + \frac{\omega^5}{30} f^{(5)}(\xi),$$

the differences $\mu\delta\, u_0$, $\mu\delta^3\, u_0$ lying on a horizontal line through the tabular value $f(x)$.

These formulae have been obtained by a special artifice which gives the remainder term in a simple manner. We now proceed to a more general method.

7·01. Derivates of Higher Order. Let

$$\phi_s(x) = (x-x_1)(x-x_2)\dots(x-x_s).$$

Then Newton's formula for interpolation with divided differences can be written

$$f(x) = f(x_1) + \sum_{s=1}^{n-1} \phi_s(x)\,[x_1x_2x_3 \dots x_{s+1}] + \phi_n(x)\,[xx_1x_2 \dots x_n].$$

Differentiate m times with respect to x. Then

$$(1) \qquad f^{(m)}(x) = \sum_{s=m}^{n-1} \phi_s^{(m)}(x)\,[x_1x_2 \dots x_{s+1}] + R_n(x),$$

$$(2) \quad \text{where} \quad R_n(x) = \frac{d^m}{dx^m}\{\phi_n(x)\,[xx_1x_2 \dots x_n]\},$$

which expresses the mth derivate in terms of divided differences.

To deal with the remainder term, let us first suppose that x is not interior to the smallest interval I which contains $x_1, x_2, \ldots, x_n$.

Since $\phi_n(x)$ has n zeros all in I, by repeated application of Rolle's Theorem we see that $\phi_n^{(m)}(x)$, if $m \leqslant n$, has exactly $n-m$ zeros all in I. Hence, if y be a point exterior to I, $\phi_n^{(m)}(y) \neq 0$.

Now consider the function

$$\psi(x) = \phi_n(x)[xx_1x_2 \ldots x_n] - \phi_n(x) R_n(y)/\phi_n^{(m)}(y). \tag{3}$$

This function vanishes for $x = x_1, x_2, \ldots, x_n$.

Let J be the smallest interval which contains $y, x_1, x_2, \ldots, x_n$. Then, by repeated application of Rolle's Theorem, $\psi^{(m)}(x)$ has at least $n-m$ zeros in I, and also the zero y which is not in I. Thus $\psi^{(m)}(x)$ has at least $n-m+1$ zeros in J. In particular, if $m = n$, then $\psi^{(n)}(x)$ has at least one zero, say η, in J. Thus

$$\frac{d^n}{d\eta^n}\{\phi_n(\eta)[\eta\, x_1x_2 \ldots x_n]\} - \frac{n!\, R_n(y)}{\phi_n^{(m)}(y)} = 0.$$

Now, from (1), $\dfrac{d^n}{d\eta^n}\{\phi_n(\eta)[\eta\, x_1x_2 \ldots x_n]\} = f^{(n)}(\eta)$.

Thus $$\frac{R_n(y)}{\phi_n^{(m)}(y)} = \frac{f^{(n)}(\eta)}{n!}.$$

(4) Hence $$R_n(x) = \frac{f^{(n)}(\eta)}{n!}\phi_n^{(m)}(x),$$

where η is some point of the interval bounded by the greatest and least of $x, x_1, x_2, \ldots, x_n$; and x is not interior to the interval bounded by the greatest and least of $x_1, x_2, \ldots, x_n$. Of course x may be an end-point of the latter interval.

If in the second place we suppose x to be interior to the least interval I which contains $x_1, x_2, \ldots, x_n$, we can proceed as follows.

By Leibniz' Theorem,

$$R_n(x) = \sum_{\nu=0}^{m} \frac{d^\nu}{dx^\nu}\phi_n(x)\binom{m}{\nu}\frac{d^{m-\nu}}{dx^{m-\nu}}[xx_1x_2 \ldots x_n].$$

Now by 1·8,

$$\frac{d^{m-\nu}}{dx^{m-\nu}}[xx_1x_2 \ldots x_n] = [xx \ldots xx_1x_2 \ldots x_n](m-\nu)!,$$

where the argument x occurs $m-\nu+1$ times and

$$[xx \dots xx_1 x_2 \dots x_n] = \frac{1}{(m+n-\nu)!} f^{(m+n-\nu)}(\xi_\nu),$$

where ξ_ν is some point of I. Thus

$$R_n(x) = \sum_{\nu=0}^{m} \frac{d^\nu}{dx^\nu} \phi_n(x) \frac{m!}{\nu!(m+n-\nu)!} f^{(m+n-\nu)}(\xi_\nu). \tag{5}$$

Comparing (4) and (5), we see that, when x is not interior to the interval I, the form of the remainder term in (1) is obtained by differentiating m times the remainder term $\phi_n(x) f^{(n)}(\xi)/n!$ as if ξ were a constant, although the value η finally used may not coincide with the original value ξ. If x be interior to the interval I we obtain the more complicated form (5).

7·02. Markoff's Formula. If $p = y/\omega$, we have by 6·4 (2)

$$\binom{p}{s} = B_s^{(s+1)}(p+1) \div (s!).$$

Thus Newton's interpolation formula can be written

$$f(x+y) = \sum_{s=0}^{n-1} \frac{1}{s!} B_s^{(s+1)}(p+1)\, \Delta^s f(x) + \frac{\omega^n}{n!} B_n^{(n+1)}(p+1) f^{(n)}(\xi),$$

where ξ is some point of the least interval containing

$$(x+y,\ x,\ x+(n-1)\omega).$$

If $y=0$, $x+y$ becomes an end-point of this interval. Thus we can determine the remainder term of the mth derivate when $y=0$ by the formula (4) of the preceding section.

Differentiating m times with respect to y and then putting $y=0$, we have

$$f^{(m)}(x) = \sum_{s=m}^{n-1} \frac{\omega^{-m}}{s!} s(s-1)\dots(s-m+1)\, B_{s-m}^{(s+1)}(1)\, \Delta^s f(x)$$

$$+ \frac{\omega^{n-m}}{n!} n(n-1)\dots(n-m+1)\, B_{n-m}^{(n+1)}(1) f^{(n)}(\eta).$$

This is Markoff's formula. Since, by 6·3 (4),

$$B_{s-m}^{(s+1)}(1) = \frac{m}{s} B_{s-m}^{(s)},$$

the formula can be written

$$(1) \quad \omega^m f^{(m)}(x) = \sum_{s=m}^{n-1} \frac{m}{(s-m)!\,s} B_{s-m}^{(s)} \Delta^s f(x) + \frac{m\,\omega^n}{(n-m)!\,n} B_{n-m}^{(n)} f^{(n)}(\eta).$$

When $m = 1$ we have, by 6·4 (1), $B_{s-1}^{(s)} = (-1)^{s-1}(s-1)!$, so that the formula agrees with 7·0 (1), which is a special case. The coefficients can be calculated with the aid of the table in 6·1.

If we write $n = m+1$, we obtain

$$\omega^m f^{(m)}(x) = B_0^{(m)} \Delta^m f(x) + \frac{m\,\omega^{m+1}}{m+1} B_1^{(m+1)} f^{(m+1)}(\eta).$$

From 6·1 (3), $B_0^{(m)} = 1$, $B_1^{(m+1)} = -\tfrac{1}{2}(m+1)$.

Thus

$$(2) \quad \omega^m f^{(m)}(x) = \Delta^m f(x) - \tfrac{1}{2} m\,\omega^{m+1} f^{(m+1)}(\eta),$$

or

$$(3) \quad f^{(m)}(x) = \overset{m}{\underset{\omega}{\Delta}} f(x) - \tfrac{1}{2} m\,\omega\, f^{(m+1)}(\eta),$$

which measures the error committed in replacing a derivate by a difference quotient.

For the case $m = 2$, $n = 6$, (1) gives

$$(4) \quad \omega^2 f''(x) = \Delta^2 f(x) - \Delta^3 f(x) + \tfrac{11}{12} \Delta^4 f(x) - \tfrac{5}{6} \Delta^5 f(x) + \tfrac{137}{180} \omega^6 f^{(6)}(\eta).$$

Example. To find $f'(\cdot 160)$, $f''(\cdot 160)$ when $f(x) = \cos x$.

Using the 10 figure tables in the example of 3·12, we have

$$(\cdot 001) f'(\cdot 160) \doteq -\cdot 0001598118 + \cdot 00000049355 + \tfrac{1}{3}(\cdot 001)^3 f'''(\xi).$$

In this range $f'''(\xi) = \sin \xi = 0\cdot 16$ approximately.

Hence

$$f'(\cdot 160) = -\cdot 1598118 + \cdot 0004936$$
$$= -\cdot 1593182,$$

which agrees with $-\sin \cdot 160$ to the last digit. The last digit is in general unreliable since the first difference in a correct table may be in error by one unit. For the second derivate we have

$$\omega^2 f''(\cdot 160) = -\cdot 0000009871 - \omega^3 f'''(\xi),$$

whence $f''(\cdot 160) = -0\cdot 9873$, which disagrees by a unit in the last place with the correct value to four places, namely

$$-\cos \cdot 160 = -0\cdot 9872.$$

Since the last digit of the second difference may be in error by two units, we cannot in any case rely upon the last digit of the calculated second derivate.

We also observe that although a 10 figure table has been used we have only determined $f'(x)$ to seven figures and $f''(x)$ to four. In any case we cannot obtain more figures of a derivate than there are digits in the difference of the corresponding order.

To obtain Markoff's formula for ascending differences we begin with Newton's backward formula,

$$f(x+y) = \sum_{s=0}^{n-1} \binom{p+s-1}{s} \Delta^s f(x-s\omega) + \binom{p+n-1}{n} \omega^n f^{(n)}(\xi).$$

Now by 6·4 (1),

$$\binom{p+s-1}{s} = \frac{1}{s!} B_s^{(s+1)}(p+s) = \frac{(-1)^s}{s!} B_s^{(s+1)}(1-p).$$

Proceeding as before, we get

$$(2) \qquad \omega^m f^{(m)}(x) = \sum_{s=m}^{n-1} \frac{(-1)^{s+m} m}{(s-m)!\, s} B_{s-m}^{(s)} \Delta^s f(x-s\omega) + \frac{(-1)^{m+n} m\, \omega^n}{(n-m)!\, n} B_{n-m}^{(n)} f^{(n)}(\eta).$$

The coefficients have the same absolute values as the coefficients in (1).

The simplicity of the remainder term in Markoff's formulae makes them often preferable to the central difference formulae which will now be obtained.

7·03. Derivates from Stirling's Formula. Writing $p = y/\omega$, Stirling's formula 3·3 (1) can be written

$$f(x+y) = u_0 + \sum_{s=0}^{n-1} a_{2s+1}(p)\, \mu\delta^{2s+1} u_0 + \sum_{s=1}^{n} a_{2s}(p)\, \delta^{2s} u_0 + a_{2n+1}(p)\, f^{(2n+1)}(\xi)\, \omega^{2n+1},$$

where $u_p = f(x+p\omega)$ and

$$a_{2s+1}(p) = \binom{p+s}{2s+1}, \quad a_{2s}(p) = \frac{p}{2s}\binom{p+s-1}{2s-1}.$$

Differentiate $2m$ times with respect to y and then put $y=0$. Then by 6·4 (7), (10), we have

$$(1)\quad \omega^{2m} f^{(2m)}(x) = \sum_{s=m}^{n} \frac{m}{s(2s-2m)!} B_{2s-2m}^{(2s)}(s)\, \delta^{2s} u_0 + R_{2n+1}(x),$$

where from 7·01 (5),

$$(2)\quad R_{2n+1}(x)$$

$$= (2n+1)! \sum_{\nu=1}^{m} \frac{\omega^{2m+2n-2\nu+2}(2m)!\, f^{(2m+2n-2\nu+2)}(\xi_\nu)\, B_{2n-2\nu+2}^{(2n+2)}(n+1)}{(2\nu-1)!\,(2m+2n-2\nu+2)!\,(2n-2\nu+2)!}.$$

Similarly, if we differentiate $(2m+1)$ times, we obtain

$$(3)\quad \omega^{2m+1} f^{(2m+1)}(x)$$

$$= \sum_{s=m}^{n-1} \frac{1}{(2s-2m)!} B_{(2s-2m)}^{(2s+2)}(s+1)\, \mu\delta^{2s+1} u_0 + R_{2n+1}(x),$$

$$(4)\quad R_{2n+1}(x)$$

$$= (2n+1)! \sum_{\nu=0}^{m} \frac{\omega^{2m+2n-2\nu+1}(2m+1)!\, f^{(2m+2n-2\nu+1)}(\xi_\nu)\, B_{2n-2\nu}^{(2n+2)}(n+1)}{(2\nu+1)!\,(2m+2n-2\nu+1)!\,(2n-2\nu)!}.$$

The following list gives the coefficients of the first few terms,

$$B_0^{(n)}(\tfrac{1}{2}n) = 1, \quad B_2^{(n)}(\tfrac{1}{2}n) = -\frac{n}{12}, \quad B_4^{(n)}(\tfrac{1}{2}n) = \frac{n(5n+2)}{240},$$

$$B_6^{(n)}(\tfrac{1}{2}n) = \frac{-n(35n^2+42n+16)}{2^6 \times 3^2 \times 7},$$

$$B_8^{(n)}(\tfrac{1}{2}n) = \frac{n(175n^3+420n^2+404n+144)}{2^8 \times 3^3 \times 5},$$

from which we easily obtain, taking 7 interpolation points,

$$\omega f'(x) = \mu\delta u_0 - \tfrac{1}{6}\mu\delta^3 u_0 + \tfrac{1}{30}\mu\delta^5 u_0 - \frac{\omega^7}{140} f^{(7)}(\xi),$$

$$\omega^2 f''(x) = \delta^2 u_0 - \tfrac{1}{12}\delta^4 u_0 + \tfrac{1}{90}\delta^6 u_0 - \frac{\omega^8}{560} f^{(8)}(\xi),$$

$$\omega^3 f'''(x) = \mu\delta^3 u_0 - \tfrac{1}{4}\mu\delta^5 u_0 + \frac{7\omega^7}{120} f^{(7)}(\xi_1) - \frac{\omega^9}{1680} f^{(9)}(\xi_2),$$

$$\omega^4 f^{(iv)}(x) = \delta^4 u_0 - \tfrac{1}{6}\delta^6 u_0 + \frac{7\omega^8}{240} f^{(8)}(\xi_1) - \frac{\omega^{10}}{4200} f^{(10)}(\xi_2),$$

$$\omega^5 f^{(v)}(x) = \mu\delta^5 u_0 - \frac{\omega^7}{3} f^{(7)}(\xi_1) + \frac{7\omega^9}{432} f^{(9)}(\xi_2) - \frac{\omega^{11}}{9240} f^{(11)}(\xi_3),$$

$$\omega^6 f^{(vi)}(x) = \delta^6 u_0 - \frac{\omega^8}{4} f^{(8)}(\xi_1) + \frac{7\omega^{10}}{720} f^{(10)}(\xi_2) - \frac{\omega^{12}}{18480} f^{(12)}(\xi_3).$$

7·04. Derivates from Bessel's Formula. With $y/\omega = p$, Bessel's formula, 3·4, can be written

$$f(x+y) = u_0 + p\,\delta u_{\frac{1}{2}} + \sum_{s=1}^{n-1} b_{2s+1}(p)\,\delta^{2s+1} u_{\frac{1}{2}} + \sum_{s=1}^{n-1} b_{2s}(p)\,\mu\delta^{2s} u_{\frac{1}{2}} + \omega^{2n} b_{2n}(p)\, f^{(2n)}(\xi),$$

where $u_p = f(x+p\omega)$ and

$$b_{2s+1}(p) = \frac{p-\frac{1}{2}}{2s+1}\binom{p+s-1}{2s}, \quad b_{2s}(p) = \binom{p+s-1}{2s}.$$

Differentiate $2m$ times with respect to y and then put $y = \frac{1}{2}\omega$. Then by 6·4 (9), (11), we have

$$\omega^{2m} f^{(2m)}(x+\tfrac{1}{2}\omega) = \sum_{s=m}^{n-1} \frac{1}{(2s-2m)!} B_{2s-2m}^{(2s+1)}(s+\tfrac{1}{2})\,\mu\delta^{2s} u_{\frac{1}{2}} + R_{2n}(x),$$

where by 7·01 (5),

$$R_{2n}(x) = (2n)! \sum_{\nu=0}^{m} \frac{\omega^{2m+2n-2\nu}(2m)!\, f^{(2m+2n-2\nu)}(\xi_\nu)\, B_{2n-2\nu}^{(2n+1)}(n+\frac{1}{2})}{(2\nu)!\,(2m+2n-2\nu)!\,(2n-2\nu)!}.$$

Similarly,

$$\omega^{2m+1} f^{(2m+1)}(x+\tfrac{1}{2}\omega) = \sum_{s=m}^{n-1} \frac{2m+1}{(2s+1)(2s-2m)!} B_{2s-2m}^{(2s+1)}(s+\tfrac{1}{2})\,\delta^{2s+1} u_{\frac{1}{2}} + R_{2n}(x),$$

$$R_{2n}(x) = (2n)! \sum_{\nu=0}^{m} \frac{\omega^{2m+2n-2\nu+1}(2m+1)!\, f^{(2m+2n-2\nu+1)}(\xi_\nu)\, B_{2n-2\nu}^{(2n+1)}(n+\frac{1}{2})}{(2\nu)!\,(2m+2n-2\nu+1)!\,(2n-2\nu)!}.$$

The formulae for $m = 0$, $m = 1$, give respectively

$$\omega f'(x+\tfrac{1}{2}\omega) = \delta u_{\frac{1}{2}} - \frac{1}{24}\delta^3 u_{\frac{1}{2}} + \frac{3\omega^5}{640} f^{(5)}(\xi),$$

$$\omega^2 f''(x+\tfrac{1}{2}\omega) = \mu\delta^2 u_{\frac{1}{2}} - \frac{5}{24}\mu\delta^4 u_{\frac{1}{2}} + \frac{259\omega^6}{5760} f^{(6)}(\xi_1) - \frac{5\omega^8}{28672} f^{(8)}(\xi_2).$$

It will be seen that the complicated form of the remainder term may often render the use of Markoff's formulae preferable to those with central differences.

7·05. Differences in Terms of Derivates. By Maclaurin's theorem

$$f(x) = \sum_{s=0}^{n-1} \frac{x^s}{s!} f^{(s)}(0) + \frac{x^n}{n!} f^{(n)}(\xi),$$

where ξ is in the interval $(0, x)$.

Now $x^s = B_s^{(0)}(x)$, so that by 6·11 (4),

$$\overset{m}{\Delta} x^s = \overset{m}{\Delta} B_s^{(0)}(x) = s(s-1)\dots(s-m+1)\, B_{s-m}^{(-m)}(x).$$

We have therefore

$$\overset{m}{\Delta} f(x) = \sum_{s=m}^{n-1} \frac{f^{(s)}(0)}{(s-m)!} B_{s-m}^{(-m)}(x) + R_n(x),$$

where, by the method of 7·01, we can prove that

$$R_n(x) = \frac{f^{(n)}(\eta)}{(n-m)!} B_{n-m}^{(-m)}(x).$$

This formula is due to Markoff. See also 2·54.

7·1. Numerical Integration. The problem of numerical integration or mechanical quadrature is that of evaluating

(1) $$\int_a^b f(x)\,dx$$

in terms of the values of $f(x)$ for a finite number of arguments $x_0, x_1, x_2, \dots, x_n$. The methods of approaching this problem fall into two main groups:

(i) Methods depending explicitly on the values

$$f(x_0), f(x_1), \dots, f(x_n).$$

(ii) Methods depending on differences or on differential coefficients.

We shall deal with each of these groups in turn, but before doing so we make the general remark that the substitution

$$x = \frac{(b-a)t + a\beta - b\alpha}{\beta - \alpha}$$

leads to

$$\int_a^b f(x)dx = \int_\alpha^\beta f\left[\frac{(b-a)\,t+a\beta-b\alpha}{\beta-\alpha}\right]\frac{b-a}{\beta-\alpha}dt,$$

so that the original limits of integration may be replaced by any others which may happen to be more convenient. In particular,

$$\int_a^b f(x)\,dx = (b-a)\int_0^1 f[(b-a)\,t+a]\,dt,$$

$$\int_a^b f(x)\,dx = \frac{b-a}{n}\int_0^n f\left[\frac{(b-a)\,t+an}{n}\right]dt,$$

$$\int_a^b f(x)\,dx = \frac{b-a}{2k}\int_{-k}^{+k} f\left[\frac{(b-a)\,t+k(b+a)}{2k}\right]dt.$$

It follows that a formula established for apparently special cases such as

$$\int_0^1 \phi(x)\,dx,\ \int_0^n \phi(x)\,dx,\ \int_{-k}^{+k} \phi(x)\,dx,$$

can be immediately applied to the general case (1) by a suitable linear change of variable.

7·101. The Mean Value Theorem. We shall make frequent use of the following theorem.

Let $f(x)$, $\phi(x)$ be integrable functions in the interval (a, b) and let $\phi(x)$ have a fixed sign in this interval. Then, if $f(x)$ be continuous for $a \leqslant x \leqslant b$, we can find a point ξ in this interval such that

$$\int_a^b f(x)\,\phi(x)\,dx = f(\xi)\int_a^b \phi(x)\,dx.$$

Let M, m be the greatest and least values of $f(x)$ in the interval $a \leqslant x \leqslant b$, and suppose that $\phi(x)$ is positive. Then we have

$$\int_a^b [M-f(x)]\,\phi(x)\,dx \geqslant 0,\ \int_a^b [f(x)-m]\,\phi(x)\,dx \geqslant 0.$$

Thus

$$M\int_a^b \phi(x)\,dx \geqslant \int_a^b f(x)\,\phi(x)\,dx \geqslant m\int_a^b \phi(x)\,dx,$$

and hence

$$\int_a^b f(x)\,\phi(x)\,dx = L\int_a^b \phi(x)\,dx,$$

where $M \geqslant L \geqslant m$. Since $f(x)$ is continuous, $f(x)$ attains the value L for some point ξ of the interval (a, b) and therefore $L = f(\xi)$, which proves the theorem when $\phi(x)$ is positive. If $\phi(x)$ be negative we reverse the above signs of inequality and obtain the same result.

7·11. Integration by Lagrange's Interpolation Formula.

We have, from 1·4,

$$(1) \qquad f(x) = \sum_{s=1}^{n} \frac{f(x_s)}{x - x_s} \frac{\phi(x)}{\phi'(x_s)} + \phi(x)\,[xx_1x_2 \ldots x_n],$$

$$(2) \qquad \phi(x) = (x - x_1)(x - x_2) \ldots (x - x_n).$$

Thus, integrating from a to b,

$$(3) \qquad \int_a^b f(x)\,dx = \sum_{s=1}^{n} h_s^{(n)} f(x_s) + R_n,$$

where

$$(4) \qquad h_s^{(n)} = \int_a^b \frac{\phi(x)}{\phi'(x_s)} \frac{dx}{x - x_s}, \quad R_n = \int_a^b \phi(x)\,[xx_1x_2 \ldots x_n]\,dx.$$

Thus the coefficients $h_s^{(n)}$ depend upon the interpolation points $x_1, x_2, \ldots, x_n$, but are independent of the particular form of $f(x)$. Formula (3), like the identity (1) from which the formula arises, is a pure identity and therefore of general application. The utility is, however, limited unless an adequate estimate can be made of the remainder term R_n.

Denote by I the interval bounded by the greatest and least of the numbers $a, b, x_1, x_2, \ldots, x_n$. When x lies in I we have, by 1·2 (2),

$$[xx_1x_2 \ldots x_n] = \frac{1}{n!} f^{(n)}(\eta),$$

where η also lies in I. Thus if $\phi(x)$ have a fixed sign when x is in (a, b), we have by the mean value theorem, 7·101,

$$(5) \qquad R_n = \frac{f^{(n)}(\xi)}{n!} \int_a^b \phi(x)\,dx,$$

where ξ lies in I.

If the sign of $\phi(x)$ be not fixed we can proceed as follows. The zeros of the polynomial $\phi(x)$ are $x_1, x_2, \ldots, x_n$, which we suppose arranged in order of ascending magnitude. In the interval (x_{s-1}, x_s), $\phi(x)$ has a constant sign and we have

$$\int_{x_{s-1}}^{x_s} f(x)\,dx = \frac{f^{(n)}(\xi_s)}{n!}\int_{x_{s-1}}^{x_s} \phi(x)\,dx.$$

Hence if x_ν be the first interpolation point such that $a \leqslant x_\nu$, and x_μ the last such that $x_\mu \leqslant b$, we have

$$(6) \qquad R_n = \frac{f^{(n)}(\xi_\nu)}{n!}\int_a^{x_\nu} \phi(x)\,dx + \frac{f^{(n)}(\xi_{\nu+1})}{n!}\int_{x_\nu}^{x_\nu+1} \phi(x)\,dx + \dots$$

$$+ \frac{f^{(n)}(\xi_\mu)}{n!}\int_{x_\mu-1}^{x_\mu} \phi(x)\,dx + \frac{f^{(n)}(\xi_{\mu+1})}{n!}\int_{x_\mu}^{b} \phi(x)\,dx,$$

where $\xi_\nu, \xi_{\nu+1}, \dots, \xi_{\mu+1}$, all lie in I.

7·12. Equidistant Arguments. If in the formulae of the last section we take

$$x_s = \alpha + s\omega, \quad s = 1, 2, 3, \dots, n,$$

we obtain

$$(1) \quad \int_a^b f(x)\,dx = \sum_{s=1}^{n} K_s^{(n)} f(\alpha + s\omega)$$

$$+ \int_a^b (x-\alpha-\omega)\dots(x-\alpha-n\omega)\,[x, \alpha+\omega, \dots, \alpha+n\omega]\,dx,$$

$$K_s^{(n)} = \frac{(-1)^{n-s}}{\omega^{n-1}}\int_a^b \frac{(x-\alpha-\omega)\dots(x-\alpha-n\omega)}{(x-\alpha-s\omega)(s-1)!(n-s)!}\,dx.$$

Now put

$$(2) \qquad a = \alpha + (1-k)\,\omega, \quad b = \alpha + (n+k)\,\omega, \quad x = \alpha + y\omega$$

and write $F(y) = f(\alpha + y\omega)$. We then have

$$(3) \qquad \omega = \frac{b-a}{n+2k-1},$$

$$(4) \qquad K_s^{(n)} = \omega(-1)^{n-s}\, n\binom{n-1}{s-1}\int_{1-k}^{n+k}\binom{y-1}{n}\frac{dy}{y-s} = \omega J_{s,k}^{(n)},$$

$$[x, \alpha+\omega, \dots, \alpha+n\omega] = \frac{1}{n!}f^{(n)}(\xi) = \frac{1}{n!}f^{(n)}(\alpha+\omega\eta)$$

$$= \frac{\omega^{-n}}{n!}F^{(n)}(\eta) = \omega^{-n}\,[y, 1, 2, \dots, n].$$

Thus

$$(5)\qquad \omega\int_{1-k}^{n+k} F(y)\,dy = \omega\sum_{s=1}^{n} J_{s,k}^{(n)} F(s) + \omega R_n,$$

$$(6)\qquad R_n = \int_{1-k}^{n+k} (y-1)\dots(y-n)\,[y,\,1,\,2,\,\dots,\,n]\,dy.$$

The formula (1) is completely equivalent to (5), but we note that the remainder term of (1) is ωR_n.

If in (5) we take $k = 0$, we have

$$(7)\quad \int_{1}^{n} F(y)\,dy = J_{1,0}^{(n)} F(1) + J_{2,0}^{(n)} F(2) + \dots + J_{n,0}^{(n)} F(n) + \text{remainder},$$

while if $k = 1$, we have

$$(8)\int_{0}^{n+1} F(y)dy = J_{1,1}^{(n)} F(1) + J_{2,1}^{(n)} F(2) + \dots + J_{n,1}^{(n)} F(n) + \text{remainder}.$$

The essential distinction here is that in (7) the values $F(1)$, $F(n)$ correspond to the end-points of the interval of integration, while in (8) the values $F(1)$, $F(n)$ correspond to points within the interval of integration. Steffensen has given the convenient epithets "closed" and "open" to the first and second of these types of formulae.

Formulae of the open type are useful in the numerical solution of differential equations where it is necessary to extend the range of integration beyond the values already calculated. In order to obtain practical formulae from (5), we must proceed to a discussion of the remainder term.

7·13. The Remainder Term, n odd. In 7·12 we suppose that $n = 2m-1$. Then

$$R_{2m-1} = \int_{1-k}^{2m+k-1} (y-1)(y-2)\dots(y-2m+1)\,[y,\,1,\,2,\,\dots,\,2m-1]\,dy.$$

Put $$\chi(x) = \int_{1-k}^{x} (y-1)\dots(y-2m+1)\,dy.$$

By 6·401 (2), $\chi(2m+k-1) = \chi(1-k) = 0$. Hence, integrating by parts, we have

$$R_{2m-1} = -\int_{1-k}^{2m+k-1} \chi(y)\,[y,\,y,\,1,\,2,\,\dots,\,2m-1]\,dy,$$

since $$\frac{d}{dy}[y,\,1,\,2,\,\dots,\,2m-1] = [y,\,y,\,1,\,2,\,\dots,\,2m-1].$$

Since $\chi(y)$ has a fixed sign (see 6·401), we have, by use of the mean value theorem,

$$R_{2m-1} = -[\eta_1, \eta_1, 1, \dots, 2m-1] \int_{1-k}^{2m+k-1} \chi(y)\, dy$$

$$= -\frac{F^{(2m)}(\eta)}{(2m)!} \int_{1-k}^{2m+k-1} \chi(y)\, dy$$

$$= -\frac{F^{(2m)}(\eta)}{(2m+1)!} \left\{ B_{2m+1}^{(2m+1)}(2-k) + B_{2m+1}^{(2m+1)}(1-k) \right\},$$

by use of 6·401 (3). Thus we have

(1) $$R_{2m-1} = -C_{2m-1,k} F^{(2m)}(\eta),$$

where $0 < \eta < 2m$; and using 6·11 (7),

(2) $$C_{2m-1,0} = \frac{2B_{2m+1}^{(2m+1)}}{(2m+1)!} + \frac{3B_{2m}^{(2m)}}{(2m)!} + \frac{B_{2m-1}^{(2m-1)}}{(2m-1)!},$$

(3) $$C_{2m-1,1} = \frac{2B_{2m+1}^{(2m+1)}}{(2m+1)!} + \frac{B_{2m}^{(2m)}}{(2m)!}.$$

7·14. The Remainder Term, n even. In 7·12 we now take $n = 2m$. Then

$$R_{2m} = \int_{1-k}^{2m+k} (y-1) \dots (y-2m)[y, 1, 2, \dots, 2m]\, dy = S_1 + S_2,$$

$$S_1 = \int_{1-k}^{2m+k-1} (y-1)(y-2) \dots (y-2m)[y, 1, \dots, 2m]\, dy,$$

$$S_2 = \int_{2m+k-1}^{2m+k} (y-1)(y-2) \dots (y-2m)[y, 1, \dots, 2m]\, dy.$$

By the definition of divided differences, we have

$$(y-2m)[y, 1, \dots, 2m] = [y, 1, \dots, 2m-1] - [1, 2, \dots, 2m].$$

S_1 can therefore be expressed as the sum of two integrals of which, by 6·401 (2), the second vanishes. Thus

$$S_1 = \int_{1-k}^{2m+k-1} (y-1) \dots (y-2m+1)[y, 1, 2, \dots, 2m-1] = R_{2m-1}$$

$$= -\frac{F^{(2m)}(\eta_1)}{(2m+1)!} \left\{ B_{2m+1}^{(2m+1)}(2-k) + B_{2m+1}^{(2m+1)}(1-k) \right\}.$$

Again by the mean value theorem,

$$S_2 = [\eta_2, 1, \dots, 2m] \int_{2m+k-1}^{2m+k} (y-1)(y-2)\dots(y-2m)\,dy$$

$$= \frac{F^{(2m)}(\eta_2)}{(2m+1)!} \left\{ B_{2m+1}^{(2m+1)}(2-k) - B_{2m+1}^{(2m+1)}(1-k) \right\},$$

since $B_{2m+1}^{(2m+1)}(2m+k) = -B_{2m+1}^{(2m+1)}(1-k)$ by the complementary argument theorem. Now, by 6·401 (8), the coefficients of the derivates in S_1 and S_2 have the same sign. Hence in the sum S_1+S_2 we can replace the derivates by a mean value and we obtain

$$R_{2m} = -\frac{2F^{(2m)}(\eta)}{(2m+1)!} B_{2m+1}^{(2m+1)}(1-k),$$

(1) $$R_{2m} = -C_{2m,k} F^{(2m)}(\eta),$$

where $0 < \eta < 2m+1$ and

(2) $$C_{2m,0} = \frac{2B_{2m+1}^{(2m+1)}}{(2m+1)!} + \frac{2B_{2m}^{(2m)}}{(2m)!},$$

(3) $$C_{2m,1} = \frac{2B_{2m+1}^{(2m+1)}}{(2m+1)!}.$$

7·2. Cotes' Formulae. If in 7·12 we put $k=0$, we have

$$\omega = \frac{b-a}{n-1},$$

and consequently

$$\int_a^b f(x)\,dx = (b-a) \sum_{\nu=1}^{n} H_\nu^{(n)} f[a+(\nu-1)\omega] + R_n,$$

where

(1) $$H_\nu^{(n)} = (-1)^{n-\nu} \frac{n}{n-1} \binom{n-1}{\nu-1} \int_1^n \frac{1}{t-\nu} \binom{t-1}{n}\,dt.$$

The remainder term is obtained from the formulae of the last two sections.

We have, with the previous notation,

$$F^{(\nu)}(y) = \omega^\nu f^{(\nu)}(x).$$

Thus
$$R_{2m-1} = -\omega^{2m+1} f^{(2m)}(\xi)\, C_{2m-1,\,0},$$
$$R_{2m} = -\omega^{2m+1} f^{(2m)}(\xi)\, C_{2m,\,0}.$$

If, for brevity, we put

(2)
$$y_\nu = f[a+(\nu-1)\omega],$$

we have Cotes' formulae, namely,

(3)
$$\int_a^b f(x)\,dx = (b-a)\sum_{\nu=1}^{2m-1} H_\nu^{(2m-1)} y_\nu - \left(\frac{b-a}{2m-2}\right)^{2m+1} f^{(2m)}(\xi)\, C_{2m-1,\,0},$$

(4)
$$\int_a^b f(x)\,dx = (b-a)\sum_{\nu=1}^{2m} H_\nu^{(2m)} y_\nu - \left(\frac{b-a}{2m-1}\right)^{2m+1} f^{(2m)}(\xi)\, C_{2m,\,0}.$$

Expressions for $C_{2m-1,\,0}$, $C_{2m,\,0}$ in terms of generalised Bernoulli's numbers are given in sections 7·13, 7·14. Numerical values can be obtained from the table of 6·43.

Cotes' formulae are of the closed type, the functional values for the end-points of the range being used in the formulae.

The coefficients $H_\nu^{(n)}$ have the property

$$H_\nu^{(n)} = H_{n-\nu+1}^{(n)},$$

which expresses that coefficients equidistant from the ends of the interval are equal. To prove this we have

$$H_{n-\nu+1}^{(n)} = (-1)^{\nu-1}\frac{n}{n-1}\binom{n-1}{n-\nu}\int_1^n \frac{1}{t-n+\nu-1}\binom{t-1}{n}dt.$$

Put $t = 1+n-z$, then

$$H_{n-\nu+1}^{(n)} = (-1)^{\nu-1}\frac{n}{n-1}\binom{n-1}{\nu-1}\int_n^1 \frac{1}{z-\nu}\binom{n-z}{n}dz$$

$$= (-1)^{n+\nu}\frac{n}{n-1}\binom{n-1}{\nu-1}\int_1^n \frac{1}{z-\nu}\binom{z-1}{n}dz = H_\nu^{(n)}.$$

That the coefficients are rational numbers is evident from the definition.

The values of the coefficients were calculated by Cotes for

$$n = 2, 3, \ldots, 11.$$

The values in the following table are taken from Pascal's *Repertorium.* The last column gives the remainder term with the coefficient abbreviated to two significant figures.

$n \backslash \nu$	1	2	3	4	Remainder
2	$\frac{1}{2}$	$\frac{1}{2}$			$-\frac{1}{12}(b-a)^3 f^{(2)}(\xi)$
3	$\frac{1}{6}$	$\frac{4}{6}$	$\frac{1}{6}$		$-3{\cdot}5(b-a)^5 f^{(4)}(\xi)\times 10^{-4}$
4	$\frac{1}{8}$	$\frac{3}{8}$	$\frac{3}{8}$	$\frac{1}{8}$	$-1{\cdot}6(b-a)^5 f^{(4)}(\xi)\times 10^{-4}$
5	$\frac{7}{90}$	$\frac{32}{90}$	$\frac{12}{90}$	$\frac{32}{90}$	$-5{\cdot}2(b-a)^7 f^{(6)}(\xi)\times 10^{-7}$
6	$\frac{19}{288}$	$\frac{75}{288}$	$\frac{50}{288}$	$\frac{50}{288}$	$-3{\cdot}0(b-a)^7 f^{(6)}(\xi)\times 10^{-7}$
7	$\frac{41}{840}$	$\frac{216}{840}$	$\frac{27}{840}$	$\frac{272}{840}$	$-6{\cdot}4(b-a)^9 f^{(8)}(\xi)\times 10^{-10}$
8	$\frac{751}{17280}$	$\frac{3577}{17280}$	$\frac{1323}{17280}$	$\frac{2989}{17280}$	$-4{\cdot}0(b-a)^9 f^{(8)}(\xi)\times 10^{-10}$

The remaining values for $n = 5, 6, 7, 8$ are obtained by using the relation $H_\nu^{(n)} = H_{n-\nu+1}^{(n)}$.

Comparison of the remainder terms shews that there is little to be gained by taking $2m$ ordinates instead of $2m-1$.

7·21. The Trapezoidal Rule. Cotes' formula for $n = 2$ gives

$$\int_a^b f(x)\,dx = \tfrac{1}{2}[f(a)+f(b)] - \frac{(b-a)^3}{12} f''(\xi).$$

To apply this rule to a given interval (a, b) we may suppose (a, b) divided into n equal parts, so that $b-a = nh$, say. To each point of division, including the end-points, there will correspond a value y of $f(x)$. If to each separate part we apply the rule we obtain with an obvious notation

$$\int_a^b y\,dx = \sum_{\nu=1}^{n}\left(\frac{h}{2}(y_\nu + y_{\nu+1}) - \frac{h^3}{12} f''(\xi_\nu)\right)$$

$$= h\left[\tfrac{1}{2} y_1 + y_2 + y_3 + \dots + y_n + \tfrac{1}{2} y_{n+1}\right] - \frac{nh^3}{12} f''(\xi)$$

$$= \frac{b-a}{n}\left[\tfrac{1}{2} y_1 + y_2 + \dots + y_n + \tfrac{1}{2} y_{n+1}\right] - \frac{b-a}{12} f''(\xi) \,.\, h^2,$$

which is the trapezoidal rule.

7·22. Simpson's Rule. This well-known and useful formula of mechanical quadrature is the special case $m = 3$ of Cotes' formula. We have then

$$\int_a^b f(x)\,dx = \frac{b-a}{6}\left[f(a) + 4f\left(\frac{a+b}{2}\right) + f(b)\right] - \frac{(b-a)^5}{2880} f^{(4)}(\xi).$$

The remainder term is zero and the formula exact when $f(x)$ is a polynomial of the third or lower degree. If we divide the interval (a, b) into $2n$ equal parts, so that $2nh = b - a$, we have, applying Simpson's rule to each successive pair,

$$\int_a^b y\,dx = \frac{b-a}{6n}\left[y_1 + 4y_2 + 2y_3 + 4y_4 + \dots + 2y_{2n-1} + 4y_{2n} + y_{2n+1}\right] + R(2n, h),$$

where

$$R(2n, h) = -\frac{n(2h)^5}{2880} f^{(4)}(\xi).$$

7·23. Formulae of G. F. Hardy and Weddle. Cotes' formula for $n = 7$ gives

(1) $$\int_a^b f(x)\,dx = \frac{b-a}{840}\{41y_1 + 216y_2 + 27y_3 + 272y_4 + 27y_5 + 216y_6 + 41y_7\} - 6{\cdot}4\,(b-a)^9 f^{(8)}(\xi) \times 10^{-10}.$$

Now we have the central difference

(2) $$\delta^6 y_4 = y_1 - 6y_2 + 15y_3 - 20y_4 + 15y_5 - 6y_6 + y_7.$$

Between (1) and (2) we can eliminate any pair of functional values which are equidistant from the central value y_4. If, from (1), we subtract

$$\frac{27}{15}\,\frac{(b-a)}{840}\,\delta^6 y_4$$

and thus eliminate y_3, y_5, we obtain G. F. Hardy's formula, namely,

$$(3) \quad \int_a^b f(x)\,dx = \tfrac{1}{3}(b-a)\{0{\cdot}14(y_1+y_7)+0{\cdot}81(y_2+y_6)+1{\cdot}10y_4\}$$
$$+4{\cdot}6(b-a)^7 f^{(6)}(\xi_1)\times 10^{-8} - 6{\cdot}4(b-a)^9 f^{(8)}(\xi)\times 10^{-10},$$

since, from 3·0,

$$\delta^6 y_4 = \left(\frac{b-a}{6}\right)^6 f^{(6)}(\xi_1).$$

The coefficients of the remainder term are given to two significant figures.

If, instead of eliminating one of the values, we add

$$(b-a)\,\delta^6 y_4 / 840$$

to (1) we obtain Weddle's Formula, namely,

$$\int_a^b f(x)\,dx = \tfrac{1}{20}(b-a)\{(y_1+y_7)+5(y_2+y_6)+(y_3+y_5)+6y_4\}$$
$$-2{\cdot}6(b-a)^7 f^{(6)}(\xi_1)\times 10^{-8} - 6{\cdot}4(b-a)^9 f^{(8)}(\xi)\times 10^{-10}.$$

The merit of this formula is the simplicity of the coefficients, the disadvantage is the complicated form of the remainder term.

The principle here exemplified could be used to obtain an endless variety of quadrature formulae.

7·3. Quadrature Formulae of the Open Type. If in 7·12 we put $k = 1$, we have

$$\omega = \frac{b-a}{n+1},$$

and consequently

$$\int_a^b f(x)\,dx = (b-a)\sum_{\nu=1}^{n} K_\nu^{(n)} f(a+\nu\omega) + R_n,$$

where

$$K_\nu^{(n)} = (-1)^{n-\nu}\frac{n}{n+1}\binom{n-1}{\nu-1}\int_0^{n+1}\frac{1}{t-\nu}\binom{t-1}{n}dt.$$

This leads to the two sets of formulae,

$$\int_a^b f(x)\,dx = (b-a)\sum_{\nu=1}^{2m-1} K_\nu^{(2m-1)} y_\nu - \left(\frac{b-a}{2m}\right)^{2m+1} f^{(2m)}(\xi)\,C_{2m-1,\,1},$$

$$\int_a^b f(x)\,dx = (b-a)\sum_{\nu=1}^{2m} K_\nu^{(2m)} y_\nu - \left(\frac{b-a}{2m+1}\right)^{2m+1} f^{(2m)}(\xi)\,C_{2m,\,1}.$$

The expressions for $C_{2m-1,1}$, $C_{2m,1}$ are given in sections 7·13, 7·14. In the formulae the functional values $f(a)$, $f(b)$ correspond to $\nu = 0$, $\nu = n+1$, and these values are not used in the formulae. The coefficients satisfy the relation

$$K_\nu^{(n)} = K_{n-\nu+1}^{(n)},$$

which can be proved in the same way as for Cotes' coefficients.

The following table gives the coefficients and remainder terms of some of these formulae:

n \ ν	1	2	3	Remainder
2	$\frac{1}{2}$	$\frac{1}{2}$		$2{\cdot}8(b-a)^3 f^{(2)}(\xi)\times 10^{-2}$
3	$\frac{2}{3}$	$-\frac{1}{3}$	$\frac{2}{3}$	$3{\cdot}1(b-a)^5 f^{(4)}(\xi)\times 10^{-4}$
4	$\frac{11}{24}$	$\frac{1}{24}$	$\frac{1}{24}$	$2{\cdot}2(b-a)^5 f^{(4)}(\xi)\times 10^{-4}$
5	$\frac{11}{20}$	$-\frac{14}{20}$	$\frac{26}{20}$	$1{\cdot}1(b-a)^7 f^{(6)}(\xi)\times 10^{-6}$
6	$\frac{611}{1440}$	$-\frac{453}{1440}$	$\frac{562}{1440}$	$7{\cdot}4(b-a)^7 f^{(6)}(\xi)\times 10^{-7}$

7·31. The Method of Gauss. From 7·11, we have

$$(1)\quad \int_a^b f(x)\,dx = \sum_{s=1}^{n} f(x_s)\int_a^b \frac{\phi(x)}{\phi'(x_s)}\,\frac{dx}{x-x_s} + \int_a^b \phi(x)\,[xx_1x_2\dots x_n]\,dx,$$

where
$$\phi(x) = (x-x_1)(x-x_2)\dots(x-x_n).$$

If in the above formula we neglect the remainder term, the approximation obtained is equivalent to the approximation obtained by replacing $f(x)$ by an interpolation polynomial of degree $n-1$, which coincides with $f(x)$ at the points $x_1, x_2, \dots, x_n$. Gauss has shewn that by a proper choice of the interpolation points

$$x_1, x_2, \dots, x_n$$

we can obtain an approximation to the given integral equivalent to the approximation obtained by replacing $f(x)$ by a polynomial of degree $2n-1$. This means that if the n interpolation points be properly chosen, the remainder in (1) will vanish when $f(x)$ is a polynomial of degree $2n-1$ at most.

Let $P(x)$ denote the polynomial of degree $2n-1$ which coincides with $f(x)$ at the points $x_1, x_2, \ldots, x_{n+1}, x_{n+2}, \ldots, x_{2n}$, and let

$$Q(x) = \sum_{s=1}^{n} \frac{f(x_s)}{x-x_s} \frac{\phi(x)}{\phi'(x_s)}.$$

$Q(x)$ is thus a polynomial of degree $n-1$ which coincides with $f(x)$ at $x_1, x_2, \ldots, x_n$.

Let c be a constant. Then $P(x)-Q(x)$ and $c\,\phi(x)$ both vanish when $x = x_1, x_2, \ldots, x_n$, and therefore we have

(2) $$P(x) - Q(x) = c\,\phi(x)\,N(x),$$

where $N(x)$ is a polynomial of degree $n-1$. Then, as in 7·11, we have

$$\int_a^b f(x)\,dx = \int_a^b P(x)\,dx + R,$$

where

(3) $$R = \int_a^b (x-x_1)(x-x_2)\ldots(x-x_{2n})\,[xx_1x_2\ldots x_{2n}]\,dx.$$

Using (2) we therefore have

(4) $$\int_a^b f(x)\,dx = \int_a^b Q(x)\,dx + \int_a^b c\,\phi(x)\,N(x)\,dx + R.$$

We now prove that by proper choice of $x_1, x_2, \ldots, x_n$ the second integral on the right will vanish.

Let the polynomial resulting from k successive indefinite integrations of $\phi(x)$ be denoted by $\phi_k(x)$.

Then, by repeated integration by parts, we have

$$\int_a^b c\,\phi(x)\,N(x)\,dx$$
$$= c\Big[\phi_1(x)\,N(x) - \phi_2(x)\,N'(x) + \ldots + (-1)^{n-1}\phi_n(x)\,N^{(n-1)}(x)\Big]_a^b,$$

since $N^{(n)}(x) = 0$. The integrated expression will vanish if we take for $c\,\phi(x)$ a polynomial such that

$$\phi_k(a) = 0, \quad \phi_k(b) = 0, \quad k = 1, 2, 3, \ldots, n.$$

This result is therefore attained if we take

$$c\,\phi(x) = \frac{d^n}{dx^n}[(x-a)^n(x-b)^n].$$

Since $\phi(x) = (x-x_1)(x-x_2)\dots(x-x_n)$, we have

(5) $$(x-x_1)(x-x_2)\dots(x-x_n) = \frac{n!}{(2n)!}\frac{d^n}{dx^n}[(x-a)^n(x-b)^n],$$

so that the required interpolation points are determined as the roots of the equation

(6) $$\frac{d^n}{dx^n}[(x-a)^n(x-b)^n] = 0.$$

That the roots are all real and lie between a and b is seen at once by successive applications of Rolle's Theorem beginning with $(x-a)^n(x-b)^n$, which has n zeros at a and n at b.

The divided difference in the remainder term (3) is zero if $f(x)$ be a polynomial of degree $2n-1$ at most, and we have therefore proved Gauss' result. It should be noted that when $x_1, x_2, \dots, x_n$ have been determined by (5) the remaining interpolation points $x_{n+1}, \dots, x_{2n}$ remain arbitrary. If we take $x_{n+s} = x_s$, $s = 1, 2, \dots, n$, the remainder term becomes

$$R = \int_a^b (x-x_1)^2(x-x_2)^2\dots(x-x_n)^2\,[xx_1x_1\,x_2x_2\dots x_nx_n]\,dx$$

$$= \frac{f^{2n}(\xi)}{(2n)!}\int_a^b (x-x_1)^2(x-x_2)^2\dots(x-x_n)^2\,dx$$

by use of the mean value theorem.

Since $(x-x_1)^2(x-x_2)^2\dots(x-x_n)^2 = (\phi(x))^2$, the integral in the remainder term after n integrations by parts becomes

$$(-1)^n\int_a^b \phi_n(x)\,\phi^{(n)}\,dx = \frac{(-1)^n\,n!\,n!}{(2n)!}\int_a^b (x-a)^n(x-b)^n\,dx.$$

Integrating by parts n more times this becomes

$$\frac{(-1)^{2n}(n!)^3}{(2n!)}\int_a^b \frac{(x-a)^{2n}}{(n+1)(n+2)\dots 2n}\,dx = \frac{(n!)^4(b-a)^{2n+1}}{[(2n)!]^2(2n+1)}.$$

Thus finally we have the formula of Gauss, namely,

$$\int_a^b f(x)\,dx = \sum_{s=1}^{n} g_s^{(n)} f(x_s) + \frac{(n!)^4(b-a)^{2n+1}}{[(2n)!]^3(2n+1)}\,f^{(2n)}(\xi),$$

where ξ lies in the interval (a, b) and $x_1, x_2, \dots, x_n$ are the zeros of (6), while, by 7·11 (4),

$$g_s^{(n)} = \int_a^b \frac{\phi(x)}{\phi'(x_s)} \frac{dx}{x - x_s}.$$

The advantage of this formula lies in the fact that by the use of n points only we are attaining the accuracy which would ordinarily result from the use of $2n$ points. The disadvantages lie in the fact that the interpolation points in general correspond to irrational numbers and their use leads to excessive labour in numerical calculation.

If we make the change of variable

$$x = \tfrac{1}{2}(b-a)\,t + \tfrac{1}{2}(b+a),$$

the new interpolation points $t_1, t_2, \dots, t_n$ are given by

$$(t-t_1)(t-t_2)\dots(t-t_n) = \frac{n!}{(2n)!}\frac{d^n}{dt^n}(t^2-1)^n$$

$$= \frac{n!}{1.3.5\dots(2n-1)} P_n(t),$$

where $P_n(t)$ is Legendre's polynomial * of degree n, and we have

$$g_s^{(n)} = \tfrac{1}{2}(b-a)\int_{-1}^{+1} \frac{P_n(t)}{P'_n(t_s)}\frac{dt}{t-t_s} = (b-a)\,G_s^{(n)},$$

where the coefficients $G_s^{(n)}$ are independent of the particular interval (a, b).

The zeros of $P_n(t)$ can be arranged in the order $t_1, t_2, \dots, t_n$ in such a way that

$$t_s + t_{n-s+1} = 0,$$

and if n be odd the middle member of the sequence is zero. With the aid of this property it is easy to prove that

$$G_s^{(n)} = G_{n-s+1}^{(n)}.$$

The following list gives the first six Legendre polynomials:

$P_0(x) = 1, \quad P_1(x) = x, \quad P_2(x) = \tfrac{1}{2}(3x^2-1), \quad P_3(x) = \tfrac{1}{2}x(5x^2-3),$
$P_4(x) = \tfrac{1}{8}(35x^4 - 30x^2 + 3), \qquad P_5(x) = \tfrac{1}{8}x(63x^4 - 70x^2 + 15).$

---

* E. W. Hobson, *Theory of Spherical and Ellipsoidal Harmonics*, (1931), p. 18. See also pp. 76-81, for a discussion of Gauss' formula and for numerical data.

With the aid of these expressions the zeros and the coefficients $G_s^{(n)}$ can be calculated. For the numerical values of the zeros and coefficients to 16 decimal places for $n = 1, 2, \dots, 7$, the reader is referred to Hobson (*loc. cit.*).

7·33. The Method of Tschebyscheff.* Let $F(x)$ be a given function, and $\phi(x)$ an arbitrary function which is assumed to have differential coefficients up to and including the $(n+1)$th. We seek to determine points $x_1, x_2, \dots, x_n$ such that

$$(1) \qquad \int_{-1}^{+1} F(x)\,\phi(x)\,dx = k[\phi(x_1)+\phi(x_2)+\dots+\phi(x_n)]+R_n,$$

where k and the points $x_1, x_2, \dots, x_n$ are independent of the particular function $\phi(x)$ and where the remainder term R_n depends upon $\phi^{(n+1)}(x)$ only.

We have, by Maclaurin's Theorem,

$$\phi(x) = \phi(0)+x\,\phi'(0)+\frac{x^2}{2!}\phi''(0)+\dots+\frac{x^n}{n!}\phi^{(n)}(0)+\frac{x^{n+1}}{(n+1)!}\phi^{(n+1)}(\xi),$$

where $0 \leqslant \xi \leqslant x$. Consider

$$R_n = \int_{-1}^{+1} F(x)\,\phi(x)\,dx - k[\phi(x_1)+\dots+\phi(x_n)].$$

If we put

$$T_s = \int_{-1}^{+1} \frac{x^s}{s!}F(x)\,dx,$$

we have

$$\begin{aligned} R_n = {} & T_0\,\phi(0)+T_1\,\phi'(0)+\dots+T_n\,\phi^{(n)}(0) \\ & + \int_{-1}^{+1}\frac{x^{n+1}}{(n+1)!}F(x)\,\phi^{(n+1)}(\xi)\,dx - nk\,\phi(0) \\ & - k\,\phi'(0)[x_1+x_2+\dots+x_n] - \frac{k\,\phi''(0)}{2!}[x_1^{\,2}+x_2^{\,2}+\dots+x_n^{\,2}] - \dots \\ & - \frac{k\,\phi^{(n)}(0)}{n!}[x_1^n+x_2^n+\dots+x_n^n] \\ & - \frac{k}{(n+1)!}[x_1^{n+1}\,\phi^{(n+1)}(\xi_1)+\dots+x_n^{n+1}\,\phi^{(n+1)}(\xi_n)], \end{aligned}$$

where ξ_s is a number in the interval $(0, x_s)$, $s = 1, 2, \dots, n$.

---

* P. Tschebyscheff, *Journal de Math.* (2), 19 (1874).

The terms containing $\phi(0), \phi'(0), \ldots, \phi^{(n)}(0)$ will therefore disappear if we take

$$(2) \qquad nk = \int_{-1}^{+1} F(x)\,dx,$$

$$k[x_1+x_2+\ldots+x_n] = \int_{-1}^{+1} x\,F(x)\,dx,$$

$$\cdot \quad \cdot \quad \cdot \quad \cdot \quad \cdot \quad \cdot \quad \cdot \quad \cdot \quad \cdot$$

$$k[x_1^n+x_2^n+\ldots+x_n^n] = \int_{-1}^{+1} x^n\,F(x)\,dx.$$

The $n+1$ numbers $k, x_1, x_2, \ldots, x_n$ having been determined in this way, (1) constitutes Tschebyscheff's formula, the remainder term being

$$(3)\ R_n = \int_{-1}^{+1} \frac{x^{n+1}}{(n+1)!} F(x)\,\phi^{(n+1)}(\xi)\,dx - \frac{k}{(n+1)!}\sum_{s=1}^{n} x_s^{\,n+1}\,\phi^{(n+1)}(\xi_s),$$

which vanishes when $\phi(x)$ is a polynomial of degree n at most. In this case Tschebyscheff's formula is exact, that is to say, there is no remainder term.

To determine $x_1, x_2, \ldots, x_n$, we proceed as follows:

Put $f(z) = (z-x_1)(z-x_2)\ldots(z-x_n)$, so that $x_1, x_2, \ldots, x_n$ are the roots of the equation

$$(4) \qquad f(z) = 0.$$

Taking $\phi(x) = (z-x)^{-1}$, we have

$$\phi^{(n+1)}(x) = (n+1)!\,(z-x)^{-n-2}$$

so that

$$(5) \qquad R_n = \frac{c_1}{z^{n+2}} + \frac{c_2}{z^{n+3}} + \ldots,$$

where $c_1, c_2, \ldots$ are independent of z.

Also, by taking the logarithmic derivate of $f(z)$, we have

$$\frac{1}{z-x_1} + \frac{1}{z-x_2} + \ldots + \frac{1}{z-x_n} = \frac{f'(z)}{f(z)},$$

and thus from (1) and (5), we have

$$\int_{-1}^{+1} \frac{F(x)}{z-x}\,dx = k\frac{f'(z)}{f(z)} + \frac{c_1}{z^{n+2}} + \frac{c_2}{z^{n+3}} + \ldots.$$

Integrating with respect to z, this gives

$$\int_{-1}^{+1} F(x)\log(z-x)\,dx = k\log\frac{f(z)}{C} - \frac{c_1}{(n+1)\,z^{n+1}} - \frac{c_2}{(n+2)\,z^{n+2}} - \dots,$$

where C is a constant. Taking the exponential of both sides, we have

$$f(z)\exp\left[-\frac{c_1}{(n+1)\,k\,z^{n+1}} - \frac{c_2}{(n+2)\,k\,z^{n+2}} - \dots\right]$$
$$= C\exp\left[\frac{1}{k}\int_{-1}^{+1} F(x)\log(z-x)\,dx\right].$$

Since the expansion of $\exp\left[-\frac{c_1}{(n+1)\,k\,z^{n+1}} - \frac{c_2}{(n+2)\,k\,z^{n+2}} - \dots\right]$ differs from unity by powers of z lower than z^{-n}, and since $f(z)$ is, by definition, of degree n, it follows that the polynomial part of the first member is equal to $f(z)$, and therefore

(6) $$f(z) = P\left\{C\exp\left[\frac{1}{k}\int_{-1}^{+1} F(x)\log(z-x)\,dx\right]\right\},$$

where P denotes the polynomial part of the expression in curled brackets when expanded in descending powers of z.

Since the coefficient of z^n in $f(z)$ is unity, the constant C is determined so that the coefficient of z^n in the right-hand member of (6) shall be unity.

By giving particular values to $F(x)$ we can obtain a variety of quadrature formulae. The most important case is $F(x) = 1$, which gives, from (2), $k = \frac{2}{n}$. Also, integrating by parts,

$$\int_{-1}^{+1} \log(z-x)\,dx = (z+1)\log(z+1) - (z-1)\log(z-1) - 2$$
$$= 2\log z + (z+1)\log\left(1+\frac{1}{z}\right) + (1-z)\log\left(1-\frac{1}{z}\right) - 2$$
$$= 2\log z - \frac{2}{2\,.\,3z^2} - \frac{2}{4\,.\,5z^4} - \frac{2}{6\,.\,7z^6} - \dots,$$

using the logarithmic series. Thus, from (6),

$$f(z) = P\left\{C\exp\left[n\log z - \frac{n}{2\,.\,3z^2} - \frac{n}{4\,.\,5z^4} - \dots\right]\right\}$$
$$= P\left\{z^n\exp\left[-\frac{n}{2\,.\,3z^2} - \frac{n}{4\,.\,5z^4} - \frac{n}{6\,.\,7z^6} - \dots\right]\right\},$$

where we have taken $C = 1$ in order to make the coefficient of z^n unity.

Taking $n = 2, 3, 4, 5$, we obtain the polynomials

$$z^2 - \tfrac{1}{3},\ z(z^2 - \tfrac{1}{2}),\ z^4 - \tfrac{2}{3}z^2 + \tfrac{1}{45},\ z(z^4 - \tfrac{5}{6}z^2 + \tfrac{7}{72}).$$

The polynomials are evidently even and odd alternately.

Solving the corresponding equations, we obtain the positions of the ordinates as follows :

$$\begin{aligned}
n = 2, &\quad -x_1 = x_2 = 0{\cdot}57735027,\\
n = 3, &\quad -x_1 = x_3 = 0{\cdot}70710678, \quad x_2 = 0.\\
n = 4, &\quad -x_1 = x_4 = 0{\cdot}79465447,\\
&\quad -x_2 = x_3 = 0{\cdot}18759247.\\
n = 5, &\quad -x_1 = x_5 = 0{\cdot}83249749,\\
&\quad -x_2 = x_4 = 0{\cdot}37454141, \quad x_3 = 0.
\end{aligned}$$

Tschebyscheff's formulae, like those of Gauss, have the disadvantage that the positions of the ordinates correspond to irrational numbers. They have the practical advantage of simplicity. Moreover, when the ordinates are obtained from observation or measurement and are therefore subject to error, the method has the advantage that all the errors are equally weighted.

7·4. Quadrature Formulae Involving Differences. From the interpolation formula with divided differences, we have

$$(1)\quad f(x) = f(x_1) + \sum_{s=1}^{n-1} (x - x_1)(x - x_2) \ldots (x - x_s)\,[x_1 x_2 \ldots x_{s+1}]$$
$$+ (x - x_1)(x - x_2) \ldots (x - x_n)\,[x x_1 x_2 \ldots x_n].$$

Let a and $a + \omega$ be numbers such that in the interval

$$a < x < a + \omega$$

the product $(x - x_1)(x - x_2) \ldots (x - x_n)$ has no zeros. In this interval the product has a constant sign, and hence by the mean value theorem

$$\int_a^{a+\omega} (x - x_1) \ldots (x - x_n)\,[x x_1 \ldots x_n]\,dx$$
$$= \frac{f^{(n)}(\xi_1)}{n!} \int_a^{a+\omega} (x - x_1) \ldots (x - x_n)\,dx,$$

where ξ_1 lies in the interval bounded by the greatest and least of $a, a+\omega, x_1, x_2, \ldots, x_n$. Thus we have, from (1),

$$(2)\quad \frac{1}{\omega}\int_a^{a+\omega} f(x)\,dx = f(x_1)+A_1[x_1x_2]+A_2[x_1x_2x_3] + \ldots + A_{n-1}[x_1x_2\ldots x_n]+A_n f^n(\xi_1)/n!,$$

where

$$(3)\qquad A_s = \frac{1}{\omega}\int_a^{a+\omega}(x-x_1)(x-x_2)\ldots(x-x_s)\,dx.$$

From this result a variety * of quadrature formulae can be deduced by assigning suitable values to $x_1, x_2, \ldots, x_n$.

7·41. Laplace's Formula.

In (2) of the last section put

$$x_1 = a, \quad x_s = a+(s-1)\,\omega.$$

Then

$$A_s = \frac{1}{\omega}\int_a^{a+\omega}(x-a)(x-a-\omega)\ldots(x-a-s\omega+\omega)\,dx$$

$$= \omega^s\int_0^1 t(t-1)\ldots(t-s+1)\,dt.$$

Thus, by 6·4 (4), we have

$$A_s = \omega^s B_s^{(s)}(1).$$

Also by 3·0,

$$[x_1x_2\ldots x_{s+1}] = \omega^{-s}\Delta^s f(a)/s!.$$

Thus, since $B_1^{(1)}(1) = \frac{1}{2}$, we have

$$(1)\quad \frac{1}{\omega}\int_a^{a+\omega} f(x)\,dx = \tfrac{1}{2}\{f(a)+f(a+\omega)\}+\frac{1}{2!}B_2^{(2)}(1)\,\Delta^2 f(a)+\ldots + \frac{1}{(n-1)!}B_{n-1}^{(n-1)}(1)\,\Delta^{n-1}f(a)+\frac{1}{n!}\,\omega^n B_n^{(n)}(1)\,f^{(n)}(\xi_1).$$

Now

$$\sum_{\nu=0}^{r-1}\Delta^s f(a+\nu\omega) = \Delta^{s-1}f(a+r\omega)-\Delta^{s-1}f(a),$$

$$\sum_{\nu=1}^{r} f^{(n)}(\xi_\nu) = r f^{(n)}(\xi).$$

---

* H. P. Nielsen, *Arkiv. för Mat. Ast. och Fys.* 4 (1908), No. 21.

Hence, if in (1) we replace a in succession by

$$a+\omega,\ a+2\omega,\ \ldots,\ a+(r-1)\,\omega$$

and then add the results, we obtain Laplace's formula, namely,

$$(2)\quad \frac{1}{\omega}\int_a^{a+r\omega} f(x)\,dx$$

$$= [\tfrac{1}{2} f(a)+f(a+\omega)+f(a+2\omega)+\ldots+f(a+(r-1)\,\omega)+\tfrac{1}{2} f(a+r\omega)]$$

$$+\sum_{s=2}^{n-1}\frac{1}{s!}B_s^{(s)}(1)\ \{\Delta^{s-1} f(a+r\omega)-\Delta^{s-1} f(a)\}+\frac{r\omega^n}{n!}B_n^{(n)}(1)\ f^{(n)}(\xi).$$

This formula gives the definite integral of a given function in terms of differences. Alternatively, the formula gives the sum

$$f(a)+f(a+\omega)+\ldots+f(a+r\omega)$$

if the integral can be evaluated. The differences employed are the forward differences of $f(a), f(a+r\omega)$.

To calculate these we require the functional values $f(a+\nu\omega)$ from $\nu=0$ to $\nu=n+r-2$, and therefore ξ lies in the interval $(a,\ a+(n+r-2)\,\omega)$.

To find the coefficients we have, from 6·43,

$$\sum_{\nu=0}^{\infty}\frac{B_\nu^{(\nu)}(1)}{\nu!}\,t^\nu=\frac{t}{\log(1+t)}.$$

Thus we have

ν	2	3	4	5	6	7
$B_\nu^{(\nu)}(1)/\nu!$	$-\frac{1}{12}$	$\frac{1}{24}$	$-\frac{19}{720}$	$\frac{3}{160}$	$-\frac{863}{60480}$	$\frac{275}{24192}$

That the signs alternate follows from 6·4 (4).

A corresponding formula for backward differences is easily obtained by taking $x_s = a-(s-1)\,\omega$. We then obtain

$$A_s=\frac{1}{\omega}\int_a^{a+\omega}(x-a)\ldots(x-a+(s-1)\,\omega)\,dx$$

$$=\omega^s\int_0^1(t+s-1)\ldots t\,dt=\omega^s B_s^{(s)}(s).$$

By the complementary argument theorem, $B_s^{(s)}(s)=(-1)^s B_s^{(s)}$.

Thus 7·4 (2) gives

$$\frac{1}{\omega}\int_a^{a+\omega} f(x)\,dx = f(a) - B_1^{(1)}\,\Delta f(a-\omega) + \frac{1}{2!}B_2^{(2)}\,\Delta^2 f(a-2\omega) - \dots$$

$$+(-1)^{n-1}\frac{1}{(n-1)!}B_{n-1}^{(n-1)}\,\Delta^{n-1}f(a-(n-1)\omega) + \frac{(-1)^n}{n!}\,\omega^n B_n^{(n)} f^{(n)}(\xi),$$

which is an integration formula with ascending differences.

In particular, for $n = 4$, we have

$$(3)\quad \frac{1}{\omega}\int_a^{a+\omega} f(x)\,dx = f(a) + \tfrac{1}{2}\,\Delta f(a-\omega) + \tfrac{5}{12}\,\Delta^2 f(a-2\omega)$$

$$+\tfrac{3}{8}\,\Delta^3 f(a-3\omega) + \tfrac{251}{720}\,\omega^4 f^{(4)}(\xi).$$

Formulae of this type can of course be obtained by direct integration of the appropriate interpolation formula.

7·42. Formula of Laplace Applied to Differential Equations.

Laplace's formula with ascending differences is the basis of the Adams-Bashforth method of integrating numerically a given system of ordinary differential equations. Such a system can always be reduced to the first order by introduction of new variables. Consider the single equation

$$y' = \frac{dy}{dx} = F(x, y).$$

From this equation by successive differentiation we can obtain y'', y''', ..., in terms of x, y. Let it be required to find the solution with the initial conditions $y = y_0$, $x = x_0$.

We first calculate y_0', y_0'', y_0''', ..., and then, by Taylor's Theorem,

$$y = y_0 + (x-x_0)\,y_0' + \frac{1}{2!}(x-x_0)^2 y_0'' + \dots .$$

Taking an interval ω for x, we calculate from this series y_1, y_2, y_3 corresponding to $x_0+\omega$, $x_0+2\omega$, $x_0+3\omega$, and from the given differential equation the corresponding derivates

$$y_1' = F(x_1, y_1),\quad y_2' = F(x_2, y_2),\quad y_3' = F(x_3, y_3),$$

where

$$x_1 = x_0+\omega,\quad x_2 = x_0+2\omega,\quad x_3 = x_0+3\omega.$$

We can now form the table :

x_0	y_0/ω	y_0'			
			$\Delta y_0'$		
$x_0+\omega$	y_1/ω	y_1'		$\Delta^2 y_0'$	
			$\Delta y_1'$		$\Delta^3 y_0'$
$x_0+2\omega$	y_2/ω	y_2'		$\Delta^2 y_1'$	
			$\Delta y_2'$		
$x_0+3\omega$	y_3/ω	y_3'			
$x_0+4\omega$					

If we can find y_4/ω, the table can be extended another line. Now by (3) of the last section, if we put $f(x) = y'$, $a = x_0+3\omega$, we have

$$\frac{1}{\omega}y_4 - \frac{1}{\omega}y_3 = y_3' + \tfrac{1}{2}\Delta y_2' + \tfrac{5}{12}\Delta^2 y_1' + \tfrac{3}{8}\Delta^3 y_0' + \tfrac{251}{720}\omega^4\,\eta^{(iv)},$$

where $\eta^{(iv)}$ is a value of d^4y/dx^4. If ω be sufficiently small to allow the error term to be neglected, we have the value of y_4/ω, and hence we can find $y_4' = F(x_4, y_4) = F(x_0+4\omega, y_4)$. We can then write in a new line of differences and proceed to the value of y_5/ω by the same method. This is the Adams-Bashforth process. The extension to systems of equations leads to greater complexity in the calculations, but the principle is the same. For an account of the present state of this subject the reader is referred to a lecture by H. Levy * on the numerical study of differential equations.

7·43. Central Difference Formulae In 7·4, take

$$n = 2m, \quad x_{2s} = a+s\omega, \quad x_{2s+1} = a-s\omega.$$

Then, writing $x = a+t\omega$,

$$A_{2s} = \omega^{2s}\int_0^1 (t+s-1)(t+s-2)\dots(t-s)\,dt = \omega^{2s} B_{2s}^{(2s)}(s),$$

$$A_{2s+1} = \omega^{2s+1}\int_0^1 (t+s)\dots(t-s)\,dt = \omega^{2s+1} B_{2s+1}^{(2s+1)}(s+1).$$

* H. Levy, *Journal London Math. Soc.* 7 (1932), p. 305.

From 6·3 (1), putting $x = s$, $n+1 = \nu = 2s+1$, we have

$$B_{2s+1}^{(2s+1)}(s+1) = \tfrac{1}{2}(2s+1)\, B_{2s}^{(2s)}(s).$$

Also

$$[x_1 x_2 \ldots x_{2s}] = \frac{\omega^{-2s+1}}{(2s-1)!}\, \Delta^{2s-1} f(a-(s-1)\,\omega),$$

$$[x_1 x_2 \ldots x_{2s+1}] = \frac{\omega^{-2s}}{(2s)!}\, \Delta^{2s} f(a-s\omega).$$

Thus

$$\frac{1}{\omega}\int_a^{a+\omega} f(x)\,dx = \sum_{s=0}^{m-1} \frac{B_{2s}^{(2s)}(s)}{(2s)!}\left\{\Delta^{2s} f(a-s\omega)+\tfrac{1}{2}\,\Delta^{2s+1} f(a-s\omega)\right\}$$

$$+\frac{1}{(2m)!}\,\omega^{2m}\, B_{2m}^{(2m)}(m)\, f^{(2m)}(\xi_1).$$

Now

$$\Delta^{2s} f(a-s\omega)+\tfrac{1}{2}\,\Delta^{2s+1} f(a-s\omega)$$

$$= \tfrac{1}{2}\,\Delta^{2s} f(a-s\omega)+\tfrac{1}{2}\,\Delta^{2s} f(a-(s-1)\,\omega)$$

$$= \tfrac{1}{2}\,\Delta^{2s-1} f(a-(s-2)\,\omega)-\tfrac{1}{2}\,\Delta^{2s-1} f(a-s\omega)$$

$$= \mu\delta^{2s-1} f(a+\omega)-\mu\delta^{2s-1} f(a),$$

in the notation of central differences.

Thus we have

$$\frac{1}{\omega}\int_a^{a+\omega} f(x)\,dx = \tfrac{1}{2}\left\{f(a)+f(a+\omega)\right\}$$

$$+\sum_{s=1}^{m-1} \frac{B_{2s}^{(2s)}(s)}{(2s)!}\left\{\mu\delta^{2s-1} f(a+\omega)-\mu\delta^{2s-1} f(a)\right\}$$

$$+\frac{\omega^{2m}}{(2m)!}\, B_{2m}^{(2m)}(m)\, f^{(2m)}(\xi_1).$$

If we write in turn for a the values $a+\omega$, $a+2\omega$, ... , $a+(r-1)\,\omega$ and then add the results, we get the central difference formula

$$\frac{1}{\omega}\int_a^{a+r\omega} f(x)\,dx = \{\tfrac{1}{2} f(a)+f(a+\omega)+\ldots+f(a+(r-1)\,\omega)+\tfrac{1}{2} f(a+r\omega)\}$$

$$+\sum_{s=1}^{m-1} \frac{B_{2s}^{(2s)}(s)}{(2s)!}\left\{\mu\delta^{2s-1} f(a+r\omega)-\mu\delta^{2s-1} f(a)\right\}$$

$$+\frac{r\,\omega^{2m}}{(2m)!}\, B_{2m}^{(2m)}(m)\, f^{(2m)}(\xi).$$

The differences actually used with this formula are shewn schematically as follows :

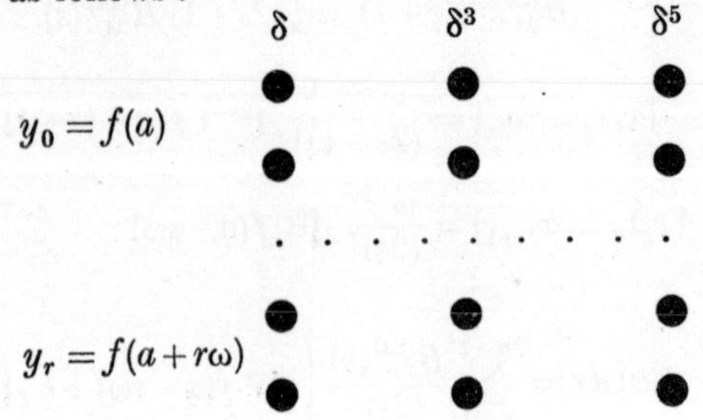

Thus, for $m = 3$, we have

$$\frac{r}{b-a}\int_a^b f(x)\,dx = [\tfrac{1}{2}y_0 + y_1 + y_2 + \dots + y_{r-1} + \tfrac{1}{2}y_r]$$
$$-\frac{1}{12}\{\tfrac{1}{2}(\delta y_{r-\frac{1}{2}} + \delta y_{r+\frac{1}{2}}) - \tfrac{1}{2}(\delta y_{-\frac{1}{2}} + \delta y_{\frac{1}{2}})\}$$
$$+\frac{11}{720}\{\tfrac{1}{2}(\delta^3 y_{r-\frac{1}{2}} + \delta^3 y_{r+\frac{1}{2}}) - \tfrac{1}{2}(\delta^3 y_{-\frac{1}{2}} + \delta^3 y_{\frac{1}{2}})\}$$
$$-\frac{191}{60480}\,r\left(\frac{b-a}{r}\right)^6 f^{(6)}(\xi).$$

Example. Calculate $\int_{\cdot 160}^{\cdot 164} \sin x\,dx$,

using the table

x	$\sin x$	Δ	Δ^2	Δ^3
		9873068		−10
0·160	0·15931 82066		−1593	
		9871475		−11
·161	·16030 53541		−1604	
		9869871		−8
·162	·16129 23412		−1612	
		9868259		−11
·163	·16227 91671		−1623	
		9866636		−10
·164	·16326 58307		−1633	
		9865003		−9

Thus, since $r = 4$, $b - a = 0{\cdot}004$, we have

$$1000 \int_{\cdot 160}^{\cdot 164} \sin x\, dx = 0{\cdot}64516888105 + 0{\cdot}00000005377$$
$$+ \cdot 0032 \times 4 \times (\cdot 001)^6 \times \cdot 16.$$

The remainder term affects only the 21st decimal place on the right. We therefore obtain

$$\int_{\cdot 160}^{\cdot 164} \sin x\, dx = 0{\cdot}00064\ 51689\ (348),$$

the figures in brackets being actually given by the above numbers. The correct value to 15 places, namely,

$$\cos \cdot 160 - \cos \cdot 164 \quad \text{is} \quad 0{\cdot}00064\ 51689\ 34801,$$

so that the above result is correct to 13 places. The precision of this result may be contrasted with the loss of accuracy in differentiating a table, as in the example of 7·02.

7·5. The Euler-Maclaurin Formula. Denote by $P_\nu(x)$ the periodic function of period unity which coincides with $B_\nu(x)$ in the interval $0 \leqslant x < 1$, so that

$$P_\nu(x) = B_\nu(x), \quad 0 \leqslant x < 1,$$
$$P_\nu(x+1) = P_\nu(x).$$

Since $B_\nu(1) = B_\nu(0)$ if $\nu > 1$, we have

$$P_\nu(1) = P_\nu(0) = B_\nu(0) = B_\nu(1),$$

so that $P_\nu(x)$ is a continuous function at $x = 1$ and therefore at $x = 0, 1, 2, \ldots$, provided that $\nu > 1$. $P_1(x)$ is, however, discontinuous at these points, for $B_1(x) = x - \frac{1}{2}$, and hence

$$P_1(x) = x - \tfrac{1}{2}, \quad 0 \leqslant x < 1,$$
$$P_1(+0) = -\tfrac{1}{2}, \qquad P_1(-0) = +\tfrac{1}{2}.$$

Again, from 6·5 (5),

$$D\, B_\nu(x) = \nu\, B_{\nu-1}(x).$$

Thus
$$D\, P_\nu(x) = \nu\, P_{\nu-1}(x)$$

and therefore $D\, P_\nu(x)$ is continuous at $0, 1, 2, \ldots$, when $\nu = 3, 4, 5, \ldots$, but $D\, P_2(x) = 2P_1(x)$ is discontinuous at these points.

Now consider the expression

(1) $$R_m = -\frac{\omega^m}{m!}\int_0^1 P_m(y-t)\, f^{(m)}(x+\omega t)\, dt, \quad 0 \leqslant y \leqslant 1.$$

Integrating by parts, we get

$$R_m = -\frac{\omega^{m-1}}{m!}\Big[P_m(y-t)\, f^{(m-1)}(x+\omega t)\Big]_0^1$$
$$-\frac{\omega^{m-1}}{m!}\int_0^1 m\, P_{m-1}(y-t)\, f^{(m-1)}(x+\omega t)\, dt.$$

Since $P_m(y-1) = P_m(y) = B_m(y)$, we have

$$R_m = -\frac{\omega^m}{m!} B_m(y) \underset{\omega}{\Delta} f^{(m-1)}(x) + R_{m-1},$$

$$R_{m-1} = -\frac{\omega^{m-1}}{(m-1)!} B_{m-1}(y) \underset{\omega}{\Delta} f^{(m-2)}(x) + R_{m-2},$$

. . . .

$$R_2 = -\frac{\omega^2}{2!} B_2(y) \underset{\omega}{\Delta} f'(x) + R_1.$$

Now

$$R_1 = -\omega\int_0^1 P_1(y-t)\, f'(x+\omega t)\, dt$$

$$= -\omega\int_0^y (y-t-\tfrac{1}{2})\, f'(x+\omega t)\, dt - \omega\int_y^1 (y-t+\tfrac{1}{2})\, f'(x+\omega t)\, dt$$

$$= f(x+y\omega) - B_1(y)\, \omega \underset{\omega}{\Delta} f(x) - \frac{1}{\omega}\int_x^{x+\omega} f(t)\, dt,$$

the last line being obtained by integration by parts and then writing t for $x+\omega t$ in the integral.

Thus, by addition of all the above equations, we have

(2) $$\frac{1}{\omega}\int_x^{x+\omega} f(t)\, dt = f(x+y\omega) - B_1(y)\, \omega \underset{\omega}{\Delta} f(x) - \frac{\omega^2}{2!} B_2(y) \underset{\omega}{\Delta} f'(x)$$
$$-\frac{\omega^3}{3!} B_3(y) \underset{\omega}{\Delta} f''(x) - \dots - \frac{\omega^m}{m!} B_m(y) \underset{\omega}{\Delta} f^{(m-1)}(x) - R_m.$$

This is the general Euler-Maclaurin formula, of which 6·511 (3), (6) are particular cases when $f(x)$ is a polynomial.

If we put $y = 0$ and write $2m$ for m, we have, since

$$B_1 = -\tfrac{1}{2}, \quad B_{2s+1} = 0, \quad s > 0,$$

$$(3) \quad \frac{1}{\omega}\int_x^{x+\omega} f(t)\,dt = \tfrac{1}{2}\{f(x)+f(x+\omega)\} - \sum_{s=1}^{m} \frac{\omega^{2s}}{(2s)!} B_{2s} \mathop{\Delta}_{\omega} f^{(2s-1)}(x)$$

$$+\frac{\omega^{2m}}{(2m)!}\int_0^1 P_{2m}(t)\, f^{(2m)}(x+\omega t)\,dt,$$

since

$$P_{2m}(-t) = P_{2m}(1-t) = B_{2m}(1-t) = B_{2m}(t) = P_{2m}(t).$$

If in (3) we write in turn $x+\omega$, $x+2\omega, \dots, x+(n-1)\omega$ for x and add the results we obtain

$$(4) \quad \frac{1}{\omega}\int_x^{x+n\omega} f(t)\,dt = \{\tfrac{1}{2} f(x) + f(x+\omega) + f(x+2\omega) + \dots$$

$$+ f(x+(n-1)\omega) + \tfrac{1}{2} f(x+n\omega)\}$$

$$-\sum_{s=1}^{m-1} \frac{\omega^{2s-1}}{(2s)!} B_{2s}\{f^{(2s-1)}(x+n\omega) - f^{(2s-1)}(x)\} + S_{2m},$$

where

$$S_{2m} = -\frac{\omega^{2m-1}}{(2m)!} B_{2m}\{f^{(2m-1)}(x+n\omega) - f^{(2m-1)}(x)\}$$

$$+\sum_{s=0}^{n-1} \frac{\omega^{2m}}{(2m)!}\int_0^1 P_{2m}(t) f^{(2m)}(x+\omega t+s\omega)\,dt.$$

Now $P_{2m}(t+s) = P_{2m}(t)$, and therefore

$$\sum_{s=0}^{n-1}\int_0^1 P_{2m}(t) f^{(2m)}(x+\omega t+s\omega)\,dt = \int_0^n P_{2m}(t)\, f^{(2m)}(x+\omega t)\,dt.$$

Thus we have

$$(5) \qquad S_{2m} = \frac{\omega^{2m}}{(2m)!}\int_0^n (P_{2m}(t) - B_{2m})\, f^{(2m)}(x+\omega t)\,dt.$$

Now

$$\int_0^n (P_{2m}(t) - B_{2m})\,dt$$

$$= \sum_{s=0}^{n-1}\int_s^{s+1} (P_{2m}(t) - B_{2m})\,dt = n\int_0^1 (P_{2m}(t) - B_{2m})\,dt,$$

since $P_{2m}(t) = P_{2m}(t+s)$, and $P_{2m}(t) = B_{2m}(t)$ in the interval $0 \leqslant t < 1$, so that the last integral is equal to $-nB_{2m}$. Also, by 6·53, $P_{2m}(t)-B_{2m}$ does not change sign. Hence by the mean value theorem

$$(6) \qquad S_{2m} = -\frac{n\,\omega^{2m}\,B_{2m}}{(2m)!} f^{(2m)}(x+\theta n\omega), \quad 0<\theta<1.$$

Thus if $f^{(2m)}(t)$, $f^{(2m+2)}(t)$ have the same constant sign in the interval $x<t<x+n\omega$, S_{2m}, S_{2m+2} have opposite signs (since B_{2m}, B_{2m+2} have opposite signs). In this case it follows, as in 3·12 (c), that the error in (4) due to neglect of the remainder term is less numerically than the first term omitted from the series (4) and is of the same sign. Again, if $f^{(2m)}(t)$ have a fixed sign in the interval $x<t<x+n\omega$, we have, from (5), by the mean value theorem

$$S_{2m} = \frac{\omega^{2m-1}}{(2m)!}\{f^{(2m-1)}(x+n\omega)-f^{(2m-1)}(x)\}\,M,$$

where M denotes a mean value of $P_{2m}(t)-B_{2m}$.

Now, by 6·52,

$$\left|P_{2m}(t)-B_{2m}\right| \leqslant \left|-\left(2-\frac{1}{2^{m-1}}\right)B_{2m}\right|.$$

Thus $|M| \leqslant |2B_{2m}|$, so that the error in (4) due to neglect of the remainder term is in this case numerically less than twice the first omitted term and has the same sign.

If in (2) we put $y=\frac{1}{2}$ and proceed as before, we deduce another formula which is sometimes useful, namely,

$$(7) \quad \frac{1}{\omega}\int_x^{x+n\omega} f(t)\,dt = \{f(x+\tfrac{1}{2}\omega)+f(x+\tfrac{3}{2}\omega)+\ldots+f(x+(n-\tfrac{1}{2})\,\omega)\}$$
$$-\sum_{s=1}^{m-1}\frac{\omega^{2s-1}}{(2s)!}B_{2s}(\tfrac{1}{2})\,\{f^{(2s-1)}(x+n\omega)-f^{(2s-1)}(x)\}$$
$$-\frac{n\,\omega^{2m}}{(2m)!}B_{2m}(\tfrac{1}{2})\,f^{(2m)}(x+\theta n\omega).$$

As an example of (4) applied to the interval (a, b), we have for $n=3$, $m=3$, $\omega=(b-a)/3$,

$$\int_a^b f(x)\,dx = \frac{b-a}{3}\left\{\tfrac{1}{2}f(a)+f\left(\frac{2a+b}{3}\right)+f\left(\frac{a+2b}{3}\right)+\tfrac{1}{2}f(b)\right\}$$
$$-\frac{1}{12}\left(\frac{b-a}{3}\right)^2\left\{f'(b)-f'(a)\right\}+\frac{1}{720}\left(\frac{b-a}{3}\right)^4\left\{f'''(b)-f'''(a)\right\}$$
$$-\frac{1}{10080}\left(\frac{b-a}{3}\right)^7 f^{(6)}(\xi), \quad a<\xi<b.$$

7·51. Application to Finite Summation. With the notation of 2·6, 2·7, we have from 7·5 (4),

$$\mathsf{P}_{(n)}^{-1} u_{t+1} = \int_1^n u_t\,dt + \tfrac{1}{2}(u_1+u_n) + \sum_{s=1}^{m-1} \frac{B_{2s}}{(2s)!}\left(u_n^{(2s-1)} - u_1^{(2s-1)}\right) + R_{2m},$$

$$R_{2m} = \frac{(n-1)}{(2m)!} B_{2m}\, u_\xi^{(2m)}, \quad 1 < \xi < n.$$

This formula gives the value of

$$\mathsf{P}_{(n)}^{-1} u_{t+1} = u_1 + u_2 + \dots + u_n.$$

For example, taking $m = 1$,

$$\mathsf{P}_{(n)}^{-1} \frac{1}{(x+t+1)^2} = \frac{1}{x+1} - \frac{1}{x+n} + \frac{1}{2(x+1)^2} + \frac{1}{2(x+n)^2} + R_2.$$

Since $u_t^{(2)}$ and $u_t^{(4)}$ have the same constant sign, we have

$$R_2 = \frac{\theta B_2}{2!}\left[-\frac{2}{(x+n)^3} + \frac{2}{(x+1)^3}\right], \quad 0 < \theta < 1.$$

If we let $n \to \infty$, we have therefore

$$\sum_{s=1}^{\infty} \frac{1}{(x+s)^2} = \frac{1}{x+1} + \frac{1}{2(x+1)^2} + \frac{\theta}{6(x+1)^3}, \quad 0 < \theta < 1.$$

By taking x large enough we can make the last term as small as we please. We can therefore find by this method the value of $\sum_{s=1}^{\infty} \frac{1}{s^2}$ to any required degree of accuracy by first calculating $\sum_{s=1}^{x} \frac{1}{s^2}$ by addition, having chosen x sufficiently large. If we take a larger value of m the calculation is of course made more expeditious.

7·6. Gregory's Formula. With an obvious notation, 7·5 (4) can be written in the form

$$(1) \quad I = \frac{1}{\omega}\int_a^{a+n\omega} f(x)\,dx - \left(\tfrac{1}{2}f_0 + f_1 + f_2 + \dots + f_{n-1} + \tfrac{1}{2}f_n\right)$$

$$= -\sum_{s=1}^{m-1} \frac{B_{2s}}{(2s)!}\left(f_n^{(2s-1)} - f_0^{(2s-1)}\right) - \frac{n\,\omega^{2m}}{(2m)!} B_{2m}\, f^{(2m)}(a+\theta n\omega).$$

If we use Markoff's formulae of 7·02 we can express $f_n^{(2s-1)}$ in ascending differences and $f_0^{(2s-1)}$ in descending differences. We thus obtain

$$-\omega^{2s-1}(f_n^{(2s-1)}-f_0^{(2s-1)}) = \sum_{\nu=2s-1}^{2m-3} \frac{B_{\nu-2s+1}^{(\nu+1)}(1)}{(\nu-2s+1)!} \Delta^\nu\{(-1)^\nu f_{n-\nu}+f_0\}$$
$$+\frac{\omega^{2m-2}}{(2m-2s-1)!} B_{2m-2s-1}^{(2m-1)}(1)\{f^{(2m-2)}(\xi)+f^{(2m-2)}(\eta)\}.$$

Thus we have

$$I-R = \sum_{s=1}^{m-1} \frac{B_{2s}}{(2s)!} \sum_{\nu=2s-1}^{2m-3} \frac{B_{\nu-2s+1}^{(\nu+1)}(1)}{(\nu-2s+1)!} \Delta^\nu\{(-1)^\nu f_{n-\nu}+f_0\},$$

where

$$(2) \quad R = -\frac{n\,\omega^{2m}}{(2m)!} B_{2m} f^{(2m)}(a+\theta n\omega)$$
$$+\sum_{s=1}^{m-1} \frac{B_{2s}\, B_{2m-2s-1}^{(2m-1)}(1)}{(2s)!\,(2m-2s-1)!} 2\omega^{2m-2} f^{(2m-2)}(\xi_s),$$

where $0<\theta<1$ and ξ_s lies in the interval $(a, a+n\omega)$.

Hence we can write

$$I-R = \sum_{\nu=1}^{2m-3} K_\nu\{\Delta^\nu f_{n-\nu}+(-1)^\nu \Delta^\nu f_0\},$$

where

$$(-1)^\nu K_\nu = \frac{B_2\, B_{\nu-1}^{(\nu+1)}(1)}{2!\,(\nu-1)!}+\frac{B_4\, B_{\nu-3}^{(\nu+1)}(1)}{4!\,(\nu-3)!}+\frac{B_6\, B_{\nu-5}^{(\nu+1)}(1)}{6!\,(\nu-5)!}+\dots,$$

the series ceasing when the suffix becomes negative.

If in (1) we put $f(x) = B_{\nu+1}^{(\nu+2)}(x+1)/(\nu+1)!$, $a=0$, $n=1$, the remainder term will be zero if m be chosen large enough, since $f(x)$ is a polynomial. Also, by 6·4 (1), $f(1)=f(2)=0$.

We have, therefore,

$$\int_0^1 \frac{B_{\nu+1}^{(\nu+2)}(x+1)}{(\nu+1)!}dx = -\sum_{s=1} \frac{B_{2s}}{(2s)!} \frac{B_{\nu-2s+2}^{(\nu+2)}(2)-B_{\nu-2s+2}^{(\nu+2)}(1)}{(\nu-2s+2)!}$$
$$= -\sum_{s=1} \frac{B_{2s}}{(2s)!} \frac{B_{\nu-2s+1}^{(\nu+1)}}{(\nu-2s+1)!} = (-1)^{\nu+1} K_\nu.$$

Thus

$$K_\nu = (-1)^{\nu+1} B_{\nu+1}^{(\nu+1)}(1)/(\nu+1)!,$$

and we see from 7·41 that the K_ν are all negative but numerically equal to the coefficients in Laplace's formula.

We thus obtain Gregory's formula, namely,

$$\frac{1}{\omega}\int_a^{a+n\omega} f(x)\,dx = (\tfrac{1}{2}f_0+f_1+f_2+\dots+f_{n-1}+\tfrac{1}{2}f_n)-\tfrac{1}{12}(\Delta f_{n-1}-\Delta f_0)$$

$$-\tfrac{1}{24}(\Delta^2 f_{n-2}+\Delta^2 f_0)-\tfrac{19}{720}(\Delta^3 f_{n-3}-\Delta^3 f_0)-\tfrac{3}{160}(\Delta^4 f_{n-4}+\Delta^4 f_0)$$

$$-\dots+\frac{B_{2m-2}^{(2m-2)}(1)}{(2m-2)!}(\Delta^{2m-3} f_{n-2m+3}-\Delta^{2m-3} f_0)+R,$$

where R is given by (2).

The advantage of Gregory's formula, as compared with that of Laplace or the central difference formula, lies in the fact that the differences employed are the descending differences of $f(a)$ and the ascending differences of $f(a+n\omega)$, all of which can be formed from values of the function within the range of integration. The disadvantage lies in the somewhat complicated form of the remainder term.

7·7. The Summation Formula of Lubbock. Suppose that we are given a table of a function in the form

n	$f(n)$		
0	$f(0)$		
		$\Delta f(0)$	
ω	$f(1)$		$\Delta^2 f(0)$
		$\Delta f(1)$	
2ω	$f(2)$		.
.	.	.	.
$(r-1)\,\omega$	$f(r-1)$		.
		$\Delta f(r-1)$	
$r\omega$	$f(r)$		.
		$\Delta f(r)$	
			$\Delta^2 f(r)$

and that we wish to subdivide the interval into h equal parts and then form the sum

$$f(0)+f\left(\frac{1}{h}\right)+f\left(\frac{2}{h}\right)+\dots+f\left(\frac{rh}{h}\right).$$

The summation can be effected in the following manner by a formula due to Lubbock.

We have, by Newton's Interpolation formula,

$$f\left(n+\frac{s}{h}\right)=f(n)+\binom{s/h}{1}\Delta f(n)+\binom{s/h}{2}\Delta^2 f(n)$$

$$+\binom{s/h}{3}\Delta^3 f(n)+\binom{s/h}{4}\omega^4 f^{(4)}(\xi).$$

Summing from $s=0$ to $h-1$, we get

$$\sum_{s=0}^{h-1} f\left(n+\frac{s}{h}\right)=hf(n)+\frac{h-1}{2}\Delta f(n)+\lambda_2\Delta^2 f(n)$$

$$+\lambda_3\Delta^3 f(n)+\lambda_4\omega^4 f^{(4)}(\xi_1),$$

where $$\lambda_2=\sum_{s=0}^{h-1}\binom{s/h}{2},\quad \lambda_3=\sum_{s=0}^{h-1}\binom{s/h}{3},\text{ etc.}$$

If we now sum both sides from $n=0$ to $n=r-1$, we get

$$\sum_{\nu=0}^{rh-1} f\left(\frac{\nu}{h}\right)=h\sum_{\nu=0}^{r-1} f(\nu)+\frac{h-1}{2}\sum_{\nu=0}^{r-1}\Delta f(\nu)$$

$$+\lambda_2\sum_{\nu=0}^{r-1}\Delta^2 f(n)+\lambda_3\sum_{\nu=0}^{r-1}\Delta^3 f(\nu)+r\lambda_4 f^{(4)}(\xi_2)$$

$$=h\sum_{\nu=0}^{r-1} f(\nu)+\frac{h-1}{2}(f(r)-f(0))+\lambda_2(\Delta f(r)-\Delta f(0))$$

$$+\lambda_3(\Delta^2 f(r)-\Delta^2 f(0))+r\lambda_4\omega^4 f^{(4)}(\xi_2).$$

Adding $f\left(\frac{rh}{h}\right)$ to each side, we have

$$\sum_{\nu=0}^{rh} f\left(\frac{\nu}{h}\right)=h\sum_{\nu=0}^{r} f(\nu)-\frac{h-1}{2}(f(r)+f(0))+\lambda_2(\Delta f(r)-\Delta f(0))$$

$$+\lambda_3(\Delta^2 f(r)-\Delta^2 f(0))+r\lambda_4\omega^4 f^{(4)}(\xi_2),$$

which expresses the required sum in terms of the given difference table.

The above formula has been arranged to include second differences Clearly any required number of differences may be included by taking further terms in the original interpolation formula. To calculate λ_2, λ_3, ... , etc., we observe that

$$h+\frac{h-1}{2}x+\lambda_2 x^2+\lambda_3 x^3+\ldots = \sum_{s=0}^{h-1}(1+x)^{\frac{s}{h}} = \frac{x}{(1+x)^{1/h}-1}.$$

Thus

$$x \equiv (h+\tfrac{1}{2}(h-1)x+\lambda_2 x^2+\ldots)\left((1+x)^{1/h}-1\right),$$

whence

$$\binom{1/h}{1}\lambda_s+\binom{1/h}{2}\lambda_{s-1}+\ldots+\binom{1/h}{s-1}\lambda_2 + \binom{1/h}{s}\left(\frac{h-1}{2}\right)+\binom{1/h}{s+1}h = 0,$$

so that the coefficients λ_s may be successively evaluated.

We have in this way

$$\lambda_2 = -\frac{h^2-1}{12h}, \quad \lambda_3 = \frac{h^2-1}{24h}, \quad \lambda_4 = -\frac{(h^2-1)(19h^2-1)}{720h^3}.$$

Example. Calculate, by Lubbock's formula,

$$\sum_{3500}^{3530}\frac{1}{n}.$$

Taking $h = 10$, $r = 3$, we form the table :

n	$\frac{1}{n}$	Δ	Δ^2
		−	+
3500	0·0002857143*		
		8140*	
3510	2849003*		46*
		8094	
3520	2840909*		46
		8048	
3530	2832861*		46
		8002*	
3540	2824859		44*
		7958	
3550	2816901		

The numbers used in the formula are indicated by an asterisk.

The required sum multiplied by 10^{10} is equal to

$$10 \times 11379916 - 4{\cdot}5 \times 5690004 - \tfrac{99}{120} \times 138 - \tfrac{99}{240} \times 2 + R,$$

where $$R < \frac{10^{10} \times 3 \times 10^4 \times 99 \times 1899 \times 24}{10^3 \times 720 \times (3500)^5} < {\cdot}004,$$

which is negligible. Thus the required sum is 0·0088194027.

EXAMPLES VII

1. Taking 10 figure logarithms to base 10 from $x = 300$ to $x = 310$ by unit increments, calculate the first three derivates of $\log x$ when $x = 300$, $x = 305$, $x = 310$.

2. From a table of $\sin x$ verify, to the number of figures which the tables permit, that

$$\frac{d}{dx} \sin x = a \cos x,$$

where $a = 1$ if x be measured in radians and $a = \pi / 180$ if x be measured in degrees.

3. By means of tables, calculate

$$\int_0^{\frac{\pi}{2}} \sin x \, dx, \quad \int_{0^0}^{90^0} \sin x \, dx,$$

using an approximate integration formula.

4. The two radii which form a diameter of a circle are bisected, and perpendicular ordinates are raised at the points of bisection. Required the area of that portion of the circle included between the two ordinates, the diameter, and the curve, the radius being supposed equal to unity. Compare the result found by Weddle's rule with the exact result.

5. Prove that

$$\int_0^{\frac{\pi}{2}} \log \sin \theta \, d\theta = - \int_0^{\frac{\pi}{2}} \theta \cot \theta \, d\theta,$$

and hence calculate the value of the integral by Weddle's rule and estimate the error.

6. Shew that Simpson's rule is tantamount to considering the curve between two consecutive odd ordinates as parabolic. Also, if we assume that the curve between each ordinate is parabolic and that the curve passes through the extremity of the next ordinate (the axes of the parabolae being in all cases parallel to the axis of y), the area will be given by

$$h[\Sigma y - \tfrac{1}{24}\{15(y_0+y_n)-4(y_1+y_{n-1})+(y_2+y_{n-2})\}].$$

[Boole.]

7. Prove that approximately

$$\frac{8}{3h}\int_0^{3ph} y\,dx = y_0+3(y_1+y_2+y_4+y_5+y_7+y_8+\dots)+y_{3p} \\ +2(y_3+y_6+y_9+\dots+y_{3p-3}),$$

and find the error term. [Newton.]

8. Prove that approximately

$$\frac{45}{2h}\int_0^{4ph} y\,dx = 7y_0+14(y_4+y_8+\dots+y_{4p-4})+7y_{4p} \\ +32(y_1+y_3+y_5+\dots+y_{4p-1}) \\ +12(y_2+y_6+y_{10}+\dots+y_{4p-2}),$$

and find an expression for the remainder term. [Boole.]

9. Prove that approximately

$$\int_0^{nh} y\,dx = h(y_{\frac{1}{2}}+y_{\frac{3}{2}}+\dots+y_{n-\frac{1}{2}})-\tfrac{1}{8}h(y_{\frac{1}{2}}-y_0+y_{n-\frac{1}{2}}-y_n),$$

and find the error term. [Poncelet.]

10. Prove that approximately

$$\int_0^{nh} y\,dx = h(y_{\frac{1}{2}}+y_{\frac{3}{2}}+\dots+y_{n-\frac{1}{2}})-\tfrac{1}{12}h(y_{\frac{1}{2}}-y_0+y_{n-\frac{1}{2}}-y_n),$$

and find the error term. [Parmentier.]

11. If $f(x)$ be a polynomial of degree $2n-1$ at most, prove that

$$\frac{n}{\pi}\int_{-1}^{+1}\frac{f(x)}{\sqrt{1-x^2}} = f\left(\cos\frac{\pi}{2n}\right)+f\left(\cos\frac{3\pi}{2n}\right)+\dots+f\left(\cos\frac{(2n-1)\pi}{2n}\right).$$

[Bronwin.]

12. Find an expression for the sum to n terms of

$$1+\frac{1}{5^2}+\frac{1}{9^2}+\frac{1}{13^2}+\dots,$$

and calculate approximately the sum to infinity.

13. Find the sum to infinity of

$$1+\frac{1}{2^5}+\frac{1}{3^5}+\frac{1}{4^5}+\dots$$

correct to 10 decimal places.

14. Find approximately the value of

$$\mathsf{P}_{(n)}^{-1}\frac{1}{(t+1)^2-a^2}$$

and obtain an exact formula when a is an integral multiple of $\frac{1}{2}$.

15. Shew that the sum of all the integral negative powers of all the positive integers (unity being excluded in both cases) is unity; if odd powers be excluded the sum is $\frac{3}{4}$.

16. Prove Burnside's * formula for double integration:

$$\int_{-1}^{+1}\int_{-1}^{+1} f(x,y)\,dx\,dy = \tfrac{40}{49}\{f(a,0)+f(0,a)+f(-a,0)+f(0,-a)\} + \tfrac{9}{49}\{f(b,b)+f(b,-b)+f(-b,b)+f(-b,-b)\},$$

where $a=\sqrt{\tfrac{7}{15}}$, $b=\sqrt{\tfrac{7}{9}}$, and $f(x,y)$ is a polynomial of degree 5 at most.

17. By successive applications of Simpson's rule obtain the formula for double integration:

$$9\int_{2c}^{2d} dy\int_{2a}^{2b} f(x,y)\,dx = (b-a)(d-c)\{f(2a,2c)+f(2a,2d) + f(2b,2c)+f(2b,2d)+4[f(2a,c+d)+f(2b,c+d) + f(a+b,2c)+f(a+b,2d)]+16f(a+b,c+d)\},$$

and investigate the form of the remainder term.

* W. Burnside, *Mess. of Math.*, (2), 37 (1908).

18. Prove that:

(*a*) By elimination of the error term in h^2 between two trapezoidal formulae corresponding to sub-intervals h and $2h$, the Simpson Rule is obtained.

(*b*) By a similar elimination between formulae corresponding to h and $3h$, Cotes' formula for $n=4$ (the "Three-Eighths" Rule, Ex. 7 above) is obtained.

(*c*) By elimination of the error term in h^4 between the Simpson and the Three-Eighths rules for 7 ordinates, Weddle's Rule is obtained.

[Sheppard.]

19. By eliminating the error term in h^4 between two Simpson formulae of $2p+1$ and $4p+1$ ordinates, obtain the Newton-Cotes' formula for $n = 5$.

20. Obtain the following table of quadrature formulae of open type, in which the ordinates used are at the midpoints of equal sub-divisions of the range (*e.g.* for 4 points and range 0 to 1, the ordinates used would be $\frac{1}{8}, \frac{3}{8}, \frac{5}{8}, \frac{7}{8}$):

n \ ν	1	2	3	Remainder
1	1			$\frac{1}{24}(b-a)^3 f^{(2)}(\xi)$
2	$\frac{1}{2}$	$\frac{1}{2}$		$\frac{1}{96}(b-a)^3 f^{(2)}(\xi)$
3	$\frac{3}{8}$	$\frac{2}{8}$	$\frac{3}{8}$	$1 \cdot 4(b-a)^5 f^{(4)}(\xi) \times 10^{-4}$
4	$\frac{13}{48}$	$\frac{11}{48}$	$\frac{11}{48}$	$7 \cdot 0(b-a)^5 f^{(4)}(\xi) \times 10^{-5}$
5	$\frac{275}{1152}$	$\frac{100}{1152}$	$\frac{402}{1152}$	$3 \cdot 7(b-a)^7 f^{(6)}(\xi) \times 10^{-7}$

The remainders in all cases have positive sign. [Aitken.]

CHAPTER VIII

THE SUMMATION PROBLEM

CONSIDER the difference equation

$$\mathop{\Delta}_{\omega} u(x) = \phi(x),$$

where $\phi(x)$ is a given function. The summation problem consists in determining $u(x)$. If $u^*(x)$ be a particular function which satisfies the equation, and if $\varpi(x)$ be an arbitrary periodic function of x of period ω, it is evident that $u^*(x)+\varpi(x)$ is also a solution. That this solution is the most general possible is seen from the remark that the difference of any two solutions is a solution of $\mathop{\Delta}_{\omega} u(x) = 0$, so that any two solutions differ by an arbitrary periodic function of period ω. Thus if $\phi(x) = 2x$, the most general solution of the given equation is $x^2-\omega x+\varpi(x)$, particular solutions being

$$x^2-\omega x, \quad x^2-\omega x+\sin(2\pi x/\omega), \quad x^2-\omega x+\tfrac{1}{6}\omega^2.$$

That particular solutions of the given equation always exist is seen (in the case of the real variable) by considering that $u(x)$ being arbitrarily defined at every point of the interval $0 \leqslant x < \omega$, the equation defines $u(x)$ for every point exterior to this interval. Such solutions are in general not analytic. The problem of determining analytic solutions has been studied by many mathematicians. In this chapter we shall consider solely Nörlund's theory of the equation. By an extremely elegant method Nörlund has succeeded in defining a " principal solution " which has specially simple and definite properties. In particular, when $\phi(x)$ is a polynomial so is the principal solution. Moreover, the solution is defined by an algorithm which supplies the means of obtaining the solution. We can only study here the more important outlines of the theory. For further details the reader is referred to Nörlund's memoir.*

8·0. Definition of the Principal Solution or Sum. Consider the difference equation

(1) $$\underset{\omega}{\Delta} u(x) = \phi(x),$$

or $$u(x+\omega) - u(x) = \omega\, \phi(x).$$

The expression, (where A is constant),

$$f(x) = A - \omega\,[\phi(x) + \phi(x+\omega) + \phi(x+2\omega) + \phi(x+3\omega) + \dots]$$

$$= A - \omega \sum_{s=0}^{\infty} \phi(x+s\omega)$$

is a *formal* solution of the difference equation, since

$$f(x+\omega) = A - \omega\,[\phi(x+\omega) + \phi(x+2\omega) + \phi(x+3\omega) + \dots]$$

and therefore $$f(x+\omega) - f(x) = \omega\, \phi(x).$$

If for A we write $\int_c^\infty \phi(t)\,dt$, and if this infinite integral and the infinite series both converge, we define the *principal solution* of the difference equation, or *sum of the function* $\phi(x)$, as

(2) $$F(x \mid \omega) = \int_c^\infty \phi(t)\,dt - \omega \sum_{s=0}^{\infty} \phi(x+s\omega).$$

The reason for the introduction of the infinite integral will appear shortly. The principal solution thus defined depends on an arbitrary constant c. We may thus consider the principal solution as being formed by "summing" the function $\phi(x)$, and from this point of view, by analogy with the notation of the integral calculus, Nörlund writes

(3) $$F(x \mid \omega) = \mathop{S}_{c}^{x} \phi(z) \underset{\omega}{\Delta} z = \int_c^\infty \phi(t)\,dt - \omega \sum_{s=0}^{\infty} \phi(x+s\omega),$$

and the process may be referred to as "summing $\phi(x)$ from c to x."

* N. E. Nörlund, "Mémoire sur le calcul aux différences finies," *Acta Math.* 44, (1923), pp. 71-211. See also *Differenzenrechnung*, ch. iii. The examples at the end of this chapter are all due to Nörlund.

As an example, consider

$$\underset{\omega}{\Delta}\, u(x) = e^{-x},$$

x and ω being real and positive. Here

$$(4) \qquad F(x \mid \omega) = \mathop{\mathbf{S}}_{c}^{x} e^{-z} \underset{\omega}{\Delta} z = \int_c^{\infty} e^{-t}\, dt - \omega \sum_{s=0}^{\infty} e^{-x-s\omega}$$

$$= e^{-c} - \frac{\omega\, e^{-x}}{1-e^{-\omega}},$$

after evaluating the integral, and summing the Geometrical Progression.

The necessary and sufficient conditions for the existence of the sum $F(x \mid \omega)$ as defined above are the convergence of the integral and of the series.

In general, neither of these conditions is satisfied and the definition fails. In order to extend the definition of the sum, Nörlund adopts an ingenious and powerful artifice. This consists in replacing $\phi(x)$ by another function, of x and of a parameter $\mu\ (>0)$, say $\phi(x, \mu)$, which is so chosen that

(i) $\lim\limits_{\mu \to 0} \phi(x, \mu) = \phi(x)$;

(ii) $\int_c^{\infty} \phi(t, \mu)\, dt$ and $\sum\limits_{s=0}^{\infty} \phi(x+s\omega, \mu)$ both converge.

For this function $\phi(x, \mu)$, the difference equation

$$(5) \qquad \underset{\omega}{\Delta}\, u(x) = \phi(x, \mu)$$

has a principal solution, given by the definition (3),

$$(6) \qquad F(x \mid \omega\,;\ \mu) = \int_c^{\infty} \phi(t, \mu)\, dt - \omega \sum_{s=0}^{\infty} \phi(x+s\omega, \mu).$$

If in this relation we let $\mu \to 0$, the difference equation (5) becomes the difference equation (1) and the principal solution of the latter is defined by

$$F(x \mid \omega) = \lim_{\mu \to 0} F(x \mid \omega\,;\ \mu),$$

provided that this limit exists uniformly and, subject to conditions (i) and (ii), is independent of the particular choice of $\phi(x, \mu)$. It is of course assumed throughout that the domain of variation of x and ω may be subject to restrictions depending on the nature of the function $\phi(x)$. The nature of these restrictions will be more apparent when we consider particular classes of functions. It may also be observed that the success of the method of definition just described depends on the *difference* of the infinite integral and the infinite series having a limit when $\mu \to 0$. Each separately may diverge when $\mu = 0$ and the choice of $\phi(x, \mu)$ has to be so made that when we take the difference of the integral and the series the divergent part disappears.

When $\phi(x)$ is such that the sum exists, it is still possible that the result obtained may depend upon the particular method of summation adopted. In this connection it has been shewn * that, for a wide class of summation methods, the result is independent of the method adopted. Among these methods is the one given in the following definition, which will suffice for our purposes.

If for x variable in a certain interval and for positive values of ω, we can find $p \geqslant 1$, $q \geqslant 0$, such that for $\lambda(x) = x^p (\log x)^q$,

$$\int_c^\infty \phi(t)\, e^{-\mu\lambda(t)}\, dt, \qquad \sum_{s=0}^{\infty} \phi(x+s\omega)\, e^{-\mu\lambda(x+s\omega)}$$

both converge for $\mu > 0$, then the principal solution of the difference equation $\underset{\omega}{\Delta}\, u(x) = \phi(x)$ is

$$(7) \quad F(x \mid \omega) = \underset{c}{\overset{x}{S}} \phi(z) \underset{\omega}{\Delta} z$$

$$= \lim_{\mu \to 0} \left\{ \int_c^\infty \phi(t)\, e^{-\mu\lambda(t)}\, dt - \omega \sum_{s=0}^{\infty} \phi(x+s\omega)\, e^{-\mu\lambda(x+s\omega)} \right\}$$

provided that this limit exists.

When the limit exists $\phi(x)$ is said to be *summable*.

As a simple illustration, consider

$$\underset{\omega}{\Delta}\, u(x) = a,$$

where a is constant.

* N. E. Nörlund, *Acta Univ. Lund.* (2), 14, 1918 ; 16, 1919.

The series $a+a+a+\dots$ obviously diverges, but for $\mu > 0$

$$\int_c^\infty a\,e^{-\mu t}\,dt, \quad \sum_{s=0}^{\infty} a\,e^{-\mu(x+s\omega)}$$

both converge if ω be positive, so that we can take $\lambda(x) = x$, *i.e.* $p = 1$, $q = 0$. Hence

$$\mathop{S}_{c}^{x} a \mathop{\Delta}_{\omega} z = \lim_{\mu\to 0}\left\{\int_c^\infty a\,e^{-\mu t}\,dt - \omega\sum_{s=0}^{\infty} a\,e^{-\mu(x+s\omega)}\right\}$$

$$= \lim_{\mu\to 0}\left\{\frac{a\,e^{-\mu c}}{\mu} - \frac{a\,\omega\,e^{-\mu x}}{1-e^{-\mu\omega}}\right\}$$

$$= \lim_{\mu\to 0}\frac{a\,e^{-\mu c}(\mu\omega - \frac{1}{2}\mu^2\omega^2 + \dots - \mu\omega + \mu^2\omega(x-c) - \dots)}{\mu\left(\mu\omega - \dfrac{\mu^2\omega^2}{2} + \dots\right)}.$$

$$(8) \qquad \mathop{S}_{c}^{x} a \mathop{\Delta}_{\omega} z = a(x - c - \tfrac{1}{2}\omega),$$

which is the principal solution. It should be noted that both the integral and the series diverge when $\mu = 0$. For $\omega = 1$, $c = 0$, $a = 1$, we have

$$\mathop{S}_{0}^{x} 1 \mathop{\Delta}_{\omega} z = x - \tfrac{1}{2} = B_1(x).$$

Thus Bernoulli's polynomial $B_1(x)$ is a principal solution. That all Bernoulli's polynomials are principal solutions will be proved later.

8·1. Properties of the Sum. We shall now consider some of the general properties of the sum which are directly derivable from the definition.

If in 8·0 (6) we write for x successively the values

$$x+\frac{\omega}{m}, \quad x+\frac{2\omega}{m}, \quad \dots, \quad x+\frac{(m-1)\,\omega}{m}$$

and add the results, we get

$$\sum_{s=0}^{m-1} F\left(x+\frac{s\omega}{m}\,\middle|\,\omega;\ \mu\right) = m\,F\left(x\,\middle|\,\frac{\omega}{m};\ \mu\right),$$

which when $\mu \to 0$ gives

$$(1) \qquad \sum_{s=0}^{m-1} F\left(x+\frac{s\omega}{m} \,\middle|\, \omega\right) = m\, F\left(x \,\middle|\, \frac{\omega}{m}\right)$$

and also

$$(2) \qquad F(x \mid \omega) = \frac{1}{m} \sum_{s=0}^{m-1} F(x+s\omega \mid m\omega).$$

These results constitute the Multiplication Theorem of the Sum (cf. 6·52).

Again, from the definition,

$$F\left(x \,\middle|\, \frac{\omega}{m};\ \mu\right) = \int_c^\infty \phi(t,\mu)\,dt - \frac{\omega}{m} \sum_{s=0}^{\infty} \phi\left(x+\frac{s\omega}{m},\ \mu\right),$$

so that if $m \to \infty$,

$$\lim_{m\to\infty} F\left(x \,\middle|\, \frac{\omega}{m};\ \mu\right) = \int_c^\infty \phi(t,\mu)\,dt - \int_x^\infty \phi(t,\mu)\,dt$$

$$= \int_c^x \phi(t,\mu)\,dt,$$

so that when $\mu \to 0$,

$$(3) \qquad \lim_{m\to\infty} F\left(x \,\middle|\, \frac{\omega}{m}\right) = \int_c^x \phi(t)\,dt.$$

Again, from (1),

$$\lim_{m\to\infty} F\left(x \,\middle|\, \frac{\omega}{m}\right) = \lim_{m\to\infty} \frac{1}{\omega}\cdot\frac{\omega}{m} \sum_{s=0}^{m-1} F\left(x+\frac{s\omega}{m} \,\middle|\, \omega\right)$$

$$= \frac{1}{\omega}\int_x^{x+\omega} F(t \mid \omega)\,dt.$$

Thus we have the result

$$(4) \qquad \frac{1}{\omega}\int_x^{x+\omega} F(t \mid \omega)\,dt = \int_c^x \phi(t)\,dt.$$

From the definition of the sum it follows that

$$(5) \qquad \mathop{\Delta}_{\omega} \mathop{\mathbf{S}}_{c}^{x} \phi(t) \mathop{\Delta}_{\omega} t = \phi(x).$$

Thus the operator $\underset{\omega}{\Delta}$ cancels the operator $\displaystyle\mathop{S}^{x}\underset{\omega}{\Delta} t$. On the other hand, these operators are not commutative, for

$$(6)\qquad \mathop{S}_{c}^{x}\left[\underset{\omega}{\Delta}\phi(t)\right]\underset{\omega}{\Delta} t=\frac{1}{\omega}\mathop{S}_{c}^{x}\phi(t+\omega)\underset{\omega}{\Delta} t-\frac{1}{\omega}\mathop{S}_{c}^{x}\phi(t)\underset{\omega}{\Delta} t$$

$$=\frac{1}{\omega}\mathop{S}_{c+\omega}^{x+\omega}\phi(t)\underset{\omega}{\Delta} t-\frac{1}{\omega}\mathop{S}_{c}^{x}\phi(t)\underset{\omega}{\Delta} t$$

$$=\underset{\omega}{\Delta}\mathop{S}_{c}^{x}\phi(t)\underset{\omega}{\Delta} t-\frac{1}{\omega}\int_{c}^{c+\omega}\phi(t)\,dt$$

$$=\phi(x)-\frac{1}{\omega}\int_{c}^{c+\omega}\phi(t)\,dt.$$

From this formula we can derive a rule for summation by parts of the product of two functions. For writing

$$\phi(z)=u(z)\mathop{S}_{c}^{z}v(t)\underset{\omega}{\Delta} t,$$

we have

$$\underset{\omega}{\Delta}\phi(z)=\frac{1}{\omega}u(z+\omega)\mathop{S}_{c}^{z+\omega}v(t)\underset{\omega}{\Delta} t-\frac{1}{\omega}u(z)\mathop{S}_{c}^{z}v(t)\underset{\omega}{\Delta} t.$$

Thus

$$\underset{\omega}{\Delta}\phi(z)=[\underset{\omega}{\Delta}u(z)]\mathop{S}_{c}^{z+\omega}v(t)\underset{\omega}{\Delta} t+u(z)\underset{\omega}{\Delta}\mathop{S}_{c}^{z}v(t)\underset{\omega}{\Delta} t,$$

so that by using (5),

$$u(z)\,v(z)=\underset{\omega}{\Delta}\phi(z)-[\underset{\omega}{\Delta}u(z)]\mathop{S}_{c}^{z+\omega}v(t)\underset{\omega}{\Delta} t.$$

Sum both sides from c to x, using (6), and we have

$$(7)\qquad \mathop{S}_{c}^{x}u(z)\,v(z)\underset{\omega}{\Delta} z=u(x)\mathop{S}_{c}^{x}v(t)\underset{\omega}{\Delta} t-\frac{1}{\omega}\int_{c}^{c+\omega}u(z)\mathop{S}_{c}^{z}v(t)\underset{\omega}{\Delta} t\,dz$$
$$-\mathop{S}_{c}^{x}\left\{[\underset{\omega}{\Delta}u(z)]\mathop{S}_{c}^{z+\omega}v(t)\underset{\omega}{\Delta} t\right\}\underset{\omega}{\Delta} z.$$

This formula is quite analogous to the formula of the integral calculus for integration by parts.

As an illustration, take $u(z) = z$, $v(z) = e^{-z}$. Then, by 8·0 (4),

$$\mathop{S}_{c}^{x} z\,e^{-z} \mathop{\Delta}_{\omega} z = x\left(e^{-c} - \frac{\omega\, e^{-x}}{1-e^{-\omega}}\right) - \frac{1}{\omega}\int_{c}^{c+\omega} z\left(e^{-c} - \frac{\omega\, e^{-z}}{1-e^{-\omega}}\right) dz$$

$$- \mathop{S}_{c}^{x} \left\{e^{-c} - \frac{\omega\, e^{-z-\omega}}{1-e^{-\omega}}\right\} \mathop{\Delta}_{\omega} z.$$

To evaluate $\mathop{S}_{c}^{x} e^{-c} \mathop{\Delta}_{\omega} z$, we use 8·0 (8), so that after reduction

$$\mathop{S}_{c}^{x} z\,e^{-z} \mathop{\Delta}_{\omega} z = -\frac{\omega\, x\, e^{-x}}{1-e^{-\omega}} - \frac{\omega^2\, e^{-x-\omega}}{(1-e^{-\omega})^2} + c\,e^{-c} + e^{-c}.$$

We have thus found the principal solution of the difference equation

$$\mathop{\Delta}_{\omega} u(x) = x\,e^{-x}.$$

We also note that when $\omega \to 0$,

$$\lim_{\omega\to 0} \mathop{S}_{c}^{x} z\,e^{-z} \mathop{\Delta}_{\omega} z = -x\,e^{-x} - e^{-x} + c\,e^{-c} + e^{-c} = \int_{c}^{x} z\,e^{-z}\,dz,$$

a result which we should expect in view of (3), which points to the result

$$\lim_{\omega\to 0} \mathop{S}_{c}^{x} \phi(z) \mathop{\Delta}_{\omega} z = \int_{c}^{x} \phi(z)\,dz.$$

That this is true when ω tends to zero by positive values will be proved in 8·22.

The following identities are often useful and are easily proved:

(8) $$\mathop{S}_{a}^{x} \phi(z) \mathop{\Delta}_{\omega} z = \mathop{S}_{b}^{x} \phi(z) \mathop{\Delta}_{\omega} z + \int_{a}^{b} \phi(z)\,dz,$$

$$\mathop{S}_{c}^{x+a} \phi(z) \mathop{\Delta}_{\omega} z = \mathop{S}_{c-a}^{x} \phi(z+a) \mathop{\Delta}_{\omega} z.$$

In this connection we note, in contrast with the known result

$$\int_c^c \phi(z)\, dz = 0, \quad \text{that} \quad \underset{c}{\overset{c}{\mathbf{S}}} \phi(z) \underset{\omega}{\Delta} z \quad \text{is not zero in general.}$$

8·11. The Sum of a Polynomial.

Consider the equation

$$\Delta\, u(x) = n x^{n-1} e^{-\mu x}.$$

Taking $c = 0$, the principal solution of this is

$$\begin{aligned} F(x \mid 1;\ \mu) &= \int_0^\infty n\, t^{n-1} e^{-\mu t} dt - \sum_{s=0}^{\infty} n (x+s)^{n-1} e^{-\mu(x+s)} \\ &= (-1)^{n-1} n \frac{\partial^{n-1}}{\partial \mu^{n-1}} \left\{ \int_0^\infty e^{-\mu t} dt - \sum_{s=0}^{\infty} e^{-\mu(x+s)} \right\} \\ &= (-1)^{n-1} n \frac{\partial^{n-1}}{\partial \mu^{n-1}} \left\{ \frac{1}{\mu} + \frac{e^{-\mu x}}{e^{-\mu} - 1} \right\} \\ &= (-1)^{n-1} n \frac{\partial^{n-1}}{\partial \mu^{n-1}} \left\{ \sum_{\nu=1}^{\infty} (-\mu)^{\nu-1} \frac{B_\nu(x)}{\nu!} \right\} \\ &= n \sum_{\nu=n}^{\infty} \frac{(-\mu)^{\nu-n}}{\nu(\nu-n)!} B_\nu(x). \end{aligned}$$

Thus when $\mu \to 0$, we have

$$F(x \mid 1) = B_n(x).$$

We have thus proved that Bernoulli's polynomials are principal solutions or that the sum of $n x^{n-1}$ from 0 to x is $B_n(x)$. It follows that the sum of a polynomial is a polynomial.

8·12. Repeated Summation.

Consider

$$F_n(x \mid \omega) = \omega^{n-1} \underset{c}{\overset{x}{\mathbf{S}}} \binom{\frac{x-t}{\omega} - 1}{n-1} \phi(t) \underset{\omega}{\Delta} t.$$

We have

$$F_n(x+\omega \mid \omega) = \omega^{n-1} \underset{c}{\overset{x+\omega}{\mathbf{S}}} \binom{\frac{x-t}{\omega}}{n-1} \phi(t) \underset{\omega}{\Delta} t.$$

Now

$$\binom{\frac{x-t}{\omega} - 1}{n-1} = \binom{\frac{x-t}{\omega}}{n-1} - \binom{\frac{x-t}{\omega} - 1}{n-2},$$

so that

$$F_n(x+\omega \mid \omega) - F_n(x \mid \omega)$$

$$= \omega^{n-1} \left\{ \mathop{\mathbf{S}}_c^{x+\omega} \binom{\frac{x-t}{\omega}}{n-1} \phi(t) \mathop{\Delta}_\omega t - \mathop{\mathbf{S}}_c^{x} \binom{\frac{x-t}{\omega}}{n-1} \phi(t) \mathop{\Delta}_\omega t \right\}$$

$$+ \omega^{n-1} \mathop{\mathbf{S}}_c^{x} \binom{\frac{x-t}{\omega} - 1}{n-2} \phi(t) \mathop{\Delta}_\omega t.$$

The expression in the curled bracket is zero, for if

$$\psi(t) = \binom{\frac{x-t}{\omega}}{n-1} \phi(t),$$

we have $\psi(x) = 0$. Hence

$$\mathop{\Delta}_\omega F_n(x \mid \omega) = F_{n-1}(x \mid \omega).$$

Thus

$$\mathop{\Delta}_\omega^n F_n(x \mid \omega) = \phi(x).$$

We shall call $F_n(x \mid \omega)$ the nth successive sum of $\phi(x)$, and write

$$F_n(x \mid \omega) = \mathop{\mathbf{S}}_c^{x} \phi(t) \mathop{\Delta}_\omega^n t = \omega^{n-1} \mathop{\mathbf{S}}_c^{x} \binom{\frac{x-t}{\omega} - 1}{n-1} \phi(t) \mathop{\Delta}_\omega t.$$

8·15. Proof of the Existence of the Principal Solution (Real Variable). We prove that, under certain restrictions on $\phi(x)$, and for positive values of ω,

(1) $$\mathop{\mathbf{S}}_c^{x+h\omega} \phi(t)\, e^{-\mu\lambda(t)} \mathop{\Delta}_\omega t$$

$$= \int_c^\infty \phi(t)\, e^{-\mu\lambda(t)}\, dt - \omega \sum_{s=0}^{\infty} \phi(x+h\omega+s\omega)\, e^{-\mu\lambda(x+h\omega+s\omega)},$$

where $0 \leqslant h \leqslant 1$, exists and, when $\mu \to 0$, tends uniformly to a limit $\mathop{\mathbf{S}}_c^{x+h\omega} \phi(t) \mathop{\Delta}_\omega t$.

The proof is based on the use of the Euler-Maclaurin formula 7·5 (2).

To fix ideas we make the following assumptions :

(A) For $x \geqslant c$, $D^m \phi(x)$ exists and is continuous, where D denotes the operator $\frac{d}{dx}$, m being a fixed positive integer.

(B) $\lim_{x \to \infty} D^m \phi(x) = 0.$

(C) $\sum_{s=0}^{\infty} D^m \phi(x+s\omega)$ is uniformly convergent in the interval $c \leqslant x \leqslant c+\omega$, and consequently by (B) in every interval $c \leqslant x \leqslant b$ however great b may be.

From (B) it follows that

(2) $$\lim_{x \to \infty} \frac{D^{m-\nu} \phi(x)}{x^\nu} = 0, \quad \lim_{x \to \infty} \frac{\phi(x)}{x^m} = 0.$$

With these restrictions on $\phi(x)$, the convergence of the integral and series in (1) is assured if we take $\lambda(t) = t$, and both sides of (1) exist.

From the periodic property of Bernoulli's function $P_m(x)$, we have, as in 7·5,

(3) $$\int_n^{n+p+1} P_m(-t)\, D^m \phi(x+t\omega)\, dt = \int_0^1 P_m(-t) \sum_{s=n}^{n+p} D^m \phi(x+t\omega+s\omega)\, dt.$$

By (C), given $\varepsilon > 0$, we can choose n_0, so that

$$\left| \sum_{s=n}^{n+p} D^m \phi(x+t\omega+s\omega) \right| < \varepsilon, \text{ for } n \geqslant n_0.$$

Also $P_m(-t)$ is bounded. Hence the left-hand member of (3) can be made arbitrarily small by choice of n only, and consequently

(4) $$\int_0^\infty P_m(-t)\, D^m \phi(x+t\omega)\, dt$$

is uniformly convergent.

For brevity, we define operators Q, T_n by the following relations:

(5) $$Qf(x) = \sum_{\nu=1}^{m} \frac{\omega^{\nu-1}}{\nu!} B_\nu(h)\, D^{\nu-1} f(x), \quad 0 \leqslant h \leqslant 1,$$

(6) $$T_n f(x) = \frac{\omega^m}{m!} \int_0^n P_m(h-t)\, D^m f(x+\omega t)\, dt.$$

Then, from the Euler-Maclaurin formula 7·5 (2), we have

$$\phi(x+h\omega) = \frac{1}{\omega}\int_x^{x+\omega} \phi(t)\, dt + Q(\phi(x+\omega) - \phi(x)) - T_1 \phi(x).$$

Writing in succession $x+\omega$, $x+2\omega$, ..., $x+(n-1)\omega$ for x and adding, we get

(7) $$\sum_{s=0}^{n-1} \phi(x+h\omega+s\omega)$$
$$= \frac{1}{\omega}\int_x^{x+n\omega} \phi(t)\, dt + Q\,\phi(x+n\omega) - Q\,\phi(x) - T_n \phi(x).$$

Now, by Leibniz' Theorem,

(8) $$D^{\nu-1}(e^{-\mu x}\phi(z)) = e^{-\mu x} \sum_{s=0}^{\nu-1} \binom{\nu-1}{s} (-\mu)^s D^{\nu-1-s} \phi(x).$$

If therefore in (7) we write $\phi(x)\, e^{-\mu x}$ for $\phi(x)$ and let $n \to \infty$, we have $Q\,\phi(x+n\omega)\, e^{-\mu(x+n\omega)} \to 0$ and therefore, from (1),

(9) $$\mathop{\mathrm{S}}_{c}^{x+h\omega} \phi(t)\, e^{-\mu t} \mathop{\Delta}_{\omega} t$$
$$= \int_c^x \phi(t)\, e^{-\mu t}\, dt + \sum_{\nu=1}^{m} \frac{\omega^\nu}{\nu!} B_\nu(h)\, D^{\nu-1}(\phi(x)\, e^{-\mu x})$$
$$+ \omega\, T_\infty \phi(x)\, e^{-\mu x},$$

where, by (6) and (8),

(10) $$\omega\, T_\infty \phi(x)\, e^{-\mu x}$$
$$= \frac{\omega^{m+1}}{m!} \left\{ \int_0^\infty P_m(h-t)\, [D^m \phi(x+\omega t)]\, e^{-\mu(x+\omega t)}\, dt \right.$$
$$\left. + e^{-\mu x} \sum_{\nu=1}^{m} I_\nu (-1)^\nu \binom{m}{\nu} \right\},$$

$$I_\nu = \mu^\nu \int_0^\infty P_m(h-t) [D^{m-\nu} \phi(x+\omega t)]\, e^{-\mu\omega t}\, dt.$$

We now prove that $I_\nu \to 0$ uniformly, when $\mu \to 0$.

Put

$$f(t, \mu) = \mu \int_t^\infty P_m(h-y)\, e^{-\mu\omega y}\, dy.$$

This integral converges when $\mu > 0$, since $P_m(h-y)$ is bounded. Then

$$f(t, \mu) = \mu \int_0^\infty P_m(h-y-t)\, e^{-\mu\omega(y+t)}\, dy$$

$$= \mu\, e^{-\mu\omega t} \sum_{s=0}^{\infty} \int_s^{s+1} P_m(h-y-t)\, e^{-\mu\omega y}\, dy$$

$$= \mu\, e^{-\mu\omega t} \sum_{s=0}^{\infty} e^{-\mu s\omega} \int_0^1 P_m(h-y-t)\, e^{-\mu\omega y}\, dy$$

$$= \frac{\mu\, e^{-\mu\omega t}}{1-e^{-\mu\omega}} \int_0^1 P_m(h-y-t)\, e^{-\mu\omega y}\, dy.$$

Hence $\displaystyle \lim_{\mu\to 0} f(t, \mu) = \frac{1}{\omega} \int_0^1 P_m(h-y-t)\, dy = 0,$

since $P_m(x)$ has period unity. Now, integrating by parts,

$$I_\nu = \mu^{\nu-1} D^{m-\nu} \phi(x)\, f(0, \mu) + \omega\, \mu^{\nu-1} \int_0^\infty D^{m-\nu+1} \phi(x+\omega t)\, f(t, \mu)\, dt.$$

Thus $I_\nu \to 0$ when $\mu \to 0$.

We have now to consider the first term in (10),

$$I_0 = \int_0^\infty P_m(h-t)\, [D^m \phi(x+\omega t)]\, e^{-\mu(x+\omega t)}\, dt.$$

Put $\displaystyle \psi(t) = \int_t^\infty P_m(h-y)\, D^m \phi(x+\omega y)\, dy,$

which by (4) is uniformly convergent. Then, integrating by parts,

$$I_0 = e^{-\mu x} \psi(0) - \mu\omega\, e^{-\mu x} \int_0^\infty e^{-\mu\omega t} \psi(t)\, dt.$$

Thus when $\mu \to 0$,

$$I_0 \to \psi(0) = \int_0^\infty P_m(h-t)\, D^m \phi(x+\omega t)\, dt.$$

Thus finally, from (9), we have

$$(11) \qquad \mathop{\large S}_{c}^{x+h\omega} \phi(t) \mathop{\Delta}_{\omega} t = \int_c^x \phi(t)\, dt + \sum_{\nu=1}^{m} \frac{\omega^\nu}{\nu!} B_\nu(h)\, D^{\nu-1} \phi(x)$$

$$+ \frac{\omega^{m+1}}{m!} \int_0^\infty P_m(h-t)\, D^m \phi(x+\omega t)\, dt, \quad 0 \leqslant h \leqslant 1.$$

We have thus proved the existence of the principal solution or sum under the restrictions on $\phi(x)$ enumerated above, in particular for all functions which increase less rapidly than a polynomial of arbitrary degree.

8·16. Bernoulli's Polynomials.

In 8·15 (11), take

$$h = 0, \quad \phi(x) = \nu x^{\nu-1}, \quad m = \nu, \quad c = 0.$$

Then we have

$$\underset{0}{\overset{x}{S}} \nu t^{\nu-1} \underset{\omega}{\Delta} t = \int_0^x \nu t^{\nu-1} dt + \sum_{s=1}^{\nu} x^{\nu-s} \binom{\nu}{s} \omega^s B_s$$

$$\doteqdot \omega^\nu \left(\frac{x}{\omega} + B\right)^\nu = \omega^\nu B_\nu \left(\frac{x}{\omega}\right),$$

which again shews that Bernoulli's polynomials are principal solutions, a result already obtained in 8·11 for the case $\omega = 1$. If we define Bernoulli's polynomial of the first order, of degree ν, by the relation

$$B_\nu(x \mid \omega) = \underset{0}{\overset{x}{S}} \nu t^{\nu-1} \underset{\omega}{\Delta} t,$$

we have proved that

$$B_\nu(x \mid \omega) = \omega^\nu B_\nu\left(\frac{x}{\omega} \middle| 1\right),$$

which gives $B_\nu(x \mid \omega)$ in terms of the polynomials of Chapter VI. We have quite readily

$$\sum_{\nu=0}^{\infty} \frac{t^\nu}{\nu!} B_\nu(x \mid \omega) = \frac{\omega t e^{xt}}{e^{\omega t} - 1}.$$

8·2. Differentiation of the Sum.

From 8·15 (11) we have, on account of the periodicity of $P_m(t)$ and the uniform convergence of the infinite series,

$$(1) \quad \underset{c}{\overset{x+h\omega}{S}} \phi(t) \underset{\omega}{\Delta} t = \int_c^x \phi(t)\, dt + \sum_{\nu=1}^{m} \frac{\omega^\nu}{\nu!} B_\nu(h) D^{\nu-1} \phi(x)$$

$$+ \frac{\omega^{m+1}}{m!} \int_0^1 P_m(h-t) \sum_{s=0}^{\infty} D^m \phi(x + s\omega + \omega t)\, dt.$$

Taking $m > 1$, differentiate both sides with respect to the parameter h and divide by ω. Then by 6·5 (5), we obtain

$$\frac{d}{dx}\mathop{\mathrm{S}}_{c}^{x+h\omega}\phi(t)\mathop{\Delta}_{\omega} t = \sum_{\nu=1}^{m}\frac{\omega^{\nu-1}}{(\nu-1)!}B_{\nu-1}(h)\,D^{\nu-1}\phi(x)$$

$$+\frac{\omega^m}{(m-1)!}\int_0^1 P_{m-1}(h-t)\sum_{s=0}^{\infty}D^m\phi(x+s\omega+\omega t)\,dt.$$

Putting $h=0$ and writing ν for $\nu-1$ this can be expressed in the form

$$\frac{d}{dx}\mathop{\mathrm{S}}_{c}^{x}\phi(t)\mathop{\Delta}_{\omega} t = \phi(c)+\int_c^x \phi'(t)\,dt+\sum_{\nu=1}^{m-1}\frac{\omega^\nu}{\nu!}B_\nu D^{\nu-1}\phi'(x)$$

$$+\frac{\omega^m}{(m-1)!}\int_0^1 P_{m-1}(-t)\sum_{s=0}^{\infty}D^{m-1}\phi'(x+s\omega+\omega t)\,dt.$$

Comparing the expression on the right with (1) when $h=0$, and $m-1$, $\phi'(x)$ are written for m and $\phi(x)$, we have

$$(2)\qquad \frac{d}{dx}\mathop{\mathrm{S}}_{c}^{x}\phi(t)\mathop{\Delta}_{\omega} t = \mathop{\mathrm{S}}_{c}^{x}\phi'(t)\mathop{\Delta}_{\omega} t+\phi(c),$$

which shews that the differential coefficient of the sum differs from the sum of the differential coefficient by the constant $\phi(c)$.

8·21. Asymptotic Behaviour of the Sum for Large Values of x. With the same hypotheses as in 8·15, we have from 8·15 (11),

$$F(x\,|\,\omega) = \mathop{\mathrm{S}}_{c}^{x}\phi(t)\mathop{\Delta}_{\omega} t = Q_m(x)+R_m(x),$$

$$(1)\qquad \text{where}\quad Q_m(x) = \int_c^x\phi(t)\,dt+\sum_{\nu=1}^{m}\frac{\omega^\nu}{\nu!}B_\nu D^{\nu-1}\phi(x),$$

$$R_m(x) = \frac{\omega^{m+1}}{m!}\int_0^\infty P_m(-t)\,D^m\phi(x+\omega t)\,dt.$$

We have seen, 8·15 (4), that the integral is uniformly convergent. Changing the variable, we have

$$R_m(x) = \frac{\omega^m}{m!}\int_x^\infty P_m\left(\frac{x-y}{\omega}\right)\frac{d^m}{dy^m}\phi(y)\,dy,$$

and since this integral also converges uniformly corresponding to an arbitrary $\varepsilon > 0$, we can find x_0 such that

$$|R_m(x)| < \varepsilon, \text{ for } x \geqslant x_0.$$

Thus for $x \geqslant x_0$,

$$(2) \qquad |F(x\,|\,\omega) - Q_m(x)| < \varepsilon.$$

Thus we conclude that, for large values of x, $F(x\,|\,\omega)$ is asymptotically represented by $Q_m(x)$.

As an illustration, consider $\displaystyle \mathop{\mathrm{S}}_{1}^{x} \frac{1}{t} \mathop{\Delta}_{\omega} t$.

Since $\displaystyle\sum_{s=0}^{\infty} \frac{1}{(t+s\omega)^2}$ is uniformly convergent for $t \geqslant 1$, it is sufficient to take $m = 1$, and we have approximately, when x is large,

$$(3) \qquad \mathop{\mathrm{S}}_{1}^{x} \frac{1}{t} \mathop{\Delta}_{\omega} t = \log x - \frac{1}{2x}.$$

Again consider $\displaystyle \mathop{\mathrm{S}}_{0}^{x} \log t \,\Delta\, t$.

Here taking $m = 2$, condition (C) of 8·15 is satisfied and we have approximately, when x is large,

$$(4) \qquad \mathop{\mathrm{S}}_{0}^{x} \log t \,\Delta\, t = (x - \tfrac{1}{2}) \log x - x + \frac{1}{12x}.$$

Evidently a grosser approximation is $(x - \frac{1}{2}) \log x - x$, which corresponds to the case $m = 1$.

Actually for $m = 1$ condition (C) is not satisfied, but

$$\int_0^{\infty} P_1(-t) \frac{1}{x + \omega t}\, dt$$

is still uniformly convergent.

Condition (C) is in fact a sufficient but not necessary condition for the convergence of the integral, which is all that is actually required in 8·15.

We can utilise the asymptotic property of the sum for values of x which are not large in the following way.

From the definition it is clear that

$$F(x \mid \omega) = F(x+n\omega \mid \omega) - \omega \sum_{s=0}^{n-1} \phi(x+s\omega),$$

so that

$$F(x \mid \omega) = Q_m(x+n\omega) - \omega \sum_{s=0}^{n-1} \phi(x+s\omega)$$

$$+[F(x+n\omega \mid \omega) - Q_m(x+n\omega)]$$

$$= Q_m(x) + \omega \sum_{s=0}^{n-1} [\underset{\omega}{\Delta} Q_m(x+s\omega) - \phi(x+s\omega)]$$

$$+[F(x+n\omega \mid \omega) - Q_m(x+n\omega)].$$

If we now let $n \to \infty$, the term in the last bracket $\to 0$ by the asymptotic property proved above, so that we have the development

(5) $$F(x \mid \omega) = Q_m(x) - \omega \sum_{s=0}^{\infty} [\phi(x+s\omega) - \underset{\omega}{\Delta} Q_m(x+s\omega)],$$

which is valid for $x \geqslant c$. We have also the equivalent form

(6) $$F(x \mid \omega) = \lim_{n\to\infty} [Q_m(x+n\omega) - \omega \sum_{s=0}^{n-1} \phi(x+s\omega)].$$

8·22. Asymptotic Behaviour of the Sum for Small Values of ω. To study the behaviour of $F(x \mid \omega)$ for small values of ω, we have from 8·21 (1),

$$F(x \mid \omega) = Q_{m-1}(x) + \frac{\omega^m}{m!} B_m \phi^{(m-1)}(x) + R_m(x),$$

$$R_m(x) = \frac{\omega^{m+1}}{m!} \int_0^\infty P_m(-t)\, \phi^{(m)}(x+\omega t)\, dt,$$

so that

$$\omega^{-m+1} [F(x \mid \omega) - Q_{m-1}(x)] = \omega^{-m+1} R_{m-1}(x),$$

where

$$\omega^{-m+1} R_{m-1}(x) = \omega \left[\frac{B_m}{m!} \phi^{(m-1)}(x) + \omega^{-m} R_m(x) \right].$$

We now assume

$$\int_c^\infty | \phi^{(m)}(y) | \, dy$$

to be bounded, less than A say. Since $|P_m(-t)|$ is bounded, less than B say, we have

$$|\omega^{-m} R_m(x)| < \frac{B}{m!}\int_0^\infty |\omega\,\phi^{(m)}(x+\omega t)|\,dt$$
$$= \frac{B}{m!}\int_x^\infty |\phi^{(m)}(y)|\,dy < \frac{AB}{m!}.$$

It follows that

$$\left[\frac{B_m}{m!}\phi^{(m-1)}(x) + \omega^{-m} R_m(x)\right]$$

is bounded, and hence

$$\lim_{\omega\to 0} \omega^{-m+1} R_{m-1}(x) = 0,$$

so that

$$\lim_{\omega\to 0} \omega^{-m+1}[F(x\,|\,\omega) - Q_{m-1}(x)] = 0,$$

and hence, taking $m = 1$, that

$$\lim_{\omega\to 0} \mathop{\mathbf{S}}_{c}^{x} \phi(t) \mathop{\Delta}_{\omega} t = \int_c^x \phi(t)\,dt.$$

Moreover, if $\phi(x)$ possess derivates of every order, and if an integer n_0 exist such that, for $n \geqslant n_0$,

$$\int_c^\infty |\phi^{(n)}(y)|\,dy$$

is bounded, the above argument shews that

$$\lim_{\omega\to 0} \omega^{-m+1}[F(x\,|\,\omega) - Q_{m-1}(x)] = 0$$

for every fixed value of m, such that $m > n_0 + 1$, and consequently in accordance with Poincaré's definition of asymptotic expansion *

$$F(x\,|\,\omega) \sim \int_c^x \phi(t)\,dt + \sum_{\nu=1}^{\infty} \frac{\omega^\nu}{\nu!} B_\nu\, \phi^{(\nu-1)}(x)$$

for small values of ω. Poincaré's definition is as follows. A divergent series

$$A_0 + \frac{A_1}{z} + \frac{A_2}{z^2} + \ldots + \frac{A_n}{z^n} + \ldots,$$

* *Modern Analysis* (4th edition), p. 151.

in which the sum of the first $(n+1)$ terms is $S_n(z)$ is said to be an asymptotic expansion of $f(z)$ for a given range of values of arg z if the expression $R_n(z) = z^n[f(z) - S_n(z)]$ satisfy the condition

$$\lim_{|z|\to\infty} R_n(z) = 0 \quad (n \text{ fixed}),$$

even though

$$\lim_{n\to\infty} |R_n(z)| = \infty \quad (z \text{ fixed}).$$

When this is the case we can make

$$|z^n[f(z) - S_n(z)]| < \varepsilon,$$

where ε is arbitrarily small, by taking $|z|$ sufficiently large. We then write

$$f(z) \sim \sum_{n=0}^{\infty} A_n z^{-n}.$$

In the case above, when $\omega \to 0$, $\omega^{-1} \to \infty$.

We shall also use the symbol $\sim$ in a slightly different sense, which will cause no confusion, as follows. Let $f(x)$, $g(x)$ be two functions, such that

$$\lim_{x\to\infty} \frac{f(x)}{g(x)}$$

is finite. We shall then write

$$f(x) \sim g(x).$$

In our applications of this notation the limit in question will generally (but not invariably) be unity. In case the limit is unity, we can say that $f(x)$ and $g(x)$ are asymptotically equal. Thus the result of 8·21 (2) can be written

$$F(x \mid \omega) \sim Q_m(x),$$

and these expressions are asymptotically equal.

8·3. Fourier Series for the Sum. To obtain a Fourier Series valid in the interval $c \leqslant x_0 < x < x_0 + \omega$, we can proceed as follows :

By 8·0 (6) we have the uniformly convergent series

$$F(x \mid \omega\,;\, \mu) = \int_c^{\infty} \phi(t, \mu)\, dt - \omega \sum_{s=0}^{\infty} \phi(x + s\omega, \mu).$$

Put $F(x \mid \omega ; \mu)=\frac{1}{2}\alpha_0+\sum_{n=1}^{\infty}\left(\alpha_n \cos \frac{2n\pi x}{\omega}+\beta_n \sin \frac{2n\pi x}{\omega}\right)$,

Then
$$\alpha_n=\frac{2}{\omega} \int_{x_0}^{x_0+\omega} F(x \mid \omega ; \mu) \cos \frac{2n\pi x}{\omega}\, dx,$$

$$\beta_n=\frac{2}{\omega} \int_{x_0}^{x_0+\omega} F(x \mid \omega ; \mu) \sin \frac{2n\pi x}{\omega}\, dx,$$

and therefore
$$\alpha_n+i\beta_n=\frac{2}{\omega} \int_{x_0}^{x_0+\omega} F(x \mid \omega ; \mu)\, e^{\frac{2n\pi x i}{\omega}}\, dx$$

$$=-2 \int_{x_0}^{x_0+\omega} \sum_{s=0}^{\infty} \phi(x+s\omega, \mu)\, e^{\frac{2n\pi x i}{\omega}}\, dx.$$

Since the series is uniformly convergent we may integrate term by term, so that
$$\alpha_n+i\beta_n=-2 \sum_{s=0}^{\infty} \int_{x_0}^{x_0+\omega} \phi(x+s\omega, \mu)\, e^{\frac{2n\pi x i}{\omega}}\, dx$$

$$=-2 \sum_{s=0}^{\infty} \int_{x_0+s\omega}^{x_0+s\omega+\omega} \phi(x, \mu)\, e^{\frac{2n\pi x i}{\omega}}\, dx.$$

Thus $\alpha_n+i\beta_n=-2 \int_{x_0}^{\infty} \phi(x, \mu)\, e^{\frac{2n\pi x i}{\omega}}\, dx.$

Now when $\mu \rightarrow 0$, $F(x \mid \omega ; \mu) \rightarrow F(x \mid \omega)$.

If then, when $\mu \rightarrow 0$, $\alpha_n \rightarrow a_n$, $\beta_n \rightarrow b_n$, we have
$$F(x \mid \omega)=\frac{1}{2} a_0+\sum_{n=1}^{\infty}\left(a_n \cos \frac{2n\pi x}{\omega}+b_n \sin \frac{2n\pi x}{\omega}\right),$$

where
$$a_0=2 \int_c^{x_0} \phi(x)\, dx,$$

$$a_n=-2 \lim_{\mu \rightarrow 0} \int_{x_0}^{\infty} \phi(x, \mu) \cos \frac{2n\pi x}{\omega}\, dx,$$

$$b_n=-2 \lim_{\mu \rightarrow 0} \int_{x_0}^{\infty} \phi(x, \mu) \sin \frac{2n\pi x}{\omega}\, dx.$$

Denoting the Fourier Series of $F(x \mid \omega)$ by $S(x)$, we have by a known property of such series *

$$\begin{aligned} 2S(x_0) &= S(x_0-0)+S(x_0+0) \\ &= F(x_0+\omega \mid \omega)+F(x_0 \mid \omega) \\ &= 2F(x_0 \mid \omega)+\omega\,\phi(x_0). \end{aligned}$$

Thus

$$F(x_0 \mid \omega) = S(x_0) - \tfrac{1}{2}\omega\,\phi(x_0).$$

Writing x for x_0 and noting that

$$\int_x^\infty \phi(t, \mu)\left(\cos\frac{2n\pi t}{\omega}\cos\frac{2n\pi x}{\omega}+\sin\frac{2n\pi t}{\omega}\sin\frac{2\pi n x}{\omega}\right)dt$$
$$= \int_0^\infty \phi(x+t, \mu)\cos\frac{2n\pi t}{\omega}\,dt,$$

we have the following series which is valid for $x \geqslant c$,

$$F(x \mid \omega) = \int_c^x \phi(t)\,dt - \tfrac{1}{2}\omega\,\phi(x) - 2\sum_{n=1}^{\infty}\lim_{\mu\to 0}\int_0^\infty \phi(x+t, \mu)\cos\frac{2n\pi t}{\omega}\,dt.$$

8·4. Complex Variable. Notation. We now proceed to a discussion of the equation

(1) $$\mathop{\Delta}_{\omega} u(z) = \phi(z),$$

on the supposition that the variable and ω may both be complex. We shall denote the complex variable by z, ζ, x according to convenience, and in particular we shall write

$$\zeta = \xi + i\eta = \rho\, e^{i\psi},$$
$$\omega = \sigma\, e^{i\tau}.$$

The expression $R(z)$ denotes the real part of z.

To avoid repetition we shall understand by ϵ, μ arbitrary positive numbers which can, in particular, be taken as small as we please.

The letters m, n, s will denote positive integers, while α will denote a positive number, such that $0 < \alpha < 1$.

When $\zeta = \rho\, e^{i\psi}$, where ρ is real and positive and where ψ is real, we call ρ the modulus and ψ the argument of ζ. We then write

$$\operatorname{mod}\zeta = |\zeta| = \rho, \quad \arg\zeta = \psi.$$

* E. W. Hobson, *Theory of Functions of a Real Variable* (2nd edition, 1926), chap. viii.

The complex number $\zeta = \xi + i\eta$ can be represented geometrically by the point (ξ, η) referred to rectangular Cartesian axes or by the point whose polar coordinates are (ρ, ψ). The figure which thus represents ζ is called the Argand diagram and we can speak of the *point* ζ. It is easy to prove, and is in fact obvious from the diagram, that

$$|\zeta_1 + \zeta_2| \leqslant |\zeta_1| + |\zeta_2|,$$

where ζ_1, ζ_2 are any two numbers, real or complex and therefore that

$$|\zeta_1| - |\zeta_2| \leqslant |\zeta_1 - \zeta_2|.$$

Take a point a represented on the Argand diagram and surround a with a small region, say a circle whose centre is a. This region will be called a *neighbourhood* of a.

A function $f(\zeta)$ is said to be *holomorphic in a region* when $f(\zeta)$ has a unique finite value and a unique finite derivate at every point of the region. The function is said to be *holomorphic at a point*, if a neighbourhood of the point exist, in which the function is holomorphic. A point at which the function is not holomorphic is called a *singular point* or *singularity* of the function.

Let $f(\zeta)$ be a given function, a a given point and N a neighbourhood of a. If in N an expansion exist of the form

$$f(\zeta) = g(\zeta) + \frac{r}{\zeta - a} + \frac{a_2}{(\zeta - a)^2} + \dots + \frac{a_m}{(\zeta - a)^m},$$

where $g(\zeta)$ is holomorphic in N, then a is said to be a *pole* of order m of the function $f(\zeta)$.

The coefficient r of $(\zeta - a)^{-1}$ in the above expansion is called the *residue* at a of the function $f(\zeta)$.

If $m = 1$, a is a simple pole, and in this case

$$r = \lim_{\zeta \to a} (\zeta - a) f(\zeta).$$

A function which is holomorphic in a region R except at poles, of which every finite sub-region of R contains only a finite number, is said to be *meromorphic* in R.

We now state

Cauchy's Residue Theorem. *Let C be a simple closed contour, such that a function $f(\zeta)$ is holomorphic at every point of C and in the* *interior of C, except at a finite number of poles inside the contour. Then*

$$\frac{1}{2\pi i}\int_C f(\zeta)\,d\zeta = \Sigma R,$$

where ΣR denotes the sum of the residues of $f(\zeta)$ at those poles which are situated within the contour C.

For the proof of this theorem and for a full discussion of the subjects of the above summary the reader is referred to a treatise on Analysis.*

8·41. Application of Cauchy's Residue Theorem. In Fig. 1, A is the point $(-\alpha, 0)$ BC, ED are the lines $\eta = h$, $\eta = -h$; CPD is a circular arc centre O which cuts the real axis at a point P between n and $n+1$ say, for definiteness, at the point $n+\frac{1}{2}$.

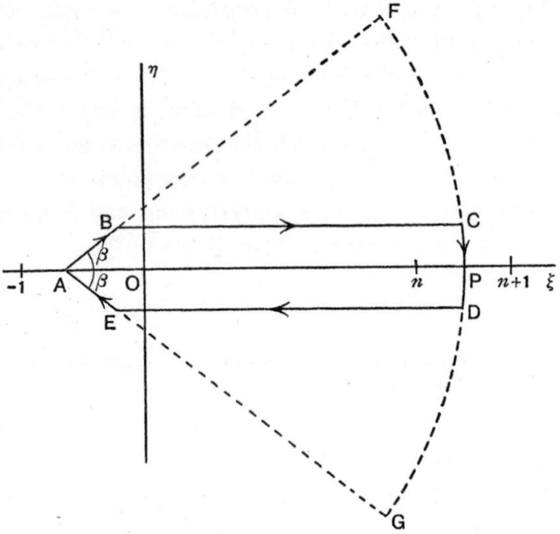

FIG. 1.

As ζ describes the contour $ABCDEA$, we shall suppose that the point $z+\omega\zeta$ describes a contour which lies entirely in a region of the plane in which the function $\phi(z+\omega\zeta)$ is holomorphic. Since

$$\pi\cot\pi\zeta = \frac{1}{\zeta}+\frac{1}{\zeta-1}+\frac{1}{\zeta+1}+\dots+\frac{1}{\zeta-n}+\frac{1}{\zeta+n}+\dots,$$

* For example, *Modern Analysis*, 1, 5, 6.

t follows that the only singularities of the function

$$\phi(z+\omega\zeta)\,\pi\cot\pi\zeta$$

which lie inside the contour $ABCDEA$ are simple poles at the points 0, 1, 2, ..., n.

We have therefore, by Cauchy's Residue Theorem,

$$\sum_{s=0}^{n}\phi(z+s\omega) = -\frac{1}{2\pi i}\int_{ABCDEA}\phi(z+\omega\zeta)\,\pi\cot\pi\zeta\,d\zeta,$$

since the contour is described clockwise.

Now

$$\frac{1}{2i}\cot\pi\zeta = -\frac{1}{2}+\frac{1}{1-e^{-2\pi i\zeta}} = \frac{1}{2}-\frac{1}{1-e^{2\pi i\zeta}}.$$

Hence

$$-\sum_{s=0}^{n}\phi(z+s\omega) = \int_{ABCP}\left(-\frac{1}{2}+\frac{1}{1-e^{-2\pi i\zeta}}\right)\phi(z+\omega\zeta)\,d\zeta - \int_{AEDP}\left(\frac{1}{2}-\frac{1}{1-e^{2\pi i\zeta}}\right)\phi(z+\omega\zeta)\,d\zeta$$

$$= -\tfrac{1}{2}\int_{ABCP}\phi(z+\omega\zeta)\,d\zeta - \tfrac{1}{2}\int_{AEDP}\phi(z+\omega\zeta)\,d\zeta + \int_{ABCP}\frac{\phi(z+\omega\zeta)}{1-e^{-2\pi i\zeta}}\,d\zeta + \int_{AEDP}\frac{\phi(z+\omega\zeta)}{1-e^{2\pi i\zeta}}\,d\zeta.$$

Since $\phi(z+\omega\zeta)$ has no singularities inside $ABCDEA$, we can hrink the paths $ABCP$, $AEDP$ in the first two integrals until they oincide with AP. We now suppose further that, when ζ describes he contour $ABFCPDGEA$ (obtained by producing AB, AE to neet the circle CPD), $z+\omega\zeta$ describes a contour lying entirely in region in which $\phi(z+\omega\zeta)$ is holomorphic. We can then replace n the second two integrals the path $ABCP$ by $AFCP$, and $AEDP$ y $AGDP$.

Thus we obtain

$$-\sum_{s=0}^{n}\phi(z+s\omega) = -\int_{-a}^{n+\frac{1}{2}}\phi(z+\omega\zeta)\,d\zeta + \int_{AF}\frac{\phi(z+\omega\zeta)}{1-e^{-2\pi i\zeta}}\,d\zeta + \int_{AG}\frac{\phi(z+\omega\zeta)}{1-e^{2\pi i\zeta}} + I_{n+\frac{1}{2}},$$

where

$$I_{n+\frac{1}{2}} = \int_{FCP} \frac{\phi(z+\omega\zeta)}{1-e^{-2\pi i\zeta}}\,d\zeta + \int_{GDP} \frac{\phi(z+\omega\zeta)}{1-e^{2\pi i\zeta}}\,d\zeta.$$

We now make the following hypotheses :

(i) For every n, however large, and for a fixed value of the angle β in Fig. 1, when ζ describes the contour $AGDPFA$, $z+\omega\zeta$ describes a contour lying entirely in a region in which $\phi(z+\omega\zeta)$ is holomorphic.

(ii) That $\int_c^\infty \phi(\zeta)\,d\zeta$ is convergent.

(iii) That $\sum_{s=0}^{\infty} \phi(z+s\omega)$ is convergent.

(iv) That $|I_{n+\frac{1}{2}}| \to 0$ when $n \to \infty$.

The principal solution of the difference equation of 8·4 is then

$$F(z\,|\,\omega) = \int_c^\infty \phi(\zeta)\,d\zeta - \omega \sum_{s=0}^{\infty} \phi(z+s\omega)$$

$$= \int_c^\infty \phi(\zeta)\,d\zeta - \omega \int_{-a}^{\infty} \phi(z+\omega\zeta)\,d\zeta$$

$$+\omega \int_{AF\infty} \frac{\phi(z+\omega\zeta)}{1-e^{-2\pi i\zeta}}\,d\zeta + \omega \int_{AG\infty} \frac{\phi(z+\omega\zeta)}{1-e^{2\pi i\zeta}}\,d\zeta.$$

Thus we have

(1) $F(z\,|\,\omega)$

$$= \int_c^{z-\omega a} \phi(\zeta)\,d\zeta + \omega \int_{R_1} \frac{\phi(z+\omega\zeta)}{1-e^{-2\pi i\zeta}}\,d\zeta + \omega \int_{R_2} \frac{\phi(z+\omega\zeta)}{1-e^{2\pi i\zeta}}\,d\zeta,$$

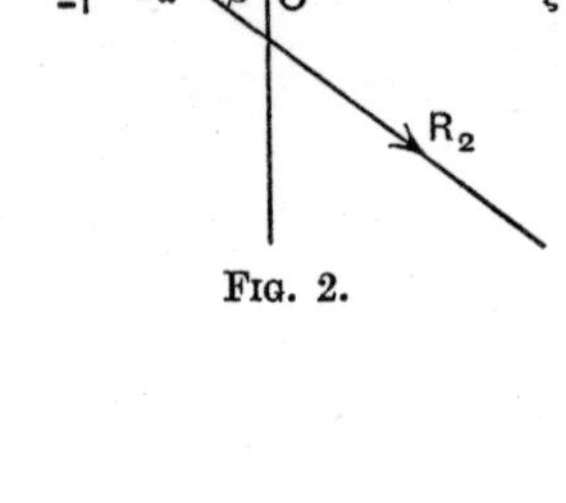

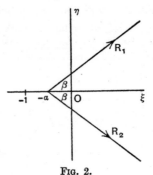

FIG. 2.

where R_1 and R_2 are rays from $-\alpha$ to infinity, each inclined at an angle β to the real axis, Fig. 2. If we now put

(2) $$f(\zeta) = \int_c^\zeta \phi(t)\,dt,$$

we can write (1) in the form

$$F(z\,|\,\omega) = f(z-\alpha\omega) + \int_{R_1} \frac{1}{1-e^{-2\pi i\zeta}} \frac{d}{d\zeta} f(z+\omega\zeta)\,d\zeta$$
$$+ \int_{R_2} \frac{1}{1-e^{2\pi i\zeta}} \frac{d}{d\zeta} f(z+\omega\zeta)\,d\zeta.$$

Integrating by parts, we obtain for $F(z\,|\,\omega)$ the expression

$$f(z-\alpha\omega) + \left[\frac{f(z+\omega\zeta)}{1-e^{-2\pi i\zeta}}\right]_{R_1} + \left[\frac{f(z+\omega\zeta)}{1-e^{2\pi i\zeta}}\right]_{R_2}$$
$$+ \int_{R_1} \frac{2\pi i\, e^{-2\pi i\zeta} f(z+\omega\zeta)}{(1-e^{-2\pi i\zeta})^2}\,d\zeta - \int_{R_2} \frac{2\pi i\, e^{2\pi i\zeta} f(z+\omega\zeta)}{(1-e^{2\pi i\zeta})^2}\,d\zeta.$$

Now when $\zeta \to \infty$ along R_1, $|e^{-2\pi i\zeta}| \to \infty$, since $R(-i\zeta)$ is positive. Similarly, $|e^{2\pi i\zeta}| \to \infty$ when $\zeta \to \infty$ along R_2. Thus the values of the contents of the square brackets vanish at infinity.

Again,

$$-\frac{1}{1-e^{-2\pi i a}} - \frac{1}{1-e^{2\pi i a}} = -1,$$

$$\frac{2\pi i\, e^{-2\pi i\zeta}}{(1-e^{-2\pi i\zeta})^2} = \frac{2\pi i}{(e^{\pi i\zeta}-e^{-\pi i\zeta})^2} = \frac{1}{2\pi i}\,\frac{\pi^2}{\sin^2 \pi\zeta}.$$

Thus we have

(3) $$F(z\,|\,\omega) = \frac{1}{2\pi i} \int_C f(z+\omega\zeta) \left(\frac{\pi}{\sin \pi\zeta}\right)^2 d\zeta,$$

where C is the line of integration shewn in Fig. 3.

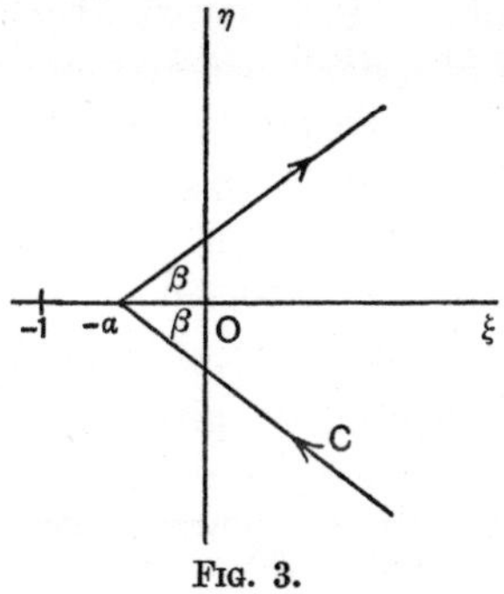

FIG. 3.

8·5. Extension of the Theory. Having established the form which the principal solution of the difference equation

$$(1) \qquad \underset{\omega}{\Delta} u(z) = \phi(z)$$

takes under the hypotheses (i)-(iv) of the preceding section, we now consider some cases in which these hypotheses are not fulfilled. That such cases of exception are numerous and important may be seen by considering such simple functions as e^z, $\sinh z$, z^{-1}.

When we are given an equation of form (1) where $\phi(z)$ does not satisfy the conditions of convergence enumerated above, we replace the equation by

$$(2) \qquad \underset{\omega}{\Delta} u(z) = \phi(z)\, e^{-\mu\lambda(z)},$$

and we then attempt to determine a function $\lambda(z)$ such that this new equation may have a principal solution of the form already found.

Denoting this principal solution by $F(z \mid \omega;\, \mu)$, we examine the behaviour when $\mu \to 0$. If $F(z \mid \omega;\, \mu)$ tend to a definite limit function $F(z \mid \omega)$ which is independent of $\lambda(z)$, we have the required principal solution of (1).

To study this process, we consider the function $\phi(z)$, which satisfies the following conditions :

(A) In the half plane $R(z) \geqslant a$, $\phi(z)$ is holomorphic.

(B) When $R(z) \geqslant a$, there exist positive constants C and k, such that

$$|\phi(z)| < C\, e^{(k+\epsilon)|z|},$$

however small the positive number ϵ may be.

The class of functions which satisfy these conditions includes all integral functions of order * one and, in particular, all rational functions and functions of the form $P(z)\, e^{lz}$ where $P(z)$ is rational.

We shall now prove that in this case it is sufficient to take $\lambda(z) = z^p$, $p > 1$, in order to ensure convergence of the integrals, provided that ω be suitably restricted.

We shall denote by δ a *real or complex* number, such that $|\delta| \to 0$ when $|\zeta| \to \infty$. More precisely, given a positive number h, we

* For the definition of order of an integral function, see, for example, P. Dienes, *The Taylor Series*, 1931, p. 290.

can find a positive number ρ_0, such that $|\delta| < h$, if $\rho = |\zeta| \geqslant \rho_0$. If δ occur more than once in the same formula, its value is not necessarily the same in each place where it occurs. With this convention we can, for example, write

$$\lambda(z+\omega\zeta) = (\omega\zeta)^p \left(1+\frac{z}{\omega\zeta}\right)^p = (\rho\sigma)^p e^{ip(\psi+\tau)}(1+\delta),$$

$$(k+\varepsilon)\rho - \mu\rho^p(1+\delta) = -\mu\rho^p(1+\delta), \quad p > 1.$$

Consider $\int_c^\infty \phi(\zeta)e^{-\mu\lambda(\zeta)}d\zeta$ taken along the real axis. We have

$$|\phi(\zeta)e^{-\mu\lambda(\zeta)}| < C e^{(k+\epsilon)\rho - \mu\rho^p(1+\delta)},$$
$$< C e^{-\mu\rho^p(1+\delta)}.$$

It follows from this that the integral converges since its modulus is more convergent than $\int_c^\infty e^{-\rho}d\rho$.

Again,

$$\left|\sum_{s=0}^\infty \phi(z+\omega s)e^{-\mu\lambda(z+\omega s)}\right|$$
$$< C e^{(k+\epsilon)|z|} \sum_{s=0}^\infty e^{(k+\epsilon)\sigma s - (\mu(\sigma s)^p \cos p\tau)(1+\delta)}$$

and

$$(k+\varepsilon)\sigma s - (\mu(\sigma s)^p \cos p\tau)(1+\delta) = -(\mu(\sigma s)^p \cos p\tau)(1+\delta).$$

Hence the series is more convergent than $\sum_{s=0}^\infty e^{-s}$, provided that $\cos p\tau > 0$, that is, provided that $|p\tau| < \frac{\pi}{2}$. Since p is arbitrarily near to unity, this gives

(3) $$|\tau| < \frac{\pi}{2},$$

which is the first restriction on ω.

Since the integral and the series both converge, it follows that

(4) $$F(z|\omega;\mu) = \int_c^\infty \phi(\zeta)e^{-\mu\lambda(\zeta)}d\zeta - \omega\sum_{s=0}^\infty \phi(z+\omega s)e^{-\mu\lambda(z+\omega s)}$$

exists as an analytic function of z, provided that (3) be satisfied.

Now consider Fig. 3. As ζ describes the path C it is easy to see that $R(z+\omega\zeta) \geqslant R(z-\alpha\omega)$, provided that

5) $$\beta < \frac{\pi}{2} - |\tau|.$$

Hence, as ζ describes C, we shall have $R(z+\omega\zeta) \geqslant a$, provided that α be chosen so that

(6) $$R(z-\alpha\omega) \geqslant a.$$

We shall suppose conditions (3), (5), (6) to be fulfilled so that condition (i) of 8·41 is satisfied. We now turn to (see Fig. 2)

$$I_{R_1} = \int_{R_1} \frac{\phi(z+\omega\zeta)e^{-\mu\lambda(z+\omega\zeta)}}{1-e^{-2\pi i\zeta}}\, d\zeta.$$

With ζ on R_1, $\zeta = \rho\, e^{i\beta} . e^{i(\psi-\beta)} = \rho\, e^{i\beta}(1+\delta)$,

$$\left| \frac{1}{1-e^{-2\pi i\zeta}} \right| = \frac{1}{2}\, \frac{e^{-\pi\eta}}{(\sin^2 \pi\xi + \sinh^2 \pi\eta)^{\frac{1}{2}}} = e^{-2\pi\eta}(1+\delta).$$

Hence

$$| I_{R_1} | < C\, e^{(k+\epsilon)|z|} \int_{R_1} (1+\delta)\, e^{-u(\rho)}\, d\rho,$$

where

$$u(\rho) = 2\pi\eta - (k+\varepsilon)\,\rho\sigma + \mu\,[\,(\rho\sigma)^p \cos p\,(\psi+\tau)\,]\,(1+\delta).$$

The integral certainly converges if $u(\rho)$ be positive, and this condition is satisfied for all positive values of μ and for $\mu = 0$, provided that

$$\cos p\,(\psi+\tau) > 0 \quad \text{and} \quad 2\pi\rho \sin\psi - (k+\varepsilon)\,\sigma\rho > 0.$$

Since on R_1 we have $\psi > \beta$ and $\psi - \beta \to 0$ when $\rho \to \infty$, these conditions lead to

$$\psi < \frac{\pi}{2p} - \tau, \quad \sigma < \frac{2\pi \sin\psi}{k+\varepsilon},$$

that is, to

(7) $$\beta < \frac{\pi}{2} - |\tau|, \quad \sigma < \frac{2\pi\cos\tau}{k}.$$

If these conditions be satisfied, I_{R_1} converges, and, when $\mu \to 0$,

$$I_{R_1} \to \int_{R_1} \frac{\phi(z+\omega\zeta)}{1-e^{-2\pi i\zeta}}\, d\zeta.$$

In the same way we may shew that, if conditions (7) be satisfied,

$$\int_{R_2} \frac{\phi(z+\omega\zeta)e^{-\mu\lambda(z+\omega\zeta)}}{1-e^{2\pi i\zeta}}\,d\zeta$$

converges and, when $\mu\to 0$, has the limit

$$\int_{R_2} \frac{\phi(z+\omega\zeta)}{1-e^{2\pi i\zeta}}\,d\zeta.$$

The proof that condition 8·41 (iv) is satisfied by the function $\phi(z)\,e^{-\mu\lambda(z)}$ presents no difficulties and is left to the reader.

We have thus proved that the principal solution of

$$\underset{\omega}{\Delta}\, u(z) = \phi(z),$$

when $|\phi(z)| < C\,e^{(k+\epsilon)|z|}$ for $R(z) \geqslant a$ can be put into the form 8·41 (3).

(8) $$F(z\,|\,\omega) = \frac{1}{2\pi i}\int_C f(z+\omega\zeta)\left(\frac{\pi}{\sin \pi\zeta}\right)^2 d\zeta,$$

provided that

$$\sigma < \frac{2\pi \cos\tau}{k}, \quad |\tau| < \frac{\pi}{2}, \quad \beta < \frac{\pi}{2} - |\tau|.$$

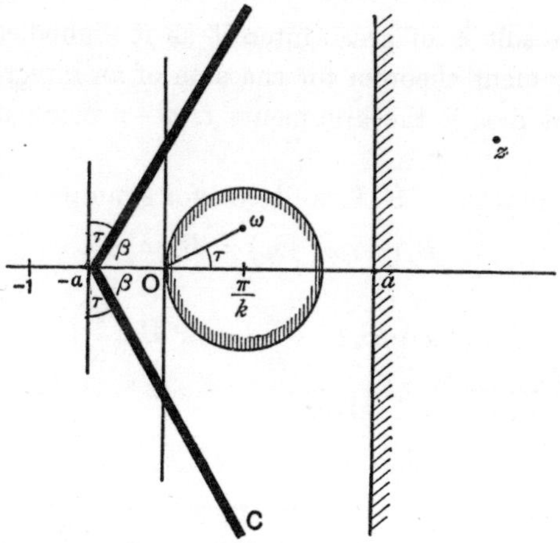

FIG. 4.

Fig. 4 illustrates what we have proved.

Expression (8) represents the principal solution for z in the half plane $R(z) \geqslant a$, and ω inside a circle whose centre is the point $\frac{\pi}{k}$ and whose radius is $\frac{\pi}{k}$. The particular contour C depends on the value of ω inside this circle.

When $\tau = 0$, ω is real and the contour C becomes a parallel to the imaginary axis. We have thus, for $\omega < \frac{2\pi}{k}$,

$$(9) \qquad F(z \mid \omega) = \frac{1}{2\pi i}\int_{-a-i\infty}^{-a+i\infty} f(z+\omega\zeta)\left(\frac{\pi}{\sin \pi\zeta}\right)^2 d\zeta.$$

From this we can at once draw the important conclusion that, if $\phi(z)$ be an *integral function* (of order one), that is to say, holomorphic in the whole plane (excluding the point ∞), (9) represents the principal solution not only for $\omega < \frac{2\pi}{k}$, but for every ω inside the circle $|\omega| = \frac{2\pi}{k}$. Also,

$$(10) \quad F(z-\omega \mid -\omega) = \frac{1}{2\pi i}\int_{-a-i\infty}^{-a+i\infty} f(z-\omega-\omega\zeta)\left(\frac{\pi}{\sin \pi\zeta}\right)^2 d\zeta$$

$$= \frac{1}{2\pi i}\int_{a-1-i\infty}^{a-1+i\infty} f(z+\omega\zeta)\left(\frac{\pi}{\sin \pi\zeta}\right)^2 d\zeta = F(z \mid \omega).$$

This last result is of great interest as it embodies the complementary argument theorem for the sum of an integral function of order one (at most), the arguments z, $\omega - z$ being called complementary.

With the notation of 8·16, we have, for example,

$$B_\nu(x-\omega \mid -\omega) = B_\nu(x \mid \omega).$$

That is,

$$(-\omega)^\nu B_\nu\left(1-\frac{x}{\omega}\right) = \omega^\nu B_\nu\left(\frac{x}{\omega}\right),$$

which, in the case $\omega = 1$, gives

$$B_\nu(1-x) = (-1)^\nu B_\nu(x),$$

the formula of 6·5 (8). It thus appears that the complementary argument theorem of Bernoulli's polynomials (of the first order) is a particular case of the general complementary argument theorem (10), and is shared by Bernoulli's polynomials in virtue of the fact that they are principal solutions of the equation

$$\underset{\omega}{\Delta} u(x) = \nu x^{\nu-1}.$$

8·53. The Sum of the Exponential Function. We have by 8·5 (9), 8·41 (2),

(1) $$I = \underset{c}{\overset{z}{S}} e^{m\zeta} \underset{\omega}{\Delta} \zeta = \frac{1}{2\pi i}\int_{-a-i\infty}^{-a+i\infty} f(z+\omega\zeta)\left(\frac{\pi}{\sin \pi\zeta}\right)^2 d\zeta,$$

$$f(z) = \int_c^z e^{m\zeta}\, d\zeta = \frac{e^{mz}-e^{mc}}{m}.$$

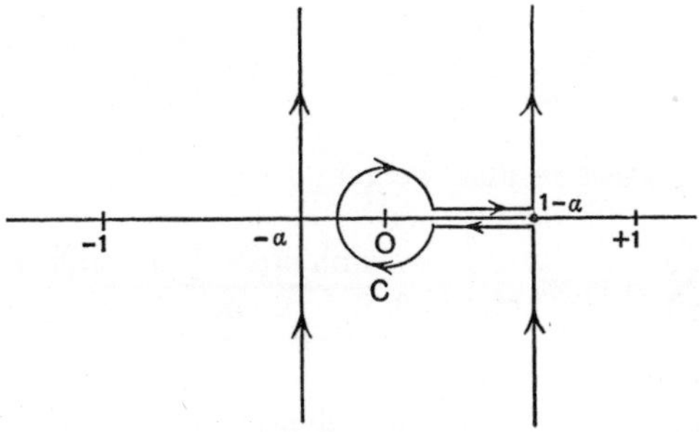

FIG. 5.

If we deform the path as shewn in Fig. 5, we obtain

$$I = \frac{1}{2\pi i}\int_C + \frac{1}{2\pi i}\int_{-a+1-i\infty}^{-a+1+i\infty},$$

where the integrand is the same as in (1) and C denotes the loop, the straight parts of which are supposed to coincide with the real axis.

The residue at $\zeta = 0$ of the integrand is $\omega\, e^{mz}$. If in the second integral we write $\zeta+1$ for ζ, we obtain

$$I = -\omega\, e^{mz} + \frac{1}{2\pi i}\int_{-a-i\infty}^{-a+i\infty} \frac{e^{m(z+\omega\zeta)+m\omega} - e^{mc}}{m}\left(\frac{\pi}{\sin \pi\zeta}\right)^2 d\zeta$$

$$= -\omega\, e^{mz} + e^{m\omega}\, I + \frac{e^{m(c+\omega)} - e^{mc}}{2\pi i\, m}\int_{-a-i\infty}^{-a+i\infty}\left(\frac{\pi}{\sin \pi\zeta}\right)^2 d\zeta.$$

The last integral is equal to

$$2\pi i\left[-\frac{1}{1-e^{-2\pi i\zeta}}\right]_{-a-i\infty}^{-a+i\infty} = 2\pi i.$$

Thus

$$\underset{c}{\overset{z}{S}} e^{m\zeta} \underset{\omega}{\Delta} \zeta = \frac{\omega\, e^{mz}}{e^{m\omega}-1} - \frac{e^{mc}}{m}, \quad |\,\omega\,| < \left|\frac{2\pi}{m}\right|.$$

Regarded as a function of ω the sum is meromorphic,* with simple poles at the points $\omega = \dfrac{2s\pi i}{m}$, s an integer. The poles nearest the origin are at $\pm\dfrac{2\pi i}{m}$, so that the inequality stated for $|\omega|$ is in fact the best possible.

If we write $-m$ for m, we get

$$\mathop{\mathbf{S}}_{c}^{z} e^{-m\zeta} \underset{\omega}{\Delta} \zeta = \frac{\omega\, e^{-mz}}{e^{-m\omega}-1} + \frac{e^{-mc}}{m}.$$

Combining these results, we get

$$\mathop{\mathbf{S}}_{c}^{z} \cosh m\zeta \underset{\omega}{\Delta} \zeta = \frac{\omega}{2}\,\frac{\sinh m(z-\frac{1}{2}\omega)}{\sinh \dfrac{m\omega}{2}} - \frac{\sinh mc}{m},$$

$$\mathop{\mathbf{S}}_{c}^{z} \sinh m\zeta \underset{\omega}{\Delta} \zeta = \frac{\omega}{2}\,\frac{\cosh m(z-\frac{1}{2}\omega)}{\sinh \dfrac{m\omega}{2}} - \frac{\cosh mc}{m}.$$

We may observe that neither of these sums vanishes when $z = c$.

If we write im for m, we obtain

$$\mathop{\mathbf{S}}_{c}^{z} \cos m\zeta \underset{\omega}{\Delta} \zeta = \frac{\omega}{2}\,\frac{\sin m(z-\frac{1}{2}\omega)}{\sin \dfrac{m\omega}{2}} - \frac{\sin mc}{m},$$

$$\mathop{\mathbf{S}}_{c}^{z} \sin m\zeta \underset{\omega}{\Delta} \zeta = -\frac{\omega}{2}\,\frac{\cos m(z-\frac{1}{2}\omega)}{\sin \dfrac{m\omega}{2}} + \frac{\cos mc}{m}.$$

8·6. Functions with only one Singular Point. Let $\phi(z)$ have only one singular point, at the point $z_1 = r_1 e^{i\theta_1}$, where r_1 is finite. Then $\phi(z)$ is holomorphic outside the circle whose centre is the origin and whose radius is r_1. Let a_1 and a be two real numbers such that $a_1 < r_1 \cos\theta_1$, $a > r_1 \cos\theta_1$.

Then $\phi(z)$ is holomorphic in each of the half planes,

$$R(z) \leqslant a_1, \quad R(z) \geqslant a.$$

---

* See 8·4, p. 221.

We shall suppose that outside the circle radius r_1,

$$|\phi(z)| < C\, e^{(k+\epsilon)|z|},$$

where C and k are fixed positive constants and ϵ is positive and arbitrarily small. Then, if $0 < \omega < 2\pi/k$, $R(x) > a - \alpha\omega$, we have

$$(1) \qquad F(x\,|\,\omega) = \frac{1}{2\pi i}\int_{L_1} f(x+\omega z)\left(\frac{\pi}{\sin \pi z}\right)^2 dz,$$

where L_1 is the line through $-\alpha$ parallel to the imaginary axis described in the direction $-i\infty - \alpha$ to $+i\infty - \alpha$. Provided that $R(x) > a$, α can always be chosen to satisfy the above condition.

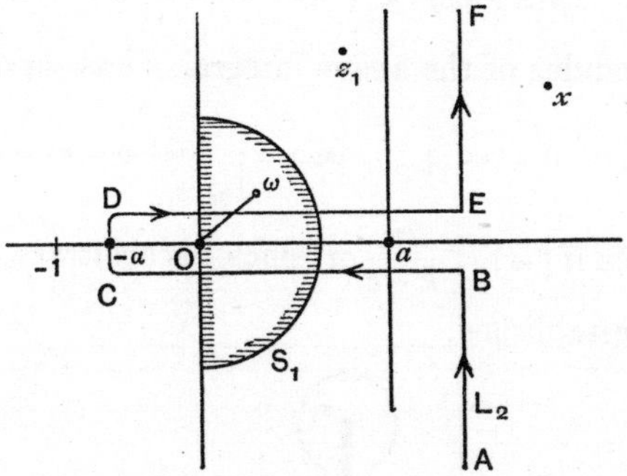

FIG. 6.

Now consider Fig. 6, where we have deformed the contour L_1 into L_2, the lines AB, EF being straight, collinear, parallel to the imaginary axis, and at distance l from it.

S_1 is a semicircle, radius $2\pi/k$, centre O. By taking the straight portions DE, BC long enough and sufficiently near to the real axis we can always arrange, for any fixed value of ω interior to S_1 and for $R(x) > a$, that, as z describes L_2, $x+\omega z$ describes a contour to the right of which $\phi(x+\omega z)$ has no singularity.

In the extreme case, $\omega = 2\pi i/k$, the contour described by $x+\omega z$ is L_2 turned through a right angle with the origin moved to x. We can now shew that

$$(2) \quad F(x\,|\,\omega) = \frac{1}{2\pi i}\int_{L_2} f(x+\omega z)\left(\frac{\pi}{\sin \pi z}\right)^2 dz, \quad |\omega| < \frac{2\pi}{k}, \quad R(\omega) \geqslant 0.$$

In order to do this we must shew that the integral converges. To do this it is sufficient to shew that

$$\left| \int_{PF\infty} \frac{\phi(x+\omega z)}{1-e^{-2\pi i z}}\, dz \right|$$

is finite where P is an arbitrary point, $l+iy_0$, on EF.

If y be the imaginary part of z,

$$|(1-e^{-2\pi i z})^{-1}| = e^{-\pi y}(\sin^2 \pi l + \sinh^2 \pi y)^{-\frac{1}{2}}$$
$$< e^{-\pi y} / \sinh \pi y$$
$$< 2e^{-2\pi y}(1-e^{-2\pi y_0})^{-1},$$
$$|\phi(x+\omega z)| < C\, e^{(k+\epsilon)|x+\omega l| + (k+\epsilon)|\omega| y}$$

so that the modulus of the above integral is less than

$$2\, C\, e^{(k+\epsilon)|x+\omega l|}(1-e^{-2\pi y_0})^{-1} \int_{y_0}^{\infty} e^{(k+\epsilon)|\omega| y - 2\pi y}\, dy,$$

and this is finite if $|\omega| < \dfrac{2\pi}{k+\varepsilon}$ or, since ε is arbitrary, if $|\omega| < \dfrac{2\pi}{k}$.

Thus (2) is established.

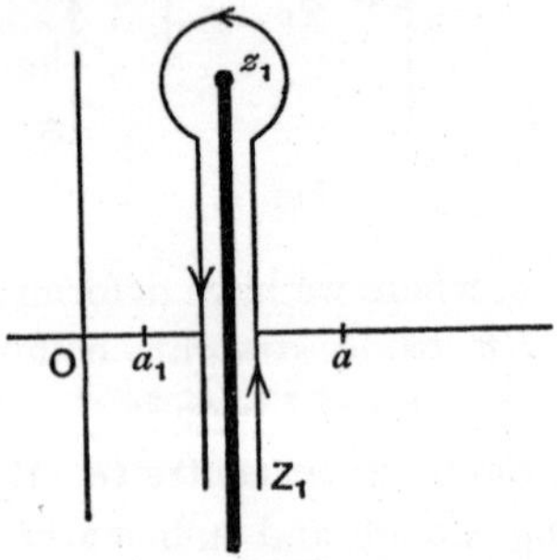

FIG. 7.

Consider now

(3) $$f(x) = \int_c^x \phi(z)\, dz, \quad R(c) > a.$$

Since z_1 is a singular point of $\phi(z)$, $f(x)$ is, in general, many-valued. To avoid this we make a cut * in the z plane from z_1 to

* A cut is an impassable barrier. The variable may not move along any curve which crosses this barrier.

$-\infty$ parallel to the negative imaginary axis (see Fig. 7). In the cut plane $f(x)$ is single-valued.

Changing the variable in (1), we have for $R(x) > a$, and for $0 < \omega < 2\pi / k$,

$$(4) \qquad F(x \mid \omega) = \frac{1}{2\pi i \omega} \int_{x - \omega a - \omega i \infty}^{x - \omega a + \omega i \infty} f(z)\, \pi^2 \operatorname{cosec}^2 \frac{\pi}{\omega}(z - x)\, dz.$$

Now keep ω fixed and move x to the left from $R(x) > a$ to $R(x) < a_1$. When we cross the singular point z_1, we increase $F(x \mid \omega)$ by

$$(5) \qquad P(x \mid \omega) = \frac{1}{2\pi i \omega} \int_{Z_1} f(z)\, \pi^2 \operatorname{cosec}^2 \frac{\pi}{\omega}(z - x) dz,$$

where Z_1 is an infinite loop round z_1 as shewn in Fig. 7.

Thus for $R(x) < a_1$, $0 < \omega < 2\pi / k$, we have

$$(6) \qquad F(x \mid \omega) = P(x \mid \omega) + \frac{1}{2\pi i} \int_{-a - i\infty}^{-a + i\infty} f(x + \omega z) \left(\frac{\pi}{\sin \pi z} \right)^2 dz.$$

By suitably deforming the path of integration in (2), we can consider this result as established for all values of ω interior to the semicircle S_1 of Fig. 6, and for the modified path.

To evaluate $P(x \mid \omega)$, we have from (5), on integrating by parts,

$$P(x \mid \omega) = -\frac{1}{2i} \left[f(z) \cot \frac{\pi}{\omega}(z - x) \right]_{Z_1} + \frac{1}{2\pi i} \int_{Z_1} \pi\, \phi(z) \cot \frac{\pi}{\omega}(z - x)\, dz.$$

Since $\cot \frac{\pi}{\omega}(z_1 - i\infty - x) = +i$, we have, if z_1 be a simple pole

$$(7) \qquad P(x \mid \omega) = -\pi i R_1 - \pi R_1 \cot (x - z_1) \frac{\pi}{\omega},$$

where R_1 is the residue at z_1 of $\phi(z)$. Evidently then

$$(8) \qquad P(x \mid \omega) + P(x \mid -\omega) = -2\pi i R_1,$$

and from the definition (5)

$$P(x + \omega \mid \omega) = P(x \mid \omega),$$

so that $P(x \mid \omega)$ is a periodic function of x with period ω.

To extend our results to values of ω inside the circle $\mid \omega \mid = 2\pi / k$, consider (4). Taking $R(x) > a$ and keeping x fixed, let us make ω describe the path p_1 inside the semicircle S_2, radius $2\pi/k$, in Fig. 8. The path of integration then passes from l_1 via l_2 to l_3, remaining

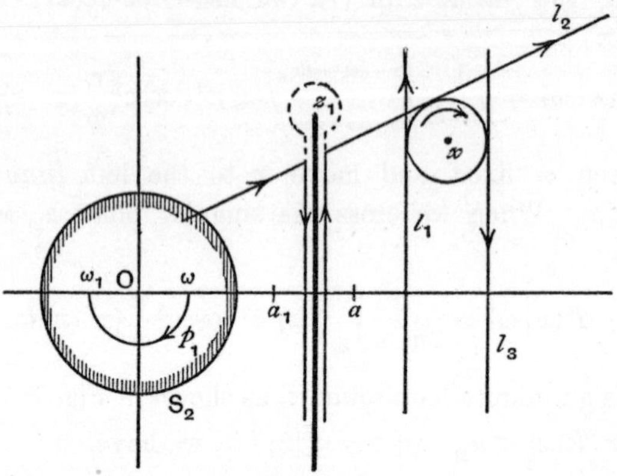

FIG. 8.

tangential to a circle centre x, radius $|\alpha\omega|$. As soon as l_2 has passed the singular point z_1 the integral on the right of (4) increases by an amount equal to an integral round the infinite loop Z_1, thus

$$(9)\qquad F(x\,|\,\omega_1) = P(x\,|\,\omega_1) + \frac{1}{2\pi i}\int_{-a-i\infty}^{-a+i\infty} f(x+\omega_1 z)\left(\frac{\pi}{\sin \pi z}\right)^2 dz,$$

for the path p_1, since, for this path, (5) still transforms in (7).

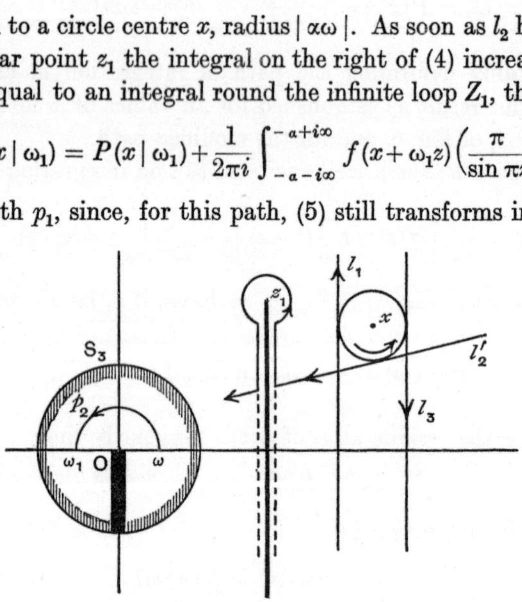

FIG. 9.

If, on the other hand, we go from ω to ω_1 by the path p_2, Fig. 9, inside the semicircle S_3, radius $2\pi/k$, l_1 passes via l_2' to l_3, and the right of (4) again increases by an amount equal to an integral round the infinite loop Z_1, but now we must evaluate (5) for a negative value of ω, and then we obtain, for the path p_2,

(10) $F(x \mid \omega_1)$

$$=2\pi i R_1+P(x \mid \omega_1)+\frac{1}{2\pi i}\int_{-a-i\infty}^{-a+i\infty} f(x+\omega_1 z)\left(\frac{\pi}{\sin \pi z}\right)^2 dz,$$

where $P(x \mid \omega_1)$ is still given by (7).

Thus $F(x \mid \omega)$ exists but is not one-valued when ω varies inside the circle $|\omega| = 2\pi / k$ in the ω plane. If, however, we make a cut in the ω plane (but not in the z plane) from 0 to $-2\pi i / k$, $F(x \mid \omega)$ is one-valued for ω inside the circle $|\omega| = 2\pi / k$ in the cut ω plane and the value of $F(x \mid \omega)$ for negative values of ω, $\omega_1 = -\omega$, is given by (10). Finally, if we now let x recede to the half plane $R(x) < a_1$, keeping a fixed negative value of ω, we arrive once more at (2), which, by a simple deformation of the path of integration, is seen to be holomorphic for all values of ω inside the circle $|\omega| = 2\pi/k$ in the cut ω plane and for all values of x in the cut z plane. We have thus obtained the analytic continuation of $F(x \mid \omega)$ in the above regions.

If $\phi(z)$, instead of having one singularity, have a finite number n, all at a finite distance, with residues $R_1, R_2, \dots, R_n$, we can proceed in exactly the same way and we shall arrive at similar results, the function $P(x \mid \omega)$ of (7) being replaced (for simple poles) by

$$P(x \mid \omega) = -\pi i \sum_{s=1}^{n} R_s - \pi \sum_{s=1}^{n} R_s \cot(x-z_s)\frac{\pi}{\omega}.$$

In the case we have considered above, ($n = 1$), the numbers a_1 and a can each approach $R(z_1)$ as near as we please. If $n > 1$ this is, of course, not the case.

We can now obtain a generalisation of 8·5 (10) connecting the sums for complementary arguments. We have from (10), writing $-\omega$ for ω_1, $x-\omega$ for x, and $-1-z$ for z,

$$F(x-\omega \mid -\omega) = 2\pi i R_1+P(x-\omega \mid -\omega)$$
$$+\frac{1}{2\pi i}\int_{-1+a-i\infty}^{-1+a+i\infty} f(x+\omega z)\left(\frac{\pi}{\sin \pi z}\right)^2 dz.$$

Using (8), and observing that $-1<-1+\alpha<0$, we have

(11) $$F(x-\omega \mid -\omega) = -P(x \mid \omega)+F(x \mid \omega).$$

8·7. An Expression for $F(x\,|\,-\omega)$. Consider

$$F_1(x\,|\,\omega) = \underset{-c}{\overset{x}{\mathbf{S}}}\, \phi(-z)\,\underset{\omega}{\Delta} z = \int_{-a-i\infty}^{-a+i\infty} f(x+\omega z)\left(\frac{\pi}{\sin \pi z}\right)^2 dz,$$

where

$$f(x+\omega z) = \int_{-c}^{x+\omega z} \phi(-z)\,dz = -\int_{c}^{-x-\omega z} \phi(z)\,dz.$$

Now we have

$$F(x\,|\,-\omega) = \underset{c}{\overset{x}{\mathbf{S}}}\, \phi(z)\,\underset{-\omega}{\Delta} z = \int_{-a-i\infty}^{-a+i\infty} g(x-\omega z)\left(\frac{\pi}{\sin \pi z}\right)^2 dz,$$

where

$$g(x-\omega z) = \int_{c}^{x-\omega z} \phi(z)\,dz = -f(-x+\omega z).$$

It follows that

$$F(x\,|\,-\omega) = -F_1(-x\,|\,\omega).$$

If then in 8·5 (4) we take $\lambda(t) = t^2$, we have, if $\omega > 0$,

$$F(x\,|\,-\omega) = -F_1(-x\,|\,\omega)$$

$$= \lim_{\mu\to 0}\left\{\omega \sum_{s=0}^{\infty} \phi(x-s\omega)\,e^{-\mu(x-s\omega)^2} - \int_{-\infty}^{c} \phi(z)\,e^{-\mu z^2}\,dz\right\},$$

which expresses $F(x\,|\,-\omega)$ as the limit of a sum.

EXAMPLES VIII

1. Prove that

$$\underset{a}{\overset{x}{\mathbf{S}}}\,(z-1)(z-2)\ldots(z-n+1)\,\Delta z = \frac{1}{n}(x-1)\ldots(x-n) - \frac{1}{n}B_n^{(n)}(a).$$

2. Prove that

$$\underset{a}{\overset{x}{\mathbf{S}}}\,\frac{\Delta z}{z(z+1)\ldots(z+n)} = \frac{-1}{nx(x+1)\ldots(x+n-1)}$$

$$+\frac{1}{n}\int_a^{a+1} \frac{dz}{z(z+1)\ldots(z+n-1)},$$

and by means of the identity

$$\frac{1}{x(x+1)\dots(x+n)} = \frac{1}{n!}\sum_{s=0}^{n}(-1)^s\binom{n}{s}\frac{1}{x+s},$$

shew that the constant can be written in the form

$$\frac{(-1)^{n+1}}{n}\overset{n}{\Delta}\log a.$$

3. Prove that

$$\underset{a}{\overset{x}{S}}\,[\underset{\omega}{\nabla}\phi(z)]\underset{2\omega}{\Delta}z = \underset{a}{\overset{x}{S}}\,\phi(z)\underset{\omega}{\Delta}z - \tfrac{1}{2}\int_a^{a+\omega}\phi(z)\,dz.$$

4. Obtain the following expressions for the periodic Bernoullian functions,

$$P_{2\nu}(x) = (-1)^{\nu+1}\frac{2(2\nu)!}{(2\pi)^{2\nu}}\sum_{n=1}^{\infty}\frac{\cos 2n\pi x}{n^{2\nu}},$$

$$P_{2\nu+1}(x) = (-1)^{\nu+1}\frac{2(2\nu+1)!}{(2\pi)^{2\nu+1}}\sum_{n=1}^{\infty}\frac{\sin 2\pi n x}{n^{2\nu+1}}.$$

5. Prove that

$$\int_0^1[B_{2\nu+1}(z) - B_{2\nu+1}(x)]\cot\pi(z-x)\,dz$$

$$= (-1)^{\nu+1}\frac{2(2\nu+1)!}{(2\pi)^{2\nu+1}}\sum_{n=1}^{\infty}\frac{\cos 2\pi n x}{n^{2\nu+1}},$$

and deduce the expansion

$$-\log(2\sin\pi x) = \sum_{n=1}^{\infty}\frac{\cos 2\pi n x}{n},\quad 0<x<1.$$

6. Shew that

$$\sum_{n=1}^{\infty}\frac{1}{n^{2\nu+1}} = (-1)^{\nu+1}\frac{(2\pi)^{2\nu+1}}{2(2\nu+1)!}\int_0^1 B_{2\nu+1}(z)\cot\pi z\,dz.$$

7. Shew that

$$\underset{0}{\overset{x}{S}}\,e^{iz}\underset{\omega}{\Delta}z = i - \frac{\omega e^{ix}}{1-e^{i\omega}}.$$

8. Prove that

$$B_\nu(x) = \frac{1}{2\pi i}\int_{-a-i\infty}^{-a+i\infty} (x+\zeta)^\nu \left(\frac{\pi}{\sin \pi\zeta}\right)^2 d\zeta.$$

9. Prove that

$$B_\nu(\tfrac{1}{2}) = \frac{1}{4\pi i}\int_{-a-i\infty}^{-a+i\infty} (\tfrac{1}{2}z)^\nu \left(\frac{\pi}{\cos\dfrac{\pi z}{2}}\right)^2 dz$$

$$B_{2\nu} = (-1)^{\nu+1}\pi\int_0^\infty \frac{x^{2\nu}}{\sinh^2 \pi x} dx,$$

$$2^{2\nu} B_{2\nu}(\tfrac{1}{2}) = (-1)^\nu \frac{\pi}{2}\int_0^\infty \frac{x^{2\nu}\, dx}{\cosh^2 \pi x}.$$

10. If $\phi(x)$ be an integral function, such that

$$|\phi(x)| < Ce^{\epsilon|x|}$$

where C is a fixed positive constant and ε is positive and arbitrarily small, prove that

$$\mathop{\mathsf{S}}_c^x \phi(z) \mathop{\Delta}_\omega z = \frac{1}{2\pi i}\int_{-a-i\infty}^{-a+i\infty} \left\{\int_c^{\omega z+x} \phi(t)\, dt\right\} \left(\frac{\pi}{\sin \pi z}\right)^2 dz$$

for all finite values of ω, real or complex.

CHAPTER IX

THE PSI FUNCTION AND THE GAMMA FUNCTION

In this chapter we consider the application of Nörlund's principal solution to two special forms of the function to be summed, namely, x^{-1} and $\log x$.

The first of these gives rise to the Psi function, the second to the logarithm of the Gamma function.

Both these functions play an important part in applications of the finite calculus, and both possess great theoretical interest.

9·0. The Psi Function. This function is defined by the relation

$$\Psi(x \mid \omega) = \mathop{\mathbf{S}}_{1}^{x} \frac{1}{z} \mathop{\Delta}_{\omega} z.$$

Taking x, ω to be real and positive, we see that the conditions of 8·15 are satisfied and the function therefore exists. When $\omega = 1$, we shall write

$$\Psi(x) = \Psi(x \mid 1).$$

We shall now illustrate the results of Chapter VIII by obtaining properties of the function $\Psi(x \mid \omega)$.

9·01. Differentiation of the Psi Function. From 8·2, we have

$$\frac{d}{dx} \Psi(x \mid \omega) = \mathop{\mathbf{S}}_{1}^{x} \left(-\frac{1}{z^2}\right) \mathop{\Delta}_{\omega} z + 1,$$

$$\frac{d^2}{dx^2} \Psi(x \mid \omega) = \mathop{\mathbf{S}}_{1}^{x} \frac{2}{z^2} \mathop{\Delta}_{\omega} z - 1,$$

and generally

$$\frac{d^n}{dx^n}\Psi(x\mid\omega) = \underset{1}{\overset{x}{S}} \frac{(-1)^n n!}{z^{n+1}} \underset{\omega}{\Delta} z + (-1)^{n-1}(n-1)!.$$

Thus we obtain

$$\underset{1}{\overset{x}{S}} \frac{\underset{\omega}{\Delta} z}{z^n} = \frac{(-1)^{n-1}}{(n-1)!}\Psi^{(n-1)}(x\mid\omega) + \frac{1}{n-1}, \quad n>1,$$

and consequently, using 8·1 (8),

$$\underset{1}{\overset{x}{S}} \frac{\underset{\omega}{\Delta} z}{(z+\alpha)^n} = \frac{(-1)^{n-1}}{(n-1)!}\Psi^{(n-1)}(x+\alpha\mid\omega) + \frac{1}{(n-1)(1+\alpha)^{n-1}}.$$

With the aid of this result and 8·16 we are now in a position to sum any rational function. For example, using 8·1 (8),

$$\underset{c}{\overset{x}{S}} \left(z+\frac{1}{z}+\frac{1}{(z+2)^2}\right) \underset{\omega}{\Delta} z$$

$$= \underset{0}{\overset{x}{S}} z \underset{\omega}{\Delta} z + \int_c^0 z\,dz + \underset{1}{\overset{x}{S}} \left(\frac{1}{z}+\frac{1}{(z+2)^2}\right) \underset{\omega}{\Delta} z + \int_c^1 \left(\frac{1}{z}+\frac{1}{(z+2)^2}\right) dz$$

$$= \tfrac{1}{2}B_2(x\mid\omega) + \Psi(x\mid\omega) - \Psi'(x+2\mid\omega) - \tfrac{1}{2}c^2 - \log c + \frac{2}{c+2} - \tfrac{1}{3}.$$

Any rational function can be expressed as the sum of terms of the types $a\,x^n$, $b\,(x+\beta)^{-n}$, and can therefore be summed. This summation property is one of the most important applications of the function.

For numerical values of $\Psi(x+1)$, $\Psi'(x+1)$, $\Psi''(x+1)$, $\Psi'''(x+1)$, the reader is referred to the *British Association Tables*, Vol. I, (1931), where they are tabulated under the respective names, di-, tri-, tetra-, and pentagamma functions.

For integration of $\Psi(x\mid\omega)$ we have, from 8·1 (4),

$$\frac{1}{\omega}\int_x^{x+\omega} \Psi(t\mid\omega)\,dt = \int_1^x \frac{1}{t}\,dt = \log x.$$

[See also 9·67.]

9·03. Partial and Repeated Summation. As an example of partial summation we have from 8·1 (7),

$$\mathop{\mathrm{S}}_1^x \frac{1}{z}\Psi(z\,|\,\omega)\mathop{\Delta}_{\omega} z = \Psi(x\,|\,\omega)\mathop{\mathrm{S}}_1^x \frac{1}{z}\mathop{\Delta}_{\omega} z$$

$$-\frac{1}{\omega}\int_1^{\omega+1}\Psi(z\,|\,\omega)\mathop{\mathrm{S}}_1^z \frac{1}{t}\mathop{\Delta}_{\omega} t\,dz - \mathop{\mathrm{S}}_1^x \frac{1}{z}\mathop{\mathrm{S}}_1^{z+\omega}\frac{1}{t}\mathop{\Delta}_{\omega} t\mathop{\Delta}_{\omega} z$$

$$= \Psi^2(x\,|\,\omega) - \frac{1}{\omega}\int_1^{\omega+1}\Psi^2(z\,|\,\omega)\,dz - \mathop{\mathrm{S}}_1^x \frac{1}{z}\Psi(z+\omega\,|\,\omega)\mathop{\Delta}_{\omega} z.$$

Now

$$\frac{1}{z}\Psi(z+\omega\,|\,\omega) = \frac{\omega}{z^2} + \frac{1}{z}\Psi(z\,|\,\omega),$$

while, from 9·01,

$$\mathop{\mathrm{S}}_1^x \frac{1}{z^2}\mathop{\Delta}_{\omega} z = -\Psi'(x\,|\,\omega)+1.$$

Thus we have

$$2\mathop{\mathrm{S}}_1^x \frac{1}{z}\Psi(z\,|\,\omega)\mathop{\Delta}_{\omega} z$$

$$= \Psi^2(x\,|\,\omega) + \omega\,\Psi'(x\,|\,\omega) - \omega - \frac{1}{\omega}\int_1^{\omega+1}\Psi^2(z\,|\,\omega)\,dz.$$

As an example of repeated summation, consider the equation

$$\mathop{\Delta}_{\omega}^{2} u(x\,|\,\omega) = \frac{1}{x}.$$

From 8·12 we have a solution,

$$\mathop{\mathrm{S}}_1^x \frac{1}{t}\mathop{\Delta}_{\omega}^{2} t = \mathop{\mathrm{S}}_1^x (x-t-\omega)\frac{1}{t}\mathop{\Delta}_{\omega} t$$

$$= (x-\omega)\mathop{\mathrm{S}}_1^x \frac{1}{t}\mathop{\Delta}_{\omega} t - \mathop{\mathrm{S}}_1^x 1\mathop{\Delta}_{\omega} t$$

$$= (x-\omega)\,\Psi(x\,|\,\omega) - (x-\tfrac{1}{2}\omega-1).$$

9·1. Asymptotic Behaviour for Large Values of x. From 8·15 (11), we have

(1) $\Psi(x \mid \omega)$

$$= \log x - \sum_{\nu=1}^{m} \frac{B_\nu \omega^\nu}{\nu} \frac{(-1)^\nu}{x^\nu} + \omega^{m+1}(-1)^m \int_0^\infty \frac{P_m(-t)}{(x+\omega t)^{m+1}} dt.$$

Write

$$Q_m(x) = \log x - \sum_{\nu=1}^{m} \frac{B_\nu \omega^\nu}{\nu} \frac{(-1)^\nu}{x^\nu}.$$

Then

$$x^m \{\Psi(x \mid \omega) - Q_m(x)\} = \omega^{m+1}(-1)^m R_m(x),$$

where

$$R_m(x) = \int_0^\infty \frac{P_m(-t)}{x+\omega t} \left(\frac{x}{x+\omega t}\right)^m dt,$$

we now shew that $R_m(x) \to 0$ when $x \to \infty$.

We have, integrating by parts,

$$\int_0^n \frac{P_m(-t)}{x+\omega t} dt = \left[\frac{-P_{m+1}(-t)}{(m+1)(x+\omega t)}\right]_0^n - \int_0^n \frac{\omega P_{m+1}(-t)}{(m+1)(x+\omega t)^2} dt.$$

Since $P_{m+1}(-t)$ is bounded, the integral on the right exists when $n \to \infty$, and, moreover, both terms $\to 0$ when $x \to \infty$. *A fortiori* $R_m(x) \to 0$.

Thus we have proved that

$$\lim_{x \to \infty} x^m \{\Psi(x \mid \omega) - Q_m(x)\} = 0.$$

It follows that asymptotically,* in the sense of Poincaré,

(2) $$\Psi(x \mid \omega) \sim \log x - \sum_{\nu=1}^{\infty} \frac{\omega^\nu}{\nu} \frac{(-1)^\nu}{x^\nu} B_\nu,$$

from which numerical values can be calculated.

In particular, for large values of x, we have

(3) $$\Psi(x \mid \omega) \sim \log x.$$

Hence

(4) $$\lim_{n \to \infty} \{\Psi(x+n\omega \mid \omega) - \log(x+n\omega)\} = 0.$$

---

* See 8·22, p. 217.

Now, from the definition,

$$\Psi(x \mid \omega) = \Psi(x+n\omega \mid \omega) - \omega \sum_{s=0}^{n-1} \frac{1}{x+s\omega}$$

$$= \left\{\log(x+n\omega) - \omega \sum_{s=0}^{n-1} \frac{1}{x+s\omega}\right\} + \Psi(x+n\omega \mid \omega) - \log(x+n\omega).$$

Thus, as in 8·21 (6),

$$\Psi(x \mid \omega) = \lim_{n\to\infty} \left\{\log(x+n\omega) - \omega \sum_{s=0}^{n-1} \frac{1}{x+s\omega}\right\}.$$

Putting $x = \omega$, we have

$$\Psi(\omega \mid \omega) = \log\omega + \lim_{n\to\infty} \left\{\log(n+1) - \sum_{s=0}^{n-1} \frac{1}{s+1}\right\}$$

$$= \log\omega - \gamma,$$

where γ denotes Euler's constant.*

In particular, if $\omega = 1$, we have

$$\Psi(1) = -\gamma.$$

We also note that the asymptotic series (2) is valid for all positive ω however small, so that, when $\omega \to 0$ by positive values, we have

$$\lim_{\omega\to 0} \Psi(x \mid \omega) = \log x.$$

9·11. Partial Fraction Development. From 8·21 (5), with $m = 0$, $Q_0(x) = \log x$, we have

$$\Psi(x \mid \omega) = \log x - \omega \sum_{s=0}^{\infty} \left\{\frac{1}{x+s\omega} - \Delta_{\omega} \log(x+s\omega)\right\}$$

$$= \log x - \sum_{s=0}^{\infty} \left\{\frac{1}{\frac{x}{\omega}+s} - \log\left(1+\frac{1}{\frac{x}{\omega}+s}\right)\right\}.$$

Putting $x = \omega$, we have, from 9·1,

$$\log\omega - \gamma = \log\omega - \sum_{s=0}^{\infty} \left\{\frac{1}{1+s} - \log\left(1+\frac{1}{1+s}\right)\right\}.$$

Subtracting, we obtain

$$\Psi(x \mid \omega) - \log\omega + \gamma = -\sum_{s=0}^{\infty} \left(\frac{\omega}{x+\omega s} - \frac{1}{1+s}\right) + S,$$

* *Modern Analysis*, 12·1.

where

$$S = \log\frac{x}{\omega} + \sum_{s=0}^{\infty}\left\{\log\left(1+\frac{1}{\frac{x}{\omega}+s}\right) - \log\left(1+\frac{1}{1+s}\right)\right\}$$

$$= \log\frac{x}{\omega}$$

$$+\sum_{s=0}^{\infty}\left\{\log\left(\frac{x}{\omega}+s+1\right) - \log\left(\frac{x}{\omega}+s\right) - \log(s+2) + \log(s+1)\right\} = 0.$$

Thus we have

$$\Psi(x\,|\,\omega) = \log\omega - \gamma - \sum_{s=0}^{\infty}\left(\frac{\omega}{x+\omega s} - \frac{1}{1+s}\right).$$

This expression of Psi in partial fractions is valid not only for x real and positive, but in the whole complex plane, and shews that $\Psi(x\,|\,\omega)$ is a meromorphic function of x with simple poles at the points $0, -\omega, -2\omega, -3\omega, \ldots,$ at each of which the residue is $-\omega$.

Regarded as a function of ω (x fixed), we see that $\Psi(x\,|\,\omega)$ has poles at the points $-x, -\frac{1}{2}x, -\frac{1}{3}x, -\frac{1}{4}x, \ldots,$ and that these poles have the point $\omega = 0$ as a limit point, so that $\omega = 0$ is an essential singularity.

9·2. The Multiplication Theorem. From 9·1 (1), we have

$$\Psi(x\,|\,\omega) - \log\omega = \log\frac{x}{\omega} - \sum_{\nu=1}^{m}\frac{(-1)^\nu B_\nu}{\nu}\left(\frac{\omega}{x}\right)^\nu$$

$$+(-1)^m\int_0^\infty \frac{P_m(-t)}{\left(\frac{x}{\omega}+t\right)^{m+1}}\,dt = \Psi\left(\frac{x}{\omega}\right).$$

Thus

(1) $$\Psi(x\,|\,\omega) = \Psi\left(\frac{x}{\omega}\right) + \log\omega.$$

From 8·1 (1), we have

$$\frac{1}{m}\sum_{s=0}^{m-1}\Psi\left(x+\frac{s\omega}{m}\,\middle|\,\omega\right) = \Psi\left(x\,\middle|\,\frac{\omega}{m}\right) = \Psi\left(\frac{mx}{\omega}\right) + \log\frac{\omega}{m}$$

$$= \Psi(mx\,|\,\omega) - \log m,$$

by a double use of (1). This is the multiplication theorem.

In particular, for $m = 2$, we have the Duplication Theorem, namely,

$$\Psi(2x \mid \omega) = \tfrac{1}{2}\{\Psi(x \mid \omega) + \Psi(x+\tfrac{1}{2} \mid \omega)\} + \log 2,$$

and in particular, for $\omega = 1$,

$$\Psi(2x) = \tfrac{1}{2}\{\Psi(x) + \Psi(x+\tfrac{1}{2})\} + \log 2.$$

Putting $x = \frac{1}{2}$, this gives

$$\Psi(\tfrac{1}{2}) = -\gamma - \log 4.$$

9·22. Fourier Series for $\Psi(x)$. From 8·3, we have in the interval $x_0 < x < x_0 + 1$,

$$\Psi(x) = \tfrac{1}{2}a_0 + \sum_{n=1}^{\infty} (a_n \cos 2\pi n x + b_n \sin 2\pi n x),$$

where

$$\tfrac{1}{2}(a_n + ib_n) = -\lim_{\mu \to 0} \int_{x_0}^{\infty} \frac{e^{-\mu x + 2n\pi x i}}{x}\, dx$$

$$= -\int_{x_0}^{\infty} \frac{\cos 2n\pi x}{x}\, dx - i\int_{x_0}^{\infty} \frac{\sin 2n\pi x}{x}\, dx$$

$$= \mathrm{ci}\,(2n\pi x_0) + i\,\mathrm{si}\,(2n\pi x_0),$$

where $\mathrm{ci}(x)$, $\mathrm{si}(x)$ are the cosine and sine integrals, namely *

$$\mathrm{ci}(x) = -\int_{x}^{\infty} \frac{\cos t}{t}\, dt, \quad \mathrm{si}(x) = -\int_{x}^{\infty} \frac{\sin t}{t}\, dt.$$

For a_0, we have

$$\tfrac{1}{2}a_0 = \int_1^{x_0} \frac{1}{x}\, dx = \log x_0.$$

Thus

$$\Psi(x) = \log x_0 + 2\sum_{n=1}^{\infty} \{\mathrm{ci}\,(2\pi n x_0) \cos 2n\pi x + \mathrm{si}\,(2\pi n x_0) \sin 2n\pi x\}.$$

9·3. The Integral of Gauss for $\Psi(x)$. For $R(x) > 0$, $t > 0$, we have, summing the geometrical progression,

$$\sum_{s=0}^{\infty} e^{-t(x+s)} = \frac{e^{-xt}}{1 - e^{-t}}.$$

---

* For numerical values of these integrals see *British Association Mathematical Tables*, vol. i, London, 1931.

Integrating with regard to t from μ (>0) to ∞, we have

$$\sum_{s=0}^{\infty} \frac{e^{-\mu(x+s)}}{x+s} = \int_{\mu}^{\infty} \frac{e^{-xt}}{1-e^{-t}}\, dt.$$

Also,

$$\int_{1}^{\infty} \frac{e^{-\mu x}}{x}\, dx = \int_{\mu}^{\infty} \frac{e^{-t}}{t}\, dt.$$

Now, from the definition,

$$\Psi(x) = \lim_{\mu \to 0} \left\{ \int_{1}^{\infty} \frac{e^{-\mu x}}{x}\, dx - \sum_{s=0}^{\infty} \frac{e^{-\mu(x+s)}}{x+s} \right\}$$

$$= \lim_{\mu \to 0} \left\{ \int_{\mu}^{\infty} \left(\frac{e^{-t}}{t} - \frac{e^{-xt}}{1-e^{-t}} \right) \right\} dt$$

$$= \int_{0}^{\infty} \left(\frac{e^{-t}}{t} - \frac{e^{-xt}}{1-e^{-t}} \right) dt,$$

which is Gauss' Integral for $\Psi(x)$.

Putting $x = 1$, we have

$$\gamma = \int_{0}^{\infty} e^{-t} \left(\frac{1}{1-e^{-t}} - \frac{1}{t} \right) dt.$$

9·32. Poisson's Integral. As an application of 8·41, we have

$$\Psi(x \mid \omega) = \int_{1}^{x-a\omega} \frac{1}{z}\, dz$$

$$+\omega \int_{-a}^{-a+i\infty} \frac{dz}{(x+\omega z)(1-e^{-2\pi i z})} + \omega \int_{-a}^{-a-i\infty} \frac{dz}{(x+\omega z)(1-e^{2\pi i z})}.$$

Put $\alpha = \frac{1}{2}$, replace x by $x+\frac{1}{2}\omega$ and z by $z-\frac{1}{2}$.

We then obtain

$$\Psi(x+\tfrac{1}{2}\omega \mid \omega)$$

$$= \log x + \omega \int_{0}^{i\infty} \frac{dz}{(x+\omega z)(1+e^{-2\pi i z})} + \omega \int_{0}^{-i\infty} \frac{dz}{(x+\omega z)(1+e^{2\pi i z})}.$$

In the first integral write $z = it$, in the second $z = -it$, then

$$\Psi(x+\tfrac{1}{2}\omega \mid \omega) = \log x + i\omega \int_{0}^{\infty} \left(\frac{1}{x+i\omega t} - \frac{1}{x-i\omega t} \right) \frac{dt}{1+e^{2\pi t}}$$

$$= \log x + 2\omega^2 \int_{0}^{\infty} \frac{t\, dt}{(x^2+\omega^2 t^2)(1+e^{2\pi t})}$$

which is Poisson's Integral.

9·4. The Complementary Argument Theorem. From 8·6 (7) and (11), we have

$$\Psi(x-\omega \mid -\omega) = \Psi(x \mid \omega) + \pi i + \pi \cot \frac{\pi x}{\omega}.$$

Now by 8·7,

$$\Psi(x \mid -\omega) = \lim_{\mu \to 0} \left\{ \omega \sum_{s=0}^{\infty} \frac{e^{-\mu(x-s\omega)^2}}{x-s\omega} - \int_{-\infty}^{1} \frac{e^{-\mu z^2}}{z} dz \right\},$$

while

$$\Psi(-x \mid \omega) = \lim_{\mu \to 0} \left\{ \int_{1}^{\infty} \frac{e^{-\mu z^2}}{z} dz - \omega \sum_{s=0}^{\infty} \frac{e^{-\mu(x-s\omega)^2}}{-x+s\omega} \right\}.$$

By subtraction,

$$\Psi(x \mid -\omega) - \Psi(-x \mid \omega) = -\lim_{\mu \to 0} \int_{-\infty}^{+\infty} \frac{e^{-\mu z^2}}{z} dz = \pi i,$$

the integral being taken along the real axis with an indentation at the origin. Writing $x-\omega$ for x, we have

$$\Psi(x-\omega \mid -\omega) - \Psi(\omega - x \mid \omega) = \pi i.$$

Thus we have

$$\Psi(\omega - x \mid \omega) = \Psi(x \mid \omega) + \pi \cot \frac{\pi x}{\omega},$$

which is the required relation between functions of the complementary arguments ω, $\omega - x$.

9·5. The Gamma Function. We start from Nörlund's definition, namely,

(1) $$\log \Gamma(x) = \mathop{S}_{0}^{x} \log z \, \Delta z + c,$$

where the constant c is chosen so that $\log \Gamma(1) = 0$. In order to fix the determination of the logarithm, the complex plane is cut along the negative real axis and the logarithm determined by $\log 1 = 0$.

We have from (1),

$$\Delta \log \Gamma(x) = \log x,$$

whence we obtain

(2) $$\Gamma(x+1) = x\,\Gamma(x),$$

which is one of the most important properties of $\Gamma(x)$.

In particular, if n be a positive integer, we have

(3) $$\Gamma(n+1) = n!\,.$$

Again by 8·1 (8), we can write

$$\log \Gamma(x) = \mathop{\large S}_{1}^{x} \log z \, \Delta z + \text{constant}.$$

Differentiating this result by means of 8·2, we obtain

$$\text{(4)} \qquad \frac{\Gamma'(x)}{\Gamma(x)} = \mathop{\large S}_{1}^{x} \frac{1}{z} \Delta z = \Psi(x),$$

so that $\Psi(x)$ is the logarithmic derivate of $\Gamma(x)$.

For numerical values of $\Gamma(x+1)$ see the *British Association Tables*, Vol. i, where the function is tabulated under the name $x!$.

9·52. Schlömilch's Infinite Product. We have from 9·11,

$$\frac{\Gamma'(x)}{\Gamma(x)} = -\gamma - \sum_{s=0}^{\infty} \left(\frac{1}{x+s} - \frac{1}{1+s} \right).$$

Integrating from 1 to $x+1$, since $\log \Gamma(1) = 0$, we get

$$\log \Gamma(x+1) = -\gamma x - \sum_{s=1}^{\infty} \left(\log \frac{x+s}{s} - \frac{x}{s} \right)$$

$$= \log e^{-\gamma x} - \sum_{s=1}^{\infty} \left(\log \frac{x+s}{s} - \log e^{\frac{x}{s}} \right).$$

Thus we have Schlömilch's Product, namely,

$$\text{(1)} \qquad \Gamma(x+1) = e^{-\gamma x} \prod_{s=1}^{\infty} \frac{e^{\frac{x}{s}}}{1+\frac{x}{s}}.$$

Since $\Gamma(x+1) = x\,\Gamma(x)$, we have

$$\text{(2)} \qquad \frac{1}{\Gamma(x)} = x e^{\gamma x} \prod_{s=1}^{\infty} \left(1 + \frac{x}{s}\right) e^{-\frac{x}{s}}.$$

The infinite product in (2) converges absolutely at every finite point of the plane, so that $1/\Gamma(x)$ is an integral function with simple zeros at the points $0, -1, -2, -3, \dots$. It follows at once that $\Gamma(x)$ is a meromorphic function with simple poles at the points $0, -1, -2, \dots$.

The above product (2) was taken by Weierstrass as the definition of the Gamma function.

9·53. Certain Infinite Products. Consider the infinite product,

$$P = \prod_{s=1}^{\infty} \frac{(s+x_1)(s+x_2)}{(s+y_1)(s+y_2)},$$

where $x_1+x_2 = y_1+y_2$.

The product is then absolutely convergent * and, moreover,

$$e^{(y_1+y_2-x_1-x_2)/s} = 1.$$

Hence we can write

$$P = \prod_{s=1}^{\infty} e^{\frac{y_1}{s}}\left(1+\frac{y_1}{s}\right)^{-1} e^{\frac{y_2}{s}}\left(1+\frac{y_2}{s}\right)^{-1} e^{-\frac{x_1}{s}}\left(1+\frac{x_1}{s}\right) e^{-\frac{x_2}{s}}\left(1+\frac{x_2}{s}\right).$$

Using Schlömilch's Product we have, therefore,

$$\prod_{s=1}^{\infty} \frac{(s+x_1)(s+x_2)}{(s+y_1)(s+y_2)} = \frac{\Gamma(y_1+1)\,\Gamma(y_2+1)}{x_1\Gamma(x_1)\,x_2\,\Gamma(x_2)} = \frac{\Gamma(y_1+1)\,\Gamma(y_2+1)}{\Gamma(x_1+1)\,\Gamma(x_2+1)},$$

provided that $$x_1+x_2 = y_1+y_2.$$

In the same way we can evaluate

$$\prod_{s=1}^{\infty} \frac{(s+x_1)(s+x_2)\,\ldots\,(s+x_n)}{(s+y_1)(s+y_2)\,\ldots\,(s+y_n)},$$

where $$x_1+x_2+\ldots+x_n = y_1+y_2+\ldots+y_n.$$

9·54. Complementary Argument Theorem. The infinite product 9·52 (1) converges absolutely and uniformly in any bounded region from which the poles are excluded.

Now

$$\Gamma(1-x) = e^{\gamma x} \prod_{s=1}^{\infty} \frac{e^{-\frac{x}{s}}}{1-\frac{x}{s}},$$

$$\Gamma(x) = \frac{e^{-\gamma x}}{x} \prod_{s=1}^{\infty} \frac{e^{\frac{x}{s}}}{1+\frac{x}{s}}.$$

Thus we have †

$$\Gamma(x)\,\Gamma(1-x) = \frac{1}{x}\prod_{s=1}^{\infty} \frac{1}{1-\frac{x^2}{s^2}} = \frac{\pi}{\sin \pi x},$$

* *Modern Analysis*, 2·7.

† *Modern Analysis*, 7·5.

which is the required relation between the functions of the complementary arguments x, $1-x$. The result is originally due to Euler.

Putting $x = \frac{1}{2}$, we have

$$\Gamma(\tfrac{1}{2}) = \sqrt{\pi}.$$

9·55. The Residues of $\Gamma(x)$. The residue at the pole $x = -n$ is r_n, where

$$r_n = \lim_{x \to -n} (x+n)\Gamma(x) = \lim_{x \to -n} \frac{(x+n)\pi}{\sin \pi x\, \Gamma(1-x)}.$$

Now

$$\frac{x+n}{\sin \pi x} = (-1)^n \frac{\pi(x+n)}{\sin \pi(x+n)} \cdot \frac{1}{\pi} \to \frac{(-1)^n}{\pi}.$$

Thus

$$r_n = \frac{(-1)^n}{\Gamma(1+n)} = \frac{(-1)^n}{n!},$$

using 9·5 (3).

We have therefore proved that in the neighbourhood of the pole $x = -n$ the principal part * of $\Gamma(x)$ is $P\{\Gamma(x)\}$, where

$$P\{\Gamma(x)\} = \frac{(-1)^n}{(x+n)n!}.$$

9·56. Determination of the Constant c. To determine the constant c of 9·5, we have, from 8·21 (6), with $m = 1$,

$$\log \Gamma(x) - c = \lim_{n \to \infty} \left\{ \int_0^{x+n} \log z\, dz - \tfrac{1}{2} \log(x+n) - \sum_{s=0}^{n-1} \log(x+s) \right\}.$$

Now, integrating by parts,

$$\int_0^{x+n} \log z\, dz - \tfrac{1}{2}\log(x+n) = (x+n-\tfrac{1}{2})\log(x+n) - (x+n)$$

$$= (x+n-\tfrac{1}{2})\log n - n + (x+n-\tfrac{1}{2})\log\left(1+\frac{x}{n}\right) - x.$$

Also

$$(x+n-\tfrac{1}{2})\log\left(1+\frac{x}{n}\right) - x = (x-\tfrac{1}{2})\log\left(1+\frac{x}{n}\right) - \frac{x^2}{n} + \frac{x^3}{3n^2} - \dots,$$

and this tends to zero when $n \to \infty$. Thus

$$(1) \qquad \log \Gamma(x) - c = \lim_{n \to \infty} \left\{ (x+n-\tfrac{1}{2})\log n - n - \sum_{s=0}^{n-1} (x+s) \right\}.$$

---

* *Modern Analysis*, 5·61.

Thus, with $x = 1$,

$$\text{(2)} \qquad \log \Gamma(1) - c = \lim_{n\to\infty} \left\{ (n+\tfrac{1}{2}) \log n - n - \log n! \right\}.$$

Writing $2n$ for n, we have also

$$\log \Gamma(1) - c = \lim_{n\to\infty} \left\{ (2n+\tfrac{1}{2}) \log n - 2n + (2n+\tfrac{1}{2}) \log 2 - \log (2n)! \right\}.$$

Again, putting $x = \frac{1}{2}$, we get

$$\log \Gamma(\tfrac{1}{2}) - c = \lim_{n\to\infty} \left\{ n \log n - n - \log \frac{1.3.5 \ldots 2n-1}{2^n} \right\}$$

$$= \lim_{n\to\infty} \left\{ n \log n - n - \log (2n)! + \log (n!) + 2n \log 2 \right\}.$$

Adding the first and last of these three equations and subtracting the middle one, we have

$$\log \Gamma(\tfrac{1}{2}) - c = -\tfrac{1}{2} \log 2.$$

Thus

$$c = \log \{ \sqrt{2}\, \Gamma(\tfrac{1}{2}) \} = \log \sqrt{2\pi},$$

from 9·54. We have, therefore,

$$\log \Gamma(x) = \mathop{\mathbf{S}}_{0}^{x} \log z \, \Delta z + \log \sqrt{2\pi}$$

as the complete definition of 9·5.

9·6. Stirling's Series. From 8·15 (11) we have Stirling's series,

$$\log \Gamma(x+h) = \log \sqrt{2\pi} + x \log x - x + B_1(h) \log x$$

$$- \sum_{\nu=1}^{m-1} (-1)^{\nu} \frac{B_{\nu+1}(h)}{\nu(\nu+1) x^{\nu}} - \frac{1}{m} \int_0^{\infty} \frac{P_m(z-h)}{(x+z)^m} dz.$$

This series is valid not only for real x, but also for

$$-\pi + \varepsilon < \arg x < \pi - \varepsilon,$$

ε being arbitrarily small but positive.

Putting $h = 0$, we have

$$\log \Gamma(x) = \log \sqrt{2\pi} + (x - \tfrac{1}{2}) \log x - \log e^x + \ldots.$$

Thus

$$\log \Gamma(x) - \log(\sqrt{2\pi}\, x^{x-\frac{1}{2}} e^{-x}) \to 0,$$

when $|x| \to \infty$. Hence we have Stirling's formula, namely,

$$\lim_{|x|\to\infty} \frac{\Gamma(x)}{\sqrt{2\pi}\, x^{x-\frac{1}{2}} e^{-x}} = 1.$$

9·61. An Important Limit. Taking $m = 2$, in Stirling's series, we have

$$\log \Gamma(x+h) = \log \sqrt{2\pi} + (x+h-\tfrac{1}{2}) \log x - x + \frac{B_2(h)}{2x}$$

$$- \tfrac{1}{2}\int_0^\infty \frac{P_2(z-h)}{(x+z)^2}\, dz.$$

Put $h = 0$, and subtract the result from the above. We then get

$$\log \frac{\Gamma(x+h)}{\Gamma(x)} = h \log x + \frac{B_2(h) - B_2}{2x} - \tfrac{1}{2}\int_0^\infty \frac{P_2(z-h) - P_2(z)}{(x+z)^2}\, dz.$$

Thus we have

$$\lim_{|x|\to\infty} \frac{\Gamma(x+h)}{x^h \Gamma(x)} = 1, \quad 0 \leqslant h \leqslant 1.$$

This result can be generalised as follows.

Let s be a positive integer, and let δ denote a number real or complex which tends to zero when $s \to \infty$. The number δ is not necessarily the same in each formula in which δ occurs.

By Stirling's formula, we have

$$\Gamma(s+x) = \sqrt{(2\pi)}\,(s+x)^{s+x-\frac{1}{2}} e^{-s-x}(1+\delta).$$

Hence

$$\frac{\Gamma(s+x)}{\Gamma(s+y)} = \frac{(s+x)^{s+x-\frac{1}{2}}}{(s+y)^{s+y-\frac{1}{2}}} e^{y-x}(1+\delta)$$

$$= s^{x-y}\left(1+\frac{x}{s}\right)^s \left(1+\frac{x}{s}\right)^{x-\frac{1}{2}} \left(1+\frac{y}{s}\right)^{-s} \left(1+\frac{y}{s}\right)^{-y+\frac{1}{2}} e^{y-x}(1+\delta).$$

Now

$$\left(1+\frac{x}{s}\right)^s = e^x(1+\delta), \quad \left(1+\frac{y}{s}\right)^{-s} = e^{-y}(1+\delta),$$

$$\left(1+\frac{x}{s}\right)^{x-\frac{1}{2}} = 1+\delta, \quad \left(1+\frac{y}{s}\right)^{-y+\frac{1}{2}} = 1+\delta.$$

Hence we have

$$\frac{\Gamma(s+x)}{\Gamma(s+y)} = s^{x-y}(1+\delta).$$

Now $|s^{a+ib}| = s^a$, when a, b are real.

Hence

$$\left|\frac{\Gamma(s+x)}{\Gamma(s+y)}\right| = s^{\sigma}(1+\delta),$$

where $\sigma = R(x) - R(y) = R(x-y)$.

9·66. The Generalised Gamma Function. If we define the function $\Gamma(x \mid \omega)$ by the relation

$$(1) \qquad \omega \log \Gamma(x \mid \omega) = \mathop{S}_{0}^{x} \log z \mathop{\Delta}_{\omega} z + \omega \log \sqrt{\frac{2\pi}{\omega}},$$

we have by differencing

$$(2) \qquad \Gamma(x+\omega \mid \omega) = x\,\Gamma(x \mid \omega),$$

so that, if n be a positive integer,

$$\Gamma(n\omega+\omega \mid \omega) = \omega^n\,\Gamma(\omega \mid \omega)\, n!.$$

From 8·15 (11), with $h = 0$, we have

$$\omega \log \Gamma(x \mid \omega) = \omega \log \sqrt{\frac{2\pi}{\omega}} + (x - \tfrac{1}{2}\omega) \log x - x$$

$$- \omega \sum_{\nu=1}^{m-1} (-1)^{\nu} \frac{B_{\nu+1}}{\nu(\nu+1)} \left(\frac{\omega}{x}\right)^{\nu} - \frac{\omega}{m} \int_0^{\infty} \frac{P_m(z)}{\left(\frac{x}{\omega}+z\right)^m} dz$$

$$= \omega \log \Gamma\left(\frac{x}{\omega}\right) + (x-\omega) \log \omega,$$

from Stirling's series. Thus we have

$$(3) \qquad \log \Gamma(x \mid \omega) = \log \Gamma\left(\frac{x}{\omega}\right) + \frac{1}{\omega}(x-\omega) \log \omega,$$

so that $\Gamma(\omega \mid \omega) = 1$, and therefore

$$\Gamma(n\omega+\omega \mid \omega) = \omega^n\, n!,$$

when n is a positive integer. Also

$$\Gamma(x \mid \omega) = \Gamma\left(\frac{x}{\omega}\right) \exp\left(\frac{x-\omega}{\omega} \log \omega\right).$$

Again, from (1),

$$(4) \qquad \frac{\omega\,\Gamma'(x\,|\,\omega)}{\Gamma(x\,|\,\omega)} = \mathop{\mathrm{S}}_{1}^{x} \frac{1}{z} \mathop{\Delta}_{\omega} z = \Psi(x\,|\,\omega)$$

$$= \log\omega - \gamma - \sum_{s=0}^{\infty}\left(\frac{\omega}{x+\omega s} - \frac{1}{s+1}\right).$$

Integrating from ω to $x+\omega$, we have

$$\omega \log\Gamma(x+\omega\,|\,\omega) = x(\log\omega - \gamma) - \sum_{s=1}^{\infty}\left(\omega\log\frac{x+\omega s}{\omega s} - \frac{x}{s}\right),$$

whence

$$\Gamma(x+\omega\,|\,\omega) = e^{\frac{-\gamma+\log\omega}{\omega}x} \prod_{s=1}^{\infty} \frac{e^{\frac{x}{s\omega}}}{\left(\frac{x}{s\omega}+1\right)},$$

and, by (2),

$$\frac{1}{\Gamma(x\,|\,\omega)} = e^{\frac{\gamma-\log\omega}{\omega}x}\, x \prod_{s=1}^{\infty}\left(1+\frac{x}{s\omega}\right) e^{-\frac{x}{s\omega}},$$

which shews that $1/\Gamma(x\,|\,\omega)$ is an integral transcendent function, with simple zeros at the points $0,\ -\omega,\ -2\omega,\ -3\omega,\ \ldots$, and therefore that $\Gamma(x\,|\,\omega)$ is a meromorphic function of x with simple poles at the same points.

9·67. Some Definite Integrals. From 8·1 (4), we have

$$\frac{1}{\omega}\int_{x}^{x+\omega}\left(\omega\log\Gamma(z\,|\,\omega) - \omega\log\sqrt{\frac{2\pi}{\omega}}\right)dz = \int_{0}^{x}\log z\,dz.$$

Thus we have Raabe's integral, namely,

$$\int_{x}^{x+\omega}\log\Gamma(z\,|\,\omega)\,dz = x\log x - x + \omega\log\sqrt{\frac{2\pi}{\omega}},$$

and for $x=0$,

$$\int_{0}^{\omega}\log\Gamma(z\,|\,\omega)\,dz = \omega\log\sqrt{\frac{2\pi}{\omega}}.$$

Again, from 9·66 (4), we have the integral of the Psi function, namely,

$$\int_{\omega}^{x}\Psi(z\,|\,\omega)\,dz = \omega\log\Gamma(x\,|\,\omega).$$

From this and 9·3, we have, when $\omega = 1$,

$$\log \Gamma(x+1) = \int_1^{x+1} \left\{ \int_0^\infty \left(\frac{e^{-t}}{t} - \frac{e^{-xt}}{1-e^{-t}} \right) dt \right\} dx.$$

Integrating, under the sign of integration, we obtain

$$\log \Gamma(x+1) = \int_0^\infty \frac{e^{-t}}{t} \left(x + \frac{e^{-xt}-1}{1-e^{-t}} \right) dt, \quad R(x) > -1,$$

a formula due to Plana.

9·68. The Multiplication Theorem. If m be a positive integer, we have, from 8·1 (1),

$$\sum_{s=0}^{m-1} \left\{ \log \Gamma\left(x + \frac{s}{m}\right) - \log \sqrt{2\pi} \right\} = \log \Gamma\left(x \,\middle|\, \frac{1}{m}\right) - \log \sqrt{2m\pi}$$

$$= \log \Gamma(mx) + m\left(x - \frac{1}{m}\right) \log \frac{1}{m} - \log \sqrt{2m\pi},$$

from 9·66 (3).

This yields Gauss' Multiplication theorem,

$$\Gamma(mx) = (2\pi)^{-\frac{m-1}{2}} m^{mx-\frac{1}{2}} \prod_{s=0}^{m-1} \Gamma\left(x + \frac{s}{m}\right).$$

In particular, for $m = 2$, we have Legendre's duplication formula,

$$\Gamma(2x) = 2^{2x-1} \pi^{-\frac{1}{2}} \Gamma(x) \Gamma(x + \tfrac{1}{2}).$$

9·7. Euler's Integral for Γ(x). Subtracting (2) from (1) in 9·56, we have

$$\log \Gamma(x) = \lim_{n\to\infty} \left\{ (x-1) \log n + \log n! - \sum_{s=0}^{n-1} \log(x+s) \right\}$$

$$= \lim_{n\to\infty} \left\{ x \log n + \log(n-1)! - \sum_{s=0}^{n-1} \log(x+s) \right\}$$

Hence

$$\Gamma(x) = \lim_{n\to\infty} \frac{n^x (n-1)!}{x(x+1)\ldots(x+n-1)}.$$

Let t be a real positive variable and let $\log t$ denote the real logarithm of t. We define the many-valued function t^x by

$$t^x = \exp(x \log t).$$

Then, if $R(x) > 0$, we have

$$\int_0^1 t^{x-1}\,dt = \frac{1}{x} = (x-1)^{(-1)},$$

and consequently, from 2·11 (7), differencing with respect to x, we obtain

$$\overset{n}{\Delta}\int_0^1 t^{x-1}\,dt = (-1)^n (x-1)^{(-n)}\, n!.$$

But
$$\overset{n}{\Delta}\, t^{x-1} = t^{x-1}(t-1)^n.$$

Thus we have

$$\int_0^1 t^{x-1}(1-t)^n\,dt = \frac{n!}{x(x+1)\dots(x+n)}.$$

Writing $\frac{t}{n}$ for t, we obtain

$$\int_0^n t^{x-1}\left(1-\frac{t}{n}\right)^n dt = \frac{n!\,n^x}{x(x+1)\dots(x+n)}.$$

Hence

$$\Gamma(x) = \lim_{n\to\infty}\int_0^n t^{x-1}\left(1-\frac{t}{n}\right)^n dt.$$

Thus we obtain *

$$\Gamma(x) = \int_0^\infty t^{x-1}e^{-t}\,dt$$

which is Euler's Integral for $\Gamma(x)$. This integral is known as the Eulerian Integral of the Second Kind.

9·72. The Complementary Gamma Function. We give the name Complementary Gamma Function to the function $\Gamma_1(x)$ defined by

$$\Gamma_1(x) = -\int_L t^{x-1}e^{-t}\,dt, \quad 0 \leqslant \arg t \leqslant 2\pi,$$

where L is the contour shewn in Fig. 10.

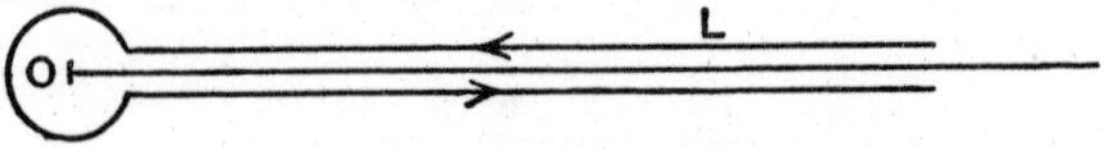

FIG. 10.

This contour consists of two straight parts ultimately coincident with the positive real axis and an infinitesimal circle round the

* For the justification of this passage to the limit, see *Modern Analysis*, 12·2.

origin. If $R(x) > 0$, the integral round the circle tends to zero as the radius tends to zero.

Thus, if we start at infinity with $\arg t = 0$, we have

$$\Gamma_1(x) = -\int_\infty^0 t^{x-1}\, e^{-t}\, dt - \int_0^\infty e^{2\pi i(x-1)}\, t^{x-1}\, e^{-t}\, dt,$$

since t^{x-1} is multiplied by $e^{2\pi i(x-1)} = e^{2\pi i x}$, after passing round the origin. Thus we have

$$\Gamma_1(x) = \Gamma(x) - e^{2\pi i x}\,\Gamma(x) = (1 - e^{2\pi i x})\,\Gamma(x),$$

and therefore

$$\Gamma(x) = \frac{1}{e^{2\pi i x} - 1}\int_L t^{x-1}\, e^{-t}\, dt.$$

The loop L can be deformed in any manner provided that it starts and terminates at ∞ and does not cross the real axis between 0 and ∞. We now can write

$$\Gamma(x) = \frac{1}{e^{2\pi i x} - 1}\int_\infty^{(0+)} t^{x-1}\, e^{-t}\, dt,$$

where the notation indicates * that the path of integration starts at "infinity" on the real axis, encircles the origin in the positive sense and returns to the starting point.

The above is Hankel's integral for $\Gamma(x)$. Although proved in the first instance for $R(x) > 0$, the integral is valid in the whole plane (since L does not pass through the origin) with the exception of the points $x = 0, \pm 1, \pm 2, \ldots$.

From 9·55, we see that near the pole $x = -n$ of $\Gamma(x)$, the function $\Gamma_1(x)$ behaves like

$$\frac{1 - e^{2\pi i x}}{x+n}\,\frac{(-1)^n}{n!} = -\frac{2i \sin \pi x\, e^{\pi i x}}{x+n}\,\frac{(-1)^n}{n!}.$$

Also

$$\frac{(-1)^n \sin \pi x}{x+n} = \frac{\sin \pi (x+n)}{x+n},$$

which is holomorphic at $x = -n$, so that $\Gamma_1(x)$ is holomorphic at the poles of $\Gamma(x)$. It follows that the complementary Gamma function is an integral function of x.

---

* *Modern Analysis*, 12·22.

Again,

$$\Gamma_1(x+1) = (1-e^{2\pi i(x+1)})\,\Gamma(x+1) = (1-e^{2\pi i x})\,x\,\Gamma(x) = x\,\Gamma_1(x).$$

Consequently, $\Gamma_1(x)$ satisfies the same difference equation as $\Gamma(x)$, namely,

$$u(x+1) = x\,u(x).$$

9·8. The Hypergeometric Series. This name is given to the series

$$(1)\quad 1+\frac{a\,.\,b}{1\,.\,c}x+\frac{a(a+1)\,b(b+1)}{1\,.\,2\,.\,c(c+1)}x^2 + \frac{a(a+1)(a+2)\,b(b+1)(b+2)}{1\,.\,2\,.\,3\,.\,c(c+1)(c+2)}x^3+\dots,$$

where we assume that none of a, b, c is a negative integer.

Denote the coefficient of x^n by u_n. Then when $n \to \infty$,

$$\left|\frac{u_{n+1}\,x^{n+1}}{u_n\,x^n}\right| = \left|\frac{(a+n)(b+n)}{(n+1)(c+n)}\,x\right| \to |\,x\,|.$$

Thus the series is absolutely convergent if $|\,x\,| < 1$, and divergent when $|\,x\,| > 1$.

When $|\,x\,| = 1$, we have *

$$\frac{u_{n+1}}{u_n} = 1+\frac{a+b-c-1}{n}+O\left(\frac{1}{n^2}\right),$$

where $O\left(\frac{1}{n^2}\right)$ denotes a function of n whose absolute value is less than $K\,/\,n^2$ (where K is independent of n), provided that n be sufficiently large. We conclude from Weierstrass' criterion that the series is absolutely convergent when $|\,x\,| = 1$, provided that

$$R(-a-b+c+1) > 1,$$

that is to say, provided that the real part of $c-a-b$ shall be positive.

Weierstrass' criterion is as follows: †

* If ζ_n, z_n be functions of the positive integer n, the relation

$$\zeta_n = O(z_n)$$

means that an integer n_0 and a positive number K independent of n exist, such that $|\,\zeta_n\,| < K\,|\,z_n\,|$ when $n \geqslant n_0$. See *Modern Analysis*, 2·1.

† See K. Knopp, *Theory of Infinite Series* (1928), § 228.

A series $\sum_{n=0}^{\infty} u_n$ *of complex terms for which*

$$\frac{u_{n+1}}{u_n} = 1 - \frac{\alpha}{n} + O\left(\frac{1}{n^{\lambda}}\right)$$

where $\lambda > 1$, *and* α *is independent of* n, *is absolutely convergent if, and only if,* $R(\alpha) > 1$.

For $R(\alpha) \leqslant 0$ *the series is invariably divergent. If* $0 < R(\alpha) \leqslant 1$, *each of the series*

$$\sum_{n=0}^{\infty} |u_n - u_{n+1}|, \quad \sum_{n=0}^{\infty} (-1)^n u_n$$

is convergent.

If we denote the sum function of the above power series by $F(a, b; c; x)$, we infer that this, *the hypergeometric function,* is an analytic function of x within the circle $|x| = 1$, and if $R(c-a-b) > 0$, we have, by Abel's limit theorem,*

$$F(a, b; c; 1) = \lim_{x \to 1} F(a, b; c; x). \tag{2}$$

Gauss has proved the following relations satisfied by the hypergeometric function $F(a, b; c; x)$:

$$\{c - 2a - (b-a)x\} F(a, b; c; x) + a(1-x) F(a+1, b; c; x) - (c-a) F(a-1, b; c; x) = 0,$$

$$c\{c - 1 - (2c - a - b - 1)x\} F(a, b; c; x) + (c-a)(c-b) x F(a, b; c+1; x) - c(c-1)(1-x) F(a, b; c-1; x) = 0,$$

$$c(c+1) F(a, b; c; x) - (c+1)\{c - (a+b+1)x\} F(a+1, b+1; c+1; x) - (a+1)(b+1) x(1-x) F(a+2, b+2; c+2; x) = 0,$$

each of which easily follows by considering the coefficient of x^n in the left-hand member. The verification is left to the reader.

9·82. The Hypergeometric Function when x = 1. We now prove that, if $R(c-a-b) > 0$,

$$F(a, b; c; 1) = \frac{\Gamma(c)\,\Gamma(c-a-b)}{\Gamma(c-a)\,\Gamma(c-b)}.$$

* K. Knopp, *loc. cit.* § 100.

We have, from the second of Gauss' relations, which holds when $x \to 1$,

$$F(a, b; c; 1) = \frac{(c-a)(c-b)}{c(c-a-b)} F(a, b; c+1; 1).$$

In this relation, write in turn $c+1, c+2, \dots, c+n-1$ for c, and multiply the results. We then get

$$F(a, b; c; 1) = \frac{(c-a)\dots(c+n-1-a)(c-b)\dots(c+n-1-b)}{c(c+1)\dots(c+n-1)(c-a-b)\dots(c+n-1-a-b)} F(a, b; c+n; 1).$$

Hence from 9·53, we have, when $n \to \infty$,

$$F(a, b; c; 1) = \frac{\Gamma(c)\,\Gamma(c-a-b)}{\Gamma(c-a)\,\Gamma(c-b)},$$

provided that

$$\lim_{n\to\infty} F(a, b; c+n; 1) = 1.$$

To prove that this is so we observe that $|F(a, b; c+n; 1)|$ cannot decrease if we replace a, b, c by $|a|, |b|, n-|c|$, so that

$$|F(a, b; c+n; 1)-1|$$

$$\leqslant \sum_{s=1}^{\infty} \frac{\{|a|\dots(|a|+s-1)\}\{|b|\dots(|b|+s-1)\}}{s!\,(n-|c|)\dots(n+s-1-|c|)}$$

$$\leqslant \frac{|ab|}{n-|c|} \sum_{s=1}^{\infty} \frac{(|a|+1)\dots(|a|+s-1)(|b|+1)\dots(|b|+s-1)}{s!\,(n+1-|c|)\dots(n+s-1-|c|)}.$$

Exactly as in 9·8, we prove that this series converges if

$$n-|c|-|a|-|b|>0,$$

a condition which is always realised if n be chosen large enough. Also as n increases each term diminishes, and $1/(n-|c|) \to 0$ when $n \to \infty$. From this the required result follows.

9·84. The Beta Function. The Beta function is defined by

$$\mathrm{B}(x, y) = \frac{\Gamma(x)\,\Gamma(y)}{\Gamma(x+y)}.$$

This function has the obvious properties:

$$\mathrm{B}(x, y) = \mathrm{B}(y, x),$$

$$\mathrm{B}(x+1,\,y) = \frac{x}{x+y}\,\mathrm{B}(x,\,y),$$

$$\mathrm{B}(x,\,y+1) = \frac{y}{x+y}\,\mathrm{B}(x,\,y).$$

Differencing with respect to x, we have also

$$\Delta_x \mathrm{B}(x,\,y) = -\frac{y}{x+y}\,\mathrm{B}(x,\,y) = -\mathrm{B}(x,\,y+1).$$

If $x = n+1$, a positive integer, we have

$$\mathrm{B}(n+1,\,y) = \frac{\Gamma(n+1)\,\Gamma(y)}{(y+n)(y+n-1)\dots y\,\Gamma(y)} = \frac{n!}{y(y+1)\dots(y+n)},$$

so that, from 9·7,

$$\mathrm{B}(n+1,\,y) = \int_0^1 t^{y-1}\,(1-t)^n\,dt.$$

This is a particular case of the more general result,

$$\mathrm{B}(x,\,y) = \int_0^1 t^{x-1}(1-t)^{y-1}\,dt, \quad R(x) > 0, \quad R(y) > 0,$$

which we shall now prove.

The binomial theorem gives

$$(1-t)^{y-1} = \sum_{s=0}^{\infty} (-1)^s \binom{y-1}{s} t^s$$

$$= \sum_{s=0}^{\infty} \frac{x(x+1)\dots(x+s-1)(1-y)(2-y)\dots(s-y)}{s!\,x(x+1)\dots(x+s-1)}\,t^s.$$

This series is uniformly convergent in the interval

$$0 < \varepsilon \leqslant t \leqslant z < 1.$$

Multiply by t^{x-1} and integrate from ε to z. We then have

$$\int_\epsilon^z t^{x-1}(1-t)^{y-1}\,dt$$

$$= \sum_{s=0}^{\infty} \frac{x(x+1)\dots(x+s-1)(1-y)(2-y)\dots(s-y)}{s!\;x(x+1)\dots(x+s)}\,(z^{s+x} - \varepsilon^{s+x})$$

$$= \frac{z^x}{x} F(x,\,1-y\,;\,x+1\,;\,z) - \frac{\varepsilon^x}{x} F(x,\,1-y\,;\,x+1\,;\,\varepsilon).$$

Since $R(x+1-x-(1-y)) = R(y) > 0$, we have, from 9·8 (2),

$$\lim_{z\to 1} F(x,\, 1-y;\; x+1;\; z) = F(x,\, 1-y;\; x+1;\; 1).$$

Also since $R(x) > 0$, we have $\varepsilon^x \to 0$ when $\varepsilon \to 0$, and the integral converges. Thus, when $z \to 1$, $\varepsilon \to 0$, we have

$$\int_0^1 t^{x-1}(1-t)^{y-1}\,dt = \frac{1}{x} F(x,\, 1-y;\; x+1;\; 1)$$

$$= \frac{\Gamma(x+1)\,\Gamma(x+1-x-1+y)}{x\,\Gamma(x+1-x)\,\Gamma(x+1-1+y)} = \frac{\Gamma(x)\,\Gamma(y)}{\Gamma(x+y)},$$

where we have used 9·82. This is the required result. The integral is known as the Eulerian Integral of the First Kind.

9·86. Definite Integral for the Hypergeometric Function. Suppose that $|x| < 1$. Then the binomial series

$$(1-xt)^{-b} = \sum_{s=0}^{\infty} \frac{b(b+1)\ldots(b+s-1)}{s!} x^s t^s$$

is uniformly convergent for $0 \leqslant t \leqslant 1$.

Multiply both sides by $t^{a-1}(1-t)^{c-a-1}$, where

$$R(a) > 0, \quad R(c-a) > 0,$$

and integrate from 0 to 1.

We then obtain, using 9·84,

$$\int_0^1 t^{a-1}(1-t)^{c-a-1}(1-xt)^{-b}\,dt$$

$$= \sum_{s=0}^{\infty} \frac{b(b+1)\ldots(b+s-1)}{s!}\cdot\frac{\Gamma(a+s)\,\Gamma(c-a)}{\Gamma(c+s)} x^s$$

$$= \sum_{s=0}^{\infty} \frac{a(a+1)\ldots(a+s-1)\,b(b+1)\ldots(b+s-1)}{s!\,c(c+1)\ldots(c+s-1)} x^s \cdot \frac{\Gamma(a)\,\Gamma(c-a)}{\Gamma(c)}$$

$$= \frac{\Gamma(a)\,\Gamma(c-a)}{\Gamma(c)} F(a,\, b;\; c;\; x)$$

$$= \mathrm{B}(a,\, c-a)\, F(a,\, b;\; c;\; x),$$

which expresses the hypergeometric function as a definite integral.

9·88. Single Loop Integral for the Beta Function. Consider the loop contour l shewn in Fig. 11.

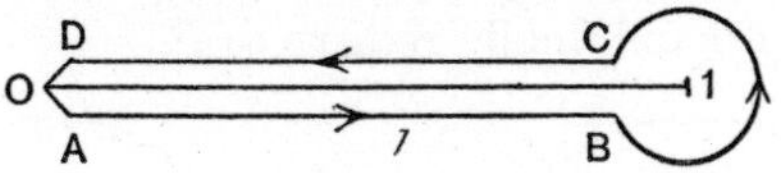

FIG. 11.

We shall suppose that AB, CD coincide with the segment of the real axis between 0 and 1 and that the radius of the circular part tends to zero.

Now consider

$$I = \int_l t^{x-1}(t-1)^{y-1}\,dt = \int_0^{(1+)} t^{x-1}(t-1)^{y-1}\,dt$$

with the notation of 9·72.

If we start with $\arg t = 0$ along AB, we shall have $\arg(t-1) = -\pi$ along AB and $\arg(t-1) = +\pi$ along CD.

Thus on AB, $\qquad (t-1) = re^{-i\pi} = -r,$

while on CD, $\qquad (t-1) = re^{i\pi} = -r,$

so that $t = 1 - r$.

If $R(y) > 0$, the integral round the circle tends to zero when the radius tends to zero, so that we have

$$I = \int_0^1 e^{-\pi i(y-1)}\,r^{y-1}(1-r)^{x-1}\,dr + \int_1^0 e^{\pi i(y-1)}\,r^{y-1}(1-r)^{x-1}\,dr$$

$$= (e^{-\pi i(y-1)} - e^{\pi i(y-1)})\,\mathrm{B}(x, y) = 2i\sin\pi y\,\mathrm{B}(x, y).$$

Thus

$$\mathrm{B}(x, y) = \frac{1}{2i\sin\pi y}\int_0^{(1+)} t^{x-1}(t-1)^{y-1}\,dt.$$

Since $\Gamma(y)\,\Gamma(1-y) = \pi/(\sin\pi y)$, we deduce from this the relation

$$\frac{\Gamma(x)}{\Gamma(x+y)\,\Gamma(1-y)} = \frac{1}{2\pi i}\int_0^{(1+)} t^{x-1}(t-1)^{y-1}\,dt.$$

9·89. Double Loop Integral for the Beta Function. Consider the contour shewn in Fig. 12, which starts from a point P, passes positively round the points 1 and 0, and then negatively round the points 1 and 0 and finally returns to P.

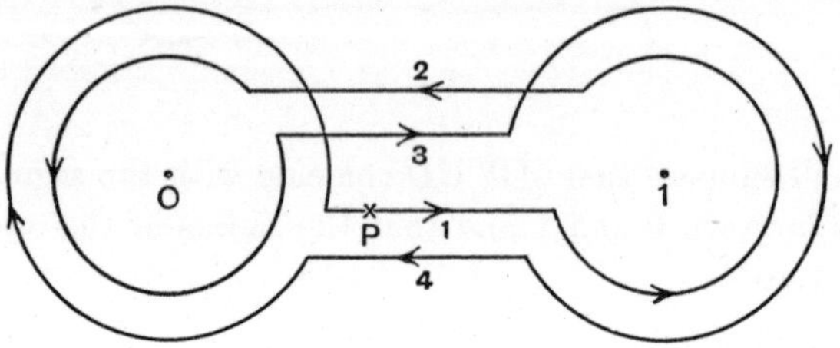

FIG. 12.

Consider

$$B_1(x, y) = \int t^{x-1}(1-t)^{y-1}\, dt,$$

taken round the above contour. To evaluate the integral, we shall suppose the contour reduced to four lines coincident with the segment 0, 1 of the real axis, the radii of the circles round 0, 1 at the same time tending to zero.

If $R(x) > 0$, $R(y) > 0$, it is easy to shew that the integral round these circles tends to zero when the radius tends to zero.

If we start at P on the real axis with $\arg t = 0$, we have, for the reduced contour,

On the path 1: $\arg t = 0$, $\arg(1-t) = 0$,

" " " 2: $\arg t = 0$, $\arg(1-t) = 2\pi$,

" " " 3: $\arg t = 2\pi$, $\arg(1-t) = 2\pi$,

" " " 4: $\arg t = 2\pi$, $\arg(1-t) = 0$.

Thus

$$B_1(x, y) = \{1 - e^{2\pi i(y-1)} + e^{2\pi i(x+y-2)} - e^{2\pi i(x-1)}\} \int_0^1 t^{x-1}(1-t)^{y-1}\, dt$$

$$= (1 - e^{2\pi i x})(1 - e^{2\pi i y})\, B(x, y).$$

Hence, with the notation of 9·72, we have proved that

$$(1 - e^{2\pi i x})(1 - e^{2\pi i y})\, B(x, y) = \int_P^{(1+),\,(0+),\,(1-),\,(0-)} t^{x-1}(1-t)^{y-1}\, dt,$$

P being any point on the contour of Fig. 12, which may be deformed in any manner provided that the branch points 0, 1 are not crossed.

The restriction $R(x) > 0$, $R(y) > 0$ can now be removed, since the contour does not pass through the points 0, 1 and the above double loop circuit integral gives the Beta function for all values of x, y, neither of which is an integer. When either x or y is an integer the integral vanishes. We also note that

$$(1-e^{2\pi i x})(1-e^{2\pi i y})\,\mathrm{B}(x, y) = \frac{\Gamma_1(x)\,\Gamma_1(y)}{\Gamma(x+y)}.$$

Since $\Gamma_1(x)$, $\Gamma_1(y)$, $\dfrac{1}{\Gamma(x+y)}$ are all integral functions, we see that the above double loop circuit integral represents an integral function of x (or y). We shall call the function $\mathrm{B}_1(x, y)$ the complementary Beta function.

EXAMPLES IX

1. Find the sum from 0 to x of the function

$$\frac{x^6+x^4+3}{(x+1)(x+2)(2x+3)}.$$

2. Prove that

(i) $\Psi(x) = \log x - \sum_{s=0}^{\infty} \left\{\frac{1}{x+s} - \log\left(1+\frac{1}{x+s}\right)\right\}$,

(ii) $\Psi(x) = \log x - \frac{1}{2x} - \sum_{s=0}^{\infty} \left\{\frac{2(x+s)+1}{2(x+s)(x+s+1)} - \log\frac{x+s+1}{x+s}\right\}$.

3. Prove that $\qquad \Psi(4) = 1+\frac{1}{2}+\frac{1}{3}-\gamma.$

4. If

$$g(x) = 2\sum_{n=0}^{\infty} \frac{(-1)^n}{x+n},$$

prove that

(i) $g(x) = \Psi\left(\frac{x+1}{2}\right) - \Psi(x)$,

(ii) $g(x)+g(1-x) = 2\pi \operatorname{cosec} \pi x$,

(iii) $g(1) = 2\log 2, \quad g(\frac{1}{2}) = \pi.$

5. With the notation of Ex. 4, prove that

$$\frac{1}{n}\sum_{\nu=0}^{2n-1}(-1)^\nu\,\Psi\left(x+\frac{\nu}{2n}\right)=-g(2nx).$$

6. Obtain the following results:

$$\Psi'(x)=\sum_{s=0}^{\infty}\frac{1}{(x+s)^2},$$

$$\Psi'(x)=\frac{1}{x}+\sum_{s=0}^{\infty}\frac{1}{(x+s)^2(x+s+1)},$$

$$\Psi'(x)=\frac{1}{x}+\frac{1}{2x^2}+\sum_{s=0}^{\infty}\frac{1}{2(x+s)^2(x+s+1)^2}.$$

7. Prove that

$$\Psi(x)=-\gamma+\int_0^1\frac{1-t^{x-1}}{1-t}\,dt.$$

[Legendre.]

8. Prove that

$$\Psi(x)=\log x-\frac{1}{2x}+2\int_0^\infty\frac{t\,dt}{(x^2+t^2)(1-e^{2\pi t})}.$$

9. By means of the last formula in 8·3, prove that

$$\Psi(x)=\log x-\frac{1}{2x}+2\sum_{n=1}^{\infty}\{\operatorname{ci}(2\pi nx)\cos 2\pi nx+\operatorname{si}(2\pi nx)\sin 2\pi nx\}.$$

10. Prove that

(i) $\Gamma(-\frac{1}{2})=-2\sqrt{\pi}$,

(ii) $\Gamma(\frac{1}{3})\,\Gamma(\frac{2}{3})=2\pi/\sqrt{3}$.

11. For large values of n, prove that, approximately,

$$\frac{3\,.\,5\,\ldots\,(2n+1)}{2\,.\,4\,\ldots\,2n}=\frac{1}{\sqrt{\pi}}\left\{2\sqrt{n}+\frac{3}{4\sqrt{n}}\right\}.$$

12. Prove Wallis' Theorem, namely

$$\frac{\pi}{2}=\frac{2\,.\,2\,.\,4\,.\,4\,.\,6\,.\,6\,.\,8\,.\,8\,\ldots}{1\,.\,3\,.\,3\,.\,5\,.\,5\,.\,7\,.\,7\,.\,9\,\ldots},$$

and deduce that for n large

$$(-1)^n\binom{-\frac{1}{2}}{n}\sim\frac{1}{\sqrt{(\pi n)}}.$$

13. Prove that, if n be a positive integer,

$$\Gamma\left(n+\tfrac{1}{2}\right) = \frac{1.3.5\ldots(2n-1)}{2^n}\sqrt{\pi}.$$

14. Shew that for real positive values of x the minimum value of $\Gamma(x)$ is $0{\cdot}88560\ldots$, when $x = 1{\cdot}46163\ldots$.

15. Prove that

$$x\,\Gamma(x)\,\Gamma(-x) = -\pi \operatorname{cosec} \pi x.$$

16. Prove that

$$\mathop{\Delta}_{-1}^{n} \frac{\Gamma(x)}{\Gamma(x+m)} = (-1)^n \frac{m(m+1)\ldots(m+n-1)}{(x-1)(x-2)\ldots(x-n)} \frac{\Gamma(x)}{\Gamma(x+m)}.$$

17. Prove that

$$\Gamma(x) = \sqrt{(2\pi)}\, x^{x-\frac{1}{2}} e^{-x} \times \left\{1 + \frac{1}{12x} + \frac{1}{288x^2} - \frac{139}{51840x^3} - \frac{571}{2488320x^4} + O\left(\frac{1}{x^5}\right)\right\}.$$

18. By means of 8·3, shew that, when $x_0 > 0$ and $x_0 < x < x_0+1$,

$$\log\Gamma(x) = \log\sqrt{2\pi} + x_0(\log x_0 - 1) + \sum_{n=1}^{\infty}(a_n \cos 2n\pi x + b_n \sin 2n\pi x)$$

where

$$a_n + ib_n = 2\lim_{\mu\to 0}\left\{\Big[-f(z)\log z\Big]_{x_0}^{\infty} + \int_{x_0}^{\infty}\frac{1}{z}f(z)\,dz\right\},$$

where

$$f(z) = -\int_z^{\infty} \exp(-\mu z + 2n\pi i z)\,dz,$$

and hence prove that

$$\pi n\, a_n = (\log x_0)\sin(2n\pi x_0) - \operatorname{si}(2\pi n x_0),$$
$$\pi n\, b_n = -(\log x_0)\cos(2n\pi x_0) + \operatorname{ci}(2n\pi x_0).$$

19. Shew that, in the interval $x_0 < x < x_0+1$,

$$x - \tfrac{1}{2} = x_0 - \frac{1}{\pi}\sum_{n=1}^{\infty}\frac{1}{n}\sin 2\pi n(x-x_0),$$

and hence prove, by means of the last example, that

$$\log\Gamma(x) = \log\sqrt{2\pi} + \left(x-\tfrac{1}{2}\right)\log x_0 - x_0 - \sum_{n=1}^{\infty}\frac{1}{n\pi}\{\operatorname{si}(2n\pi x_0)\cos(2n\pi x) - \operatorname{ci}(2n\pi x_0)\sin(2n\pi x)\}.$$

20. From Ex. 18, deduce that

$$2\pi n \int_{x_0}^{x_0+1} \log \Gamma(x) \cos(2n\pi x)\, dx = (\log x_0) \sin(2nx\pi_0) - \operatorname{si}(2\pi n x_0),$$

$$2\pi n \int_{x_0}^{x_0+1} \log \Gamma(x) \sin(2n\pi x)\, dx = -(\log x_0) \cos(2n\pi x_0) + \operatorname{ci}(2\pi n x_0).$$

21. Prove that

$$\operatorname{ci}(x) - \log x + \int_0^x \frac{1-\cos z}{z}\, dz = \lim_{n\to\infty} \left[\int_0^{\frac{1}{2}\pi} \frac{1-\cos 2nz}{z}\, dz - \log n\pi\right]$$

$$= \lim_{n\to\infty} \left\{\int_0^{\frac{1}{2}\pi} \frac{1-\cos 2nz}{\sin z}\, dz - \log 4n\right\},$$

and deduce that

$$\operatorname{ci}(x) = \gamma + \log x + \sum_{\nu=1}^{\infty} \frac{(-1)^\nu x^{2\nu}}{2\nu\,(2\nu)!}.$$

22. Use the last two examples to prove that

$$4n \int_0^1 \log \Gamma(x) \cos(2n\pi x)\, dx = 1,$$

$$2\pi n \int_0^1 \log \Gamma(x) \sin(2n\pi x)\, dx = \gamma + \log 2\pi n.$$

23. Prove that, for $0 < x < 1$,

$$\log \Gamma(x) = \log \sqrt{2\pi} + \sum_{n=1}^{\infty} \left\{\frac{\cos 2n\pi x}{2n} + (\gamma + \log(2n\pi))\frac{\sin 2n\pi x}{n\pi}\right\},$$

and deduce Kummer's series, namely,

$$\log \Gamma(x) = (\gamma + \log 2)(\tfrac{1}{2} - x) + (1-x)\log \pi - \tfrac{1}{2}\log \sin \pi x$$

$$+ \sum_{n=1}^{\infty} \frac{\log n}{n\pi} \sin 2n\pi x.$$

24. Prove that

$$B(x, 1-x) = \pi \operatorname{cosec} \pi x.$$

25. Prove that

$$B(x, y)\, B(x+y, z) = B(y, z)\, B(y+z, x).$$

[Euler.]

CHAPTER X

FACTORIAL SERIES

IN this chapter we develop some of the properties of the series

$$\frac{a_0}{x}+\frac{a_1\,1!}{x(x+1)}+\frac{a_2\,2!}{x(x+1)(x+2)}+\frac{a_3\,3!}{x(x+1)(x+2)(x+3)}+\dots,$$

which is known as a factorial series of the first kind, or series of inverse factorials; and the series

$$b_0+b_1\frac{(x-1)}{1}+\frac{b_2(x-1)(x-2)}{2!}+\frac{b_3(x-1)(x-2)(x-3)}{3!}+\dots,$$

which is variously called a factorial series of the second kind, a series of binomial coefficients, or Newton's (interpolation) series. The last name arises from the fact that Newton's interpolation formula 3·1, when the series is extended to infinity, takes the above form.

Both these factorial series have many properties in common, in particular when x is a complex variable, the domain of convergence is a half-plane.

Factorial series are of importance in the theory of linear difference equations, where they play a part analogous to that of power series in the theory of differential equations.

With the notations of 2·11, we see that the series can be written in the respective forms

$$a_0(x-1)^{(-1)}+a_1(x-1)^{(-2)}\,1!+a_2(x-1)^{(-3)}\,2!+\dots,$$

$$b_0+b_1(x-1)^{(1)}/1!+b_2(x-1)^{(2)}/2!+\dots,$$

in which shape they present a marked analogy with power series in $x-1$.

While factorial series first appear in the work of Newton and Stirling, their systematic development on modern lines is due largely to Bendixson, Nielsen, Landau, Nörlund and Bohr.

The present chapter is based mainly upon Nörlund's *Leçons sur les séries d'interpolation* (Paris, 1926), to which the reader is referred for a more detailed treatment.

10·0. Associated Factorial Series. With the sequence of coefficients

$$a_0, a_1, a_2, a_3, \dots,$$

we can associate the factorial series

$$(1) \qquad \sum_{s=0}^{\infty} \frac{a_s\, s!}{x(x+1)\dots(x+s)},$$

$$(2) \qquad \sum_{s=0}^{\infty} (-1)^s a_s \binom{x-1}{s},$$

which we shall call associated factorial series. We now prove a fundamental theorem due to Landau.*

Theorem I. *Associated factorial series simultaneously converge or diverge for every value of x which is not an integer.*

In the first place, suppose that (1) converges.

Put

$$b_s = \frac{a_s\, s!}{x(x+1)\dots(x+s)}, \quad c_s = \frac{(-1)^s x(x^2-1)\dots(x^2-s^2)}{s!\, s!}.$$

We have

$$c_s = x\left(1-\frac{x^2}{1}\right)\left(1-\frac{x^2}{2^2}\right)\dots\left(1-\frac{x^2}{s^2}\right).$$

Thus †

$$\lim_{s\to\infty} c_s = \frac{\sin \pi x}{\pi}.$$

Hence a constant K exists such that $|c_s| < K$.

* E. Landau, *Sitzsber. Akad. München*, 36 (1906), pp. 151-218. Landau also proves that the Dirichlet series

$$\sum_{s=1}^{\infty} \frac{a_s}{s^x}$$

formed with the same coefficients can be included in the enunciation of the theorem.

† *Modern Analysis*, 7·5.

Also

$$c_s - c_{s+1} = \frac{x^2}{(s+1)^2} c_s,$$

and consequently

$$|c_s - c_{s+1}| < K \frac{|x|^2}{(s+1)^2},$$

and hence the series $\Sigma(c_s - c_{s+1})$ is absolutely convergent. By hypothesis, Σb_s converges. Hence by du Bois-Reymond's test * $\Sigma b_s c_s$ converges, that is to say (2) converges.

Secondly, suppose that (2) converges.

Put

$$d_s = (-1)^s a_s \binom{x-1}{s}, \quad f_s = \frac{(-1)^s s!\, s!}{x(x^2-1)\dots(x^2-s^2)}.$$

As before,

$$\lim_{s\to\infty} f_s = \frac{\pi}{\sin \pi x},$$

so that a constant K exists such that $|f_s| < K$. Also

$$f_s - f_{s+1} = f_s \frac{x^2}{x^2-(s+1)^2}.$$

Hence $\Sigma(f_s - f_{s+1})$ converges absolutely and therefore we again infer that $\Sigma d_s f_s$ converges, that is to say (1) converges.

10·02. The Convergence of Factorial Series. Let

(1) $$u_s = \frac{x_0(x_0+1)\dots(x_0+s)}{x(x+1)\dots(x+s)} = \frac{\Gamma(x_0+s+1)\Gamma(x)}{\Gamma(x+s+1)\Gamma(x_0)},$$

(2) $$v_s = \frac{(x-1)\dots(x-s)}{(x_0-1)\dots(x_0-s)} = \frac{\Gamma(s-x+1)\Gamma(1-x_0)}{\Gamma(s-x_0+1)\Gamma(1-x)},$$

and let σ denote the real part of $x - x_0$ which we take to be positive.

Then, from 9·61,

$$|u_s| = s^{-\sigma} \left| \frac{\Gamma(x)}{\Gamma(x_0)} \right| (1+\delta),$$

$$|v_s| = s^{-\sigma} \left| \frac{\Gamma(1-x_0)}{\Gamma(1-x)} \right| (1+\delta),$$

where $\delta \to 0$ when $s \to \infty$.

---

* See p. 274 for the statement of this test.

In the case of u_s, we suppose that x is not one of the numbers $0, -1, -2, -3, \ldots$, and in the case of v_s, that x_0 is not one of the numbers $1, 2, 3, \ldots$.

From these results it is clear, when x and x_0 are given, that both u_s and v_s are bounded.

Let w_s denote either u_s or v_s.

Then

$$\frac{w_{s+1}}{w_s} = 1 - \frac{x - x_0}{s} + O\left(\frac{1}{s^2}\right).$$

It follows from Weierstrass' criterion (9·8), that

(i) when $0 < \sigma \leqslant 1$,

$$\sum_{s=0}^{\infty} (w_s - w_{s+1})$$

is absolutely convergent.

(ii) when $\sigma > 1$,

$$\sum_{s=0}^{\infty} w_s$$

is absolutely convergent, and, *a fortiori*,

$$\sum_{s=0}^{\infty} (w_s - w_{s+1})$$

is absolutely convergent.

Now let $\sum_{s=0}^{\infty} \alpha_s$ be a (not necessarily absolutely) convergent series.

We have du Bois-Reymond's test,* namely that

$\Sigma\, a_s\, b_s$ is convergent if $\Sigma (b_s - b_{s+1})$ be absolutely convergent and if $\Sigma\, a_s$ converge at least conditionally.

If follows that

$$\sum_{s=0}^{\infty} \alpha_s\, w_s$$

is convergent.

Moreover, w_s is bounded, and in fact we have

$$|w_s| < C s^{-\sigma},$$

where C is independent of s. Also $|\alpha_s|$ is bounded, since $\Sigma\, \alpha_s$ converges.

---

* K. Knopp, *Infinite Series*, 184. The test is substantially due to Abel and is also known as Abel's Test.

Thus we have

$$\sum_{s=n}^{m} |\alpha_s w_s| < C \sum_{s=n}^{m} \frac{1}{s^{\sigma}},$$

where C is independent of s.

Therefore if $\sigma > 1$, $\Sigma s^{-\sigma}$ converges, and consequently $\Sigma \alpha_s w_s$ converges absolutely.

If we take:

(A) $$\alpha_s = \frac{a_s \,.\, s!}{x_0(x_0+1) \ldots (x_0+s)}, \quad w_s = u_s,$$

we have

$$\alpha_s w_s = \frac{a_s \,.\, s!}{x(x+1) \ldots (x+s)};$$

(B) $$\alpha_s = (-1)^s a_s \binom{x_0-1}{s}, \quad w_s = v_s,$$

we have

$$\alpha_s w_s = (-1)^s a_s \binom{x-1}{s}.$$

We therefore have the following theorems:

Theorem II. *If a factorial series converge for $x = x_0$, the series converges for every x, such that $R(x) > R(x_0)$.*

Theorem III. *If a factorial series converge for $x = x_0$, the series converges absolutely for every x, such that $R(x) > R(x_0+1)$.*

Theorem IV. *If a factorial series converge absolutely for $x = x_0$, the series converges absolutely for every x, such that $R(x) > R(x_0)$.*

For in this case $\Sigma |\alpha_s|$ converges and $|w_s|$ is bounded so that

$$\sum_{s=n}^{m} |\alpha_s w_s| < M \sum_{s=n}^{m} |\alpha_s|,$$

where M is positive and greater than every $|w_s|$.

10·04. The Region of Convergence. We can now prove that the region of convergence of a factorial series is a half-plane.

For we can divide all rational numbers, excluding zero and positive and negative integers, into two classes L and R, such that L contains all numbers which make the series divergent and R contains all numbers which make the series convergent. From Theorem II we see that each member of L is less than every member of R.

The above classification therefore determines a Dedekind section of the rational numbers and therefore defines a real number λ, such that the series converges for $x = \lambda + \varepsilon$, where ε is positive and arbitrarily small, and diverges for $x = \lambda - \varepsilon$.

This number λ is called the *abscissa of convergence*. By Theorem II the series converges for every point in the half-plane which is limited on the left by $R(x) = \lambda$. Theorem I can now be stated in the form: *two associated factorial series have the same convergence abscissa.*

Of the classes L and R by which λ is defined one may be empty, that is, may contain no members. If L be empty, we have $\lambda = +\infty$, that is, the series is everywhere divergent. If R be empty, $\lambda = -\infty$, and the series converges in the whole complex plane. In both cases the integral points are possibly excluded.

10·06. The Region of Absolute Convergence. The region of absolute convergence is likewise a half-plane. If in the definitions of the classes L and R of 10·04 we substitute the words " absolutely convergent " for " convergent," the Dedekind section, by Theorem IV, determines a real number μ called the abscissa of absolute convergence. The series converges absolutely in the half-plane limited on the left by $R(x) = \mu$.

From Theorem III we conclude that

$$0 \leqslant \mu - \lambda \leqslant 1.$$

In the strip defined by

$$\lambda < R(x) < \mu,$$

the series converges, but not absolutely.

We now proceed to determine the value of λ, but before doing so we investigate some preliminary results.

10·07. Abel's Identities. The two following identities, which are due to Abel, are of frequent use in the transformation of series.

(I) If $A_s = a_n + a_{n+1} + \dots + a_s$, then

$$\sum_{s=p}^{m} a_s b_s = \sum_{s=p}^{m} (b_s - b_{s+1}) A_s - b_p A_{p-1} + b_{m+1} A_m.$$

(II) If $A'_s = a_s + a_{s+1} + a_{s+2} + \dots$, then

$$\sum_{s=p}^{m} a_s b_s = \sum_{s=p}^{m-1} (b_{s+1} - b_s) A'_{s+1} + b_p A'_p - b_m A'_{m+1}.$$

To prove these identities, we observe that

$$a_s b_s = (b_s - b_{s+1})(A_s - A_{s-1}) + b_{s+1}(A_s - A_{s-1})$$
$$= (b_s - b_{s+1}) A_s - b_s A_{s-1} + b_{s+1} A_s,$$

and that

$$a_s b_s = (b_{s+1} - b_s) A'_{s+1} + b_s A'_s - b_{s+1} A'_{s+1}.$$

From these results the identities follow at once by summation.

10·08. The Upper Limit of a Sequence. Consider a sequence of real numbers,

$$(x_n) = x_1, x_2, x_3, \dots .$$

Divide all rational numbers into two classes L and R, such that if l be a member of the class L there is an unlimited number of terms x_n, such that $x_n \geqslant l$, while if r be a member of the class R, there is only a finite number of terms x_n, such that $x_n > r$. It is clear that each l is less than every r, and this classification involving, as it does, *all* rational numbers, therefore determines a Dedekind section of the rational numbers. This section defines a real number λ, such that, if ε be an arbitrary positive number,

(i) $x_n > \lambda - \varepsilon$ for an infinite number of x_n,

(ii) $x_n > \lambda + \varepsilon$ for a finite number only of x_n.

The number λ defined in this way is called the greatest of the limits, the upper limit, or *limes superior* of the sequence (x_n), and we write *

$$\lambda = \limsup_{n \to \infty} x_n.$$

In this chapter we shall be concerned with sequences whose nth term is of the form

$$\frac{\log x_n}{\log n},$$

* See K. Knopp, *Infinite Series*, p. 90. Also *Modern Analysis*, 2·21.

where x_n is real and positive. Let

$$\lambda = \limsup_{n\to\infty} \frac{\log x_n}{\log n},$$

and let ε be an arbitrarily small positive number.

Then we can find an integer n_0, such that

$$\frac{\log x_n}{\log n} < \lambda + \varepsilon, \text{ if } n \geqslant n_0,$$

$$\frac{\log x_n}{\log n} > \lambda - \varepsilon,$$

for an infinite number of increasing suffixes $n_1, n_2, n_3, \ldots,$ where $n_1 \geqslant n_0$.

Thus

$$x_n < n^{\lambda+\epsilon}, \text{ if } n \geqslant n_0,$$

$$x_n > n^{\lambda-\epsilon}, \text{ if } n = n_1, n_2, n_3, \ldots .$$

If a real number σ, other than zero, exist, such that

$$\lim_{n\to\infty} \frac{x_n}{n^\sigma} = 0,$$

we find a suffix N, such that

$$x_n < \varepsilon n^\sigma, \text{ if } n \geqslant N.$$

Hence if n_r be the first of $n_1, n_2, n_3, \ldots,$ such that $n_r \geqslant N$, we have $n^{\lambda-\epsilon} < \varepsilon n^\sigma$, if $n = n_r, n_{r+1}, n_{r+2}, \ldots,$ that is to say, $n^{\lambda-\sigma-\epsilon} < \varepsilon$ for these values of n.

Hence we must have $\lambda - \sigma - \varepsilon < 0$. Since ε is arbitrarily small, we have

$$\lambda \leqslant \sigma.$$

Again, if x_n be such that

$$\lim_{n\to\infty} \frac{x_n}{\log n} = 0,$$

we have in the same way $n^{\lambda-\epsilon} < x_n < \varepsilon \log n$, if $n = n_r, n_{r+1}, \ldots .$

Thus $n^\lambda < n^\epsilon \log n^\epsilon < n^{2\epsilon}$, which necessitates $\lambda < 2\varepsilon$, and since ε is arbitrarily small, we must have

$$\lambda \leqslant 0.$$

10·09. The Abscissa of Convergence; Landau's Theorem. The convergence abscissa of the associated factorial series 10·0, (1), (2) is determined by the following theorem.*

Theorem V. *Let*

$$\alpha = \limsup_{n\to\infty} \log\left|\sum_{s=0}^{n} a_s\right| \Big/ \log n, \quad \beta = \limsup_{n\to\infty} \log\left|\sum_{s=n}^{\infty} a_s\right| \Big/ \log n.$$

The abscissa of convergence, λ, of the associated factorial series is equal to α if $\lambda \geqslant 0$ and is equal to β if $\lambda < 0$.

We consider the series

$$(1) \qquad \sum_{s=0}^{\infty} (-1)^s a_s \binom{x-1}{s},$$

and divide the proof into four stages.

Suppose that the series converges at a point x, where x is not a positive integer. Let $R(x) = \sigma$.

(i) We prove that if $\sigma \geqslant 0$, then $\alpha \leqslant \sigma$; and consequently that $\alpha \leqslant \lambda$, if $\lambda \geqslant 0$.

Write

$$b_s = (-1)^s a_s \binom{x-1}{s}, \quad c_s = \frac{(-1)^s s!}{(x-1)\dots(x-s)} = \frac{\Gamma(s+1)\,\Gamma(1-x)}{\Gamma(s-x+1)}.$$

Then we have

$$c_{s+1} - c_s = \left(\frac{s+1}{s-x+1} - 1\right) c_s = \frac{x}{s-x+1} c_s,$$

so that, from 9·61,

$$c_s = \Gamma(1-x)\, s^x (1+\delta), \quad c_{s+1} - c_s = x\,\Gamma(1-x)\, s^{x-1}(1+\delta),$$

where $|\delta| \to 0$ when $s \to \infty$. Thus we can find a positive number K independent of s, such that

$$|c_s| < Ks^{\sigma}, \quad |c_{s+1} - c_s| < Ks^{\sigma-1}.$$

Let $B_s = b_s + b_{s+1} + b_{s+2} + \dots$. Since $a_s = b_s c_s$, we have by Abel's Identity

$$\sum_{s=p}^{m} a_s = \sum_{s=p}^{m-1} (c_{s+1} - c_s) B_{s+1} + c_p B_p - c_m B_{m+1},$$

* E. Landau, *Sitzsber. Akad. München*, 36 (1906), pp. 151-218.

and hence

$$A_{m,p} = \left|\sum_{s=p}^{m} a_s\right| \leqslant \sum_{s=p}^{m-1} \left|c_{s+1} - c_s\right| \times \left|B_{s+1}\right| + \left|c_p B_p\right| + \left|c_m B_{m+1}\right|.$$

By hypothesis, Σb_s converges, and hence, given $\varepsilon > 0$, we can find p, such that $|B_s| < \varepsilon$, if $s \geqslant p$. Hence we have

$$(2) \qquad A_{m,p} < \varepsilon K\left(\sum_{s=p}^{m-1} s^{\sigma-1} + m^\sigma + p^\sigma\right).$$

Now $\int_s^{s+1} x^{\sigma-1}\,dx$ lies between $s^{\sigma-1}$ and $(s+1)^{\sigma-1}$, and hence

$$\int_p^m x^{\sigma-1}\,dx \text{ lies between } \sum_{s=p}^{m-1} s^{\sigma-1} \text{ and } m^{\sigma-1} - p^{\sigma-1} + \sum_{s=p}^{m-1} s^{\sigma-1},$$

whence we easily conclude, if $\sigma > 0$, that

$$\sum_{s=p}^{m-1} s^{\sigma-1} < \frac{m^\sigma}{\sigma}.$$

Thus

$$A_{m,p} < \varepsilon K\left\{p^\sigma + m^\sigma\left(1 + \frac{1}{\sigma}\right)\right\},$$

and hence

$$\frac{A_{m,0}}{m^\sigma} < \frac{A_{p-1,0}}{m^\sigma} + \varepsilon K\left(\frac{p^\sigma}{m^\sigma} + 1 + \frac{1}{\sigma}\right).$$

Now let $m \to \infty$. We then have

$$\lim_{m\to\infty} \frac{A_{m,0}}{m^\sigma} = 0,$$

and hence, from 10·08, $\alpha \leqslant \sigma$.

Again, if $\sigma = 0$ and $s < x < s+1$, then

$$\frac{1}{s} > \int_s^{s+1} \frac{dx}{x} > \frac{1}{s+1},$$

so that

$$\sum_{s=p}^{m-1} s^{-1} > \log m - \log p > \sum_{s=p}^{m-1} s^{-1} + \frac{1}{m} - \frac{1}{p},$$

and hence, if $p > 0$,

$$\sum_{s=p}^{m-1} s^{-1} < \log m.$$

Thus, from (2), we have

$$A_{m,p} < \varepsilon K(2+\log m),$$

whence

$$\frac{A_{m,0}}{\log m} < \frac{A_{p-1,0}}{\log m} + \varepsilon K\left(\frac{2}{\log m}+1\right).$$

It follows that

$$\lim_{m\to\infty} \frac{A_{m,0}}{\log m} = 0,$$

and therefore again, by 10·08, we have $\alpha \leqslant \sigma$. Thus (i) is established.

(ii) We now prove that when α is finite the series converges for $x = \alpha+\varepsilon$, where ε is an arbitrarily small positive number, and consequently that $\lambda \leqslant \alpha$.

Let

$$d_s = (-1)^s \frac{(x-1)(x-2)\ldots(x-s)}{s!} = \frac{\Gamma(s-x+1)}{\Gamma(s+1)\,\Gamma(1-x)}.$$

Then, by 9·61,

$$d_s = \frac{s^{-x}}{\Gamma(1-x)}(1+\delta), \quad d_s - d_{s+1} = \frac{s^{-x-1}}{\Gamma(1-x)}(1+\delta),$$

so that if $x = \alpha+\varepsilon$ we can find a positive number K, independent of s, such that

$$|\,d_s\,| < Ks^{-\alpha-\epsilon} < Ks^{-\alpha-\frac{1}{2}\epsilon},$$

$$|\,d_s - d_{s+1}\,| < Ks^{-\alpha-1-\frac{1}{2}\epsilon},$$

and further by 10·08, such that

$$\left|\sum_{n=0}^{s} a_n\right| < Ks^{\alpha+\frac{1}{2}\epsilon}.$$

Let

$$A_s = a_0 + a_1 + a_2 + \ldots + a_s.$$

Then, since $b_s = a_s d_s$, we have by Abel's Identity,

$$\sum_{s=p}^{m} b_s = \sum_{s=p}^{m} (d_s - d_{s+1}) A_s - d_p A_{p-1} + d_{m+1} A_m.$$

Thus we have

$$(3) \qquad \left|\sum_{s=p}^{m} b_s\right| < K^2 \left\{ \sum_{s=p}^{m} s^{-1-\frac{1}{2}\epsilon} + \frac{(p-1)^{\alpha+\frac{1}{2}\epsilon}}{p^{\alpha+\frac{1}{2}\epsilon}} + \frac{m^{\alpha+\frac{1}{2}\epsilon}}{(m+1)^{\alpha+\frac{1}{2}\epsilon}} \right\}.$$

The right-hand member $\to 0$ when $p \to \infty$, and consequently Σb_s converges. Thus (ii) is established.

Combining (i) and (ii) we have, if $\lambda \geqslant 0$, $\alpha \leqslant \lambda$, and when α is finite, $\lambda \leqslant \alpha$. Consequently we must have $\lambda = \alpha$, if $\lambda \geqslant 0$.

(iii) We now consider the case $\sigma < 0$, and prove that if $\sigma < 0$, then $\beta \leqslant \sigma$; and consequently that $\beta \leqslant \lambda$.

When $\sigma < 0$, we can let $m \to \infty$ in (2), which then gives

$$A_{\infty, p} = \left| \sum_{s=p}^{\infty} a_s \right| < \varepsilon K \left(p^\sigma + \sum_{s=p}^{\infty} s^{\sigma-1} \right).$$

Now, if $s < x < s+1$, and $\sigma < 0$, we have

$$s^{\sigma-1} > \int_s^{s+1} x^{\sigma-1} \, dx > (s+1)^{\sigma-1}.$$

Thus

$$\sum_{s=p}^{\infty} s^{\sigma-1} < p^{\sigma-1} - \frac{p^\sigma}{\sigma}.$$

Hence

$$p^{-\sigma} A_{\infty, p} < \varepsilon K \left(1 - \frac{1}{\sigma} + \frac{1}{p} \right),$$

so that

$$\lim_{p \to \infty} \frac{1}{p^\sigma} \left| \sum_{s=p}^{\infty} a_s \right| = 0,$$

and therefore, from 10·08, we have $\beta \leqslant \sigma$, so that (iii) is proved.

(iv) Lastly, we prove that when β is finite the series converges, for $x = \beta + \varepsilon$, where ε is an arbitrarily small positive number, and consequently that $\lambda \leqslant \beta$.

Let

$$A_s' = a_s + a_{s+1} + a_{s+2} + \dots .$$

Then by Abel's Identity we have, with the notation of (ii),

$$\sum_{s=p}^{m} b_s = \sum_{s=p}^{m-1} (d_{s+1} - d_s) A'_{s+1} + d_p A'_p - d_m A'_{m+1},$$

and we can now find K, such that

$$\left| \sum_{n=s}^{\infty} a_n \right| < K s^{\beta + \frac{1}{2}\epsilon}.$$

We thus get an inequality of the same type as (3) and we conclude in precisely the same way that the series converges.

Combining (iii) and (iv) we have, if $\lambda < 0$, then $\beta \leqslant \lambda$, and when β is finite, $\lambda \leqslant \beta$. Thus if $\lambda < 0$, we have $\lambda = \beta$.

Another way of stating the theorem is the following:

$\lambda = \alpha$ *if the series* Σa_s *diverge, and* $\lambda = \beta$ *if the series* Σa_s *converge.*

10·091. Majorant Inverse Factorial Series. With the notation of Theorem V, we have

$$\alpha = \lambda, \text{ if } \lambda \geqslant 0,$$
$$\alpha = 0, \text{ if } \lambda < 0,$$

for in the latter case Σa_s converges.

Hence if λ' denote the greater of the numbers 0, λ, we have $\lambda' = \alpha$, that is to say,

$$\limsup_{n\to\infty} \log \left| \sum_{s=0}^{n} a_s \right| \Big/ \log n = \lambda'.$$

Hence from 10·08, given $\varepsilon > 0$, we can find n_0, such that

$$\left| \sum_{s=0}^{n} a_s \right| < n^{\lambda'+\epsilon}, \quad n \geqslant n_0.$$

Now, from 9·61,

$$\binom{\lambda'+\varepsilon+n}{n} = \frac{(\lambda'+\varepsilon+1)(\lambda'+\varepsilon+2)\dots(\lambda'+\varepsilon+n)}{n!}$$
$$= \frac{\Gamma(\lambda'+\varepsilon+n+1)}{\Gamma(n+1)\,\Gamma(\lambda'+\varepsilon+1)} \sim \frac{n^{\lambda'+\epsilon}}{\Gamma(\lambda'+\varepsilon+1)}.$$

Hence we can find a positive constant M, independent of n, such that

$$\left| \sum_{s=0}^{n} a_s \right| < M \binom{\lambda'+\varepsilon+n}{n}$$

for all values of n.

Now consider the series *

$$(1) \qquad \frac{M}{x-\lambda'-\varepsilon} = \frac{M}{x} + \frac{M(\lambda'+\varepsilon)}{x(x+1)} + \frac{M(\lambda'+\varepsilon)(\lambda'+\varepsilon+1)}{x(x+1)(x+2)} + \dots,$$

which is absolutely convergent, for $R(x) > \lambda'+\varepsilon$.

---

* This series is obtained in 10·2, example 2.

The sth term of this series is

$$\frac{b_s\, s!}{x(x+1)\ldots(x+s)}, \quad b_s = M\binom{\lambda'+\varepsilon+s-1}{s}.$$

If we call the b_s the coefficients of the series, all the coefficients are positive and the sum of the first $n+1$ of them is given by

$$M\sum_{s=0}^{n}\binom{\lambda'+\varepsilon+s-1}{s} = M\binom{\lambda'+\varepsilon+n}{n},$$

since this sum is equal to the coefficient of t^n in

$$(1-t)^{-\lambda'-\epsilon}\times(1-t)^{-1}.$$

Thus, whatever the value of n, the sum of the first $n+1$ coefficients of (1) is greater than the modulus of the sum of the first $n+1$ coefficients a_s of the series

$$\sum_{s=0}^{\infty}\frac{a_s\, s!}{x(x+1)\ldots(x+s)}. \tag{2}$$

We shall call the factorial series (1) a majorant series for the factorial series (2).

10·1. Series of Inverse Factorials. We shall now consider the function defined by

$$\Omega(x) = \sum_{s=0}^{\infty}\frac{a_s\, s!}{x(x+1)\ldots(x+s)}.$$

The region of convergence has already been shewn to be a half-plane limited on the left by the line

$$R(x) = \lambda,$$

where λ is the convergence abscissa.

Since terms of the series become infinite when $x = 0, -1, -2, \ldots$, we shall always suppose that such of these points as may lie in the half-plane of convergence are excluded from the region by small circles drawn round them. Unless $\lambda = -\infty$ it is evident that only a finite number of these points can lie in the half-plane of convergence.

10·11. Uniform Convergence of Inverse Factorial Series. We shall now prove the following theorem due to Nörlund:*

* *Séries d'interpolation*, p. 171.

Theorem VI. *If a series of inverse factorials converge at the point x_0, the series is uniformly convergent when x lies in the angle A, vertex at x_0, such that*

$$-\tfrac{1}{2}\pi+\eta \leqslant \arg(x-x_0) \leqslant \tfrac{1}{2}\pi-\eta,$$

where η is positive and arbitrarily small.

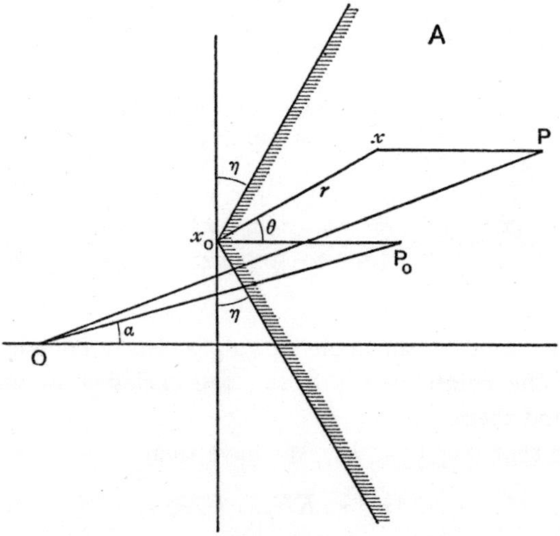

FIG. 13.

Let

$$u_s = \frac{x_0(x_0+1)\dots(x_0+s)}{x(x+1)\dots(x+s)},$$

$$R(x_0)=\sigma_0, \quad \arg(x-x_0)=\theta, \quad |x-x_0|=r.$$

It is clear from Fig. 13 that we can find a positive integer n, such that

$$\alpha = |\arg(x_0+s)| < \tfrac{1}{2}\eta, \quad \text{if } s \geqslant n.$$

Denote by P, P_0 the points $x+s$, x_0+s. Then the length of OP is not less than the length of the projection of OP on OP_0, so that

$$|x+s| \geqslant |x_0+s| + r\sin(\tfrac{1}{2}\pi-\theta+\alpha).$$

Hence, if $s \geqslant n$,

(1) $$|x+s| > |x_0+s| + r\sin\tfrac{1}{2}\eta,$$

whence we obtain

$$(2)\quad \left|\frac{x_0+s}{x+s}\right| < \frac{|x_0+s|}{|x_0+s|+r\sin\frac{1}{2}\eta}\cdot\frac{\cos\alpha}{\cos\alpha} < \frac{\sigma_0+s}{\sigma_0+s+\frac{1}{2}r\sin\eta} < 1,$$

$$(3)\quad \left|\frac{x-x_0}{x+s+1}\right| < \frac{r}{|x_0+s+1|+r\sin\frac{1}{2}\eta} < \frac{r}{\sigma_0+s+1+\frac{1}{2}r\sin\eta},$$

since $\frac{1}{2}\sin\eta < \sin\frac{1}{2}\eta$.

Now,

$$u_s = u_{n-1}\frac{(x_0+n)\dots(x_0+s)}{(x+n)\dots(x_0+s)},$$

and by (2),

$$\left|\frac{(x_0+n)\dots(x_0+s)}{(x+n)\dots(x+s)}\right| < \frac{(\sigma_0+n)\dots(\sigma_0+s)}{(\sigma_0+n+\frac{1}{2}r\sin\eta)\dots(\sigma_0+s+\frac{1}{2}r\sin\eta)} = U_s,$$

say.

Also when x lies in the angle A, u_{n-1} is clearly bounded since n is fixed and the points, $-1, -2, \dots$, are excluded by small circles drawn round them.

Suppose that $|u_{n-1}| < K$. We have then

$$|u_s| < KU_s, \quad U_s < 1,$$

so that the u_s are uniformly bounded in A.

Again,

$$u_s - u_{s+1} = u_s\frac{x-x_0}{x+s+1}.$$

Hence, using (3),

$$(4)\quad |u_s-u_{s+1}| < KU_s\frac{r}{\sigma_0+s+1+\frac{1}{2}r\sin\eta} = \frac{2K}{\sin\eta}(U_s-U_{s+1}).$$

If

$$b_s = \frac{a_s\, s!}{x_0(x_0+1)\dots(x_0+s)},$$

the series $\Sigma\, b_s$ converges by hypothesis.

Hence, given $\varepsilon > 0$, we can find N such that, if $p \geqslant N$,

$$\left|\sum_{s=p}^{m} b_s\right| < \frac{\varepsilon\sin\eta}{2K}.$$

Now, if $B_s = b_p + b_{p+1} + \dots + b_s$, we have from Abel's identity, if $p \geqslant N$,

$$\left| \sum_{s=p}^{m} b_s u_s \right| \leqslant \sum_{s=p}^{m-1} |B_s| \; |u_s - u_{s+1}| + |B_m| \; |u_m|$$

$$< \varepsilon \sum_{s=p}^{m-1} (U_s - U_{s+1}) + \varepsilon U_m$$

$$< \varepsilon U_p < \varepsilon,$$

so that the series $\Sigma b_s u_s$ converges uniformly in A, that is to say,

$$\Omega(x) = \Sigma \frac{a_s s!}{x(x+1) \dots (x+s)},$$

converges uniformly in A.

It follows from this theorem that the sum function $\Omega(x)$ of the series is an analytic function of x in any closed region, which, together with its boundaries, is interior to the half-plane of convergence, for any such region can be enclosed in an angle of the type A. That the region of uniform convergence is even more extensive than that indicated by Theorem VI is shewn by

Theorem VII. *If the series of inverse factorials be convergent for $x = x_0$, the series is uniformly convergent in the half-plane*

$$R(x) = R(x_0) + \varepsilon.$$

where ε is positive and arbitrarily small.

It is clearly sufficient to suppose x_0 real. Taking $x_0 = \sigma_0$, and n an integer such that $n + \sigma_0 > 0$, we replace inequality (1) by $|x+s| \geqslant |\sigma_0 + s| + \varepsilon$, and $\frac{1}{2} r \sin \eta$ by ε in the remaining inequalities, and the proof is then entirely on the same lines as that of Theorem VI.

Thus $\Omega(x)$ is an analytic function at every point within the half-plane of convergence, with the exception of those of the points, $\dots, -3, -2, -1, 0,$ which may lie within this half-plane.

10·13. The Poles of $\Omega(x)$. The function $\Omega(x)$ can be written in the form

$$\Omega(x) = \Gamma(x) \sum_{s=0}^{\infty} \frac{a_s s!}{\Gamma(x+s+1)}.$$

Since $1/\Gamma(x)$ is an integral function, we see that $\Omega(x)$ has simple poles at such of the poles of $\Gamma(x)$ as lie within the half-plane of convergence.

If $x = -n$ be such a pole, we have from 9·55 the residue of $\Omega(x)$ at this point, namely,

$$\frac{(-1)^n}{n!}\sum_{s=0}^{\infty}\frac{a_s\, s!}{\Gamma(s-n+1)} = (-1)^n\sum_{s=n}^{\infty} a_s\binom{s}{n},$$

since $1/\Gamma(s-n+1)$ is zero, for $s = 0, 1, 2, \ldots, n-1$.

If $\lambda = -\infty$ the function $\Omega(x)$ is meromorphic in the whole complex plane.

We may note that, in terms of the Beta function,

$$\Omega(x) = \sum_{s=0}^{\infty} a_s \,\mathrm{B}(x, s+1).$$

10·15. The Theorem of Unique Development. *A function which can be developed in a series of inverse factorials can be so developed in only one manner.*

For suppose that the same function admits two distinct developments. Then we have an equality of the form

$$\sum_{s=0}^{\infty}\frac{a_s\, s!}{x(x+1)\ldots(x+s)} = \sum_{s=0}^{\infty}\frac{b_s\, s!}{x(x+1)\ldots(x+s)}.$$

Let λ, λ' be the abscissae of convergence. Multiply both sides by x and let $x \to \infty$ in such a way that $R(x) \to \infty$ in the half-plane $R(x) > \lambda$, $R(x) > \lambda'$. We then obtain

$$a_0 = b_0.$$

Remove corresponding terms and then multiply by $x(x+1)$ and let $R(x) \to \infty$ as before. We thus get $a_1 = b_1$. Proceeding in this way we see that the two series are identical.

It follows from this that *an inverse factorial series cannot vanish identically unless all the coefficients vanish.*

10·2. Application of Laplace's Integral. We have, from 10·13,

$$\Omega(x) = \sum_{s=0}^{\infty}\frac{a_s\, s!}{x(x+1)\ldots(x+s)} = \sum_{s=0}^{\infty} a_s \,\mathrm{B}(x, s+1).$$

Thus using the integral expression of 9·84 for the Beta function we have, when $R(x) > 0$,

(1) $$\Omega(x) = \sum_{s=0}^{\infty} a_s \int_0^1 t^{x-1}(1-t)^s\,dt.$$

This suggests consideration of the function

(2) $$\phi(t) = a_0 + a_1(1-t) + a_2(1-t)^2 + a_3(1-t)^3 + \dots.$$

We now prove that the series

(3) $$t^{x-1}\phi(t) = \sum_{s=0}^{\infty} a_s t^{x-1}(1-t)^s$$

is uniformly convergent in the interval $0 \leqslant t \leqslant 1$, provided that $R(x)$ be greater than the larger of the numbers 1, $\lambda+2$, where λ is, as usual, the abscissa of convergence of the factorial series. Let $R(x) = \sigma$.

Then the factorial series converges when $x = \sigma - 2$ on account of the way in which σ was determined, and consequently the sth term tends to zero when $s \to \infty$. Thus

$$\lim_{s\to\infty} \frac{|a_s|\,s!}{(\sigma-1)\,\sigma\,\dots\,(\sigma+s-2)} = 0,$$

so that

$$\lim_{s\to\infty} |a_s| \Big/ \binom{\sigma+s-2}{s} = 0,$$

and hence, given $\varepsilon > 0$, we can find n, such that

$$|a_s| < \varepsilon \binom{\sigma+s-2}{s}, \quad s \geqslant n.$$

It follows then that

$$\left| \sum_{s=n}^{\infty} a_s t^{x-1}(1-t)^s \right| < \varepsilon\, t^{\sigma-1} \sum_{s=n}^{\infty} \binom{\sigma+s-2}{s} (1-t)^s$$
$$< \varepsilon\, t^{\sigma-1}[1-(1-t)]^{-\sigma+1} = \varepsilon,$$

which proves the uniform convergence of (3).

We can therefore integrate term by term and we get from (1)

(4) $$\Omega(x) = \int_0^1 t^{x-1}\phi(t)\,dt.$$

An integral of the above form is known as Laplace's Integral.

We have thus proved that, if $R(x)$ be sufficiently large, the sum function of a series of inverse factorials can be expressed by Laplace's integral in the form (4).

Conversely, if $\phi(t)$ be given in the form (2) and if, for $R(x)$ sufficiently great, the series (3) be uniformly convergent for $0 \leqslant t \leqslant 1$, the corresponding Laplace's integral (4) can be represented by an inverse factorial series.

The function $\phi(t)$ may be called the *generating function* of the factorial series.

When the function $\Omega(x)$ is given, the generating function $\phi(t)$ is obtained by solving the integral equation (4). It is easily verified * that the solution is

$$(5) \qquad \phi(t) = \frac{1}{2\pi i}\int_{l-i\infty}^{l+i\infty} t^{-z}\Omega(z)\,dz,$$

where l is any number greater than the abscissa of absolute convergence of the factorial series for $\Omega(x)$.

Example 1. Find the sum function of the series

$$\sum_{s=1}^{\infty} \frac{(s-1)!}{x(x+1)\dots(x+s)}.$$

Here $a_s = s^{-1}$, so that

$$\phi(t) = \frac{1-t}{1} + \frac{(1-t)^2}{2} + \frac{(1-t)^3}{3} + \dots = -\log t.$$

Thus

$$\Omega(x) = -\int_0^1 t^{x-1}\log t\,dt = -\frac{\partial}{\partial x}\int_0^1 t^{x-1}\,dt = \frac{1}{x^2},$$

so that

$$\frac{1}{x^2} = \frac{0!}{x(x+1)} + \frac{1!}{x(x+1)(x+2)} + \frac{2!}{x(x+1)(x+2)(x+3)} + \dots.$$

The ratio of the $(s+1)$th term to the sth is

$$\frac{s}{x+1+s} = 1 - \frac{x+1}{s} + O\left(\frac{1}{s^2}\right),$$

so that by Weierstrass' criterion, 9·8, the series converges absolutely if $R(x) > 0$. Hence $\mu = 0$.

---

* For a more complete discussion of the generating function, see Nörlund's *Séries d'interpolation*, chap. vi.

Again,

$$\sum_{s=0}^{n} a_s = 1+\frac{1}{2}+\frac{1}{3}+\dots+\frac{1}{n} \sim \gamma+\log n,$$

hence, from Theorem V,

$$\lambda = \limsup_{n\to\infty} \log(\gamma+\log n)\,/\log n = 0,$$

so that in this case $\lambda = \mu = 0$.

Example 2. Expand $(x-a)^{-1}$ in a series of inverse factorials.

From (5), the generating function is

$$\phi(t) = \frac{1}{2\pi i}\int_{l-i\infty}^{l+i\infty} \frac{t^{-z}}{z-a}\,dz = t^{-a},$$

if l be sufficiently great. This can also be inferred trom (4), since

$$\frac{1}{x-a} = \int_0^1 t^{x-a-1}\,dt.$$

By the binomial theorem,

$$t^{-a} = [1-(1-t)]^{-a} = 1+\sum_{s=1}^{\infty}\binom{a+s-1}{s}(1-t)^s.$$

Hence, from (1),

$$\frac{1}{x-a} = \frac{1}{x}+\sum_{s=1}^{\infty}\binom{a+s-1}{s}\mathrm{B}(x,\, s+1).$$

Thus we have Waring's formula, namely

$$\frac{1}{x-a} = \frac{1}{x}+\frac{a}{x(x+1)}+\frac{a(a+1)}{x(x+1)(x+2)}+\frac{a(a+1)(a+2)}{x(x+1)(x+2)(x+3)}+\dots.$$

The formula can also be obtained from 3·1 (4), applied to the function x^{-1}, by interchanging a and x and putting $p=-a$.

By Weierstrass' criterion, the abscissa of absolute convergence is given by

$$\mu = R(a),$$

and since $(x-a)^{-1}$ has a pole at $x=a$,

$$\lambda = R(a).$$

Example 3. The series

$$\Omega(x) = \frac{1}{x}-\frac{a}{x(x+1)}+\frac{a(a+1)}{x(x+1)(x+2)}-\frac{a(a+1)(a+2)}{x(x+1)(x+2)(x+3)}+\dots$$

has the same abscissa of absolute convergence as the series for $(x-a)^{-1}$, so that

$$\mu = R(a).$$

On the other hand, by Weierstrass' criterion, the series converges conditionally if

$$0 < R(x-a+1) \leqslant 1,$$

so that

$$\lambda = R(a-1).$$

These examples illustrate the result of 10·06.

10·22. Order of Singularity and the Convergence Abscissa. If

$$f(z) = b_0 + b_1 z + b_2 z^2 + b_3 z^3 + \dots,$$

the order h of $f(z)$ on its circle of convergence whose radius is taken to be unity is by Hadamard's definition *

$$h = 1 + \limsup_{n\to\infty} \frac{\log |b_n|}{\log n}.$$

Multiply the generating function $\phi(t)$ in 10·2 (2) by

$$t^{-1} = [1-(1-t)]^{-1}$$

and we obtain

$$\frac{\phi(t)}{t} = \sum_{s=0}^{\infty} (a_0 + a_1 + a_2 + \dots + a_s)(1-t)^s,$$

so that $\phi(t)/t$ is holomorphic inside the circle $|1-t| = 1$. Thus, if $\lambda \geqslant 0$, we have from Theorem V that the order of $\phi(t)/t$ on the circle $|t-1| = 1$ is $\lambda+1$.

If $\lambda < 0$, the series Σa_s converges; thus, if $t \to 0$ along the radius joining 1 to 0,

$$\lim_{t\to 0} \phi(t) = \phi(+0),$$

and hence

$$\frac{\phi(t)-\phi(+0)}{t} = -\sum_{s=0}^{\infty} (a_{s+1} + a_{s+2} + \dots)(1-t)^s,$$

and hence, again by Theorem V, the order of $[\phi(t)-\phi(+0)]/t$ on the circle $|t-1| = 1$ is $\lambda+1$.

* P. Dienes, *The Taylor Series* (1931), p. 493.

10·3. The Transformation (x, x+m). Consider

$$\Omega(x) = \sum_{s=0}^{\infty} \frac{a_s\, s!}{x(x+1)\dots(x+s)} = \int_0^1 t^{x-1}\phi(t)\,dt,$$

where $\phi(t)$ is the generating function 10·2 (2).

We have identically

$$\Omega(x) = \int_0^1 t^{x+m-1}\, t^{-m}\, \phi(t)\,dt,$$

$$t^{-m}\phi(t) = [1-(1-t)]^{-m}\,\Sigma\, a_s(1-t)^s = \Sigma\, b_s(1-t)^s,$$

$$b_s = a_s + \binom{m}{1} a_{s-1} + \binom{m+1}{2} a_{s-2} + \dots + \binom{m+s-1}{s} a_0,$$

so that

$$\Omega(x) = \sum_{s=0}^{\infty} \frac{b_s\, s!}{(x+m)(x+m+1)\dots(x+m+s)},$$

which we call the transformation $(x,\, x+m)$.

If λ_m denote the convergence abscissa of the transformed series we can shew, from considerations of order (10·22), that

$$\lambda_m \leqslant \lambda, \text{ if } R(m) \geqslant 0,\ \lambda \geqslant 0,$$

$$\lambda_m \leqslant \lambda - R(m), \text{ if } R(m) < 0,\ \lambda \geqslant 0,$$

while in general

$$\lambda_m \geqslant 0, \text{ if } \lambda < 0.$$

The case $m = 1$ is particularly simple, for then

$$b_s = a_s + a_{s-1} + \dots + a_0,$$

so that

$$\sum \frac{a_s\, s!}{x(x+1)\dots(x+s)} = \sum \frac{(a_0+a_1+\dots+a_s)\, s!}{(x+1)(x+2)\dots(x+s+1)},$$

with $\lambda_1 \leqslant \lambda$ if $\lambda \geqslant 0$, $\lambda_1 = 0$ if $\lambda < 0$.

The transformation can sometimes be effected directly; for example, using 10·2, Ex. 2, we have

$$\frac{1}{x-a} = \frac{1}{(x+m)-(m+a)} = \frac{1}{x+m} + \frac{m+a}{(x+m)(x+m+1)}$$

$$+ \frac{(m+a)(m+a+1)}{(x+m)(x+m+1)(x+m+2)} + \dots .$$

It may be observed that if $\lambda_m < \lambda$, the transformation $(x, x+m)$ gives the analytic continuation of $\Omega(x)$ beyond the original half-plane of convergence.

10·32. The Transformation (x, x/ω). Starting from

$$\Omega(x) = \int_0^1 t^{x-1}\phi(t)\,dt,$$

we make the change of variable $t^\omega = z$, $\omega > 1$. Then

$$\Omega(x) = \frac{1}{\omega}\int_0^1 z^{\frac{x}{\omega}-1}\phi(z^{\frac{1}{\omega}})\,dz.$$

If ω be large enough, $\phi(z^{\frac{1}{\omega}})$ will be holomorphic inside and on the circle $|z-1| = 1$, except perhaps at $z = 0$. Now,

$$\phi(z^{\frac{1}{\omega}}) = \sum_{s=0}^{\infty} a_s(1-z^{\frac{1}{\omega}})^s,$$

$$1-z^{\frac{1}{\omega}} = 1-(1-1+z)^{\frac{1}{\omega}}$$

$$= \frac{1-z}{\omega} + \frac{\omega-1}{2!}\left(\frac{1-z}{\omega}\right)^2 + \frac{(\omega-1)(\omega-2)}{3!}\left(\frac{1-z}{\omega}\right)^3 + \dots,$$

so that

$$(1-z^{\frac{1}{\omega}})^s = \sum_{n=s}^{\infty} f_{n,s}(\omega)\,(1-z)^n,$$

and therefore

$$\phi(z^{\frac{1}{\omega}}) = \sum_{s=0}^{\infty} b_s(1-z)^s,$$

$$b_s = f_{s,1}(\omega)\,a_1 + f_{s,2}(\omega)\,a_2 + \dots + f_{s,s}(\omega)\,a_s.$$

It follows that

$$\Omega(x) = \sum_{s=0}^{\infty} \frac{b_s\, s!\, \omega^s}{x(x+\omega)\dots(x+s\omega)},$$

which we call the transformation * $(x, x/\omega)$.

If $\lambda > 0$, considerations of order at the point $z = 0$ shew that the series converges if $R(x) > \lambda(\omega)$ where $\lambda(\omega) \leqslant \lambda$.

* See Nörlund, *Séries d'interpolation*, chap. vi. For recent research on the analytic continuation of factorial series of both kinds, see H. K. Hughes, *American J. of Math.* liii (1931), pp. 757-780, where several new results are obtained.

10·4. Addition and Multiplication of Inverse Factorial Series. Suppose that we have the two series

$$\Omega(x) = \sum_{s=0}^{\infty} \frac{s!\,a_s}{x(x+1)\dots(x+s)}, \quad R(x) > \lambda,$$

$$\Omega_1(x) = \sum_{s=0}^{\infty} \frac{s!\,b_s}{x(x+1)\dots(x+s)}, \quad R(x) > \lambda'.$$

If l denote the greater of the numbers λ, λ', we have evidently

$$\Omega(x) \pm \Omega_1(x) = \sum_{s=0}^{\infty} \frac{s!\,(a_s \pm b_s)}{x(x+1)\dots(x+s)}, \quad R(x) > l,$$

which solves the problem of addition and subtraction.

The problem of multiplication is more difficult on account of the complexity of the coefficients in the product. The solution of the problem is given by the following theorem due to N. Nielsen.*

The product of $\Omega(x)$, $\Omega_1(x)$ is developable in a factorial series of the same form, convergent for $R(x) > 0$, $R(x) > l$. These conditions are always sufficient and generally necessary. The product is

$$\sum_{s=1}^{\infty} \frac{A_s}{x(x+1)\dots(x+s)},$$

where

$$A_{n+1} = \sum_{s=0}^{n} (n-s)!\; s!\; b_{n-s}\, C_{n-s,\,s}, \quad C_{r,\,s} = \sum_{p=0}^{r} \binom{p+r}{p} a_{s-p}.$$

To obtain a practical method of forming the product we use Laplace's Integral. Let

$$\Omega(x) = \int_0^1 \alpha^{x-1} \varphi(\alpha)\, d\alpha, \quad \Omega_1(x) = \int_0^1 \beta^{x-1} \psi(\beta)\, d\beta.$$

Then

$$\Omega(x)\,\Omega_1(x) = \int_0^1\!\!\int_0^1 (\alpha\beta)^{x-1} \varphi(\alpha)\, \psi(\beta)\, d\alpha\, d\beta.$$

Making the change of variable $\alpha\beta = t$, we have

$$\Omega(x)\,\Omega_1(x) = \int_0^1 t^{x-1} \chi(t)\, dt,$$

where

$$\chi(t) = \int_t^1 \psi\left(\frac{t}{\alpha}\right) \frac{\varphi(\alpha)}{\alpha}\, d\alpha = \int_t^1 \varphi\left(\frac{t}{\beta}\right) \frac{\psi(\beta)}{\beta}\, d\beta.$$

* *Rendiconti della R. Acc. dei Lincei* (5), 13 (1904).

This result will determine the form of the product. The convergence abscissa must be determined separately.

For example, consider

$$\frac{1}{x-p} = \frac{1}{x} + \frac{p}{x(x+1)} + \frac{p(p+1)}{x(x+1)(x+2)} + \dots = \int_0^1 t^{x-p-1}\,dt,$$

$$\frac{1}{x-q} = \frac{1}{x} + \frac{q}{x(x+1)} + \frac{q(q+1)}{x(x+1)(x+2)} + \dots = \int_0^1 t^{x-q-1}\,dt.$$

Here

$$\chi(t) = \int_t^1 \alpha^{-p-1}\left(\frac{t}{\alpha}\right)^{-q} d\alpha = \frac{t^{-p}-t^{-q}}{p-q}.$$

To obtain the coefficients we can expand $\chi(t)$ in powers of $(1-t)$, but it is simpler here to write

$$\frac{1}{x-p}\cdot\frac{1}{x-q} = \int_0^1 \frac{t^{x-p-1}-t^{x-q-1}}{p-q}\,dt$$

$$= \frac{1}{x(x+1)} + \frac{p+q+1}{x(x+1)(x+2)} + \frac{p^2+pq+q^2+3(p+q)+2}{x(x+1)(x+2)(x+3)} + \dots,$$

which is obtained by subtracting the second given series from the first and dividing by $p-q$, and in fact this result could have been obtained direct, without calculation. We infer that

$$\frac{1}{(x-p)^2} = \frac{1}{x(x+1)} + \frac{2p+1}{x(x+1)(x+2)} + \frac{3p^2+6p+2}{x(x+1)(x+2)(x+3)} + \dots,$$

which agrees with the result of differentiating the first of the given series with respect to p.

Actually, if $p = q$, we have

$$\chi(t) = \int_t^1 \alpha^{-1}\,t^{-p}\,d\alpha = -t^{-p}\log t$$

$$= \left[1+p(1-t)+\frac{p(p+1)}{2!}(1-t)^2+\dots\right]\left[(1-t)+\frac{(1-t)^2}{2}+\frac{(1-t)^3}{3}+\dots\right]$$

$$= (1-t)+(p+\tfrac{1}{2})(1-t)^2+\left(\frac{p^2}{2}+p+\frac{1}{3}\right)(1-t)^3+\dots,$$

which gives the same series as before for $(x-p)^{-2}$.

10·42. Differentiation of Inverse Factorial Series. If

$$\Omega(x) = \sum_{s=0}^{\infty} \frac{a_s\, s!}{x(x+1)\dots(x+s)} = \int_0^1 t^{x-1}\phi(t)\,dt,$$

we have

$$\Omega'(x) = \int_0^1 t^{x-1}\log t\,\phi(t)\,dt,$$

which is again developable in a factorial series.

In fact

$$\log t = -(1-t) - \tfrac{1}{2}(1-t)^2 - \tfrac{1}{3}(1-t)^3 - \dots,$$

$$\phi(t) = a_0 + a_1(1-t) + a_2(1-t)^2 + \dots,$$

so that

$$\Omega'(x) = -\sum_{s=1}^{\infty} \frac{\left(\frac{a_0}{s} + \frac{a_1}{s-1} + \dots + \frac{a_{s-1}}{1}\right)s!}{x(x+1)(x+2)\dots(x+s)}.$$

If $\lambda > 0$, the order of $t^{-1}\phi(t)\log t$ on the circle $|t-1| = 1$ is the same as the order of $t^{-1}\phi(t)$, that is to say, $\lambda+1$, so that the series for $\Omega'(x)$ has the same convergence abscissa as $\Omega(x)$, namely, λ. If, however, $\lambda < 0$, we know that $x = 0$ is in general a simple pole of $\Omega(x)$, and consequently a double pole of $\Omega'(x)$, so that $\Omega'(x)$ cannot have a convergence abscissa < 0.

Hence, if $\lambda < 0$, the convergence abscissa for $\Omega'(x)$ is in general zero.

Example.

$$\frac{1}{x-\alpha} = \sum_{s=0}^{\infty} \frac{\alpha(\alpha+1)\dots(\alpha+s-1)}{x(x+1)\dots(x+s)} = \int_0^1 t^{x-\alpha-1}\,dt;$$

$$-\frac{1}{(x-\alpha)^2} = \int_0^1 t^{x-\alpha-1}\log t\,dt.$$

The coefficient of $(1-t)^s$ in $t^{-\alpha}\log t$ is equal to the coefficient of y^s in $(1-y)^{-\alpha}\log(1-y)$, that is, in

$$-\frac{\partial}{\partial\alpha}(1-y)^{-\alpha},$$

which is equal to

$$-\frac{\partial}{\partial\alpha}\frac{\alpha(\alpha+1)\dots(\alpha+s-1)}{s!}.$$

Thus

$$\frac{1}{(x-\alpha)^2} = \sum_{s=1}^{\infty} \frac{\alpha(\alpha+1)\dots(\alpha+s-1)}{x(x+1)\dots(x+s)} \left(\frac{1}{\alpha}+\frac{1}{\alpha+1}+\dots+\frac{1}{\alpha+s-1}\right).$$

It will be seen that the direct application of the general formula for $\Omega'(x)$ leads to an equivalent but more complicated form for this result.

The convergence abscissa is $R(\alpha)$ whatever α may be, in fact $x=0$ is not a pole unless $\alpha=0$, so that this is a case of exception to the rule that the convergence abscissa is zero if $\lambda<0$.

Since $\alpha(\alpha+1)\dots(\alpha+s-1) = B_s^{(s+1)}(\alpha+s)$, the series for $(x-\alpha)^{-n}$ can also be obtained by direct differentiation with respect to α.

10·43. An Asymptotic Formula. We have

$$(1) \qquad \frac{1}{x} = \int_0^1 t^{x-1}\,dt, \quad R(x)>0.$$

Differentiate m times with respect to x and we obtain

$$\frac{\Gamma(m+1)}{x^{m+1}} = \int_0^1 t^{x-1}\left(\log\frac{1}{t}\right)^m dt$$

Now by 6·43 (1), writing $-1+t$ for t, we have

$$\left(\log\frac{1}{t}\right)^m = m(1-t)^m \sum_{\nu=0}^{\infty} \frac{(1-t)^\nu}{\nu!}\,\frac{(-1)^\nu B_\nu^{(m+\nu)}}{m+\nu}.$$

Multiply by t^{x-1} and integrate term by term, then

$$\frac{\Gamma(m+1)}{x^{m+1}} = \sum_{\nu=0}^{\infty} \frac{m(-1)^\nu B_\nu^{(m+\nu)}}{(m+\nu)\,\nu!}\,\frac{\Gamma(x)\Gamma(m+\nu+1)}{\Gamma(x+m+\nu+1)}.$$

Multiply both sides by

$$\frac{\Gamma(x+m+1)}{\Gamma(x)\Gamma(m+1)},$$

and we obtain, on writing s for ν,

$$\frac{\Gamma(x+m+1)}{\Gamma(x)\,x^{m+1}} = \sum_{s=0}^{\infty} \frac{(-1)^s \binom{m+s-1}{s} B_s^{(m+s)}}{(x+m+1)(x+m+2)\dots(x+m+s)}, \quad R(x)>0.$$

From this we can infer that the development of the reciprocal of the left side is given by a relation of the form

$$\frac{\Gamma(x)\,x^{m+1}}{\Gamma(x+m+1)}=1+\sum_{s=0}^{\infty}\frac{a_{s+1}\,s!}{x(x+1)\ldots(x+s)}=1+\Omega_0(x),\text{ say.}$$

Differentiating with respect to m, we have

$$x^{m+1}\frac{\partial}{\partial m}\frac{\Gamma(x)}{\Gamma(x+m+1)}+(\log x)(1+\Omega_0(x))$$

$$=\sum_{s=0}^{\infty}\frac{s!\,\dfrac{\partial a_{s+1}}{\partial m}}{x(x+1)(x+s)}=\Omega_1(x),\text{ say.}$$

Thus

$$x^{m+1}\frac{\partial}{\partial m}\frac{\Gamma(x)}{\Gamma(x+m+1)}=\Omega_1(x)+(1+\Omega_0(x))\log\left(\frac{1}{x}\right).$$

Proceeding in this way we can obtain a relation of the form

$$x^{m+1}\frac{\partial^s}{\partial m^s}\frac{\Gamma(x)}{\Gamma(x+m+1)}$$

$$=\Omega_s(x)+\Omega_{s-1}(x)\log\frac{1}{x}+\Omega_{s-2}(x)\left(\log\frac{1}{x}\right)^2+\ldots+(1+\Omega_0(x))\left(\log\frac{1}{x}\right)^s$$

where $\Omega_0(x)$, $\Omega_1(x)$, ... represent factorial series which vanish when $x=+\infty$.

It follows that, when $R(x)$ is large and positive, we can replace the right-hand side by its greatest term, namely $\left(\log\frac{1}{x}\right)^s$.

We have, therefore, the important asymptotic relation that, for large positive values of $R(x)$,

$$\frac{\partial^s}{\partial m^s}\frac{\Gamma(x)}{\Gamma(x+m+1)}\sim\left(\frac{1}{x}\right)^{m+1}\left(\log\frac{1}{x}\right)^s,$$

which is useful in the theory of difference equations.

10·44. Integration of Inverse Factorial Series. Let x_0 be a point interior to the half-plane of convergence. Then

$$\int_{x_0}^{x}\Omega(x)\,dx=\int_0^1(t^{x-1}-t^{x_0-1})\frac{\phi(t)}{\log t}\,dt$$

$$=\phi(1)\int_0^1\frac{t^{x-1}-1}{\log t}\,dt-\int_0^1\frac{t^{x_0-1}\phi(t)-\phi(1)}{\log t}\,dt+\int_0^1 t^{x-1}\frac{\phi(t)-\phi(1)}{\log t}\,dt.$$

The second term on the right is independent of x (= C say), and integrating 10·43 (1) with respect to x, we have

$$\int_0^1 \frac{t^{x-1}-1}{\log t}\,dt = \log x\,;$$

and therefore

$$\int_{x_0}^{x} \Omega(x)\,dx - \phi(1)\log x - C = \int_0^1 t^{x-1}\frac{\phi(t)-\phi(1)}{\log t}\,dt.$$

Now,

$$\frac{\phi(t)-\phi(1)}{1-t} = a_1 + a_2(1-t) + a_3(1-t)^2 + \dots,$$

and from 6·43 (7), in terms of Bernoulli's numbers, we have

$$\frac{1-t}{\log t} = -1 + \tfrac{1}{2}(1-t) + \sum_{\nu=2}^{\infty} \frac{B_\nu^{(\nu-1)}}{\nu-1}\,\frac{(-1)^\nu(1-t)^\nu}{\nu!}.$$

Thus

$$\frac{\phi(t)-\phi(1)}{\log t} = -a_1 + (-a_2 + \tfrac{1}{2}a_1)(1-t)$$
$$+\left(-a_3 + \tfrac{1}{2}a_2 + \frac{B_2^{(1)}}{2!}a_1\right)(1-t)^2 + \dots.$$

Hence we have

$$\int_{x_0}^{x} \Omega(x)\,dx = C + a_0\log x + \sum_{s=0}^{\infty} \frac{b_s\, s!}{x(x+1)\dots(x+s)},$$

where

$$b_0 = -a_1,\quad b_1 = -a_2 + \tfrac{1}{2}a_1,$$

$$b_s = -a_{s+1} + \tfrac{1}{2}a_s + \sum_{\nu=2}^{s} (-1)^\nu \frac{B_\nu^{(\nu-1)}}{\nu-1}\,\frac{a_{s-\nu+1}}{\nu!}.$$

This result is valid for $R(x) > 0$, $R(x) > \lambda$, unless $a_0 = 0$, in which case it holds for $R(x) > \lambda$.

10·5. Finite Difference and Sum of Factorial Series. The operations which we have hitherto considered, namely, multiplication, differentiation, and integration, are operations which are simpler in their application to power series than to factorial series. On the other hand, factorial series of both kinds are admirably adapted to the performance of the operations Δ and its inverse.

Thus we have from

$$\Omega(x) = \sum_{s=0}^{\infty} \frac{a_s\, s!}{x(x+1)\dots(x+s)},$$

$$F(x) = \sum_{s=0}^{\infty} (-1)^s a_s \binom{x-1}{s},$$

$$(-1)\,\Delta\,\Omega(x) = \sum_{s=1}^{\infty} \frac{a_{s-1}\, s!}{x(x+1)\dots(x+s)},$$

$$(-1)^n \overset{n}{\Delta}\,\Omega(x) = \sum_{s=n}^{\infty} \frac{a_{s-n}\, s!}{x(x+1)\dots(x+s)},$$

$$(-1)\,\Delta F(x) = \sum_{s=0}^{\infty} (-1)^s a_{s+1} \binom{x-1}{s},$$

$$(-1)^n \overset{n}{\Delta} F(x) = \sum_{s=0}^{\infty} (-1)^s a_{s+n} \binom{x-1}{s}.$$

Again, the equation

$$\Delta\, u(x) = \Omega(x)$$

clearly admits the general solution

$$u(x) = \varpi(x) + a_0\, \Psi(x) - \sum_{s=0}^{\infty} \frac{a_{s+1}\, s!}{x(x+1)\dots(x+s)},$$

where $\varpi(x)$ is an arbitrary periodic function of period unity, and the principal solution is obtained by replacing $\varpi(x)$ by a constant, so that

$$\mathop{\mathrm{S}}^{x} \Omega(t)\,\Delta t = C + a_0\, \Psi(x) - \sum_{s=0}^{\infty} \frac{a_{s+1}\, s!}{x(x+1)\dots(x+s)},$$

where C is a constant whose value depends on the lower limit of the summation.* Similarly, we have

$$\mathop{\mathrm{S}}^{x} F(t)\,\Delta t = C_1 - \sum_{s=1}^{\infty} (-1)^s a_{s-1} \binom{x-1}{s}.$$

It is clear that the operations Δ and S do not affect the convergence abscissa since the coefficients are merely displaced, and the limits of Theorem V are unaltered.

---

* It is convenient to indicate "indefinite summation" (the analogue of indefinite integration) by omitting the lower limit.

Example.

$$\frac{1}{x-\alpha} = \sum_{s=0}^{\infty} \frac{\alpha(\alpha+1)\dots(\alpha+s-1)}{x(x+1)\dots(x+s)}.$$

Thus

$$\Psi(x-\alpha) = \mathop{\mathrm{S}}^{x} \frac{1}{t-\alpha}\Delta t$$

$$= \Psi(x) - \sum_{s=0}^{\infty} \frac{1}{s+1} \frac{\alpha(\alpha+1)\dots(\alpha+s)}{x(x+1)\dots(x+s)},$$

the constant being zero, since both sides must agree when $\alpha = 0$.

10·6. Newton's Series. The series

$$F(x) = \sum_{s=0}^{\infty} (-1)^s a_s \binom{x-1}{s},$$

to which we shall refer as Newton's series, converges in a half-plane (10·04) limited on the left by the line $R(x) = \lambda$, and converges absolutely in a half-plane (10·06) limited on the left by the line $R(x) = \mu$, where $0 \leqslant \mu - \lambda \leqslant 1$.

When x is a positive integer, the series reduces to a polynomial and may therefore be said to converge at those of the integral points which may lie outside the half-plane of convergence, but diverges in a neighbourhood of such points. We shall therefore not include in the region of convergence those integral points which lie outside the half-plane of convergence. The convergence abscissa λ is given by Theorem V.

10·61. Uniform Convergence of Newton's Series. We now prove the following theorem due to Nörlund: *

Theorem VIII. *If Newton's series converge at the point x_0, where x_0 is not a positive integer, the series converges uniformly at every point of the sector S, vertex at x_0, such that*

$$|x-x_0| \leqslant R, \quad -\tfrac{1}{2}\pi + \eta \leqslant \arg(x-x_0) \leqslant \tfrac{1}{2}\pi - \eta,$$

where η is positive and arbitrarily small, and R is any positive number.

---

* *Séries d'interpolation*, p. 100.

Let the given convergent series be

$$\sum_{s=0}^{\infty} b_s, \quad b_s = (-1)^s a_s \binom{x_0 - 1}{s},$$

and let

$$v_s = \frac{(x-1)(x-2)\dots(x-s)}{(x_0-1)(x_0-2)\dots(x_0-s)}.$$

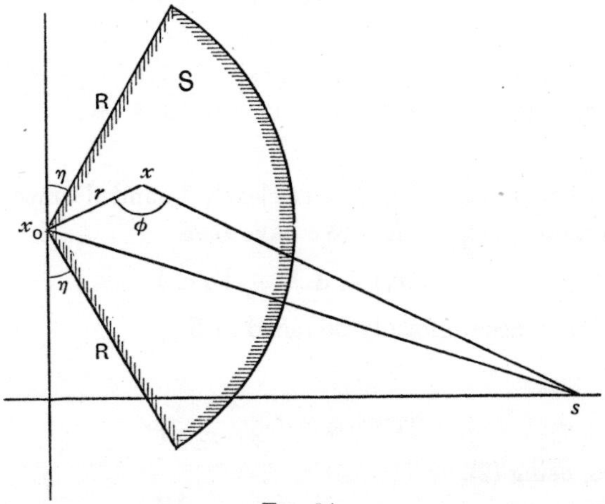

FIG. 14.

We have to prove that, if x be any point of S (see Fig. 14), $\Sigma\, b_s v_s$ converges uniformly.

It is clear from the figure that we can find an integer n, such that

$$|\arg(s-x_0)| < \tfrac{1}{2}\eta, \quad \text{if} \quad s \geqslant n,$$

and also that the line joining x_0 to s subtends at any point of S an angle ϕ greater than $\frac{1}{2}(\pi+\eta)$. The projection of this line on the line joining s to x cannot exceed the length of the line joining s to x_0; hence, if $r = |x - x_0|$,

$$|s-x_0| \geqslant |s-x| + r\cos(\pi-\phi) > |s-x| + r\sin\tfrac{1}{2}\eta,$$

so that

$$|s-x| < |s-x_0| - r\sin\tfrac{1}{2}\eta,$$

and hence

(1)
$$\left|\frac{x-s}{x_0-s}\right| < 1 - \frac{r\sin\frac{1}{2}\eta}{|s-x_0|}\,\frac{\cos\arg(s-x_0)}{\cos\arg(s-x_0)}$$

$$< 1 - \frac{\frac{1}{2}r\sin\eta}{s-\sigma_0} = \frac{s-\sigma_0-\frac{1}{2}r\sin\eta}{s-\sigma_0},$$

where $\sigma_0 = R(x_0)$, and $s \geqslant n$. Also we have

$$(2) \qquad \left|\frac{x-x_0}{s-x_0+1}\right| \leqslant \frac{r}{s-\sigma_0+1}.$$

Now,

$$v_s = v_{n-1}\frac{(x-n)\dots(x-s)}{(x_0-n)\dots(x_0-s)},$$

and by (1),

$$\left|\frac{(x-n)\dots(x-s)}{(x_0-n)\dots(x_0-s)}\right| < \frac{(n-\sigma_0-\frac{1}{2}r\sin\eta)\dots(s-\sigma_0-\frac{1}{2}r\sin\eta)}{(n-\sigma_0)\dots(s-\sigma_0)} = V_s,$$

say.

Also, when x lies in S, v_{n-1} is clearly bounded since n is fixed. Suppose that $|v_{n-1}| < K$. We have then

$$|v_s| < K V_s, \quad V_s < 1,$$

so that the v_s are uniformly bounded in S.

Again,

$$v_s - v_{s+1} = v_s \frac{x-x_0}{s-x_0+1}.$$

Hence, using (2),

$$|v_s - v_{s+1}| < K V_s \frac{r}{s-\sigma_0+1} = \frac{2K}{\sin\eta}(V_s - V_{s+1}).$$

This inequality is of exactly the same type as 10·11 (4), and the required uniform convergence follows by precisely the same steps as in that section.

It follows from this theorem that the sum function $F(x)$ of Newton's series is an analytic function of x in every closed region which, together with its boundaries, lies in the half-plane of convergence, for any such region can be enclosed within a sector of the type given in the theorem.

10·63. Null Series. Consider the binomial series *

$$(1+\alpha)^{x-1} = \sum_{s=0}^{\infty} \alpha^s \binom{x-1}{s}.$$

If $|\alpha| < 1$, the series converges everywhere, so that $\lambda = -\infty$,

* K. Knopp, *Infinite Series*, p. 426.

If $|\alpha| > 1$, the series diverges everywhere (except at the positive integer points), so that $\lambda = +\infty$.

If $|\alpha| = 1$, $\alpha \neq -1$, the series diverges if $R(x) \leqslant 0$, converges simply if $0 < R(x) \leqslant 1$, and converges absolutely if $R(x) > 1$, so that $\lambda = 0$, $\mu = 1$.

If $\alpha = -1$, we have

$$\sum_{s=0}^{\infty} (-1)^s \binom{x-1}{s} = \lim_{n\to\infty} \sum_{s=0}^{n-1} \binom{x-1}{s}.$$

Now,

$$\begin{aligned}\sum_{s=0}^{n-1} (-1)^s \binom{x-1}{s} &= \text{coefficient of } t^{n-1} \text{ in } (1-t)^{x-1}(1+t+t^2+\ldots)\\ &= \text{coefficient of } t^{n-1} \text{ in } (1-t)^{x-2}\\ &= \binom{x-2}{n-1}(-1)^{n-1}.\end{aligned}$$

Thus

$$\sum_{s=0}^{n-1} (-1)^s \binom{x-1}{s} = \frac{(n-x)\ldots(2-x)}{(n-1)!} = \frac{\Gamma(n-x+1)}{\Gamma(n)\,\Gamma(2-x)} \sim \frac{n^{1-x}}{\Gamma(2-x)}$$

for large values of n (see 9·61). Thus when $n \to \infty$, the right-hand member $\to 0$ if $R(x) > 1$, and $\to \infty$ if $R(x) < 1$. Hence the series

$$\phi(x) = \sum_{s=0}^{\infty} (-1)^s \binom{x-1}{s}$$

converges in the half-plane $R(x) > 1$, and is equal to zero for all values of x in this half-plane. To such a Newton's series we give the name *null series*. We note that when $x = 1$, $\phi(1) = 1$.

10·64. Unique Development. If a given function $f(x)$ be holomorphic in the half-plane $R(x) > l$, and if this function be capable of expansion in a Newton's series which is convergent in the half-plane $R(x) > \lambda$, we can shew that the expansion is unique, provided that $l \leqslant \lambda < 1$.

For, let the Newton's series be

$$F(x) = \sum_{s=0}^{\infty} (-1)^s \binom{x-1}{s}.$$

Then

$$\overset{s}{\Delta} F(1) = (-1)^s a_s.$$

But $F(1) = f(1)$, since $l \leqslant \lambda < 1$, and hence

$$F(x) = \sum_{s=0}^{\infty} \overset{s}{\Delta} f(1) \binom{x-1}{s}$$

and the expansion is uniquely determined.

It follows from this theorem that no null series can have a convergence abscissa which is less than unity.

10·65. Expansion in Newton's Series. Suppose that we are given a function $f(x)$ which is holomorphic in the half-plane $R(x) > l$, and that this function is representable by a Newton's series whose convergence abscissa is λ, where $n \leqslant \lambda < n+1$, n being a positive integer, and $l \leqslant \lambda$. Let $F(x)$ be the sum function of this series. Then

$$(1) \qquad F(x) = \sum_{s=0}^{\infty} (-1)^s a_s \binom{x-1}{s} = \sum_{s=0}^{\infty} \overset{s}{\Delta} F(1) \binom{x-1}{s}$$

as in the preceding section.

From 2·5 (2), we have

$$(2) \quad \overset{s}{\Delta} F(1) = F(s+1) - \binom{s}{1} F(s) + \binom{s}{2} F(s-1) - \dots + (-1)^s F(1).$$

Now, if $s \geqslant n$, we can write this in the form

$$(3) \quad \overset{s}{\Delta} F(1) = \sum_{\nu=0}^{n-1} (-1)^{s-\nu} \binom{s}{\nu} F(\nu+1) + \sum_{\nu=n}^{s} (-1)^{s-\nu} \binom{s}{\nu} f(\nu+1)$$

since by hypothesis $f(\nu+1) = F(\nu+1)$ when $\nu \geqslant n$.

If we substitute these expressions in (1), we obtain for the coefficient of $F(\nu+1)$, $\nu \leqslant n-1$, the series

$$\sum_{s=\nu}^{\infty} (-1)^{s-\nu} \binom{s}{\nu} \binom{x-1}{s} = \binom{x-1}{\nu} \sum_{s=\nu}^{\infty} (-1)^{s-\nu} \binom{x-\nu-1}{s-\nu}$$

$$= \binom{x-1}{\nu} \phi(x-\nu),$$

where $\phi(x)$ denotes the null series of 10·63.

The series $\phi(x-\nu)$ is likewise a null series whose convergence abscissa is $\nu+1$, so that the contribution to (1) of the numbers $F(1)$, $F(2)$, ... , $F(n)$ is

$$F(1)\,\phi(x) + F(2) \binom{x-1}{1} \phi(x-1) + \dots + F(n) \binom{x-1}{n} \phi(x-n+1),$$

which is also a null series whose convergence abscissa is n. Thus it appears that the sum function $F(x)$ of the series (1) is independent of the values of the sum of the series at the points $1, 2, 3, \dots, n$, and consequently that we can arbitrarily assign the values $F(1), F(2), \dots, F(n)$ without altering the value of the sum-function in the half-plane of convergence of the series.

Thus, if $\lambda > 1$, the expansion in Newton's series of a function $f(x)$ which can be so expanded is not unique but admits of infinite variety.

In some measure to restrict the choice of series, we define a *reduced series* as follows:

Let m be the smallest positive integer, such that the given function $f(x)$ is holomorphic for $R(x) > m$ and continuous on the right at $x = m$, so that

$$f(m) = \lim_{\varepsilon \to 0} f(m+\varepsilon),$$

where $\varepsilon \to 0$ through positive values. A Newton's series is said to be reduced if the sum function $F(x)$ be such that

$$F(x) = f(x), \quad x = m, m+1, m+2, \dots .$$

If the convergence abscissa λ of a reduced series be greater than the integer m, and if we add to this series a null series whose convergence abscissa is less than λ, the new series has the same convergence abscissa as the original series. A series obtained in this way may also be called reduced. In any case the convergence abscissa of a reduced series is the least possible, that is to say, no other Newton's series which represents the function can have a smaller convergence abscissa.

Example. Expand $(x-\alpha)^{-1}$ in a Newton's series. We have

$$(x-\alpha)^{-1} = (x-\alpha-1)^{(-1)},$$

so that from 2·11 (7),

$$\overset{s}{\Delta}(x-\alpha)^{-1} = (-1)^s\, s!\, (x-\alpha-1)^{(-s-1)} = \frac{(-1)^s\, s!}{(x-\alpha)\dots(x-\alpha+s)}.$$

Thus

$$\frac{1}{x-\alpha} = -\sum_{s=0}^{\infty} \frac{(x-1)\dots(x-s)}{(\alpha-1)(\alpha-2)\dots(\alpha-s-1)}.$$

The ratio of the $(s+1)$th term to the sth is

$$\frac{s-x}{s+1-\alpha} = 1 - \frac{x-\alpha+1}{s} + O\left(\frac{1}{s^2}\right),$$

so that by Weierstrass' criterion the series is absolutely convergent if $R(x) > R(\alpha)$. Also the series diverges if $R(x) < R(\alpha)$, since $(x-\alpha)^{-1}$ is infinite at $x = \alpha$, while the sum of a Newton's series is holomorphic at every point of the half-plane of convergence. Thus $\lambda = \mu = R(\alpha)$.

This series can also be deduced from 10·2, Ex. 2, by writing $1-\alpha$ for x and $1-x$ for a.

If we differentiate with respect to α, we obtain

$$\frac{1}{(x-\alpha)^2} = \sum_{s=0}^{\infty} \frac{(x-1)\dots(x-s)}{(\alpha-1)\dots(\alpha-s-1)}\left[\frac{1}{\alpha-1} + \frac{1}{\alpha-2} + \dots + \frac{1}{\alpha-s-1}\right].$$

Proceeding in this way we can obtain a Newton's series for $(x-\alpha)^{-n}$, and so any rational function can be expanded in a Newton's series.

The above method fails if $\alpha = n$, a positive integer. To obtain a reduced series, let us take the sum-function to have the values

$$\frac{1}{1-n}, \frac{1}{2-n}, \dots, \frac{1}{-1}$$

at the points $x = 1, 2, \dots, n-1$, and let us choose the value of the sum-function at $x = n$, so that the coefficient a_{n-1} is zero. We then have

$$\frac{1}{x-n} = -\sum_{s=0}^{n-2} \frac{(x-1)\dots(x-s)}{(n-1)\dots(n-s-1)} + \sum_{s=n}^{\infty} \frac{(x-1)\dots(x-s)}{s!}(-1)^s a_s,$$

where, from (3),

$$a_s = \sum_{\nu=0}^{n-2} (-1)^{\nu+1}\binom{s}{\nu}\frac{1}{n-\nu-1}$$
$$+(-1)^{n-1}\binom{s}{n-1}F(n) + \sum_{\nu=n}^{s}(-1)^{\nu}\binom{s}{\nu}\frac{1}{\nu+1-n}$$

and putting $x = n$ in the *series*, we get

$$F(n) = -\left(1 + \tfrac{1}{2} + \dots + \frac{1}{n-1}\right).$$

Thus $(-1)^n a_s$ is equal to the coefficient of t^{n-1} in

$$-(1+t)^s\log(1+t)+(-1)^n\binom{s}{n-1}\frac{\log(1+t)}{1+t}+t^{2n-s-2}(1+t)^s\log(1+t).$$

Now,

$$\frac{\partial}{\partial s}(1+t)^s=(1+t)^s\log(1+t),$$

and hence the coefficient of t^ν is

$$\frac{\partial}{\partial\nu}\binom{s}{\nu}=\binom{s}{\nu}\left(\frac{1}{s}+\frac{1}{s-1}+\ldots+\frac{1}{s-\nu+1}\right)$$

$$=\binom{s}{\nu}(S_s-S_{s-\nu}),$$

where $$S_s=1+\tfrac{1}{2}+\tfrac{1}{3}+\ldots+\frac{1}{s}.$$

Also

$$\frac{\log(1+t)}{1+t}=S_1t-S_2t^2+S_3t^3-\ldots.$$

Hence

$$(-1)^n a_s=\binom{s}{n-1}[-S_s+S_{s-n+1}+S_{n-1}+S_s-S_{n-1}]$$

$$=\binom{s}{n-1}S_{s-n+1}.$$

Hence finally we have the reduced series

$$\frac{1}{x-n}=-\sum_{s=0}^{n-2}\frac{(x-1)\ldots(x-s)}{(n-1)\ldots(n-s-1)}$$

$$+\sum_{s=n}^{\infty}(-1)^{s-n}\frac{(x-1)\ldots(x-s)}{(n-1)!\,(s-n+1)!}\left[1+\tfrac{1}{2}+\ldots+\frac{1}{s-n+1}\right],$$

of which the convergence abscissa is n.

10·67. Abscissa of Convergence of Newton's Series. Let the function $f(x)$ be represented by the Newton's series whose sum-function is $F(x)$. The method of the preceding section enables us to obtain another form for the convergence abscissa.

If n be a positive integer such that $0 \leqslant n \leqslant \lambda$, we have

$$F(x)=\sum_{s=0}^{\infty}\overset{s}{\Delta}F(1)\binom{x-1}{s},$$

$$(-1)^s a_s=\overset{s}{\Delta}F(1).$$

If we denote by $F(0)$ an arbitrary constant, which we introduce in front of the sequence

$$F(1), F(2), F(3), \ldots, F(n), f(n+1), f(n+2), \ldots,$$

we have

$$(1)\quad \sum_{s=0}^{n-1} a_s = \sum_{s=0}^{n-1} (-1)^s \overset{s}{\Delta} F(1) = \sum_{s=0}^{n-1} (-1)^s [\overset{s}{\Delta} F(0) + \overset{s+1}{\Delta} F(0)]$$

$$= F(0) + (-1)^{n-1} \overset{n}{\Delta} F(0),$$

and hence, from Theorem V,

$$(2)\qquad \lambda = \limsup_{n\to\infty} \log |\overset{n}{\Delta} F(0)| / \log n.$$

This formula for λ is still valid when $\lambda < 0$, if we remember that $F(0)$, $F(1)$, $F(2)$, ... are now the values of $f(0)$, $f(1)$, $f(2)$, ... We have in fact

$$F(0) = f(0) = \sum_{s=0}^{\infty} a_s,$$

so that, from (1),

$$\sum_{s=n}^{\infty} a_s = (-1)^n \overset{n}{\Delta} F(0),$$

and (2) therefore still yields the convergence abscissa.

10·7. Majorant Properties. We give here some theorems which indicate the nature of analytic functions which can be expanded in Newton's series. The proofs are lengthy and are omitted. They will be found in Nörlund's *Séries d'interpolation*, Chapter V. The first of these theorems is due to F. Carlson.

Theorem. *Let $F(x)$ be a function which can be expanded in a Newton's series of convergence abscissa λ. Let α be a real number greater than λ, and let $x-\alpha = r e^{i\theta}$, where $-\frac{1}{2}\pi \leqslant \theta \leqslant \frac{1}{2}\pi$. Then*

$$|F(x)| \leqslant e^{r\psi(\theta)} \frac{r^{\lambda+\frac{1}{2}+\epsilon(r)}}{(1+r\cos\theta)^{\frac{1}{2}}},$$

where

$$\psi(\theta) = \cos\theta \log(2\cos\theta) + \theta\sin\theta$$

and $\epsilon(r)$ tends uniformly to zero as $r \to \infty$.

A sufficient condition for the convergence of the Newton series of a function is contained in the following theorem due to Nörlund. We use the same notations as before.

Theorem. *Let $F(x)$ be an analytic function which is holomorphic in the half-plane $R(x) \geqslant \alpha$ and satisfying in this half-plane the inequality*

$$|F(x)| < e^{r\psi(\theta)}(1+r)^{\beta+\epsilon(r)}, \quad -\tfrac{1}{2}\pi \leqslant \theta \leqslant \tfrac{1}{2}\pi.$$

The function $F(x)$ can be expanded in a Newton's series whose convergence abscissa does not exceed the greater of the numbers α, $\beta+\frac{1}{2}$.

For the more general series,

$$\sum_{s=0}^{\infty} b_s \frac{(x-\omega)(x-2\omega)\dots(x-s\omega)}{s!},$$

Nörlund has proved the following:

Theorem. *In order that a function $F(x)$ should admit a development of the above form, it is necessary and sufficient that $F(x)$ should be holomorphic in a certain half-plane $R(x) > \alpha$ and should there satisfy the inequality*

$$|F(x)| < C\, e^{k|x|},$$

where C and k are fixed positive numbers.

It is here sufficient to take

$$k\omega < \log 2 \leqslant \psi(\theta).$$

Any function which can be developed in a Newton's series admits, *a fortiori*, a development of the above form where $0 < \omega < 1$.

10·8. Euler's Transformation of Series.

Let

$$\phi(t) = \sum_{s=0}^{\infty} \frac{F(s)}{t^{s+1}}$$

be a power series in t^{-1} which converges outside the circle $|t| = R$.

If we write $t = 1+u$ and expand each term in negative powers of u, we obtain

$$\phi(t) = \sum_{s=0}^{\infty} F(s) \sum_{\nu=s}^{\infty} (-1)^{\nu-s} \binom{\nu}{s} u^{-\nu-1}.$$

Since the original series converges if $|t| > R$, the second series will certainly converge if $|u| > 1+R$, that is to say, the power series in u^{-1} converges outside the circle whose centre is the point $t=1$ and whose radius is $1+R$. But by Weierstrass' theorem on double series * we can interchange the orders of summation.

Hence we obtain

$$\phi(t) = \sum_{s=0}^{\infty} u^{-s-1} \sum_{\nu=0}^{s} (-1)^{s-\nu} \binom{s}{\nu} F(\nu).$$

Now, from 2·5 (2), we have

$$\sum_{\nu=0}^{s} (-1)^{s-\nu} \binom{s}{\nu} F(\nu) = \overset{s}{\Delta} F(0).$$

Thus we have Euler's transformation, namely,

$$\sum_{s=0}^{\infty} \frac{F(s)}{t^{s+1}} = \sum_{s=0}^{\infty} \frac{\overset{s}{\Delta} F(0)}{(t-1)^{s+1}}.$$

The series on the right certainly converges outside the circle $|t-1| = 1+R$, but the series may also converge at points within this circle.

10·82. Generating Function. Consider the Newton's series

$$F(x) = \sum_{s=0}^{\infty} \overset{s}{\Delta} F(1) \binom{x-1}{s}. \tag{1}$$

The function $\phi(t)$ defined by

$$\phi(t) = \sum_{s=0}^{\infty} \frac{F(s)}{t^s} \tag{2}$$

is called the *generating function* of the series.

To obtain the region of convergence of the series which defines the generating function we have, by Carlson's theorem, 10·7,

$$|F(s)| < e^{s \log 2} s^{\lambda+\epsilon} = 2^s s^{\lambda+\epsilon},$$

and hence

$$\sqrt[s]{\left|\frac{F(s)}{t^s}\right|} < \frac{2 s^{\frac{\lambda+\epsilon}{s}}}{|t|} = \left|\frac{2}{t}\right| e^{\frac{(\lambda+\epsilon)\log s}{s}}.$$

Since

$$\lim_{s\to\infty} e^{\frac{\log s}{s}} = e^0 = 1,$$

* K. Knopp, *Infinite Series*, p. 430.

we see that the series for $\phi(t)$ converges if

$$|t| > 2.$$

Applying Euler's transformation to $\phi(t)/t$, we obtain

$$\frac{\phi(t)}{t} = \sum_{s=0}^{\infty} \frac{\overset{s}{\Delta} F(0)}{(t-1)^{s+1}}, \tag{3}$$

where, as in 10·67, $F(0)$ is to be replaced by an arbitrary number if $\lambda > 0$.

Multiplying both sides of (3) by $t \equiv (t-1)+1$, we have

$$\phi(t) = \sum_{s=0}^{\infty} \frac{\overset{s}{\Delta} F(0)}{(t-1)^{s}} + \sum_{s=0}^{\infty} \frac{\overset{s}{\Delta} F(0)}{(t-1)^{s+1}}$$

$$= F(0) + \sum_{s=0}^{\infty} \frac{\overset{s}{\Delta} F(1)}{(t-1)^{s+1}}, \tag{4}$$

since

$$\overset{s+1}{\Delta} F(0) + \overset{s}{\Delta} F(0) = \overset{s}{\Delta} F(1).$$

Now,

$$\binom{x-1}{s} = \frac{\Gamma(x)}{\Gamma(x-s)\,\Gamma(s+1)},$$

and by the complementary argument theorem

$$\Gamma(x-s)\,\Gamma(1-x+s) = \frac{\pi}{\sin \pi(x-s)} = \frac{(-1)^s \pi}{\sin \pi x}.$$

It follows that

$$\binom{x-1}{s} = \frac{\sin \pi x\, \Gamma(x)}{(-1)^s \pi} \, \frac{\Gamma(s+1-x)}{\Gamma(s+1)}$$

and hence, if $R(x) = \sigma$, we have from 9·61,

$$\left| \overset{s}{\Delta} F(1) \binom{x-1}{s} \right| = | C(x) \overset{s}{\Delta} F(1)\, s^{-\sigma}(1+\delta) |,$$

where $C(x)$ is independent of s and $\delta \to 0$ when $s \to \infty$.

Since the series (1) converges, the absolute value of the sth term tends to zero when $s \to \infty$. Taking $\sigma = \lambda + \varepsilon$ $(\varepsilon > 0)$, we see that for sufficiently large values of s

$$| \overset{s}{\Delta} F(1) | < s^{\lambda+\epsilon}.$$

Hence

$$\lim_{s\to\infty} \sqrt[s]{\left|\frac{\overset{s}{\Delta} F(1)}{(t-1)^{s+1}}\right|} = \frac{1}{|t-1|},$$

so that the series (4) converges at all points exterior to the circle $|t-1| = 1$, and therefore the series (3) converges in the same domain. From 10·22 and 10·67 (2), we see that the order of $\phi(t)/t$ on the circle $|t-1| = 1$ is equal to $\lambda+1$.

10·83. Laplace's Integral. We have, from 9·88,

$$(1) \quad \binom{x-1}{s} = \frac{\Gamma(x)}{\Gamma(x-s)\,\Gamma(s+1)} = \frac{1}{2\pi i}\int_0^{(1+)} t^{x-1}(t-1)^{-s-1}\,dt,$$

the path of integration being a loop which starts from the origin, makes a positive circuit round $t = 1$, and returns to the origin.

Also, the generating function is, from 10·82 (4),

$$\phi(t) = F(0) + \sum_{s=0}^{\infty} \frac{\overset{s}{\Delta} F(1)}{(t-1)^{s+1}}.$$

If we take $R(x) > 0$, $R(x) > \lambda+1$ and multiply by t^{x-1}, we can integrate term by term, provided that the contour of (1) be enlarged into a loop l which starts from the origin and encircles the circle $|t-1| = 1$ and then returns to the origin in such a way that no branch of l is tangent to this circle at $t = 0$. We thus obtain

$$F(x) = \frac{1}{2\pi i}\int_l t^{x-1}\phi(t)\,dt.$$

Conversely, every integral of this form, where $\phi(t)$ is holomorphic outside the circle $|t-1| = 1$ and is of finite order on the circle, gives rise to a Newton's series.

Example. $F(x) = a^x$.

Here

$$\phi(t) = \sum_{s=0}^{\infty} \frac{a^s}{t^s} = \frac{t}{t-a} = 1 + \frac{a}{(t-1)-(a-1)}$$

$$= 1 + a\sum_{s=0}^{\infty} \frac{(a-1)^s}{(t-1)^{s+1}},$$

and hence

$$F(x) = \frac{1}{2\pi i}\int_l \left(1 + \sum_{s=0}^{\infty} \frac{(a-1)^s a}{(t-1)^{s+1}}\right) t^{x-1}\, dt$$

$$= a \sum_{s=0}^{\infty} (a-1)^s \binom{x-1}{s}.$$

If $|a-1| = 1$, $a \neq 0$, we have

$$\frac{\phi(t)}{t} = \frac{1}{(t-1)-(a-1)},$$

so that $t = a$ is a simple pole on the circle $|t-1| = 1$ and the order of $\phi(t)/t$ is unity. Thus $\lambda = 0$. If $|a-1| < 1$, $\phi(t)/t$ is holomorphic on the circle and therefore $\lambda = -\infty$.

The expansion can also be obtained directly from the identity

$$a^x = a(1+a-1)^{x-1}.$$

10·85. Expansion of the Psi Function in Newton's Series. We have

$$\Delta\Psi(x) = \frac{1}{x}, \quad \overset{s}{\Delta}\Psi(x) = \frac{(-1)^{s-1}(s-1)!}{x(x+1)\dots(x+s-1)}.$$

Thus, from 10·82 (4), the generating function for $\Psi(1) - \Psi(x)$ is

$$\phi(t) = \sum_{s=1}^{\infty} \frac{(-1)^s}{s} \frac{1}{(t-1)^{s+1}} = -\frac{1}{t-1}\log\left(1 + \frac{1}{t-1}\right).$$

Hence

$$\Psi(1) - \Psi(x) = \frac{1}{2\pi i}\int_l t^{x-1} \sum_{s=1}^{\infty} \frac{(-1)^s}{s} \frac{1}{(t-1)^{s+1}}\, dt$$

$$= \sum_{s=1}^{\infty} \frac{(-1)^s}{s} \binom{x-1}{s}.$$

Since $\Psi(1) = -\gamma$, we have

$$\Psi(x) = -\gamma + \binom{x-1}{1} - \frac{1}{2}\binom{x-1}{2} + \frac{1}{3}\binom{x-1}{3} - \dots,$$

with convergence abscissa zero.

10·9. Application to the Hypergeometric Function. From 9·8, 9·82, we have

$$\frac{\Gamma(c)\,\Gamma(x+c-b-1)}{\Gamma(c-b)\,\Gamma(x+c-1)} = F(1-x,\, b;\, c;\, 1)$$

$$= 1 - \frac{b}{c}\binom{x-1}{1} + \frac{b(b+1)}{c(c+1)}\binom{x-1}{2} - \frac{b(b+1)(b+2)}{c(c+1)(c+2)}\binom{x-1}{3} + \dots$$

which is a Newton's series.

The function on the left is meromorphic in the whole complex plane, with simple poles at $b-c+1,\ b-c,\ b-c-1, \dots$. The convergence abscissa is therefore $b-c+1$.

Writing $c = b+1$, $b = y$, we have a Newton's series for the reciprocal of the Beta function, namely,

$$\frac{1}{\mathrm{B}(x,y)} = \frac{1}{y} - \frac{1}{y+1}\binom{x-1}{1} + \frac{1}{y+2}\binom{x-1}{2} - \frac{1}{y+3}\binom{x-1}{3} + \dots,$$

with convergence abscissa zero.

If we put $y = n+1$, where n is a positive integer, we obtain a Newton's series for the inverse factorial, namely,

$$\frac{n!}{x(x+1)\dots(x+n)} = \frac{1}{n+1} - \frac{1}{n+2}\binom{x-1}{1} + \frac{1}{n+3}\binom{x-1}{2} - \dots$$

and for $n = 0$,

$$\frac{1}{x} = 1 - \frac{1}{2}\binom{x-1}{1} + \frac{1}{3}\binom{x-1}{2} - \dots.$$

Since

$$\Psi(x) = \mathop{\mathrm{S}}_{1}^{x} \frac{\Delta t}{t},$$

we have, by summation,

$$\Psi(x) = \text{constant} + \sum_{s=0}^{\infty} \binom{x-1}{s+1} \frac{(-1)^s}{s+1}.$$

Putting $x = 1$, we have for the constant the value $\Psi(1) = -\gamma$, whence we obtain once more the result of 10·85.

EXAMPLES X

1. Prove that

$$\frac{1}{x}=\frac{1}{x+1}+\frac{1!}{(x+1)(x+2)}+\frac{2!}{(x+1)(x+2)(x+3)}+\frac{3!}{(x+1)(x+2)(x+3)(x+4)}+\dots.$$

2. Prove that the series

$$\sum_{s=0}^{\infty}\frac{2^{-s-1}\,s!}{x(x+1)\dots(x+s)}$$

represents a meromorphic function in the whole plane. Transform the series by $(x,\ x+1)$ and shew that the resulting series

$$\sum_{s=0}^{\infty}\frac{s!}{(x+1)(x+2)\dots(x+s+1)}\,\frac{2^{s+1}-1}{2^{s+1}}$$

has the convergence abscissa zero. What is the explanation of this result ?

3. Establish the transformation $\left(x,\ \dfrac{x}{\omega}\right)$ by starting from the integral $\dfrac{1}{x}=\displaystyle\int_0^1 t^{x-1}\,dt$ and its finite differences

$$\frac{s!}{x(x+1)\dots(x+s)}=\int_0^1 t^{x-1}(1-t)^s\,dt$$

with respect to x.

4. Shew that the derivate of the function

$$\sum_{s=0}^{\infty}\frac{2^{-s-1}\,s!}{x(x+1)\dots(x+s)},$$

which is meromorphic in the whole plane, has convergence abscissa zero.

5. Prove that

$$\beta(x)=\frac{1}{x}-\frac{1}{x+1}+\frac{1}{x+2}-\dots=\sum_{s=0}^{\infty}\frac{s!\,2^{-s-1}}{x(x+1)\dots(x+s)},$$

and that the factorial series represents a meromorphic function in the whole plane. (See also Ex. 4, p. 267.)

6. Prove that

$$\beta\left(\frac{x}{3}\right)-\beta(x)=\sum_{s=0}^{\infty}\frac{s!\sin\frac{2s+1}{6}\pi}{x(x+1)\dots(x+s)},\quad R(x)>0.$$

7. Prove that

$$\beta_1(x)=$$

$$\frac{1}{2x}+\frac{1}{2^2(x+1)}+\frac{1}{2^3(x+2)}+\dots=\sum_{s=1}^{\infty}\frac{(-1)^s s!}{x(x+1)\dots(x+s)},\quad R(x)>0.$$

8. Prove that

$$[\beta(x)]^2=\sum_{s=1}^{\infty}\frac{s!}{x(x+1)\dots(x+s)}\frac{2^s-1}{(s+1)2^s},\quad R(x)>0,$$

and that the series is absolutely convergent.

9. Prove that

$$[\beta_1(x)]^2=\sum_{s=1}^{\infty}\frac{s!\,b_s}{x(x+1)\dots(x+s)},\quad R(x)>0,$$

where

$$b_n=\sum_{s=1}^{n}\frac{(-1)^s-1}{s\,.\,3^{n-s+1}},$$

and that the series is absolutely convergent.

10. Prove that

$$\beta(x)\,\beta_1(x)=\sum_{s=1}^{\infty}\frac{s!\,b_s}{x(x+1)\dots(x+s)},\quad R(x)>0,$$

where

$$b_n=\sum_{s=1}^{n}\frac{1}{s\,.\,3^{n-s+1}}\left[1-(-1)^s-\frac{1}{2^s}\right],$$

and that the series is absolutely convergent.

11. Prove that

$$1-(x-1)\,\beta_1(x-1)=\sum_{s=0}^{\infty}\frac{(-1)^s(s+1)!}{x(x+1)\dots(x+s)},\quad R(x)>1,$$

and also that

$$1-(x-1)\,\beta_1(x-1)$$

$$=\sum_{s=0}^{\infty}\frac{s!\,[1-2+3-\dots+(-1)^s(s+1)]}{(x+1)(x+2)\dots(x+s+1)},\quad R(x)>0,$$

so that the second series is convergent in the strip $0<R(x)<1$, where the first series is divergent.

12. Obtain the transformation $(x, x+1)$ by taking $F_1(x) = \frac{1}{x}$ in the product $F(x)\, F_1(x)$ of two factorial series.

13. Prove that

$$\Psi(x+y) - \Psi(x) = \int_0^\infty e^{-\xi x} \frac{1-e^{-\xi y}}{1-e^{-\xi}}\, d\xi,$$

where $R(x) > 0$, $R(x+y) > 0$.

14. Prove that

$$\Psi(x+y) - \Psi(x) = \sum_{s=0}^{\infty} \frac{(-1)^s}{s+1} \frac{y(y-1)\dots(y-s)}{x(x+1)\dots(x+s)}.$$

15. Prove that

$$\frac{1}{(x-\alpha)^{n+1}} = \sum_{s=n}^{\infty} \binom{s}{n} \frac{B_{s-n}^{(s+1)}(\alpha+s)}{x(x+1)\dots(x+s)}.$$

16. By integrating $x^{-1}(x+1)^{-1}$, shew that

$$\log\left(1+\frac{1}{x}\right) = \frac{1}{x} - \frac{1}{2x(x+1)} + \sum_{s=2}^{\infty} \frac{(-1)^{s-1} B_s^{(s-1)}}{(s-1)\, x(x+1)\dots(x+s)}$$

$$= \sum_{s=1}^{\infty} \frac{(-1)^{s-1} B_{s-1}^{(s-1)}}{(x+1)(x+2)\dots(x+s)}$$

where $R(x) > 0$ in both cases.

17. By summation of both sides in Ex. 16, prove that

$$\Psi(x) = \log x - \frac{1}{2x} + \sum_{s=1}^{\infty} \frac{(-1)^s B_{s+1}^{(s)}}{s(s+1)} \frac{1}{x(x+1)\dots(x+s)}$$

$$= \log x - \frac{1}{x} + \sum_{s=1}^{\infty} \frac{(-1)^s B_s^{(s)}}{s} \frac{1}{(x+1)\dots(x+s)}.$$

18. Determine the abscissa of absolute convergence of the series

$$\sum_{s=0}^{\infty} (-1)^s \binom{x-1}{s}.$$

19. Expand in a Newton's series

$$(1+a)^x+(x-a)^{-1}, \quad |a|=1, \quad a\neq -1,$$

and determine the abscissa of absolute convergence.

20. If

$$F(x)=\sum_{s=0}^{\infty}(-1)^s a_s\binom{x-1}{s}, \quad A_s=\sum_{r=0}^{s} a_r, \quad B_s=\sum_{r=s}^{\infty} a_r,$$

shew that

$$F(x)=\sum_{s=0}^{\infty}(-1)^s A_s\binom{x}{s+1}, \qquad \lambda>0,$$

$$F(x)=F(0)+\sum_{s=1}^{\infty}(-1)^s B_s\binom{x}{s}, \quad \lambda<0,$$

and that in each case the abscissa of absolute convergence is λ.

21. Shew that the results of applying p times in succession each of the above transformations yield

$$F(x)=\sum_{s=0}^{\infty}(-1)^s A_{s,p}\binom{x+p-1}{s+p},$$

$$F(x)=\sum_{s=0}^{\infty}(-1)^s B_{s,p}\binom{x+p-1}{s},$$

where $$A_{s,p}=\sum_{r=0}^{s} a_r\binom{p+s-r-1}{s-r},$$

$$B_{s,p}=\sum_{r=s}^{\infty} a_r\binom{p+r-s-1}{r-s}.$$

22. If $f(n)=\left|\binom{x-1}{n-1}\right|\div\left|\binom{x-1}{n}\right|$, shew that the equation $f(n)=1$ has the single root $m=|x^2|\div 2R(x)$.

Hence prove that the greatest value of $\left|\binom{x-1}{n}\right|$ for fixed x occurs when $n=[m]$, where $[m]$ denotes the greatest integer which does not exceed m.

23. Prove that

$$a^x=a^{1-p}\sum_{s=0}^{\infty}(a-1)^s\binom{x+p-1}{s}.$$

24. Prove that

$$\frac{a^{x-1}}{\Gamma(x)} = \sum_{s=0}^{\infty} (-1)^s L_s(a) \binom{x-1}{s},$$

where $L_n(x)$ is Laguerre's polynomial defined by

$$L_n(x) = \frac{e^x}{n!} \frac{d^n}{dx^n}(x^n e^{-x}).$$

25. Shew that the hypergeometric function $F(1-x, b; c; \alpha)$ represents a Newton's series which converges everywhere if $|\alpha| < 1$, and that the generating function is

$$\phi(t) = F(1, b; c; \alpha) + \frac{1}{t-1} F\left(1, b; c; \frac{\alpha}{1-t}\right).$$

CHAPTER XI

THE DIFFERENCE EQUATION OF THE FIRST ORDER

11·0. The Genesis of Difference Equations. Let $\varpi(x)$ denote an arbitrary periodic function of x of period unity, so that $\varpi(x+1) = \varpi(x)$. From a relation of the form

$$F(x, u_x, \varpi(x)) = 0, \tag{1}$$

we obtain, by performing the operation Δ,

$$F(x+1, u_{x+1}, \varpi(x)) = F(x, u_x, \varpi(x)). \tag{2}$$

The elimination of $\varpi(x)$ between (1) and (2) leads to a relation of the form

$$\phi(x, u_x, u_{x+1}) = 0, \tag{3}$$

which is a difference equation of the first order, of which (1) may be regarded as a *complete primitive*. Observing that

$$u_{x+1} = u_x + \Delta u_x,$$

the equation (3) could also be exhibited in the form

$$\psi(x, u_x, \Delta u_x) = 0. \tag{4}$$

The problem to be envisaged is then, given a difference equation of the form (3) or (4), to obtain a complete primitive of the form (1). That such a problem is capable of solution is by no means obvious, nor, supposing solution to be possible, are we entitled to expect a solution in compact form. The proper attitude is rather to regard a difference equation as possibly defining a class of functions and to study the properties of these functions from the form of the equation. In Chapter VIII we have established the existence of a definite function which satisfies the simplest possible difference equation,

$$\Delta u_x = \phi(x),$$

but even there we have seen that the problem is not entirely simple and that $\phi(x)$ must be suitably restricted. In the present chapter we shall consider only equations of the first order, and it will appear that, except in the case of the linear equation, very little is known of the theory. We shall denote the independent variable by x and the dependent variable by u_x, $u(x)$, or u, according to convenience.

Example 1. Assuming as complete primitive

$$u_x = \varpi x + \varpi^2,$$

form the corresponding difference equation.

We have

$$\Delta u_x = \varpi,$$

whence

$$u_x = x \Delta u_x + (\Delta u_x)^2.$$

Example 2. Assuming as complete primitive

$$u_x = \varpi_1 a^x + \varpi_2 b^x,$$

form the corresponding difference equation.

We have

$$u_{x+1} = \varpi_1 a^{x+1} + \varpi_2 b^{x+1},$$

$$u_{x+2} = \varpi_1 a^{x+2} + \varpi_2 b^{x+2},$$

whence, eliminating $\varpi_1 a^x$, $\varpi_2 b^x$, we have

$$\begin{vmatrix} u_x & u_{x+1} & u_{x+2} \\ 1 & a & a^2 \\ 1 & b & b^2 \end{vmatrix} = 0,$$

$$u_{x+2} - (a+b)\, u_{x+1} + ab\, u_x = 0,$$

or

$$\overset{2}{\Delta} u_x - (a+b-2) \Delta u_x + (ab - a - b + 1)\, u_x = 0.$$

Either of these forms is a linear difference equation of the second order with constant coefficients.

11·01. The Linear Difference Equation of the Firs Order. The general form of the linear equation of the first order i

$$a(x)\,u(x+1)+b(x)\,u(x)=c(x), \tag{1}$$

where $a(x)$, $b(x)$ and $c(x)$ are given functions of x.

If we can find a particular function $u_1(x)$ which satisfies thi equation, we have

$$a(x)\,u_1(x+1)+b(x)\,u_1(x)=c(x). \tag{2}$$

If we now put $u(x)=u_1(x)+v(x)$ in (1), we obtain, by sub tracting (2),

$$a(x)\,v(x+1)+b(x)\,v(x)=0. \tag{3}$$

Thus the general solution of (1) can be regarded as the sum of particular solution of (1) and the general solution of the homogeneou linear equation (3).

This point of view is convenient in that it applies to linear equa tions of any order, but later we shall see how, in the case of th general equation of the *first* order, it is possible to proceed at onc to a symbolic solution.

11·1. The Homogeneous Linear Equation. The genera type of this equation is that of 11·01 (3). Dividing by $a(x)$ an changing the notation, this can be written in the form

$$u(x+1)=p(x)\,u(x). \tag{1}$$

The general method of solving this equation is as follows:

Taking logarithms

$$\log u(x+1)-\log u(x)=\log p(x).$$

Hence summing the function on the right, we obtain

$$\log u(x)=\mathop{\mathrm{S}}_{c}^{x}\log p(t)\,\Delta t+\varpi(x),$$

where $\varpi(x)$ is an arbitrary periodic function of x of period 1 Such an arbitrary periodic function we shall in future denote b

ϖ and call an arbitrary "periodic," the argument x being implied. Thus we obtain

$$u(x) = \exp\left(\varpi + \mathop{S}_{c}^{x} \log p(t)\, \Delta t\right)$$

(2) $$= \varpi_1 \exp\left(\mathop{S}_{c}^{x} \log p(t)\, \Delta t\right),$$

where $\varpi_1 = \exp(\varpi)$ is an arbitrary periodic.

The arbitrary constant c does not of course add generality to the solution. This constant c may therefore be given any particular value which is convenient for the purpose of summation. The solution obtained in this way exists in so far as $\log p(x)$ is summable in the sense described in Chapter VIII. Moreover, in view of the possible many-valued nature of the right-hand side of (2) it may be necessary to make suitable cuts in the x plane. The important point to observe is that the general solution of the homogeneous linear equation contains an arbitrary function of period unity, which can therefore be defined in a perfectly arbitrary manner in the strip $0 \leqslant R(x) < 1$.

The general solution of (1) is therefore only analytic if ϖ_1 be analytic. Moreover, the solution of (1) is only completely determined when the value of $u(x)$ in the strip $0 \leqslant R(x) < 1$ is assigned. In the case of a differential equation of the form $\dfrac{dy}{dx} = p(x)\, y$, the solution is determined when y is given for a particular value of x: in the corresponding case of a difference equation, a particular value of x for which $u(x)$ is given does not in general determine the solution.

Consider the equation

(3) $$u(x+1) = e^{2x}\, u(x).$$

Here

$$u(x) = \varpi \exp\left[\mathop{S}_{c}^{x} 2t\, \Delta t\right].$$

Taking $$c = 0,$$

$$u(x) = \varpi \exp(B_2(x))$$

$$= \varpi \exp(x^2 - x + \tfrac{1}{6}).$$

Introducing Bernoulli's function $P_2(x)$, which has the period 1 and coincides with $B_2(x)$ in the strip $0 \leqslant R(x) < 1$, we can write

(4) $$u(x) = \varpi_1 e^{-P_2(x)} \,.\, e^{x^2 - x + \frac{1}{6}},$$

where ϖ_1 is an arbitrary periodic.

Let us now seek that solution of (3) which is equal to $\cos 2\pi x$ in the strip $0 \leqslant R(x) < 1$.

Clearly we have the solution required if $\varpi_1 = \cos 2\pi x$, that is to say,

$$u(x) = \cos 2\pi x \, e^{x^2 - x + \frac{1}{6} - P_2(x)}.$$

This is an analytic solution valid for all values of x, and continuous at $x = 1$.

Suppose, again, that we require the solution of (3) which shall be equal to x in the interval $0 \leqslant x < 1$. Bernoulli's function $P_1(x)$ is equal to $x - \frac{1}{2}$ in $0 \leqslant x < 1$ and has period unity. The required solution is therefore

$$u(x) = [P_1(x) + \tfrac{1}{2}] \, e^{x^2 - x + \frac{1}{6} - P_2(x)}.$$

This solution is discontinuous at $x = \ldots -3, -2, -1, 0, 1, 2, \ldots$

More generally, if $u(x)$ is to reduce to a given function $f(x)$ in the interval $0 \leqslant x < 1$, we expand $f(x)$ in a Fourier series in this range and substitute this Fourier series for ϖ_1 in (4).

The above illustrations should sufficiently shew that the nature of the problem of solution of a difference equation is very different from the corresponding problem in differential equations.

We cannot, for example, obtain a definite answer to the problem of finding a solution of (3) which reduces to a constant k when $x = 0$, for the arbitrary periodic ϖ_1 is now subject only to the restriction that $\varpi_1 = k$ when $x = 0$. If, however, the values of x with which we are concerned be of the form $x = a + n$, where n is an arbitrary integer and a is a constant, the situation is entirely changed, for in this case we are not concerned with values of x other than those assigned, and the solution of (3) which reduces to the constant k when $x = a$ is now perfectly definite, being in fact

$$u(x) = k \, e^{x^2 - x - a^2 - a}.$$

This type of problem is of frequent occurrence in the practical applications of difference equations, but it must be borne in mind that this definiteness of the solution can only be obtained under the special circumstances mentioned.

From the form of (2) it is evident that if we have two particular solutions $u_1(x)$ and $u_2(x)$ of (1), then $u_2(x) = \varpi u_1(x)$, where ϖ is a periodic (not arbitrary), and further, that if we are in possession of any particular solution $u_1(x)$, the general solution is $\varpi u_1(x)$ where ϖ is an arbitrary periodic. We shall now investigate various particular methods of finding a particular solution of (1) which may in special cases be more conveniently applied than the general method just explained.

11·2. Solution by means of the Gamma Function. Rational Coefficients. We have seen in Chapter IX that the equation $u(x+1) = x\,u(x)$ has the particular solution $u(x) = \Gamma(x)$.

Now, consider the equation

(1) $$u(x+1) = r(x)\,u(x),$$

where $r(x)$ is a rational function. We can therefore suppose

$$r(x) = c\,\frac{(x-\alpha_1)(x-\alpha_2)\dots(x-\alpha_k)}{(x-\beta_1)(x-\beta_2)\dots(x-\beta_l)},$$

where neither the α_i nor the β_i are necessarily all distinct.

Since

$$\Gamma(x+1-\alpha_i) = (x-\alpha_i)\,\Gamma(x-\alpha_i)$$

and

$$c^{x+1} = c\,.\,c^x,$$

it is evident that (1) has the particular solution

(2) $$u(x) = c^x\,\frac{\Gamma(x-\alpha_1)\,\Gamma(x-\alpha_2)\dots\Gamma(x-\alpha_k)}{\Gamma(x-\beta_1)\,\Gamma(x-\beta_2)\dots\Gamma(x-\beta_l)}.$$

Since $\dfrac{1}{\Gamma(x)}$ is an integral function, it follows that the particular solution found in this way is meromorphic in the whole plane with poles at the points $\alpha_i - n$,

$$\begin{cases} i = 1, 2, \dots, k, \\ n = 0, 1, 2, 3 \dots . \end{cases}$$

The general solution is obtained by multiplying the above by an arbitrary periodic.

Example 1. $$x^2 u(x+1) = 2(x+1)u(x).$$

Here
$$r(x) = \frac{2(x+1)}{x^2},$$
so that
$$u(x) = \varpi\, 2^x \frac{\Gamma(x+1)}{\Gamma(x)\,\Gamma(x)} = \frac{\varpi\, 2^x\, x}{\Gamma(x)}.$$

Example 2. The equation with linear coefficients
$$(ax+b)\,u(x+1) + (cx+d)\,u(x) = 0.$$

Divide by a and write
$$u(x) = \left(-\frac{c}{a}\right)^x v(x).$$

The equation then assumes the form
$$(x+e)\,v(x+1) - (x+f)\,v(x).$$

Finally, writing x for $x+e$, we reduce the problem to the solution of the form
$$x\,w(x+1) = (x-\alpha)\,w(x).$$

A particular solution is
$$w(x) = \frac{\Gamma(1)\,\Gamma(x-\alpha)}{\Gamma(1-\alpha)\,\Gamma(x)} = F(1-x, \alpha\,;\,1\,;\,1),$$
whence, from 10·9,
$$w(x) = \sum_{s=0}^{\infty} (-1)^s \binom{\alpha+s-1}{s} \binom{x-1}{s},$$
which is a Newton's series convergent for $R(x-\alpha) > 0$.

11·3. The Complete Linear Equation of the First Order. The general form of 11·01 reduces at once to

(1) $$u(x+1) - p(x)\,u(x) = q(x).$$

We have seen that when $q(x) = 0$, we have the special solution

(2) $$u_1(x) = \exp\left[\, \mathop{\Large S}_{c}^{x} \log p(t)\,\Delta t \right].$$

To obtain the general solution of (1), put
$$u(x) = u_1(x)\,v(x),$$

and we have, from (1),

$$u_1(x+1)\,v(x+1) - p(x)\,u_1(x)\,v(x) = q(x).$$

Now, $u_1(x+1) = p(x)\,u_1(x)$. Hence we have

$$u_1(x+1)\,\Delta v(x) = q(x),$$

so that

$$v(x) = \varpi + \underset{c}{\overset{x}{\mathsf{S}}} \frac{q(t)}{u_1(t+1)}\,\Delta t.$$

Thus the general solution of (1) is $u(x) =$

$$\left[\varpi + \underset{c}{\overset{x}{\mathsf{S}}} \left\{ \frac{q(s)}{\exp\left(\underset{c}{\overset{s+1}{\mathsf{S}}} \log p(t)\,\Delta t\right)} \right\} \Delta s \right] \exp\left[\underset{c}{\overset{x}{\mathsf{S}}} \log p(t)\,\Delta t\right],$$

where ϖ is an arbitrary periodic and c an arbitrary constant to which any convenient particular value may be assigned.

Example. $u(x+1) - e^{2x}\,u(x) = 3x^2\,e^{x^2+x+\frac{1}{3}}$.

Here we take, as in 11·1 (3),

$$u_1(x) = e^{B_2(x)}.$$

Putting $u(x) = v(x)\,e^{B_2(x)}$, we obtain

$$\Delta v(x) = 3x^2,$$

$$v(x) = \varpi + B_3(x),$$

$$u(x) = \varpi\,e^{B_2(x)} + B_3(x)\,e^{B_2(x)}.$$

11·31. The Case of Constant Coefficients. The linear equation of the first order with constant coefficients is

$$u(x+1) - \lambda\,u(x) = \phi(x),$$

where λ is independent of x.

If $\phi(x) = 0$, we have

$$u(x) = \varpi\,\lambda^x,$$

so that we can take the special solution

$$u_1(x) = \lambda^{x-1}.$$

Putting $u(x) = \lambda^{x-1} v(x)$, we have

$$\Delta v(x) = \lambda^{-x} \phi(x),$$

whence

$$u(x) = \left\{ \varpi + \mathop{\mathrm{S}}_{c}^{x} \lambda^{-t} \phi(t) \Delta t \right\} \lambda^{x-1}.$$

An interesting particular case of this equation is

$$u(x+1) + u(x) = 2x^{-1},$$

corresponding to $\lambda = -1$. The general solution is

$$u(x) = (-1)^{x-1} \left[\varpi + \int_c^\infty \frac{2(-1)^{-t}}{t} dt - 2 \sum_{s=0}^{\infty} \frac{(-1)^{-x-s}}{x+s} \right].$$

The equation has therefore, as a particular solution, the function

$$g(x) = 2 \sum_{s=0}^{\infty} \frac{(-1)^s}{x+s} = 2\left(\frac{1}{x} - \frac{1}{x+1} + \frac{1}{x+2} - \dots \right).$$

This function $g(x)$ has interesting properties, some of which are given in Examples IX (4).

11·32. Application of Ascending Continued Fractions. Another method of obtaining a particular solution of the complete equation is as follows. The general equation 11·01 (3) can be written in the form

$$a(x) u(x) = u(x+1) + b(x),$$

so that

$$u(x) = \frac{b(x) + u(x+1)}{a(x)},$$

and by continued application of this result we have for $u(x)$ the ascending continued fraction *

$$u(x) = \cfrac{b(x) + \cfrac{b(x+1) + \cfrac{b(x+2) + \cfrac{b(x+3) + \cdots}{a(x+3)}}{a(x+2)}}{a(x+1)}}{a(x)}.$$

* L. M. Milne-Thomson, *Proc. Edinburgh Math. Soc.* (2) 3, 1933.

which is equivalent to the infinite series

$$u(x) = \frac{b(x)}{a(x)} + \frac{b(x+1)}{a(x)\,a(x+1)} + \frac{b(x+2)}{a(x)\,a(x+1)\,a(x+2)} + \dots .$$

The general solution is obtained by adding to this the general solution of the homogeneous equation

$$a(x)\,u(x) = u(x+1).$$

As an application, consider

$$u(x+1) - x\,u(x) = -e^{-\rho}\rho^x.$$

We have the particular solution

$$u(x) = \frac{e^{-\rho}\rho^x}{x} + \frac{e^{-\rho}\rho^{x+1}}{x(x+1)} + \frac{e^{-\rho}\rho^{x+2}}{x(x+1)(x+2)} + \dots$$

and the general solution

$$u(x) = \varpi\,\Gamma(x) + e^{-\rho}\rho^x \sum_{s=0}^{\infty} \frac{\rho^s}{x(x+1)\dots(x+s)}.$$

The above particular solution is an Incomplete Gamma Function (see the next section).

11·33. The Incomplete Gamma Functions. We saw in the last section that the equation

$$u(x+1) - x\,u(x) = -e^{-\rho}\rho^x$$

has the particular solution

(1) $$P(x;\ \rho) = e^{-\rho}\rho^x \sum_{s=0}^{\infty} \frac{\rho^s}{x(x+1)\dots(x+s)}.$$

The factorial series converges in the whole plane, that is, $\lambda = -\infty$, with the exception of the points $0, -1, -2, \dots$ which are simple poles, so that $P(x;\ \rho)$ is a meromorphic function of x in the whole plane.

The generating function of the series (10·2) is

$$\phi(t) = \sum_{s=0}^{\infty} \frac{\rho^s(1-t)^s}{s!} = e^{\rho(1-t)}.$$

Thus

$$P(x;\ \rho) = e^{-\rho}\rho^x \int_0^1 t^{x-1} e^{\rho(1-t)}\,dt$$

(2) $$= \int_0^1 (\rho t)^{x-1} e^{-\rho t}\,\rho\,dt = \int_0^{\rho} t^{x-1} e^{-t}\,dt,$$

the integral representation being valid only if $R(x) > 0$.

If we expand e^{-t} and integrate term by term, we obtain Mittag-Leffler's partial fraction development,

$$P(x;\,\rho) = \rho^x \sum_{s=0}^{\infty} \frac{(-1)^s \rho^s}{s!\,(x+s)},$$

which is valid in the whole plane and puts in evidence the poles at $0, -1, -2, \ldots$.

The residue at the pole $x = -n$ is

$$\frac{(-1)^n}{n!},$$

which is the same as the residue of $\Gamma(x)$ at $x = -n$ (see 9·55). Hence the function

$$Q(x;\,\rho) = \Gamma(x) - P(x;\,\rho)$$

has no singularities at a finite distance from the origin and is therefore an integral function.

Thus

$$Q(x;\,\rho) = \int_0^\infty t^{x-1} e^{-t}\,dt - \int_0^\rho t^{x-1} e^{-t}\,dt$$

$$(3) \qquad = \int_\rho^\infty t^{x-1} e^{-t}\,dt,$$

which is valid for all values of x.

Since

$$\Gamma(x+1) - x\,\Gamma(x) = 0,$$

it follows that $Q(x;\,\rho)$ satisfies the difference equation

$$u(x+1) - x\,u(x) = e^{-\rho}\,\rho^x.$$

On account of the properties (2) and (3) $P(x;\,\rho)$, $Q(x;\,\rho)$ are known as Incomplete Gamma Functions. The special functions which arise when $\rho = 1$ are called Prym's Functions.*

11·34. Application of Prym's Functions. We can use Prym's functions to solve the difference equation

$$(1) \qquad u(x+1) - x\,u(x) = R(x),$$

where $R(x)$ is a polynomial.

---

* F. E. Prym, *J. f. reine u. angew. Math.* 82 (1877).

Expressing $R(x)$ in factorials by the method of 2·12 or by Newton's Interpolation formula, we have

(2) $$R(x) = \sum_{s=0}^{n} s!\, a_s \binom{x}{s},$$

where n is the degree of $R(x)$.

Now, let

$$f(x) = \sum_{s=0}^{n-1} s!\, b_s \binom{x-1}{s}.$$

Then

$$f(x+1) - x f(x) = \sum_{s=0}^{n} s!\, (b_s - b_{s-1}) \binom{x}{s},$$

where $$b_n = b_{-1} = 0.$$

If we choose b_s so that

$$b_s - b_{s-1} = a_s, \quad s = 1, 2, 3, \dots\ n$$

we have, since $b_n = 0$,

$$b_s = -\sum_{t=s+1}^{n} a_t, \quad s = 0, 1, 2, \dots, n-1.$$

These equations determine $f(x)$ completely, and if we now write

$$u(x) = v(x) + f(x),$$

we have, from (1),

(3) $$v(x+1) - x\, v(x) = \sum_{s=0}^{n} a_s = A,$$

say.

Now, from 11·33, Prym's function $P(x\,;\,1)$ satisfies the equation

$$P(x+1\,;\,1) - x\, P(x\,;\,1) = -e^{-1}$$

and therefore (3) has the particular solution

$$v(x) = -e\, A\, P(x\,;\,1)$$

and consequently the general solution

$$v(x) = \varpi\, \Gamma(x) - e\, A\, P(x\,;\,1),$$

so that the general solution of (1) is

$$u(x) = f(x) + \varpi\, \Gamma(x) - e\, A\, P(x\,;\,1).$$

11·4. The Exact Difference Equation of the First Order. Very little is known about the theory of difference equations which are not linear. There is a fairly complete theory of the linear equation, including the exact linear equation, which will be considered in a later chapter. Here we propose to develop the outline of a theory of the exact difference equation of the first order, but not necessarily of the first degree.*

If we denote, as usual, the independent variable by x and the dependent variable by $u(x)$ or u, we can write

$$h = \Delta u(x) = \Delta u = u(x+1) - u(x),$$

and the general difference equation of the first order is of the form

$$\phi(x, u, h) = 0, \quad \text{or} \quad \phi(x, u, \Delta u) = 0.$$

We shall use the symbols h and Δu according to convenience to denote the same operation. We proceed to consider such equations of the first order as can be put into the form

$$M(x, u) + N(x, u, h)\, h = 0, \tag{1}$$

or its equivalent

$$M(x, u) + N(x, u, \Delta u)\, \Delta u = 0,$$

where $M(x, u)$ is independent of Δu. This is an equation of the first order, but not necessarily of the first degree.

It should be observed that Δu is not, in general, constant, so that the dependent and independent variables are not interchangeable. In this respect the problem is very different from that of the corresponding differential equation.

Definition. *The equation*

$$M(x, u) + N(x, u, \Delta u)\, \Delta u = 0$$

is said to be exact, when a function $f(x, u)$ exists which is independent of Δu and is such that

$$M(x, u) + N(x, u, \Delta u)\, \Delta u = \Delta f(x, u), \tag{2}$$

where

$$\Delta f(x, u) = f(x+1, u(x+1)) - f(x, u(x)).$$

---

* L. M. Milne-Thomson, "The exact difference equation of the first order," *Proc. Camb. Phil. Soc.*, 29 (1933).

Since $u(x+1) = u+h$, we have, from 2·105 (2),

$$\Delta f(x, u) = \Delta_x f(x, u) + h \underset{h}{\Delta_u} f(x+1, u),$$

where we regard h as unaffected by either of the partial operators

$$\Delta_x, \underset{h}{\Delta_u}.$$

The condition that (2) should be exact is clearly satisfied if, and only if,

$$M(x, u) = \Delta_x f(x, u),$$

$$N(x, u, h) = \underset{h}{\Delta_u} f(x+1, u).$$

Using 2·105 (3), we see that a necessary condition is, therefore,

(3) $$\Delta_x N(x, u, h) = \underset{h}{\Delta_u} M(x+1, u).$$

We shall now shew that this condition is sufficient to ensure that

(4) $$M(x, u) + N(x, u, \Delta u) \Delta u = \Delta f(x, u, h),$$

but that an additional condition is required in order that $f(x, u, h)$ shall be independent of h.

We write

$$V(x, u) = \mathop{S}_{c}^{x} M(t, u) \Delta t,$$

so that, from the definition of the sum,

$$\Delta_x V(x, u) = M(x, u),$$

and hence

$$\underset{h}{\Delta_u} \Delta_x V(x+1, u) = \underset{h}{\Delta_u} M(x+1, u) = \Delta_x N(x, u, h),$$

from (3). Using 2·105 (3), we can write this in the form

$$\Delta_x \{N(x, u, h) - \underset{h}{\Delta_u} V(x+1, u)\} = 0,$$

and thus

$$N(x, u, h) = \underset{h}{\Delta_u} V(x+1, u) + \varpi + \underset{h}{\Delta_u} F(u, h),$$

where the last term represents a function independent of x, and ϖ is an arbitrary periodic in x. We have, therefore,

$$M(x, u)+N(x, u, h) \Delta u$$
$$= \Delta_x V(x, u)+h \underset{h}{\Delta_u} V(x+1, u)+h \underset{h}{\Delta_u} F(u, h)+\varpi h$$
$$= \varDelta [V(x, u)+F(u, h)+\varpi u],$$

using 2·105 (2). This proves that (3) is sufficient to ensure (4). Also, from (4), we have

(5) $\Delta_x f(x, u, h) = M(x, u), \quad \underset{h}{\Delta_u} f(x+1, u, h) = N(x, u, h),$

and therefore, summing with respect to x, regarding u as constant, we have

$$f(x, u, h) = \mathop{S}_{c}^{x} M(t, u) \Delta t+\varpi_1+\phi(u, h),$$

where $\phi(u, h)$ is independent of x, and ϖ_1 is an arbitrary periodic. If we write $x+1$ for x and then operate with $\underset{h}{\Delta_u}$, we have from (5)

$$\underset{h}{\Delta_u} \phi(u, h) = N(x, u, h) - \underset{h}{\Delta_u} \mathop{S}_{c}^{x+1} M(t, u) \Delta t.$$

The left hand is independent of x, and therefore the right hand is independent of x, and $\phi(u, h)$ can be obtained by summation with respect to u. This introduces another arbitrary periodic function of u of period h, that is to say, an arbitrary periodic in x of period unity. Thus finally we have for $f(x, u, h)$ the expression

$$\varpi+ \mathop{S}_{c}^{x} M(t, u) \Delta t+ \mathop{S}_{c_1}^{u} \left[N(x, v, h) - \underset{h}{\Delta_v} \mathop{S}_{c}^{x+1} M(t,v)\Delta t\right] \underset{h}{\Delta} v,$$

where, in the summations with x in the upper limit, u, v are to be regarded as constant.

That the above expression for $f(x, u, h)$ gives

$$\Delta_x f(x, u, h) = M(x, u)$$

is obvious. To verify the second formula of (5), we have

$$\underset{h}{\Delta_u} f(x+1, u, h)$$

$$= \underset{h}{\Delta_u} \mathop{S}_{c}^{x+1} M(t, u) \Delta t + N(x+1, u, h) - \underset{h}{\Delta_u} \mathop{S}_{c}^{x+2} M(t, u) \Delta t$$

$$= N(x+1, u, h) - \underset{h}{\Delta_u} \Delta_x \mathop{S}_{c}^{x+1} M(t, u) \Delta t$$

$$= N(x+1, u, h) - \underset{h}{\Delta_u} M(x+1, u)$$

$$= N(x+1, u, h) - \Delta_x N(x, u, h) \quad \text{from (3),}$$

$$= N(x, u, h).$$

We have thus proved the following :

Theorem. *The necessary and sufficient conditions that the difference equation*

$$M(x, u) + N(x, u, \Delta u) \Delta u = 0$$

should be exact are

(A) $$\underset{h}{\Delta_u} M(x+1, u) = \Delta_x N(x, u, h), \quad h = \Delta u;$$

(B) *that*

$$\mathop{S}^{u} \left\{ N(x, v, h) - \underset{h}{\Delta_v} \mathop{S}^{x+1} M(t, v) \Delta t \right\} \underset{h}{\Delta} v$$

should be independent of h.

If these conditions be satisfied, the primitive of the given equation is

$$\mathop{S}_{c}^{x} M(t, u) \Delta t + \mathop{S}_{c_1}^{u} \left\{ N(x, v, h) - \underset{h}{\Delta_v} \mathop{S}_{c}^{x+1} M(t, v) \Delta t \right\} \underset{h}{\Delta} v = \varpi,$$

where ϖ is an arbitrary periodic, and where in those summations with x in the upper limit u and v are to be treated as constants.

The lower limits of the summations are arbitrary and may be chosen to have any convenient values.

With regard to condition (B), I have not been able to obtain any simpler formulation in the general case, but, when

$$F(u, h) = N(x, u, h) - \underset{h}{\Delta_u} \mathop{S}_{c}^{x+1} M(t, u) \Delta t$$

is a polynomial, we can use Bernoulli's polynomials, of order -1, to simplify the process. As in 6·1 (3), we write

$$\frac{(e^{ht}-1)\,e^{ut}}{ht} = \sum_{\nu=0}^{\infty} \frac{t^\nu}{\nu!} B_\nu^{(-1)}(u \mid h),$$

so that

$$\underset{h}{\Delta}_u\, u^\nu = \nu\, B_{\nu-1}^{(-1)}(u \mid h).$$

If then we can put $F(u, h)$ in the form

$$F(u, h) = \sum_{\nu=0}^{m} a_\nu\, B_\nu^{(-1)}(u \mid h),$$

where the a_ν are independent of u and h, condition (B) will be satisfied, since we then have

$$\mathop{\mathrm{S}}_{c}^{u} F(v, h) \underset{h}{\Delta} v = \sum_{\nu=0}^{m} \frac{a_\nu\, u^{\nu+1}}{\nu+1} + k,$$

where k is a constant.

Example. Find the condition that the equation

$$a(\Delta u)^2 + bu\,\Delta u + c\,\Delta u + \phi(x) = 0$$

may be exact, where a, b, c are constants.

Here

$$M(x+1) = \phi(x+1), \quad N(x, u, h) = ah + bu + c,$$

so that condition (A) is satisfied.

Condition (B) will be satisfied if we can find p and q, independent of u and h, such that

$$ah + bu + c \equiv p + q\, B_1^{(-1)}(u \mid h) \equiv p + q(u + \tfrac{1}{2}h).$$

Thus we must have $a = \frac{1}{2}q$, $b = q$, $c = p$, so that the equation is exact if, and only if, $b = 2a$, in which case the primitive is

$$\mathop{\mathrm{S}}^{x} \phi(t)\,\Delta t + \mathop{\mathrm{S}}^{u} \left\{c + 2a\, B_1^{(-1)}(v \mid h)\right\} \underset{h}{\Delta} v = \varpi,$$

that is,

$$\mathop{\mathrm{S}}^{x} \phi(t)\,\Delta t + cu + au^2 = \varpi.$$

11·41. Multipliers. When the given difference equation is not exact, we are naturally led to consider the possible existence of a multiplier which is the analogue of Euler's integrating factor for a differential equation.

Definition. *Given the difference equation*

$$M(x, u)+N(x, u, \Delta u)\Delta u = 0,$$

$\mu(x, u)$ *is said to be a multiplier when the equation*

$$\mu(x, u) M(x, u)+\mu(x, u) N(x, u, \Delta u)\Delta u = 0$$

is an exact equation.

For $\mu(x, u)$ to be a multiplier, a necessary condition is that $\mu(x, u)$ should satisfy the partial difference equation

$$\Delta_x[\mu(x, u) N(x, u, h)] = \underset{h}{\Delta_u}[\mu(x+1, u) M(x+1, u)].$$

Any particular solution of this equation is a potential multiplier, but in every case we must test whether condition (B) is satisfied. This equation can be written

$$\Delta_x[\mu N - \underset{h}{\Delta_u}(\mu M)] = \underset{h}{\Delta_u}[\mu M].$$

11·42. Multipliers Independent of x. If a multiplier independent of x exist, we must have

$$\mu \Delta_x N - \underset{h}{\Delta_u}(\mu \Delta_x M) = \underset{h}{\Delta_u}(\mu M),$$

which leads to

$$\frac{\mu(u+h)}{\mu(u)} = Q(u) = \frac{h\Delta_x N(x, u, h)+M(x+1, u)}{M(x+1, u+h)}.$$

A necessary condition for the existence of a multiplier independent of x is therefore that $Q(u)$ should be independent of x. If this be the case, we have

$$\underset{h}{\Delta}\log \mu(u) = \frac{1}{h}\log Q(u),$$

whence

$$\mu(u) = \exp\left[\overset{u}{S}\frac{1}{h}\log Q(v)\underset{h}{\Delta} v\right].$$

This is a multiplier, provided that condition (B) be satisfied.

Example. $(x+1)\Delta u\left(2+\frac{1}{u}\Delta u\right)+u=0.$

Here

$$Q(u)=\left(2h+\frac{h^2}{u}+u\right)\div(u+h)=\frac{u+h}{u}.$$

Thus

$$\frac{\mu(u+h)}{\mu(u)}=\frac{u+h}{u},$$

and we can take $\mu(u)=u$, and the equation becomes $\Delta(xu^2)=0$, whence $x\,u^2=\varpi$.

11·43. Multipliers Independent of u. For a multiplier independent of u we have, from 11·41,

$$\Delta_x[\mu(x)\,N(x,u,h)]=\mu(x+1)\,\underset{h}{\Delta_u}\,M(x+1,u),$$

whence we obtain

$$\frac{\mu(x+1)}{\mu(x)}=T(x)=\frac{N(x,u,h)}{N(x+1,u,h)-\underset{h}{\Delta_u}\,M(x+1,u)},$$

and $T(x)$ must be independent of u. If this be the case we easily obtain

$$\mu(x)=\exp\left[\overset{x}{\mathop{S}}\log T(t)\,\Delta t\right],$$

which is a multiplier, provided that condition (B) be satisfied.

Example. $(x+1)\,u^2(x+1)-(x-1)\,u^2(x)=0.$

Since $u(x+1)=u(x)+\Delta u(x)$, we have

$$(x+1)(2u+\Delta u)\,\Delta u+2u^2=0,$$

so that $T(x)=(x+1)/x$, and hence

$$\frac{\mu(x+1)}{\mu(x)}=\frac{x+1}{x}.$$

Taking $\mu(x)=x$, we have

$$x(x-1)\,u^2(x)=\varpi.$$

Alternatively

$$\mu(x)=\exp\left[\overset{x}{\mathop{S}}\{\log(t+1)-\log t\}\,\Delta t\right]$$
$$=\exp[\log x]=x.$$

11·5. The Independent Variable Absent. Haldane's Method. The general equation of this type is

$$\psi(u, \Delta u) = 0,$$

where
$$\Delta u = u(x+1) - u(x).$$

When this equation can be solved for Δu we have

(1)
$$\Delta u = u(x+1) - u(x) = \phi[u(x)].$$

An elegant method of obtaining a solution of equations of this type has been devised by Haldane.* The method is as follows:

Taking the equation

(2)
$$u(x+1) - u(x) = k\,\phi[u(x)],$$

let us try to satisfy it by assuming that

(3)
$$x = \frac{1}{k}\int_{u(0)}^{u(x)} w(v, k)\,dv,$$

where

(4)
$$w(v, k) = \sum_{s=1}^{\infty} \frac{k^{s-1}}{s!} f_s(v).$$

We have then, from (3) and (2),

$$k = \int_{u(x)}^{u(x+1)} w(v, k)\,dv = \int_{u}^{u+k\phi} \sum_{s=1}^{\infty} \frac{k^{s-1}}{s!} f_s(v)\,dv,$$

where
$$u = u(x), \quad \phi = \phi(u).$$

In order to obtain a recurrence relation for the functions $f_s(v)$ we assume that the series can be integrated term by term, which will certainly be the case whenever the series is uniformly convergent.

Put

(5)
$$F_s(u) = \int^{u} f_s(v)\,dv.$$

Then

$$\int_{u}^{u+k\phi} f_s(v)\,dv = F_s(u+k\phi) - F_s(u) = \sum_{\nu=1}^{\infty} \frac{k^{\nu}\phi^{\nu}}{\nu!} f_s^{(\nu-1)}(u)$$

* J. B. S. Haldane, *Proc. Cambridge Phil. Soc.* (28), 1932, pp. 234-243.

by Taylor's Theorem. Thus we have

$$k = \sum_{s=1}^{\infty} \frac{k^{s-1}}{s!} \sum_{\nu=1}^{\infty} \frac{k^\nu \phi^\nu}{\nu!} f_s^{(\nu-1)}(u).$$

This is an identity. Equating coefficients, we have

$$f_1(u) = \frac{1}{\phi(u)},$$

$$\sum_{\nu=1}^{s-1} \binom{s}{\nu} [\phi(u)]^{s-\nu-1} f_\nu^{(s-\nu-1)}(u) = 0. \tag{6}$$

This determines successively the functions $f_s(u)$, and the solution is complete in so far as the above operations are valid. In terms of the function $F_s(u)$ this recurrence relation can be written in the symbolic form

$$(\phi(u)\, D + F(u)\,)^s \doteq [\phi(u)\,]^s\, D^s\, F_0(u) + F_s(u), \quad s > 2,$$

where the index of $F(u)$ is to be written as a suffix after expansion and D denotes the differentiation operator.

From the recurrence relation, we obtain

$$f_1(u) = \frac{1}{\phi}, \quad f_2(u) = \frac{\phi'}{\phi}, \quad f_3(u) = -\frac{1}{2}\frac{(\phi')^2}{\phi} - \frac{1}{2}\phi'',$$

$$f_4(u) = \frac{(\phi')^3}{\phi} + 2\phi'\,\phi'',$$

$$f_5(u) = \frac{1}{6}\left[-19\frac{(\phi')^4}{\phi} - 59(\phi')^2\phi'' - \phi(\phi'')^2 + 2\phi\phi'\phi''' + \phi^2\phi^{(\mathrm{iv})}\right].$$

Thus we have

$$x = \frac{1}{k}\int_{u(0)}^{u(x)} \frac{dv}{\phi(v)} + \frac{1}{2}[\log\phi(u(x)) - \log\phi(u(0))]$$

$$- \frac{k}{12}\int_{u(0)}^{u(x)} \frac{[\phi'(v)]^2 + \phi(v)\,\phi''(v)}{\phi(v)}\, dv + \dots .$$

The arbitrary element in this solution is $u(0)$.

We give some examples taken from Haldane's paper:

Example 1. $\Delta u = u^{1+c}$.

$$w(u, k) = u^{-1-c} + \tfrac{1}{2}k(c+1)\,u^{-1} - \tfrac{1}{12}k^2\, c(c+1)(2c+1)\,u^{c-1}$$

$$+ \tfrac{1}{24}k^3\,(c+1)^2(3c+1)\,u^{2c-1} + \dots ,$$

and therefore

$$x = A - \frac{1}{ck\,u^c} + \frac{1}{2}(c+1)\log u - \frac{1}{12}(c+1)(2c+1)\,ku^c$$

$$+ \frac{1}{48c}(c+1)^2(3c+1)(ku^c)^2 + \dots,$$

where A is a function of $u(0)$.

Example 2. $\Delta u = ke^{au}.$

$$w(u, k) = e^{-au} + \tfrac{1}{2}ka - \tfrac{1}{12}k^2a^2e^{au} + \tfrac{1}{8}k^3a^3e^{2au} + \dots,$$

and hence

$$x = A - \frac{e^{-au}}{ak} + \frac{1}{2}au - \frac{1}{12}ka\,e^{au} + \frac{1}{8}k^2a^2e^{2au} + \dots.$$

11·51. Boole's Iterative Method. When the independent variable is absent, Boole writes the equation in the form

$$u_{x+1} = \psi(u_x),$$

whence

$$u_{x+2} = \psi^2(u_x),$$

where $\psi^2(u_x)$ denotes $\psi[\psi(u_x)]$.

Proceeding in this way

$$u_{x+n} = \psi^n(u_x).$$

If we assume an initial value u_a to be known, we have therefore

$$u_{a+n} = \psi^n(u_a).$$

It is evident, apart from the difficulty of application, that this method is only suitable for a variable which differs from the initial value a by a positive integer.

Example 1. $u_{x+1} = 2u_x^{\,2}.$

We have $u_{x+2} = 2(2u_x^{\,2})^2 = 2^3\,u_x^{\,4},$

and, continuing, we obtain

$$u_{x+n} = \tfrac{1}{2}(2u_x)^{2^n}.$$

Example 2.

$$u_{x+1} = \frac{1}{1-u_x}.$$

Assuming $u_a = b$, we have

$$u_{a+1} = \frac{1}{1-b}, \quad u_{a+2} = \frac{b-1}{b}, \quad u_{a+3} = b,$$

so that u_{a+n} has these values in order according as $n \equiv 1, 2, 3 \pmod 3$.

11·6. Solution by Differencing. Consider a non-linear difference equation of the first order

$$(1) \qquad f(x, u, \Delta u) = 0.$$

Writing $\Delta u = v$, where v is a function of x, and operating with Δ, we obtain a relation of the form

$$\phi(u, x, v, \Delta v) = 0.$$

If this be independent of u, and if we can solve this difference equation for v, we obtain

$$(2) \qquad \psi(x, v, \varpi) = 0,$$

where ϖ is an arbitrary periodic, the elimination of v between (1) and (2) will yield a primitive of (1).

This method may, in particular, succeed when (1) can be solved for u in terms of x, v.

Consider, for example, the form, analogous to Clairaut's differential equation,

$$u_x = x \Delta u_x + f(\Delta u_x).$$

Writing $\Delta u_x = v$, we have

$$u_x = xv + f(v).$$

Operating with Δ, this gives

$$0 = (x+1)\Delta v + f(v+\Delta v) - f(v),$$

whence either $\Delta v = 0$ or

$$(3) \qquad x+1+\frac{f(v+\Delta v)-f(v)}{\Delta v} = 0.$$

$\Delta v = 0$ gives $v = \varpi$, so that we have the primitive

$$u_x = x\varpi + f(\varpi).$$

The supposition (3) may lead to a second primitive.

Example. $$u_x = x\Delta u_x + (\Delta u_x)^2.$$

Here

$$u_x = xv + v^2,$$

whence, operating with Δ,

$$(x+1)\Delta v + 2v\Delta v + (\Delta v)^2 = 0,$$

whence either $\Delta v = 0$ so that

$$u_x = x\varpi + \varpi^2,$$

or

$$\Delta v + 2v + x + 1 = 0,$$

which gives

$$v_{x+1} + v_x = -x - 1,$$

the solution of which is easily seen to be

$$v = \varpi(-1)^x - \frac{x}{2} - \frac{1}{4}.$$

Eliminating v between this and the original equation, we have

$$u_x = [\varpi(-1)^x - \tfrac{1}{4}]^2 - \tfrac{1}{4}x^2.$$

This form of the solution may also be derived from the primitive

$$u_x = cx + c^2,$$

by supposing that c is a function of x and then taking the difference. We thus obtain

$$\Delta u = c + (x+1)\Delta c + 2c\Delta c + (\Delta c)^2.$$

On the other hand, the supposition that c is a periodic gives $\Delta u = c$. Equating these values of Δu, we have

$$\Delta c(x + 1 + 2c + \Delta c) = 0.$$

The equation $\Delta c = 0$ leads back to the original primitive, the supposition that

$$x + 1 + 2c + \Delta c = 0,$$

gives the second form obtained above. Boole gives the name "indirect solution" to a primitive obtained in this way.

11·7. Equations Homogeneous in u. The general type of such equations is

$$f\left(\frac{u_{x+1}}{u_x}, x\right) = 0,$$

which on solution for u_{x+1} / u_x leads to a linear equation.

Consider, for example,

$$u_{x+1}^2 - 3u_{x+1}u_x + 2u_x^2 = 0.$$

We have

$$u_{x+1} = 2u_x \quad \text{or} \quad u_{x+1} = u_x,$$

whence

$$u_x = \varpi\, 2^x \quad \text{or} \quad u_x = \varpi.$$

11·8. Riccati's Form. The difference equation corresponding to Riccati's differential equation is

(1) $$u(x)\, u(x+1) + p(x)\, u(x+1) + q(x)\, u(x) + r(x) = 0.$$

The substitution

$$u(x) = \frac{v(x+1)}{v(x)} - p(x)$$

gives the linear equation of the *second order*,

$$v(x+2) + [q(x) - p(x+1)]\, v(x+1) + [r(x) - p(x)\, q(x)]\, v(x) = 0,$$

the discussion of which does not belong to this chapter. We can, however, obtain the solution of (1) when three particular solutions are known. For let $u_1(x)$ be a particular solution of (1), and write

$$u(x) = u_1(x) + \frac{1}{w(x)}.$$

We then obtain, since $u_1(x)$ satisfies (1),

$$w(x+1)\,[q(x) + u_1(x+1)] + w(x)\,[p(x) + u_1(x)] + 1 = 0.$$

This is a linear equation of the first order and therefore the solution is of the form

$$w(x) = \varpi f(x) + \phi(x),$$

where ϖ is an arbitrary periodic.

Hence the complete solution of (1) is of the form

(2) $$u(x) = \frac{\varpi f_1(x) + \phi_1(x)}{\varpi f(x) + \phi(x)}.$$

Now let $u_1(x)$, $u_2(x)$, $u_3(x)$, $u_4(x)$ be four particular solutions of (1) and ϖ_1, ϖ_2, ϖ_3, ϖ_4 the corresponding periodics. Then it is easy to verify, from (2), that

$$\frac{(u_4-u_1)(u_3-u_2)}{(u_4-u_2)(u_3-u_1)} = \frac{(\varpi_4-\varpi_1)(\varpi_3-\varpi_2)}{(\varpi_4-\varpi_2)(\varpi_3-\varpi_1)} = \varpi,$$

say, where ϖ is a periodic. Thus the anharmonic ratio of four particular solutions is a periodic. If we suppose u_4 to remain arbitrary, equal to u say, we have

$$\frac{(u-u_1)(u_3-u_2)}{(u-u_2)(u_3-u_1)} = \varpi,$$

which determines u in terms of the three known solutions and an arbitrary periodic. The equation is thus solved.

11·9. Miscellaneous Forms. As examples of special artifices which may occasionally be employed we cite the following:

Example 1. $\quad u_{x+1}\,u_x - a_x(u_{x+1}-u_x)+1 = 0.$

Here we have

$$\frac{u_{x+1}-u_x}{1+u_{x+1}\,u_x} = \frac{1}{a_x}.$$

This suggests substituting $u_x = \tan v_x$, which leads to

$$\tan \Delta\, v_x = \frac{1}{a_x}.$$

Thus

$$\Delta\, v_x = \tan^{-1}\frac{1}{a^x},$$

and hence

$$u_x = \tan\left[\varpi + \mathop{\mathrm{S}}_{c}^{x} \tan^{-1}\frac{1}{a_x}\,\Delta\, x\right].$$

Example 2. $\quad u_{x+1}\,u_x + (1-u_{x+1}^2)^{\frac{1}{2}}(1-u_x^2)^{\frac{1}{2}} = a_x.$

Here we put $u_x = \cos v_x$, and we have

$$\cos \Delta\, v_x = a_x$$

and therefore

$$u_x = \cos\left[\varpi + \mathop{\mathrm{S}}_{c}^{x} \cos^{-1} a_x\,\Delta\, x\right].$$

EXAMPLES XI

1. Find the difference equations to which the following complete primitives belong :

(i) $u = cx^2+c^2$; (ii) $u = \{c(-1)^x - \frac{1}{2}x\}^2 - \frac{1}{4}x^4$;

(iii) $u = cx+c'a^x$; (iv) $u = ca^x+c^2$;

(v) $u = c^2+c\left(\frac{1-a}{1+a}\right)(-a)^x - \frac{a^{2x+1}}{(1+a)^2}$,

where in each case c, c' denote arbitrary periodics.

Solve the following equations :

2. $u_{x+1} - pa^{2x} u_x = qa^{x^2}$.

3. $u_{x+1} - au_x = \cos nx$.

4. $u_{x+1} u_x + (x+2) u_{x+1} + xu_x = -2-2x-x^2$.

5. $u_{x+1} - u_x \cos ax = \cos a \cos 2a \ldots \cos(x-2)a$,

x being a positive integer variable.

6. $u_x u_{x+1} + au_x + b = 0$.

7. $u_x u_{x+1} - au_x + b = 0$.

8. $u_{x+1} - e^{2x-1} u_x = e^{x^2}$.

9. $u_{x+1} \sin x\theta - u_x \sin(x+1)\theta = \cos(x-1)\theta - \cos(3x+1)\theta$.

10. $u_{x+1} - a\,u_x = (2x+1)\,a^x$.

11. $u_{x+1} - 2\,u_x^{\,2} + 1 = 0$.

12. $(x+1)^2(u_{x+1} - au_x) = a^x(x^2+2x)$.

13. $(u_{x+1})^2 = 4(u_x)^2\{(u_x)^2+1)\}$.

14. $u_{x+1} = m(u_x)^n$.

15. $u_x \Delta u_x = x(\Delta u_x)^2 + 1$.

16. $(u_{x+1})^3 - 3a^2x^2 u_{x+1}(u_x)^2 + 2a^3x^3(u_x)^3 = 0$.

17. If P_K be the number of permutations of n letters taken K together, repetition be allowed, but no three consecutive letters being the same, shew that

$$\Delta P_K = (n^2-n)\frac{\alpha^K-\beta^K}{\alpha-\beta},$$

where α, β are the roots of the equation

$$x^2 = (n-1)(x+1).$$

[Smith's Prize.]

18. Solve the equation

$$\overset{2}{\Delta} u_x = (u_{x+1})^2 - (u_x)^2,$$

by writing $\qquad u_x + \tfrac{1}{2} = v_x.$

19. $$\Delta u_x + 2u_x = -x-1.$$

20. $$u_{x+1} - au_x = \frac{a^x}{(x+1)^2}.$$

21. Apply Haldane's method to the equations:

$$\text{(i)} \quad \Delta u_x = k u_x^2,$$

$$\text{(ii)} \quad u_{n+1} = \frac{u_n(u_n+1)}{u_n+1-k},$$

in the latter case substituting

$$v_n = 1 + \frac{1}{u_n}.$$

22. The equation

$$u = \frac{\Delta u}{2x+1}\left(x^2 + \frac{\Delta u}{2x+1}\right)$$

has the complete primitive $u = \varpi x^2 + \varpi^2$. Shew that another complete primitive is

$$u = \{\varpi(-1)^x - \tfrac{1}{2}x\}^2 - \tfrac{1}{4}x^2.$$

23. The equation

$$\left(\frac{\Delta u}{a-1}\right)^2 + a^{2x}\left(\frac{\Delta u}{a-1}\right) - a^{2x} u = 0$$

has the complete primitive $u = \varpi a^x + \varpi^2$. Deduce another complete primitive.

24. If $u_n u_{n+1} = m/(n+1)$, shew that

$$u_n = \frac{2.4 \dots (n-1)}{1.3.5 \dots n} mC \quad \text{or} \quad \frac{1.3 \dots (n-1)}{2.4 \dots n\, C},$$

according as n is odd or even.

25. From the difference equation

$$u_n = n \Delta u_n + \frac{m}{\Delta u_n},$$

obtain the indirect solutions

$$u_n = \frac{2.4 \dots (n-1)}{1.3 \dots (n-2)} mC + \frac{1.3 \dots n}{2.4 \dots (n-1)\, C}, \text{ when } n \text{ is odd,}$$

$$u_n = \frac{1.3 \dots (n-1)}{2.4 \dots (n-2)\, C} + \frac{2.4 \dots n}{1.3 \dots (n-1)} mC, \text{ when } n \text{ is even.}$$

26. The equation

$$u = x \Delta u + (\Delta u)^2$$

has the indirect solution

$$u = \{\varpi(-1)^x - \tfrac{1}{4}\}^2 - \tfrac{1}{4}x^2;$$

shew that, assuming this as complete primitive, the equation $u = \varpi x + \varpi^2$ results as an indirect solution.

27. Shew that the equation

$$\tfrac{1}{4}u = \frac{4^{3x}(\Delta u)^3}{9} - \frac{\Delta u}{3}$$

has the complete primitive

$$u = \varpi\left(\tfrac{1}{2}\right)^{-2x} - \tfrac{3}{16}\varpi^3.$$ [Poisson.]

28. Shew that the equation

$$u_{x+1} = (1 + u_x^{\frac{1}{3}})^3$$

admits the complete primitives

$$(\varpi + x)^3, \quad \left(\varpi \alpha^x - \frac{\alpha}{\alpha - 1}\right)^3,$$

where

$$\alpha^2 + \alpha + 1 = 0.$$

29. Solve the equation

$$u_{x+2} - (a^{x+1} + a^{-x})\, u_{x+1} + u_x = 0,$$

by writing it in the form $(\mathsf{E} - a^{-x})(\mathsf{E} - a^x)\, u_x = 0$.

CHAPTER XII

GENERAL PROPERTIES OF THE LINEAR DIFFERENCE EQUATION

In this chapter we discuss properties which are common to all linear difference equations and obtain some important general theorems.

Many of the general properties are sufficiently illustrated by considering an equation of the second or third order. Whenever this method is suitable we shall adopt it.

12·0. The Homogeneous Linear Difference Equation.

The equation

$$(1)\quad p_n(x)\,u(x+n)+p_{n-1}(x)\,u(x+n-1)+\dots + p_1(x)\,u(x+1)+p_0(x)\,u(x)=0,$$

where $p_n(x)$; $p_{n-1}(x), \dots, p_0(x)$ are given analytic functions of x and where $u(x)$ is the unknown function, is called a homogeneous linear equation of order n. When there is no fear of ambiguity we shall denote the coefficients by $p_n, p_{n-1}, \dots, p_0$, thus

$$p_s(x)=p_s, \quad s=0, 1, 2, \dots, n.$$

We have taken x to proceed by unit increment. The case of increment ω is readily reduced to this by the change of variable $x=y\omega$.

The homogeneous equation (1) has the trivial solution $u(x)=0$. We shall tacitly assume that this trivial solution is excluded from all enunciations.

With regard to the coefficients $p_s(x)$, we can assume that their only singularities are essential singularities, for any poles can readily be removed by multiplying the equation by a suitable integral function which has zeros of the necessary order at these poles.

We shall call the singular points of the difference equation the three following sets of points:

(i) The zeros of $p_0(x)$, denoted by $\alpha_1, \alpha_2, \dots$.

(ii) The essential singularities of the coefficients, $\beta_1, \beta_2, \dots$.

(iii) The zeros of $p_n(x-n)$, $\gamma_1, \gamma_2, \dots$.

The points

$$\alpha_i - \nu, \quad \beta_i - \nu, \quad \beta_i + n + \nu, \quad \gamma_i + \nu,$$
$$i = 1, 2, 3, \dots, \quad \nu = 0, 1, 2, \dots$$

will be said to be *congruent* to the singular points of the equation. More generally, if a be any point, the points $a+\nu$, where ν is zero or an integer, positive or negative, will be said to be congruent to the point a.

If x be any point, and $x-a$ be neither zero nor a positive or negative integer, x is said to be *incongruent* to a.

12·01. The Existence of Solutions. Consider the second order equation

$$p_2(x)\, u(x+2) + p_1(x)\, u(x+1) + p_0(x)\, u(x) = 0.$$

Let us suppose that the value of $u(x)$ is assigned at every point of the strip $0 \leqslant R(x) < 2$.

We have

$$u(x) = -\frac{p_2(x)\, u(x+2)}{p_0(x)} - \frac{p_1(x)\, u(x+1)}{p_0(x)}.$$

Hence, if x be incongruent to the points α_i, β_i, we can find the value of $u(x)$ in the strip $-1 \leqslant R(x) < 0$, and hence in the strip $-2 \leqslant R(x) < -1$, and so on. Thus we can continue $u(x)$ indefinitely to the left.

Similarly, we have

$$u(x+2) = -\frac{p_1(x)\, u(x+1)}{p_2(x)} - \frac{p_0(x)\, u(x)}{p_2(x)},$$

and if x be incongruent to the points β_i, γ_i, we can find $u(x)$ in the strip $2 \leqslant R(x) < 3$, and hence in the strip $3 \leqslant R(x) < 4$, and so on. Thus, if we are given $u(x)$ at every point of the strip $0 \leqslant R(x) < 2$, we can continue $u(x)$ over the whole of the remaining part of the complex plane except at the points which are congruent to the singular points of the given equation. Hence, if $\varpi_1(x)$, $\varpi_2(x)$ denote periodic functions of period unity such that

$$u(x) = \varpi_1(x), \quad 0 \leqslant R(x) < 1,$$
$$u(x) = \varpi_2(x), \quad 1 \leqslant R(x) < 2,$$

the above calculations will yield for $u(x)$ a linear form in $\varpi_1(x)$, $\varpi_2(x)$ say,

$$u(x) = \varpi_1(x)\, u_1(x) + \varpi_2(x)\, u_2(x).$$

The functions $u_1(x)$ and $u_2(x)$ are particular solutions of the difference equation which satisfy the conditions,

$$u_1(x) = 1, \quad u_2(x) = 0 \text{ in } 0 \leqslant R(x) < 1,$$
$$u_1(x) = 0, \quad u_2(x) = 1 \text{ in } 1 \leqslant R(x) < 2.$$

These particular solutions are in general discontinuous. Our object is, of course, to find analytic solutions, but the above investigation shews

(1) that the given equation has particular solutions;

(2) that analytic solutions which satisfy *arbitrary* initial conditions do not in general exist.

12·1. Fundamental System of Solutions. Let

$$u_1(x), \quad u_2(x), \quad \dots, \quad u_n(x)$$

be n particular solutions of the general equation 12·0 (1). These solutions are said to form a fundamental system (or set) when there exists *no* linear relation of the form

$$\varpi_1 u_1(x) + \varpi_2 u_2(x) + \dots + \varpi_n u_n(x) = 0,$$

where $\varpi_1, \varpi_2, \dots, \varpi_n$ are periodics such that for at least one value of x, which is incongruent to the singular points of the equation, they are finite and not all simultaneously zero. The functions of a fundamental set are said to be linearly independent.

It follows that if $u_s(x)$ denote a member of a fundamental system, and a a point incongruent to the singular points, that $u_s(a)$ cannot vanish for all the points $a, a+1, \dots, a+n-1$.

For if this were the case we should have $u_s(a+m) = 0$, where m is any integer positive or negative.

If then ϖ_s denotes a periodic which does not vanish at the points $a+m$, but vanishes everywhere else, we would have

$$\varpi_s u_s(x) = 0,$$

which is contrary to the hypothesis that $u_s(x)$ belongs to the system.

12·11. Casorati's Theorem. *The necessary and sufficient condition that* $u_1(x), u_2(x), \dots, u_n(x)$ *should form a fundamental system of solutions of the homogeneous equation of order* n *is that the determinant*

$$D(x) = \begin{vmatrix} u_1(x) & u_2(x) & \dots & u_n(x) \\ u_1(x+1) & u_2(x+1) & \dots & u_n(x+1) \\ \dots & \dots & \dots & \dots \\ u_1(x+n-1) & u_2(x+n-1) & \dots & u_n(x+n-1) \end{vmatrix}$$

should not vanish for any value of x *which is incongruent to the singular points of the equation.*

For simplicity, take $n=3$. The condition is sufficient. For if $u_1(x), u_2(x), u_3(x)$ do not form a fundamental system of the equation

$$p_3 u(x+3) + p_2 u(x+2) + p_1 u(x+1) + p_0 u(x) = 0,$$

we can find a point ξ incongruent to the singular points of the equation and periodics not all zero, when $x = \xi$, such that

$$\varpi_1 u_1(\xi) + \varpi_2 u_2(\xi) + \varpi_3 u_3(\xi) = 0,$$

and consequently

$$\varpi_1 u_1(\xi+1) + \varpi_2 u_2(\xi+1) + \varpi_3 u_3(\xi+1) = 0,$$
$$\varpi_1 u_1(\xi+2) + \varpi_2 u_2(\xi+2) + \varpi_3 u_3(\xi+2) = 0,$$

and, since $\varpi_1, \varpi_2, \varpi_3$ do not all vanish, we have

$$D(\xi) = 0.$$

The condition is also necessary. For, supposing that $D(x) = 0$, let $U_1(x), U_2(x), U_3(x)$ denote the cofactors of the elements of the *last* row in $D(x)$.

We shall suppose that these do not all vanish. Then, by the property of cofactors,

$$u_1(x)\,U_1(x) + u_2(x)\,U_2(x) + u_3(x)\,U_3(x) = 0,$$
$$u_1(x+1)\,U_1(x) + u_2(x+1)\,U_2(x) + u_3(x+1)\,U_3(x) = 0,$$
$$u_1(x+2)\,U_1(x) + u_2(x+2)\,U_2(x) + u_3(x+2)\,U_3(x) = D(x) = 0.$$

Now $U_1(x+1)$, $U_2(x+1)$, $U_3(x+1)$ are the cofactors of the *first* row, and hence

$$u_1(x)\,U_1(x+1)+u_2(x)\,U_2(x+1)+u_3(x)\,U_3(x+1) = D(x) = 0,$$
$$u_1(x+1)\,U_1(x+1)+u_2(x+1)\,U_2(x+1)+u_3(x+1)\,U_3(x+1) = 0,$$
$$u_1(x+2)\,U_1(x+1)+u_2(x+2)\,U_2(x+1)+u_3(x+2)\,U_3(x+1) = 0.$$

If we suppose $U_1(x)$ to be the cofactor which does not vanish, the first set of three equations determines uniquely the ratios

$$\frac{U_2(x)}{U_1(x)},\quad \frac{U_3(x)}{U_1(x)},$$

while the second set determines uniquely

$$\frac{U_2(x+1)}{U_1(x+1)},\quad \frac{U_3(x+1)}{U_1(x+1)},$$

and since in the two sets of equations the coefficients of the unknowns are the same, we have

$$\frac{U_2(x+1)}{U_1(x+1)} = \frac{U_2(x)}{U_1(x)} = \gamma_2 \text{ say},$$

$$\frac{U_3(x+1)}{U_1(x+1)} = \frac{U_3(x)}{U_1(x)} = \gamma_3 \text{ say},$$

where γ_2, γ_3 are periodics. If we take $\gamma_2 = \dfrac{\varpi_2}{\varpi_1}$, $\gamma_3 = \dfrac{\varpi_3}{\varpi_1}$, we have, therefore,

$$\varpi_1\,u_1(x)+\varpi_2\,u_2(x)+\varpi_3\,u_3(x) = 0,$$

which shews that the solutions do not form a fundamental set.

If all the cofactors of the last row vanish we simply resume the argument with $n-1$ functions instead of n.

Example. It is easy to verify that the equation

$$u(x+2)-(\alpha+\beta)\,u(x+1)+\alpha\,\beta\,u(x) = 0, \quad \alpha \neq \beta$$

has the solutions α^x, β^x. These form a fundamental system, for

$$D(x) = \begin{vmatrix} \alpha^x & \beta^x \\ \alpha^{x+1} & \beta^{x+1} \end{vmatrix} = \alpha^x\,\beta^x(\beta-\alpha),$$

so that $D(x)$ does not vanish for any finite value of x.

Another system of solutions is

$$\alpha^x, \quad \beta^x \sin 2\pi x,$$

for which

$$D(x) = \alpha^x \beta^x (\beta - \alpha) \sin 2\pi x.$$

$D(x)$ now vanishes whenever x is an integer, so that these solutions do not form a fundamental system.

The importance of a fundamental set of solutions lies in the fact that every solution of a linear difference equation is expressible as a linear function, whose coefficients are periodics, of the solutions of a fundamental system. To see that this is so, consider the general equation

$$p_n u(x+n) + p_{n-1} u(x+n-1) + \dots + p_1 u(x+1) + p_0 u(x) = 0.$$

If $u_1(x), u_2(x), \dots, u_n(x)$ be a fundamental system of solutions, we have

$$p_n u_1(x+n) + p_{n-1} u_1(x+n-1) + \dots + p_0 u_1(x) = 0,$$
$$\cdots\cdots\cdots\cdots\cdots\cdots$$
$$p_n u_n(x+n) + p_{n-1} u_n(x+n-1) + \dots + p_0 u_n(x) = 0.$$

Eliminating the coefficients, it follows that

$$\begin{vmatrix} u(x) & u_1(x) & u_2(x) & \dots & u_n(x) \\ u(x+1) & u_1(x+1) & u_2(x+1) & \dots & u_n(x+1) \\ \dots & \dots & \dots & \dots & \dots \\ u(x+n) & u_1(x+n) & \dots & \dots & u_n(x+n) \end{vmatrix} = 0.$$

Since the solutions $u_1(x), \dots, u_n(x)$ form a fundamental set, the minors of the elements of the first column are all different from zero, provided that x be incongruent to a singular point, so that periodics $\varpi, \varpi_1, \dots, \varpi_n$ exist, such that

$$\varpi u(x) + \varpi_1 u_1(x) + \varpi_2 u_2(x) + \dots + \varpi_n u_n(x) = 0,$$

with $\varpi \neq 0$. Obviously, every expression of the form

$$u(x) = \varpi_1 u_1(x) + \varpi_2 u_2(x) + \dots + \varpi_n u_n(x)$$

satisfies the given equation. Hence the result is established.

It follows from this that the problem of solution of a linear difference equation consists in finding a set of fundamental solutions. In the case of the homogeneous linear equation of the first rder, if $u_1(x)$ be a particular solution, the general solution is $\varpi\, u_1(x)$ (cf. 11·1).

The above result can also be used to form a difference equation with a given set of fundamental solutions. For example, the quation which has the solutions x, $x(x-1)$ is

$$\begin{vmatrix} u(x) & x & x(x-1) \\ u(x+1) & x+1 & (x+1)\,x \\ u(x+2) & x+2 & (x+2)(x+1) \end{vmatrix} = 0,$$

$$x(x+1)\,u(x+2) - 2x(x+2)\,u(x+1) + (x+1)(x+2)\,u(x) = 0.$$

Here

$$D(x) = x(x+1),$$

which only vanishes when $x = 0$ or -1, but these are congruent to singular points of the equation. The singular points are -2, -1, 1, 2.

12·12. Heymann's Theorem.* Casorati's determinant $D(x)$ satisfies the linear equation of the first order,

$$D(x+1) = (-1)^n \frac{p_0(x)}{p_n(x)} D(x).$$

From 12·11,

$$D(x+1) = \begin{vmatrix} u_1(x+1) & u_2(x+1) & \dots & u_n(x+1) \\ u_1(x+2) & u_2(x+2) & \dots & u_n(x+2) \\ \dots & \dots & \dots & \dots \\ u_1(x+n) & u_2(x+n) & \dots & u_n(x+n) \end{vmatrix}.$$

From the difference equation itself,

$$-\frac{p_0}{p_n} u(x) = \frac{p_1}{p_n} u(x+1) + \frac{p_2}{p_n} u(x+2) + \dots + u(x+n).$$

Multiply the first $n-1$ rows of the above determinant by

$$\frac{p_1}{p_n},\ \frac{p_2}{p_n},\ \dots,\ \frac{p_{n-1}}{p_n}$$

and add to the last.

* W. Heymann, *J. f. reine u. angew. Math.* 109 (1892).

This row then becomes

$$-\frac{p_0}{p_n}u_1(x),\ -\frac{p_0}{p_n}u_2(x),\ \dots,\ -\frac{p_0}{p_n}u_n(x),$$

so that, moving this into the first row, we have

$$D(x+1) = \frac{(-1)^n p_0}{p_n} D(x). \tag{1}$$

It follows at once from this, that if ξ be not congruent to a singular point, $D(\xi)$ is simultaneously zero or not zero at all points congruent to ξ.

Again, solving this first order equation by the method of 11·1, we have

$$D(x) = \varpi \exp\left[\mathop{\mathrm{S}}_c^x \log\frac{(-1)^n p_0(t)}{p_n(t)}\Delta t\right]. \tag{2}$$

The periodic ϖ will depend upon the particular fundamental set which is chosen to form $D(x)$.

An application of Heymann's theorem arises in the equation of the second order when one member of a fundamental system is known. By means of this theorem a second member of the system can be found.

Consider the equation

$$p_2 u(x+2) + p_1 u(x+1) + p_0 u(x) = 0.$$

Let $u_1(x)$, $u_2(x)$ form a fundamental set and suppose $u_1(x)$ to be known. Then

$$D(x) = u_1(x)\,u_2(x+1) - u_2(x)\,u_1(x+1)$$

$$= u_1(x)\,u_1(x+1)\,\Delta\frac{u_2(x)}{u_1(x)}.$$

Thus

$$\frac{u_2(x)}{u_1(x)} = \varpi_1 + \mathop{\mathrm{S}}_c^x \frac{D(y)}{u_1(y)\,u_1(y+1)}\Delta y,$$

and $D(y)$ is given by (2), so that $u_2(x)$ is determined.

Thus, for example, the equation

$$x(x+1)\,u(x+2) - 2x(x+2)\,u(x+1) + (x+1)(x+2)\,u(x) = 0$$

as the solution $u(x) = x$, and, from (2),

$$D(x) = \varpi \exp\left[\mathop{S}_{c}^{x} \log \frac{x+2}{x} \Delta x \right]$$

$$= \varpi \exp\left(\log \frac{\Gamma(x+2)}{\Gamma(x)}\right)$$

by proper choice of c. Hence, taking $\varpi = 1$, we have

$$D(x) = x(x+1),$$

o that

$$u_2(x) = x\left[\varpi_1 + \mathop{S}_{0}^{x} 1 \, \Delta x\right] = \varpi_1 x + x(x-\tfrac{1}{2}).$$

If we wish to find a particular second member of the set, we can ake $\varpi_1 = 0$. Then

$$u_2(x) = x(x-\tfrac{1}{2}).$$

12·14. Relations between two Fundamental Systems.

f

$$u_1(x),\ u_2(x),\ \ldots,\ u_n(x),$$
$$v_1(x),\ v_2(x),\ \ldots,\ v_n(x)$$

e two fundamental systems, each solution of one system must be xpressible in terms of the members of the other system.

Thus, for example, we must have

$$\begin{aligned}
v_1(x) &= \varpi_{1,1}\, u_1(x) + \varpi_{1,2}\, u_2(x) + \ldots + \varpi_{1,n}\, u_n(x),\\
v_2(x) &= \varpi_{2,1}\, u_1(x) + \varpi_{2,2}\, u_2(x) + \ldots + \varpi_{2,n}\, u_n(x),\\
&\ldots\ldots\ldots\ldots\ldots\ldots\\
v_n(x) &= \varpi_{n,1}\, u_1(x) + \varpi_{n,2}\, u_2(x) + \ldots + \varpi_{n,n}\, u_n(x).
\end{aligned}$$

The periodics $\varpi_{r,s}$ are here not arbitrary, but depend solely on he two fundamental systems chosen. Moreover, the determinant

$$\Omega = \begin{vmatrix} \varpi_{1,1} & \varpi_{1,2} & \cdots & \varpi_{1,n} \\ \varpi_{2,1} & \varpi_{2,2} & \cdots & \varpi_{2,n} \\ \cdots & \cdots & \cdots & \cdots \\ \varpi_{n,1} & \varpi_{n,2} & \cdots & \varpi_{n,n} \end{vmatrix}$$

cannot vanish. Conversely, if $u_1(x), \dots, u_n(x)$ form a fundamenta system and we take a determinant $\Omega \neq 0$ of periodics, the syster $v_1(x), \dots, v_n(x)$ also forms a fundamental set. The proof is simpl and is left to the reader.

12·16. A Criterion for Linear Independence.

Theorem. *If n functions $u_1(x), u_2(x), \dots, u_n(x)$ be such that*

$$\lim_{r\to\infty} \frac{u_s(x+r)}{u_{s+1}(x+r)} = 0, \quad s = 1, 2, \dots, n-1,$$

where r is a positive integer, then these functions are linearly inde pendent.

Suppose the functions all to exist in a half-plane limited of th left, and suppose if possible that they are not linearly independen that is to say, that a relation of the form

$$\varpi_1 u_1(x) + \varpi_2 u_2(x) + \dots + \varpi_n u_n(x) = 0$$

exists where the periodics $\varpi_1, \varpi_2, \dots,$ are not all simultaneousl zero, x not being a singular point. Suppose that the last produc which does not vanish is $\varpi_m u_m(x)$, so that

$$\varpi_1 u_1(x) + \dots + \varpi_m u_m(x) = 0.$$

Write $x+r$ for x and divide by $u_m(x+r)$
Then

$$\varpi_1 \frac{u_1(x+r)}{u_m(x+r)} + \varpi_2 \frac{u_2(x+r)}{u_m(x+r)} + \dots + \varpi_m = 0.$$

If in this relation we let $r \to \infty$, we have, from the enunciatior

$$\lim_{r\to\infty} \frac{u_s(x+r)}{u_m(x+r)} = \lim_{r\to\infty} \frac{u_s(x+r)}{u_{s+1}(x+r)} \cdot \frac{u_{s+1}(x+r)}{u_{s+2}(x+r)} \cdots \frac{u_{m-1}(x+r)}{u_m(x+r)} = 0,$$

$s = 1, 2, \dots, m-1$. Thus we have

$$\varpi_m = 0,$$

which is contrary to the hypothesis. Thus a relation of the forn stated cannot exist and the theorem is proved.

We shall later make applications of this theorem to deduce th linear independence of solutions of a difference equation from thei asymptotic forms.

12·2. The Symbolic Highest Common Factor.* Consider the linear expressions

(1) $P[u(x)] = p_4(x)\,u(x+4) + p_3(x)\,u(x+3) + p_2(x)\,u(x+2)$
$$+ p_1(x)\,u(x+1) + p_0(x)\,u(x),$$

(2) $Q[u(x)] = q_3(x)\,u(x+3) + q_2(x)\,u(x+2)$
$$+ q_1(x)\,u(x+1) + q_0(x)\,u(x).$$

If we perform on $Q[u(x)]$ the operation E of 2·4, we get

(3) $\mathsf{E}\,Q[u(x)] = q_3(x+1)\,u(x+4) + q_2(x+1)\,u(x+3)$
$$+ q_1(x+1)\,u(x+2) + q_0(x+1)\,u(x+1).$$

If we multiply (2) by $r_1(x)$ and (3) by $r_0(x)$ and subtract from (1), we shall arrive at an expression of the form

$$Q_1[u(x)] = t_2(x)\,u(x+2) + t_1(x)\,u(x+1) + t_0(x)\,u(x),$$

in which $u(x+3)$, $u(x+4)$ do not appear, provided that $r_0(x)$, $r_1(x)$ be so chosen that

(4)
$$p_4(x) - r_0(x)\,q_3(x+1) = 0,$$
$$p_3(x) - r_0(x)\,q_2(x+1) - r_1(x)\,q_3(x) = 0.$$

Supposing this to have been done, we may write

$$P[u(x)] - \{r_0(x)\,\mathsf{E} + r_1(x)\}\,Q[u(x)] = Q_1[u(x)],$$

or, symbolically,

$$P[u(x)] = R_1\{Q[u(x)]\} + Q_1[u(x)],$$

where $R_1\{\;\}$ is put for the operator $r_0(x)\,\mathsf{E} + r_1(x)$.

Evidently, for the more general expressions,

(5)
$$P[u(x)] = \sum_{s=0}^{n} p_s(x)\,u(x+s),$$

(6)
$$Q[u(x)] = \sum_{s=0}^{m} q_s(x)\,u(x+s), \quad n \geqslant m,$$

we can find an operator

$$R_1\{\;\} = \{r_0(x)\,\mathsf{E}^{n-m} + r_1(x)\,\mathsf{E}^{n-m-1} + \dots + r_{n-m}(x)\},$$

* Pincherle and Amaldi, *Le Operazioni Distributive*, (Bologna, 1901), chap. x.

where the functions $r_0(x)$, $r_1(x)$, ..., are determined by equations of the same type as (4), such that

(7) $$P[u(x)] = R_1\{Q[u(x)]\} + Q_1[u(x)],$$

where

$$Q_1[u(x)] = \sum_{s=0}^{m-1} t_s(x)\, u(x+s).$$

The order of $Q_1[u(x)]$ may, of course, be less than $m-1$ since the coefficients $t_{m-1}(x)$, $t_{m-2}(x)$, ... may vanish identically.

Now, if the difference equations

(8) $$P[u(x)] = 0, \quad Q[u(x)] = 0$$

have a common solution $u_1(x)$, it is evident from (7) that $u_1(x)$ must also be a solution of

$$Q_1[u(x)] = 0.$$

Thus every solution which is common to the equations (8) is common also to the equations

(9) $$Q[u(x)] = 0, \quad Q_1[u(x)] = 0.$$

Treating the expressions $Q[u(x)]$, $Q_1[u(x)]$ in the same way, we can obtain

$$Q[u(x)] = R_2\{Q_1[u(x)]\} + Q_2[u(x)],$$

so that any solution common to (8), and therefore to (9), is common to

$$Q_1[u(x)] = 0, \quad Q_2[u(x)] = 0.$$

Proceeding in this way we continually lower the orders of the difference expressions, so that after a finite number of steps we must arrive at a pair of equations, say,

(10) $$Q_k[u(x)] = 0, \quad Q_{k+1}[u(x)] = 0,$$

which have in common all the solutions common to (8), and which are such that the process cannot be continued. Thus the process must terminate with either

$$\text{(A)} \quad Q_{k+1}[u(x)] \equiv 0,$$

or

$$\text{(B)} \quad Q_{k+1}[u(x)] = t(x)\, u(x).$$

In case (A), we say that $Q_k[u(x)]$ is the symbolic highest common factor of the expressions (5) and (6), and we see from (10) that the equations (8) have common solutions which are the solutions of the equation

$$Q_k[u(x)] = 0,$$

obtained by equating to zero the symbolic highest common factor.

In case (B), we can say that the expressions (5) and (6) are mutually prime. In this case the only solution common to (8) is the trivial solution $u(x) = 0$.

Corollary. If it so happen that *all* the solutions of $Q[u(x)] = 0$ satisfy $P[u(x)] = 0$, we must have the symbolic relation

$$P[u(x)] = R\{Q[u(x)]\}.$$

12·22. The Symbolic Lowest Common Multiple. As it is of some importance to ascertain whether two given equations have any common solutions we now introduce the notion of the symbolic lowest common multiple.

Consider two difference expressions (see 12·2 (5), (6)), $P[u(x)]$, $Q[u(x)]$ of orders n, m respectively. The lowest common multiple of these expressions is the expression $V[u(x)]$ of *lowest* order such that the difference equation $V[u(x)] = 0$ is satisfied by *every* solution of each of the equations $P[u(x)] = 0$, $Q[u(x)] = 0$. First, suppose $P[u(x)]$, $Q[u(x)]$ to be mutually prime. Then $V[u(x)] = 0$ must be satisfied by the n solutions of $P[u(x)] = 0$ and the m solutions of $Q[u(x)] = 0$, and since these equations have no common solution, $V[u(x)] = 0$ must be of order $m+n$. Then by the corollary of 12·2, we have

$$V[u(x)] = R\{Q[u(x)]\},$$

$$V[u(x)] = S\{P[u(x)]\},$$

where

$$R\{\ \} = \{r_0(x)\,\mathsf{E}^n + \dots + r_n(x)\},$$

$$S\{\ \} = \{s_0(x)\,\mathsf{E}^m + \dots + s_m(x)\}.$$

Hence, if we perform these operations and equate the coefficients of $u(x)$, $u(x+1)$, ..., we obtain

$$s_m(x)\,p_0(x) = r_n(x)\,q_0(x),$$

$$s_m(x)\,p_1(x) + s_{m-1}(x)\,p_0(x+1) = r_n(x)\,q_1(x) + r_{n-1}(x)\,q_0(x+1),$$

$$s_m(x)\,p_2(x)+s_{m-1}(x)\,p_1(x+1)+s_{m-2}(x)\,p_0(x+2)$$
$$= r_n(x)\,q_2(x)+r_{n-1}(x)\,q_1(x+1)+r_{n-2}(x)\,q_0(x+2),$$

. . . .

$$s_1(x)\,p_n(x+m-1)+s_0(x)\,p_{n-1}(x+m)$$
$$= r_1(x)\,q_m(x+n-1)+r_0(x)\,q_{m-1}(x+m-1),$$

$$s_0(x)\,p_n(x+m) = r_0(x)\,q_m(x+n).$$

Thus we have $m+n+1$ homogeneous linear equations to determine the $m+n+2$ unknowns $r_i(x)$, $s_j(x)$. The ratios of these functions can therefore be determined and we have the expression for $V[u(x)]$, save for a factor which is a function of x.

We have supposed that $P[u(x)]$, $Q[u(x)]$ are mutually prime. If this be not the case, the equations $P[u(x)]=0$, $Q[u(x)]=0$ will have at least one solution in common, and $V[u(x)]$ will be of order less than $m+n$. The same method may be used to determine $V[u(x)]$, but now we must suppose that $r_0(x)$, $s_0(x)$ vanish identically.

Hence eliminating $r_i(x)$, $s_j(x)$ from the remaining equations, we have the condition that $P[u(x)]=0$, $Q[u(x)]=0$ may have a common solution, namely, the vanishing of the determinant

$$\begin{vmatrix} p_0(x) & 0 & 0 & \cdots & \cdots & q_0(x) & 0 & 0 & \cdots & 0 \\ p_1(x) & p_0(x+1) & 0 & \cdots & \cdots & q_1(x) & q_0(x+1) & 0 & \cdots & 0 \\ \cdots & \cdots & \cdots & \cdots & \cdots & \cdots & \cdots & \cdots & \cdots & \cdots \\ 0 & 0 & 0 & \cdots & p_n(x+m-1) & 0 & 0 & 0 & \cdots & q_m(x+n-1) \end{vmatrix}$$

This condition is expressed directly in terms of the coefficients of the given equations.

Consider, for example, the equations

$$f[u(x)]$$
$$\equiv x(x+1)\,u(x+2)-2x(x+2)\,u(x+1)+(x+1)(x+2)\,u(x)=0,$$

$$g[u(x)]$$
$$\equiv (x-1)\,u(x+2)-(3x-2)\,u(x+1)+2x\,u(x)=0.$$

The condition for a common solution is the vanishing of

$$\begin{vmatrix} (x+1)(x+2) & 0 & 2x & 0 \\ -2x(x+2) & (x+2)(x+3) & -3x+2 & 2x+2 \\ x(x+1) & -2(x+1)(x+3) & x-1 & -3x-1 \\ 0 & (x+1)(x+2) & 0 & x \end{vmatrix}.$$

Replace the second row by the sum of all four rows, and increase the third row by twice the last row, then subtract twice the last column from the second column and we then have a determinant which clearly vanishes.

Thus the proposed equations have at least one solution in common. We now proceed to find the Highest Common Factor. Multiplying the first equation by $(x-1)$ and the second by $x(x+1)$ and subtracting, we get after suppressing a factor x^2-x+2,

$$H[u(x)] \equiv x\,u(x+1)-(x+1)\,u(x) = 0.$$

This must be the Highest Common Factor, since we know that the equations have at least one solution in common. That this is indeed the case is easily verified, for we can see at once that

$$f[u(x)] \equiv \{x\mathsf{E}-(x+2)\}\,H[u(x)],$$

$$g[u(x)] \equiv \left\{\frac{x-1}{x+1}\mathsf{E}-\frac{2x}{x+1}\right\} H[u(x)].$$

The solution of $H[u(x)]=0$ is $u(x) = \varpi x$.

The equation $f[u(x)]=0$ has already been solved by Heymann's theorem in 12·12. We can use the same method to solve $g[u(x)]=0$. We have

$$u_2(x) = \varpi_1 x + \varpi x \mathop{S}^{x} \left\{\frac{1}{y(y+1)} \exp\left[\mathop{S}^{y} \log\frac{2t}{1-t}\Delta t\right]\right\}\Delta y$$

$$= \varpi_1 x + \varpi x \mathop{S}^{x} \frac{1}{y(y+1)}\,\frac{2^y\,\Gamma(y)}{\Gamma(y-1)}\,\Delta y$$

$$= \varpi_1 x + \varpi x \mathop{S}^{x} \left(\frac{2^{y+1}}{y+1}-\frac{2^y}{y}\right)\Delta y.$$

Thus the primitive is

$$u(x) = \varpi_1 x + \varpi\,.\,2^x.$$

12·24. Reducible Equations. A homogeneous linear difference equation whose coefficients are rational functions of x is said to be reducible when it has solutions in common with an equation of lower order whose coefficients are likewise rational functions of x. An equation with rational coefficients which lacks this property is said to be irreducible.

Given two difference expressions $P[u(x)]$ of order n and $Q[u(x)]$ of order m ($\leqslant n$), we saw in 12·2 that we can form the operator

$$R\{\ \} = \{r_0(x)\,\mathsf{E}^{n-m} + \ldots + r_{n-m}(x)\},$$

such that

$$P[u(x)] = R\{Q[u(x)]\} + Q_1[u(x)].$$

If the coefficients of P and Q be rational functions, so also are the coefficients of R and Q_1.

Also, if $P[u(x)] = 0$ and $Q[u(x)] = 0$ have a solution in common, this solution satisfies $Q_1[u(x)] = 0$. It follows that if the equation $Q[u(x)] = 0$ be irreducible, the expression $Q_1[u(x)] = 0$ must vanish identically and we have

$$P[u(x)] = R\{Q[u(x)]\}.$$

Hence $P[u(x)] = 0$ is satisfied by *every* solution of $Q[u(x)] = 0$. Thus we have proved the following :

Theorem. *When a homogeneous linear equation with rational coefficients has one solution in common with an irreducible equation whose coefficients are likewise rational, then the given equation admits every solution of the irreducible equation.*

Let $P[u(x)] = 0$ be a reducible equation. By hypothesis there exists an equation $Q[u(x)] = 0$ also with rational coefficients which has solutions in common with $P[u(x)] = 0$.

If $R[u(x)] = 0$ denote the symbolic highest common factor of P and Q, the solutions common to $P = 0$, $Q = 0$ also satisfy $R = 0$.

If $R = 0$ be irreducible, all the solutions of $R = 0$ belong to $P = 0$. If $R = 0$ be itself reducible, we can continue the process until we arrive either at an equation of the first order or an irreducible equation. We regard an equation of the first order as irreducible. Thus we have the following:

Theorem. *Given a reducible equation, there exists an equation of lower order all of whose solutions belong to the given equation, and there exist one or more irreducible equations all of whose solutions belong to the given equation.*

12·3. Reduction of Order when a Solution is known.

Let $u_1(x)$ be a known particular solution of the general equation

(1) $P[u(x)] = p_n u(x+n) + p_{n-1} u(x+n-1) + \dots + p_0 u(x) = 0,$

so that

$$P[u_1(x)] = p_n u_1(x+n) + \dots + p_0 u_1(x) = 0.$$

Make the change of dependent variable

$$u(x) = u_1(x)\, v(x),$$

so that

$$p_n u_1(x+n)\, v(x+n) + p_{n-1} u_1(x+n-1)\, v(x+n-1) + \dots \\ + p_0 u_1(x)\, v(x) = 0.$$

Now, by Abel's Identity, 10·07 (I), taking

$$a_s = p_s u_1(x+s), \quad b_s = v(x+s),$$

we have

$$-q_{n-1} \Delta v(x+n-1) - q_{n-2} \Delta v(x+n-2) - \dots - q_0 \Delta v(x) \\ + v(x+n)\, P[u_1(x)] = 0,$$

where

$$q_s = p_0 u_1(x) + p_1 u_1(x+1) + \dots + p_s u_1(x+s).$$

Now $P[u_1(x)] = 0$ by hypothesis. Hence, if we put

$$\Delta v(x) = w(x),$$

we have an equation of order $n-1$ to determine $w(x)$, namely,

(2) $q_{n-1} w(x+n-1) + q_{n-2} w(x+n-2) + \dots + q_0 w(x) = 0.$

We note incidentally that

$$q_0 = p_0 u_1(x), \quad q_{n-1} = -p_n u_1(x+n).$$

If $w_2(x)$ be a particular solution of (2), we have

$$\Delta \frac{u_2(x)}{u_1(x)} = \Delta v_2(x) = w_2(x),$$

so that

$$u_2(x) = u_1(x) \underset{c}{\overset{x}{S}} w_2(t)\,\Delta t,$$

which gives the corresponding solution of (1).

Suppose now that we know m linearly independent solutions of (1), say, $u_1(x), u_2(x), \ldots, u_m(x)$. Then (2) has the $m-1$ solutions

$$\Delta\frac{u_2(x)}{u_1(x)}, \quad \Delta\frac{u_3(x)}{u_1(x)}, \quad \ldots, \quad \Delta\frac{u_m(x)}{u_1(x)}.$$

These solutions are themselves linearly independent, for if we had a relation

$$\sum_{s=2}^{m} \varpi_s\,\Delta\frac{u_s(x)}{u_1(x)} = 0,$$

we could deduce

$$\sum_{s=2}^{m} \varpi_s\,\frac{u_s(x)}{u_1(x)} = \varpi,$$

which would contradict the hypothesis that the m solutions are independent.

If $m > 1$, we can therefore proceed by the same method to lower the order of (2) and we can in this way depress the order of the original equation (1) by m units.

In particular, if we know one solution of the equation of the second order, we can reduce the equation to the first order and hence complete the solution by the methods of Chapter XI.

Example. The equation

$$(2x-1)\,u(x+2) - (8x-2)\,u(x+1) + (6x+3)\,u(x) = 0$$

has the particular solution $u_1(x) = 3^x$.

Putting $u(x) = 3^x\,v(x)$, the equation becomes on application of the foregoing method

$$-(2x-1)\,3^{x+2}\,w(x+1) + (6x+3)\,3^x\,w(x) = 0,$$

or

$$w(x+1) = \frac{(2x+1)}{3(2x-1)}\,w(x),$$

whence

$$w_2(x) = \frac{3^{-x}\Gamma(x+\frac{1}{2})}{\Gamma(x-\frac{1}{2})} = 3^{-x}(x-\tfrac{1}{2})$$

$$= \Delta\, 3^{-x+1}(-\tfrac{1}{2}x),$$

so that

$$\frac{u_2(x)}{3^x} = -\tfrac{1}{2}x\,.\,3^{-x+1},$$

$$u_2(x) = -\tfrac{3}{2}x.$$

Alternatively, $u_2(x) = x$ can also be used, as the constant has no special significance.

12·4. Functional Derivates. If P be a distributive operator, that is to say if

$$P[u+v] = P[u]+P[v],$$

Pincherle * defines the functional derivate P' by the relation

$$P'[u] = P[xu]-x\,P[u].$$

The second derivate $P''[u]$ is defined by

$$P''[u] = P'[xu]-x\,P'[u]$$

$$= P[x^2u]-2x\,P[xu]+x^2\,P[u],$$

and generally

$$P^{(n)}[u] = P^{(n-1)}[xu]-x\,P^{(n-1)}[u],$$

and it is easily proved by induction or by direct substitution that

$$P^{(n)}[u] = P[x^n u]-\binom{n}{1}x\,P[x^{n-1}u]+\binom{n}{2}x^2\,P[x^{n-2}u]-\dots$$

$$+(-1)^n x^n\,P[u].$$

If in this relation we put in turn for n the numbers

$$n,\ n-1,\ n-2,\ \dots,\ 2,\ 1,\ 0,$$

multiply the resulting equations by

$$1,\ \binom{n}{1}x,\ \binom{n}{2}x^2,\ \dots,\ \binom{n}{n}x^n$$

---

* Pincherle and Amaldi, *Le Operazioni Distributive*, p. 189.

and add the results, we get

$$P[x^n u] = P^{(n)}[u] + \binom{n}{1} x P^{(n-1)}[u] + \binom{n}{2} x^2 P^{(n-2)}[u] + \dots$$
$$+ x^n P[u].$$

12·5. Multiple Solutions of a Difference Equation. Let

$$P[u(x)] \equiv p_n u(x+n) + p_{n-1} u(x+n-1) + \dots + p_0 u(x).$$

Consider the difference equation

$$P[u(x)] = 0.$$

If a solution $u_1(x)$ exist, such that

$$u_1(x),\ x u_1(x),\ x^2 u_1(x),\ \dots,\ x^{\nu-1} u_1(x)$$

are all solutions, the solution $u_1(x)$ is said to be a solution of multiplicity ν. Since, from 12·4,

$$P[x^{\nu-1}u(x)] = P^{(\nu-1)}[u(x)] + \binom{\nu-1}{1} x P^{(\nu-2)}[u(x)] + \dots + x^{\nu-1}[Pu(x)],$$

it follows that the necessary and sufficient conditions that $u_1(x)$ should be a solution of multiplicity ν are that $u_1(x)$ should satisfy each of the equations

$$P[u(x)] = 0, \quad P'[u(x)] = 0, \quad \dots, \quad P^{(\nu-1)}[u(x)] = 0$$

and that $P^{(\nu)}[u_1(x)] \neq 0$.

Evidently, then, the condition that the equation $P[u(x)] = 0$ should have at least one multiple solution is that the equations

$$P[u(x)] = 0, \quad P'[u(x)] = 0$$

should have a common solution. If $H[u(x)]$ denote the symbolic highest common factor of the expressions

$$P[u(x)], \quad P'[u(x)],$$

the equation $H[u(x)] = 0$ will have as solutions all and only the multiple solutions of $P[u(x)] = 0$; and these multiple solutions will appear in $H[u(x)] = 0$ with one less order of multiplicity than in the equation $P[u(x)] = 0$. Suppose that $P[u(x)] = 0$ has r multiple solutions of orders $\nu_1, \nu_2, \dots, \nu_r$ respectively, where $\nu_1, \nu_2, \dots, \nu_r$ are arranged in non-descending order of magnitude. If $\nu_{r-1} \neq \nu_r$, we can find the solution of multiplicity ν_r. For

$H[u(x)] = 0$ has solutions of multiplicities $\nu_{r-1}-1$, ν_r-1, and if we find $H_2[u(x)]$ the highest common factor of $H[u(x)]$ and $H'[u(x)]$, $H_2[u(x)] = 0$ will have solutions of multiplicities $\nu_{r-1}-2$, ν_r-2.

If $\nu_{r-1} = 2$, $H_2[u(x)] = 0$ has only one solution, of multiplicity ν_r-2. If $\nu_{r-1} > 2$, we can continue the process, until we arrive at an equation which has only a single multiple solution. We thus reduce the problem to finding the solutions of an equation which has only one multiple solution.

Suppose this equation to be $H_s[u(x)] = 0$, $(s = \nu_{r-1})$, with a multiple solution of order $\nu_r - s$. This multiple solution will be a simple solution of $H_s^{(\nu_r-s+1)}[u(x)] = 0$, which is of the first order and can be solved.

The order of the original equation can now be depressed by ν_r units, and if $\nu_{r-2} \neq \nu_{r-1}$, we can proceed to find the solution of multiplicity ν_{r-1} and thus further depress the order.

Proceeding in this way we can find all the multiple solutions up to the stage if any at which $\nu_{k-1} = \nu_k$, when the process just described comes to an end.

To carry out this process it is necessary to form the derivates. By the definition

$$\begin{aligned}
P'[u(x)] &= P[x\,u(x)] - x\,P[u(x)] \\
&= (x+n)\,p_n\,u(x+n) + (x+n-1)\,p_{n-1}\,u(x+n-1) + \dots \\
&\qquad + (x+1)p_1\,u(x+1) + x\,p_0\,u(x) \\
&\quad - x\,p_n\,u(x+n) - x\,p_{n-1}u(x+n-1) - x\,p_1\,u(x+1) - x\,p_0\,u(x) \\
&= n\,p_n\,u(x+n) + (n-1)\,p_{n-1}\,u(x+n-1) + \dots + p_1\,u(x+1).
\end{aligned}$$

$$P''[u(x)] = n^2\,p_n\,u(x+n) + (n-1)^2\,p_{n-1}\,u(x+n-1) + \dots + p_1\,u(x+1),$$

and generally

$$P^{(\nu)}[u(x)] = n^\nu\,p_n\,u(x+n) + (n-1)^\nu\,p_{n-1}\,u(x+n-1) + \dots + 2^\nu\,p_2\,u(x+2) + p_1\,u(x+1).$$

As an illustration, consider

$$\begin{aligned}
P[u(x)] &= (2x^2+4x+1)\,u(x+3) - (2x^2+8x+3)\,u(x+2) \\
&\qquad - (2x^2+4x-3)\,u(x+1) + (2x^2+8x+7)\,u(x) = 0. \\
P'[u(x)] &= 3(2x^2+4x+1)\,u(x+3) - 2(2x^2+8x+3)\,u(x+2) \\
&\qquad - (2x^2+4x-3)\,u(x+1).
\end{aligned}$$

We find

$$3P[u(x)] - P'[u(x)] + \frac{2x^2+8x+3}{3(2x^2-1)} \mathsf{E}^{-1} P'[u(x)]$$

$$= -\frac{16(x+1)(2x^2+4x-3)}{3(2x^2-1)}\{x\,u(x+1)-(x+1)\,u(x)\}.$$

We can proceed to show that $x\,u(x+1)-(x+1)\,u(x)$ is the highest common factor. We can avoid the calculation by observing that $x\,u(x+1)-(x+1)\,u(x)=0$ has the solution $u(x)=x$, which is easily seen to satisfy $P[u(x)]=0$, $P'[u(x)]=0$. Hence $P[u(x)]=0$ has the solutions x, x^2. Knowing these solutions, we can depress the order by two units and so obtain an equation of the first order. The complete solution is $u(x) = \varpi_1 x + \varpi_2 x^2 + \varpi_3(-1)^x$.

12·6. Multipliers. If $P[u(x)]$ be a linear form of order n, a function $M(x)$, such that $M(x)\,P[u(x)] = \Delta\, Q[u(x)]$, where $Q[u(x)]$ is a linear form of order $n-1$, is called a multiplier of $P[u(x)]$.

For simplicity, take

$$P[u(x)] \equiv p_3\,u(x+3)+p_2\,u(x+2)+p_1\,u(x+1)+p_0\,u(x),$$

and let $u_1(x)$, $u_2(x)$, $u_3(x)$ be a fundamental set of solutions of the equation $P[u(x)]=0$.

Then, if $u(x)$ be any other solution, we have

$$\begin{aligned} u(x) &= \varpi_1 u_1(x)+\varpi_2 u_2(x)+\varpi_3 u_3(x),\\ u(x+1) &= \varpi_1 u_1(x+1)+\varpi_2 u_2(x+1)+\varpi_3 u_3(x+1),\\ u(x+2) &= \varpi_1 u_1(x+2)+\varpi_2 u_2(x+2)+\varpi_3 u_3(x+2). \end{aligned}$$

Solving these equations for ϖ_1, ϖ_2, ϖ_3, we have

$$\frac{\varpi_1}{\begin{vmatrix} u_2(x) & u_3(x) & u(x)\\ u_2(x+1) & u_3(x+1) & u(x+1)\\ u_2(x+2) & u_3(x+2) & u(x+2)\end{vmatrix}} = \frac{-\varpi_2}{\begin{vmatrix} u_1(x) & u_3(x) & u(x)\\ u_1(x+1) & u_3(x+1) & u(x+1)\\ u_1(x+2) & u_3(x+2) & u(x+2)\end{vmatrix}}$$

$$= \frac{\varpi_3}{\begin{vmatrix} u_1(x) & u_2(x) & u(x)\\ u_1(x+1) & u_2(x+1) & u(x+1)\\ u_1(x+2) & u_2(x+2) & u(x+2)\end{vmatrix}} = \frac{1}{\begin{vmatrix} u_1(x) & u_2(x) & u_3(x)\\ u_1(x+1) & u_2(x+1) & u_3(x+1)\\ u_1(x+2) & u_2(x+2) & u_3(x+2)\end{vmatrix}}$$

The last of these determinants is Casorati's determinant $D(x)$. Denote by $\mu_j^{(i)}$ the cofactor of the element in the ith row and jth column of this determinant, divided by $D(x)$. Then

$$\varpi_1 = \mu_1^{(1)} u(x) + \mu_1^{(2)} u(x+1) + \mu_1^{(3)} u(x+2) = Q_1[u(x)],$$
$$\varpi_2 = \mu_2^{(1)} u(x) + \mu_2^{(2)} u(x+1) + \mu_2^{(3)} u(x+2) = Q_2[u(x)],$$
$$\varpi_3 = \mu_3^{(1)} u(x) + \mu_3^{(2)} u(x+1) + \mu_3^{(3)} u(x+2) = Q_3[u(x)].$$

Hence

$$\Delta Q_1[u(x)] = 0, \quad \Delta Q_2[u(x)] = 0, \quad \Delta Q_3[u(x)] = 0,$$

provided that $u(x)$ be a solution of $P[u(x)] = 0$, which we have supposed to be the case throughout.

Thus taking $Q_1[u(x)]$, say, we see that $\Delta Q_1[u(x)] = 0$ has the same fundamental solutions $u_1(x)$, $u_2(x)$, $u_3(x)$ as $P[u(x)] = 0$. Hence the expressions $\Delta Q_1[u(x)]$ and $P[u(x)]$ can only differ by a factor which is a function of x, and by comparing the coefficients of $u(x+3)$, which are respectively $\mu_1^{(3)}(x+1)$ and p_3, we have

$$\Delta Q_1[u(x)] \equiv \frac{\mu_1^{(3)}(x+1)}{p_3} P[u(x)].$$

Thus $\mu_1^{(3)}(x+1) \div p_3$ is a multiplier. Clearly we can prove the same thing for

$$\mu_2^{(3)}(x+1) \div p_3, \quad \mu_3^{(3)}(x+1) \div p_3.$$

If we denote these multipliers by ν_1, ν_2, ν_3, we have

$$\Delta Q_1(x) \equiv \nu_1 P[u(x)].$$

Writing this relation in full, we have

$$\mu_1^{(1)}(x+1)\, u(x+1) + \mu_1^{(2)}(x+1)\, u(x+2) + \mu_1^{(3)}(x+1)\, u(x+3)$$
$$- \mu_1^{(1)}(x)\, u(x) - \mu_1^{(2)}(x)\, u(x+1) - \mu_1^{(3)}(x)\, u(x+2)$$
$$\equiv \nu_1 \{ p_3 u(x+3) + p_2 u(x+2) + p_1 u(x+1) + p_0 u(x) \},$$

so that, equating coefficients of $u(x)$, $u(x+1)$, ..., we obtain

$$p_0(x)\, \nu_1(x) = -\mu_1^{(1)}(x),$$
$$p_1(x)\, \nu_1(x) = \mu_1^{(1)}(x+1) - \mu_1^{(2)}(x),$$
$$p_2(x)\, \nu_1(x) = \mu_1^{(2)}(x+1) - \mu_1^{(3)}(x),$$
$$p_3(x)\, \nu_1(x) = \mu_1^{(3)}(x+1).$$

In the first, replace x by $x+3$, in the second x by $x+2$, and in the third x by $x+1$ and add. We then get the equation satisfied by $\nu_1(x)$, namely,

$$p_0(x+3)\,u(x+3)+p_1(x+2)\,u(x+2)+p_2(x+1)\,u(x+1) \\ +p_3(x)\,u(x)=0,$$

and clearly ν_2, ν_3 satisfy the same equation.

This last equation is called the adjoint equation of the given equation $P[u(x)]=0$. Introducing the operator E, the given equation can be written

$$[p_3(x)\,\mathsf{E}^3+p_2(x)\,\mathsf{E}^2+p_1(x)\,\mathsf{E}+p_0(x)]\,u(x)=0.$$

The adjoint equation is then

$$[\mathsf{E}^3\,p_0(x)+\mathsf{E}^2\,p_1(x)+\mathsf{E}\,p_2(x)+p_3(x)]\,u(x)=0,$$

and we have the important theorem :

The multipliers of a given homogeneous linear difference equation are the solutions of the corresponding adjoint equation.

We also see that the multipliers ν_1, ν_2, ν_3 are the cofactors of the last row of the determinant :

$$D(x+1)=\begin{vmatrix} u_1(x+1) & u_2(x+1) & u_3(x+1) \\ u_1(x+2) & u_2(x+2) & u_3(x+2) \\ u_1(x+3) & u_2(x+3) & u_3(x+3) \end{vmatrix},$$

each divided by $p_3\,D(x+1)$. Thus we have

$$\nu_1\,u_1(x+1)+\nu_2\,u_2(x+1)+\nu_3\,u_3(x+1)=0,$$

$$\nu_1\,u_1(x+2)+\nu_2\,u_2(x+2)+\nu_3\,u_3(x+2)=0,$$

$$\nu_1\,p_3\,u_1(x+3)+\nu_2\,p_3\,u_2(x+3)+\nu_3\,p_3\,u_3(x+3)=1.$$

12·7. The Complete Linear Equation. Denoting as usual the homogeneous linear equation by $P[u(x)]=0$, the equation

$$P[u(x)]=f(x),$$

where $f(x)$ is a given function of x, is called the complete linear equation.

Let $u_1(x), u_2(x), \ldots, u_n(x)$ be a fundamental system of solutions of $P[u(x)] = 0$, and let $v(x)$ be a particular solution of the complete equation, so that $P[v(x)] = f(x)$.

Then the general solution of the complete equation is

$$u(x) = v(x) + \varpi_1 u_1(x) + \varpi_2 u_2(x) + \ldots + \varpi_n u_n(x).$$

The problem of the solution of the complete equation therefore reduces to the problem of obtaining a fundamental set of solutions of the corresponding homogeneous equation and a particular solution of the complete equation. For simplicity, we again consider the equation of the third order,

$$(1) \qquad p_3 u(x+3) + p_2 u(x+2) + p_1 u(x+1) + p_0 u(x) = f(x),$$

and we suppose that we are in possession of a fundamental set of solutions $u_1(x)$, $u_2(x)$, $u_3(x)$ of the homogeneous equation

$$(2) \qquad p_3 u(x+3) + p_2 u(x+2) + p_1 u(x+1) + p_0 u(x) = 0.$$

The multipliers ν_1, ν_2, ν_3 can then be found from Casorati's determinant of the given solutions, or by solving the adjoint equation. Both methods have been explained in 12·6.

To find a particular solution we use Lagrange's method of variation of parameters. We seek to satisfy the complete equation by putting

$$(3) \qquad v(x) = a_1(x) u_1(x) + a_2(x) u_2(x) + a_3(x) u_3(x).$$

As we have three disposable functions a_1, a_2, a_3, we can make them satisfy two additional conditions. We therefore assume that

$$v(x+1) = a_1(x) u_1(x+1) + a_2(x) u_2(x+1) + a_3(x) u_3(x+1),$$

$$v(x+2) = a_1(x) u_1(x+2) + a_2(x) u_2(x+2) + a_3(x) u_3(x+2).$$

The conditions for this are

$$(4) \quad u_1(x+1) \Delta a_1(x) + u_2(x+1) \Delta a_2(x) + u_3(x+1) \Delta a_3(x) = 0.$$

$$(5) \quad u_1(x+2) \Delta a_1(x) + u_2(x+2) \Delta a_2(x) + u_3(x+2) \Delta a_3(x) = 0.$$

Again,

$$v(x+3) = a_1(x) u_1(x+3) + a_2(x) u_2(x+3) + a_3(x) u_3(x+3) + u_1(x+3) \Delta a_1(x) + u_2(x+3) \Delta a_2(x) + u_3(x+3) \Delta a_3(x).$$

Substituting in the given equation for $v(x+1)$, $v(x+2)$, $v(x+3)$ and noting that $u_1(x)$, $u_2(x)$, $u_3(x)$ are solutions of the homogeneous equation, we obtain

$$(6) \qquad p_3\, u_1(x+3) \Delta a_1(x) + p_3\, u_2(x+3) \Delta a_2(x) + p_3\, u_3(x+3) \Delta a_3(x) = f(x).$$

Equations (4), (5), (6) are sufficient to determine

$$\Delta a_1(x), \quad \Delta a_2(x), \quad \Delta a_3(x),$$

but as a matter of fact we already know solutions of these equations from the property (given at the end of 12·6) of the multipliers ν_1, ν_2, ν_3, which shew at once that

$$\Delta a_1(x) = \nu_1 f(x),$$
$$\Delta a_2(x) = \nu_2 f(x),$$
$$\Delta a_3(x) = \nu_3 f(x),$$

so that the required particular solution is

$$v(x) = u_1(x) \mathop{S}_{c}^{x} \nu_1 f(t) \Delta t + u_2(x) \mathop{S}_{c}^{x} \nu_2 f(t) \Delta t + u_3(x) \mathop{S}_{c}^{x} \nu_3 f(t) \Delta t.$$

For example, consider

$$x(x+1)\,u(x+2) - 2x(x+2)\,u(x+1) + (x+1)(x+2)\,u(x) = x(x+1)(x+2).$$

A fundamental set of solutions of the homogeneous equation is x, $x(x-1)$, so that

$$D(x+1) = \begin{vmatrix} x+1 & (x+1)\,x \\ x+2 & (x+2)(x+1) \end{vmatrix} = (x+1)(x+2), \quad p_3 = x(x+1).$$

The multipliers are therefore

$$\frac{-x(x+1)}{D(x+1)} \times \frac{1}{p_3}, \quad \frac{x+1}{D(x+1)} \times \frac{1}{p_3},$$

or

$$-\frac{1}{(x+1)(x+2)}, \quad \frac{1}{x(x+1)(x+2)}.$$

Hence a particular solution is

$$v(x) = -x \mathop{\mathrm{S}}_0^x \frac{t(t+1)(t+2)}{(t+1)(t+2)} \Delta t + x(x-1) \mathop{\mathrm{S}}_0^x \frac{t(t+1)(t+2)}{t(t+1)(t+2)} \Delta t$$

$$= -x \mathop{\mathrm{S}}_0^x t \Delta t + x(x-1) \mathop{\mathrm{S}}_0^x 1 \Delta t$$

$$= -\tfrac{1}{2} x B_2(x) + x(x-1) B_1(x)$$

$$= \tfrac{1}{12}(6x^3 - 12x^2 + 5x).$$

12·72. Polynomial Coefficients. When the coefficients of the complete equation are polynomials, the search for a particular solution can often be simplified by the following method.

Consider

$$(1) \qquad P[u(x)] \equiv p_n(x)\, u(x+n) + \ldots + p_0(x)\, u(x) = p(x),$$

where $p(x)$ is a polynomial of degree m, and the coefficients

$$p_0(x),\ p_1(x),\ \ldots\ ,\ p_n(x)$$

are polynomials of degree μ at most where $\mu \leqslant m$.

Put

$$u(x) = a_0 + a_1 x + \ldots + a_{m-\mu} x^{m-\mu} + w(x).$$

Substituting, we obtain

$$P[w(x)] = p(x) - f(x),$$

where $f(x)$ is a polynomial of degree m whose coefficients depend upon the $m-\mu+1$ constants $a_0, a_1, \ldots, a_{m-\mu}$. We can in general choose the constants so that the coefficients of $x^m, x^{m-1}, \ldots, x^\mu$ on the right vanish, so that we are led to consider an equation of the same form as (1), but with the right-hand member a polynomial of degree $\mu - 1$ at most.

In the case of the equation

$$q_n(x) \overset{n}{\Delta} u + q_{n-1}(x) \overset{n-1}{\Delta} u + \ldots + q_0(x)\, u = q(x).$$

where $q_s(x)$ is a polynomial of degree not exceeding s and $q(x)$ is a polynomial of degree m, we can in general find a particular solution by assuming that

$$u(x) = b_0 + b_1 \binom{x}{1} + b_2 \binom{x}{2} + \ldots + b_m \binom{x}{m}$$

and equating coefficients.

12·8. Solution by Means of Continued Fractions.* The homogeneous linear difference equation of the second order may be exhibited in the form

$$(1) \qquad u_x = a_x u_{x-1} + b_x u_{x-2},$$

a_x, b_x being given functions of the variable x whose domain is the positive integers including zero. It is assumed that a_x, b_x do not become infinite for any value of x in this domain. The general solution of (1) is a function of x, containing two independent arbitrary constants, which when substituted for u_x in (1) renders it an identity. The general solution is a homogeneous linear function of the arbitrary constants which we shall take to be the initial values of u_x, in this case, u_0, u_1.

Denote by $\frac{p_x}{q_x}$ the xth convergent of the continued fraction

$$a_1 + \frac{b_2}{a_2+} \frac{b_3}{a_3+} \cdots .$$

Then

$$p_x = a_x p_{x-1} + b_x p_{x-2},$$

$$q_x = a_x q_{x-1} + b_x q_{x-2}.$$

It follows that p_x and q_x are particular solutions of (1).

Now

$$p_2 = a_2 p_1 + b_2 p_0.$$

If we regard p_1 and p_0 as arbitrary and denote them by u_1 and u_0, we have

$$p_2 = a_2 u_1 + b_2 u_0.$$

Assigning an arbitrary value u_0 to p_0 is actually equivalent to writing u_1 for a_1 and $b_2 u_0$ for b_2.

---

* L. M. Milne-Thomson, *Proc. Royal Soc. Edinburgh,* li (1931), 91-96.

If we write $\dfrac{\beta_{x-1}}{\alpha_{x-1}}$ for the $(x-1)$th convergent of the continued fraction $\dfrac{b_2}{a_2+}\,\dfrac{b_3}{a_3+}\dots$, we have

$$\frac{p_x}{q_x} = u_1 + \frac{\beta_{x-1}}{\alpha_{x-1}}u_0,$$

and it is seen that p_x is derived from p_2 by writing α_{x-1} for a_2 and β_{x-1} for b_2, so that

$$p_x = \alpha_{x-1}u_1 + \beta_{x-1}u_0,$$

and hence the general solution of (1) is

$$u_x = \alpha_{x-1}u_1 + \beta_{x-1}u_0.$$

We have thus expressed the general solution of (1) in terms of the components of the $(x-1)$th convergent of the continued fraction $\dfrac{b_2}{a_2+}\,\dfrac{b_3}{a_3+}\dots$, which contains no arbitrary elements and which is written down from the given equation. It will be observed that the values of a_x, b_x for $x = 0, 1$ are irrelevant.

It is proposed to generalise the above result to the homogeneous equation of order m.

Milne-Thomson's matrix notation, described for the two dimensional fraction in 5·3, allows us to write the above result in the form

$$[u_x] = [u_1 \; u_0]\begin{bmatrix} a_2 & 1 \\ b_2 & 0 \end{bmatrix}\begin{bmatrix} a_3 & 1 \\ b_3 & 0 \end{bmatrix}\cdots\begin{bmatrix} a_{x-1} & 1 \\ b_{x-1} & 0 \end{bmatrix}\begin{bmatrix} a_x \\ b_x \end{bmatrix}.$$

Such a matrix product is in fact equal to a matrix of one row and one column, that is, a scalar.

This result is easily generalised, for consider the difference equation

(2) $$u_x = a_x u_{x-1} + b_x u_{x-2} + \dots + i_x u_{x-m+1} + j_x u_{x-m}$$

and the square matrix J_x (containing m rows and columns) which is equal to

$$\begin{bmatrix} a_x & 1 & 0 & 0 & \dots & 0 \\ b_x & 0 & 1 & 0 & \dots & 0 \\ c_x & 0 & 0 & 1 & \dots & 0 \\ \cdot & \cdot & \cdot & \cdot & \dots & 0 \\ i_x & 0 & 0 & 0 & \dots & 1 \\ j_x & 0 & 0 & 0 & \dots & 0 \end{bmatrix}.$$

We call the matrix product

$$J_1 J_2 J_3 \dots J_x \dots$$

a generalised continued fraction of m dimensions.

Now consider the product

$$M_k = J_1 J_2 \dots J_k = \begin{bmatrix} p_{1,k} & p_{2,k} & p_{3,k} & \dots \\ q_{1,k} & q_{2,k} & q_{3,k} & \dots \\ r_{1,k} & r_{2,k} & r_{3,k} & \dots \\ \cdot & \cdot & \cdot & \dots \end{bmatrix},$$

Writing $k+1$ for k, we have

$$M_{k+1} = M_k J_{k+1},$$

which gives, on forming the product,

$$p_{1,k+1} = a_{k+1} p_{1,k} + b_{k+1} p_{2,k} + \dots + j_{k+1} p_{m,k},$$

$$p_{2,k+1} = p_{1,k}, \quad p_{3,k+1} = p_{2,k}, \dots, \quad p_{m,k+1} = p_{m-1,k}.$$

If then we write p_k for $p_{1,k}$, it follows at once that the top row of the matrix M_k can be written

$$p_k, \quad p_{k-1}, \dots, \quad p_{k-m+1},$$

and similar results hold for every row. Thus

$$J_1 J_2 \dots J_n = \begin{bmatrix} p_n & p_{n-1} & p_{n-2} & \dots \\ q_n & q_{n-1} & q_{n-2} & \dots \\ \cdot & \cdot & \cdot & \dots \\ w_n & w_{n-1} & w_{n-2} & \dots \end{bmatrix},$$

where

(3)
$$\begin{aligned} p_n &= a_n p_{n-1} + b_n p_{n-2} + \dots + j_n p_{n-m}, \\ q_n &= a_n q_{n-1} + b_n q_{n-2} + \dots + j_n q_{n-m}, \\ &\dots \\ w_n &= a_n w_{n-1} + b_n w_{n-2} + \dots + j_n w_{n-m}. \end{aligned}$$

We call $p_n, q_n, \dots, w_n$ the components of the nth convergent of the continued fraction, and we have therefore for the xth convergent

$$\begin{bmatrix} p_x \\ q_x \\ \cdot \\ w_x \end{bmatrix} = J_1 J_2 \dots J_{x-1} \begin{bmatrix} a_x \\ b_x \\ \cdot \\ j_x \end{bmatrix}.$$

It follows from (3) that $p_x, q_x, \dots, w_x$ are particular solutions of (2).

Now, from (3),

$$p_m = a_m p_{m-1} + b_m p_{m-2} + \dots + j_m p_0.$$

If we regard $p_0, p_1, \dots, p_{m-1}$ as arbitrary and denote them by $u_0, u_1, \dots, u_{m-1}$, we have

$$p_m = a_m u_{m-1} + b_m u_{m-2} + \dots + j_m u_0,$$

which can be written

$$[p_m] = [u_{m-1}\, u_{m-2} \dots u_0] \begin{bmatrix} a_m \\ b_m \\ \cdot \\ \cdot \\ j_m \end{bmatrix}.$$

Thus we can write the general solution of (2) in the form

$$[u_x] = [u_{m-1}\, u_{m-2} \dots u_0]\, J_m J_{m+1} \dots J_{x-1} \begin{bmatrix} a_x \\ b_x \\ \cdot \\ j_x \end{bmatrix},$$

which is the required generalisation.

EXAMPLES XII

1. Form the difference equations whose fundamental systems are

$$\text{(i)}\quad a^x,\quad x\,a^x,\quad x^2 a^x;$$

$$\text{(ii)}\quad a^x,\quad \binom{x}{1} a^x,\quad \binom{x}{2} a^x,$$

and explain why the result is the same in each case.

2. Complete the proof of the statement in 12·14.

3. Prove that the equations

$$p_2 u(x+2) + p_1 u(x+1) + p_0 u(x) = 0,$$

$$q_1 u(x+1) - q_0 u(x) = 0$$

have a solution in common if

$$p_2(x)\,q_0(x)\,q_0(x+1)+p_1(x)\,q_0(x)\,q_1(x+1)$$
$$+p_0(x)\,q_1(x)\,q_1(x+1)=0.$$

4. Find the condition that

$$p_2\,u(x+2)+p_1\,u(x+1)+p_0\,u(x)=0,$$
$$q_2\,u(x+2)+q_1\,u(x+1)+q_0\,u(x)=0$$

should have a solution in common.

5. Find the solution common to the equations

$$(2x^2+4x+1)\,u(x+3)-(2x^2+8x+3)\,u(x+2)$$
$$-(2x^2+4x-3)\,u(x+1)+(2x^2+8x+7)\,u(x)=0,$$
$$u(x+2)-u(x+1)-2u(x)=0.$$

6. Given the expressions

$$P[u_x]=(2x^2+4x+1)\,u_{x+3}-(2x^2+8x+3)\,u_{x+2}$$
$$-(2x^2+4x-3)\,u_{x+1}+(2x^2+8x+7)\,u_x,$$
$$Q[u_x]=x(x+1)\,u_{x+2}-2x(x+2)\,u_{x+1}+(x+1)(x+2)\,u_x,$$

prove that

$$P[u_x]=R\{Q[u_x]\},$$

and shew that

$$R\{\;\}=\frac{2x^2+4x+1}{x^3+3x+2}\,\mathsf{E}+\frac{2x^2+8x+7}{x^3+3x+2}.$$

7. Prove that the adjoint of the adjoint equation reproduces the original equation.

8. Prove that the sum or difference of the adjoints of two linear difference expression is the adjoint of their sum or difference.

9. If $p(x)$, $q(x)$ be rational functions, shew that the equation

$$u(x+2)+p(x)\,u(x+1)-q(x)\{q(x+1)-p(x)\}\,u(x)=0$$

is reducible. Prove also that the most general equation of the second order which is reducible must have the above form.

10. Obtain a fundamental system of solutions of the equation of example 9.

11. Prove that every equation which has multiple solutions is reducible.

12. Prove that the equation

$$u(x+2) - 2\frac{x+2}{x+1}u(x+1) + \frac{x+2}{x}u(x) = 0$$

is reducible.

13. Find a particular solution of the equation

$$x^3 \overset{3}{\Delta} u + x(x-1) \overset{2}{\Delta} u + u = x^4.$$

14. Given that a particular solution of

$$u_{x+2} - a(a^x + 1)\, u_{x+1} + a^{x+1} u_x = 0$$

is

$$u_x = a^{\frac{1}{2}x(x-1)},$$

deduce the general solution.

CHAPTER XIII

THE LINEAR DIFFERENCE EQUATION WITH CONSTANT COEFFICIENTS

13·0. Homogeneous Equations. Consider the equation

$$P[u(x)] = p_n u(x+n) + p_{n-1} u(x+n-1) + \dots$$
$$+ p_1 u(x+1) + p_0 u(x) = 0,$$

where $p_n, p_{n-1}, \dots, p_1, p_0$ are constants and $p_n \neq 0$, $p_0 \neq 0$.

There is evidently no loss of generality if we take $p_n = 1$.

The equation can then be written

(1) $$P[u(x)] = [\mathsf{E}^n + p_{n-1}\mathsf{E}^{n-1} + \dots + p_1 \mathsf{E} + p_0]\, u(x) = 0.$$

Putting $u(x) = \rho^x v(x)$, we have

$$P[\rho^x v(x)] = \rho^x [\rho^n \mathsf{E}^n + p_{n-1}\rho^{n-1}\mathsf{E}^{n-1} + \dots + p_1 \rho \mathsf{E} + p_0]\, v(x).$$

Denote by $f(\rho) = \rho^n + \rho^{n-1} p_{n-1} + \dots + \rho p_1 + p_0$ the *characteristic function* of the given equation.

Then

$$P[\rho^x v(x)] = \rho^x f(\rho\,\mathsf{E})\, v(x)$$
$$= \rho^x f(\rho + \rho\,\Delta)\, v(x),$$

since $$\mathsf{E} \doteq 1 + \Delta.$$

Expanding by Taylor's theorem, the equation is equivalent to

(2) $$[f(\rho) + \rho f'(\rho)\,\Delta + \frac{\rho^2}{2!} f''(\rho)\,\overset{2}{\Delta} + \dots + \frac{\rho^n}{n!} f^{(n)}(\rho)\,\overset{n}{\Delta}]\, v(x) = 0.$$

This equation is evidently satisfied by $v(x) = 1$, provided that ρ be a root of the *characteristic equation*

(3) $$f(\rho) \equiv \rho^n + \rho^{n-1} p_{n-1} + \dots + \rho p_1 + p_0 = 0.$$

Let $\rho_1, \rho_2, \dots, \rho_n$ be the roots of the characteristic equation, which we suppose to be all different.

Then we have n particular solutions of (1), namely,

$$\rho_1^x, \ \rho_2^x, \dots, \rho_n^x.$$

These solutions form a fundamental system, since Casorati's determinant

$$D(x) = \begin{vmatrix} \rho_1^x & \rho_2^x & \dots & \rho_n^x \\ \rho_1^{x+1} & \rho_2^{x+1} & \dots & \rho_n^{x+1} \\ \cdot & \cdot & \dots & \cdot \\ \rho_1^{x+n-1} & \rho_2^{x+n-1} & \dots & \rho_n^{x+n-1} \end{vmatrix}$$

$$= (\rho_1\rho_2 \dots \rho_n)^x \begin{vmatrix} 1 & 1 & \dots & 1 \\ \rho_1 & \rho_2 & \dots & \rho_n \\ \rho_1^2 & \rho_2 & \dots & \rho_n^2 \\ \cdot & \cdot & \dots & \cdot \\ \rho_1^{n-1} & \rho_2^{n-1} & \dots & \rho_n^{n-1} \end{vmatrix}$$

$$= [(-1)^n p_0]^x \prod_{i>j} (\rho_i - \rho_j), \quad \text{(see 1·5)}.$$

Since $p_0 \neq 0$ and $\rho_i \neq \rho_j \ (i \neq j)$, $D(x)$ never vanishes for any finite x.

Example 1. $u(x+2) - 7u(x+1) + 12u(x) = 0$.

The characteristic equation is

$$\rho^2 - 7\rho + 12 = 0.$$

Hence

$$u(x) = \varpi_1 3^x + \varpi_2 4^x.$$

Suppose now that the characteristic equation has multiple roots. Let ρ_1, say, be a root of multiplicity ν.

Then

$$f(\rho_1) = 0, \ f'(\rho_1) = 0, \dots, \ f^{(\nu-1)}(\rho_1) = 0, \ f^{(\nu)}(\rho_1) \neq 0.$$

Putting $\rho = \rho_1$ in (2), we obtain

$$\left[\frac{\rho_1^\nu}{\nu!} f^{(\nu)}(\rho_1) \overset{\nu}{\Delta} + \frac{\rho_1^{\nu+1}}{(\nu+1)!} f^{(\nu+1)}(\rho_1) \overset{\nu+1}{\Delta} + \dots + \frac{\rho_1^n}{n!} f^{(n)}(\rho_1) \overset{n}{\Delta}\right] v(x) = 0.$$

We can satisfy this equation by taking $v(x)$ to be any of

$$1,\ x,\ x^2, \ldots,\ x^{\nu-1}.$$

Hence, corresponding to $\rho = \rho_1$, we have the solutions

$$\rho_1^x,\ x\,\rho_1^x, \ldots,\ x^{\nu-1}\rho_1^x,$$

so that a multiple root of multiplicity ν of the characteristic equation gives a set of ν particular solutions, and these solutions contribute to the general solution the term

$$\varpi_1\,\rho_1^x + \varpi_2\,x\,\rho_1^x + \varpi_3\,x^2\,\rho_1^x + \ldots + \varpi_{\nu-1}\,x^{\nu-1}\,\rho_1^x = q_1(x)\,\rho_1^x,$$

where $q_1(x)$ is a "polynomial" in x whose coefficients are periodics. Thus, if the characteristic equation have k distinct roots, we have the general solution

$$u(x) = q_1(x)\,\rho_1^x + q_2(x)\,\rho_2^x + \ldots + q_k(x)\,\rho_k^x,$$

where the coefficients of the "polynomials" $q(x)$ are periodics. To shew that this is indeed the general solution, we must shew that it is impossible to choose the arbitrary periodics in such a way that, when they are not all zero, $u(x)$ vanishes identically.

For simplicity, take the case of three distinct roots ρ_1, ρ_2, ρ_3, and suppose, if possible, that we can choose the periodics (not all zero) so that

$$q_1(x)\,\rho_1^x + q_2(x)\,\rho_2^x + q_3(x)\,\rho_3^x \equiv 0.$$

Writing $x+1$, $x+2$ for x, we have

$$q_1(x+1)\,\rho_1^{x+1} + q_2(x+1)\,\rho_2^{x+1} + q_3(x)\,\rho_3^{x+1} \equiv 0,$$

$$q_2(x+2)\,\rho_1^{x+2} + q_2(x+2)\,\rho_2^{x+2} + q_3(x+2)\,\rho_3^{x+2} \equiv 0.$$

Eliminating $\rho_1{}^x$, $\rho_2{}^x$, $\rho_3{}^x$,

$$\begin{vmatrix} q_1(x) & q_2(x) & q_3(x) \\ \rho_1\,q_1(x+1) & \rho_2\,q_2(x+1) & \rho_3\,q_3(x+1) \\ \rho_1^2\,q_1(x+2) & \rho_2^2\,q_2(x+2) & \rho_3^2\,q_3(x+2) \end{vmatrix} \equiv 0,$$

that is

$$\begin{vmatrix} q_1(x) & \cdot & \cdot \\ \rho_1\,q_1(x) + \rho_1\,\Delta q_1(x) & \cdot & \cdot \\ \rho_1^2\,q_1(x) + 2\rho_1^2\,\Delta\,q_1(x) + \rho_1^2\,\overset{2}{\Delta}\,q_1(x) & \cdot & \cdot \end{vmatrix} \equiv 0.$$

The coefficient of the highest power of x in this is

$$\varpi \begin{vmatrix} 1 & 1 & 1 \\ \rho_1 & \rho_2 & \rho_3 \\ \rho_1^2 & \rho_2^2 & \rho_3^2 \end{vmatrix}$$

where ϖ is a periodic which is not identically zero. The determinant never vanishes, so that the coefficient of the highest power of x cannot vanish identically and the supposition is untenable.

Example 2. $u(x+3)-3u(x+1)-2u(x)=0$.

The characteristic equation is

$$\rho^3-3\rho-2=(\rho+1)^2(\rho-2)=0,$$

so that

$$u(x)=(\varpi_1+\varpi_2 x)(-1)^x+\varpi_3 2^x.$$

Example 3. $u(x+6)+2u(x+3)+u(x)=0$.

The characteristic equation is

$$\rho^6+2\rho^3+1=(\rho+1)^2(\rho+e^{\frac{2}{3}\pi i})^2(\rho+e^{-\frac{2}{3}\pi i})^2=0,$$

so that each root is repeated once and

$$u(x)=(\varpi_1+x\,\varpi_2)(-1)^x+(\varpi_3+x\,\varpi_4)\,e^{\frac{2}{3}\pi ix}+(\varpi_5+x\,\varpi_6)\,e^{-\frac{2}{3}\pi ix},$$

or in a real form

$$u(x)=(\varpi_1+x\,\varpi_2)(-1)^x+(\varpi_3+x\,\varpi_4)\cos\frac{2\pi x}{3}+(\varpi_5+x\,\varpi_6)\sin\frac{2\pi x}{3}.$$

13·02. Boole's Symbolic Method. The general equation of 13·0 can be written in the operational form

$$f(\mathbf{E})\,u(x)=0,$$

where $f(\rho)$ is the characteristic function.

Thus, factorising $f(\rho)$, we can write the equation in the form

(1) $$(\mathbf{E}-\rho_1)^a(\mathbf{E}-\rho_2)^b\ldots(\mathbf{E}-\rho_k)^h\,u(x)=0,$$

where $\rho_1, \rho_2, \ldots, \rho_k$ are the distinct roots of the characteristic equation. The order in which the factors in (1) are written is immaterial, since all the coefficients are constants.

If we choose $u(x)$ to satisfy

(2) $$(\mathbf{E}-\rho_k)^h\,u(x)=0,$$

we have a solution of the given difference equation. Since ar factor may be put last in the form (1) we obtain altogeth k equations of the type (2).

Now, by the theorem of 2·43, we have

$$(\mathsf{E}-\rho_k)^h u(x) = \rho_k^x(\rho_k \mathsf{E}-\rho_k)^h \rho_k^{-x} u(x)$$

$$= \rho_k^{x+h} \overset{h}{\Delta} [\rho_k^{-x} u(x)].$$

Hence, to satisfy (2), we must have

$$\overset{h}{\Delta} [\rho_k^{-x} u(x)] = 0,$$

or

$$\rho_k^{-x} u(x) = \varpi_1 + \varpi_2 x + \dots \varpi_{h-1} x^{h-1},$$

whence

$$u(x) = \rho_k^x(\varpi_1 + \varpi_2 x + \dots + \varpi_{h-1} x^{h-1}).$$

Treating each factor of (1) in the same way, we arrive at th same solution as in 13·0.

Corresponding to a root ρ of multiplicity ν of the characteristi equation, we have the fundamental set of solutions

$$\rho^x, \quad x\rho^x, \dots, \quad x^{\nu-1}\rho^x.$$

By suitably combining these we obtain a second fundamental se

$$\rho^x, \quad \binom{x-1}{1}\rho^x, \quad \binom{x-1}{2}\rho^x, \dots, \quad \binom{x-1}{\nu-1}\rho^x,$$

so that we can write the general solution in the form

$$u(x) = \left[\varpi_1 + \varpi_2\binom{x-1}{1} + \dots + \varpi_{\nu-1}\binom{x-1}{\nu-1}\right]\rho_1^x$$

$$+\left[\varpi_\nu + \varpi_{\nu+1}\binom{x-1}{1} + \dots\right]\rho_2^x + \dots,$$

which is sometimes convenient.

13·1. The Complete Equation. Let the given equation b

$$u(x+n) + p_{n-1} u(x+n-1) + \dots + p_1 u(x+1) + p_0 u(x) = \phi(x).$$

As we have seen in 12·7, to obtain the general solution we need only find a particular solution of the complete equation and add to this the general solution of the homogeneous equation obtained by utting $\phi(x)$ zero. This latter may be called the complementary olution.

Let $f(\rho)$ be the characteristic function. If the roots $\rho_1, \rho_2, \dots, \rho_n$ f $f(\rho) = 0$ be all different, we have the fundamental set of solutions $\rho_1^x, \rho_2^x, \dots, \rho_n^x$. To obtain the required particular solution we use agrange's method of variation of parameters. As we have seen in 2·7, the solution is then

$$\rho_1^x \underset{c}{\overset{x}{S}} \nu_1 \phi(t) \Delta t + \dots + \rho_n^x \underset{c}{\overset{x}{S}} \nu_n \phi(t) \Delta t,$$

here $\nu_1, \nu_2, \dots, \nu_n$ are the multipliers corresponding to the fundaiental set of solutions.

Forming Casorati's determinant

$$D(x+1) = \begin{vmatrix} \rho_1^{x+1} & \rho_2^{x+1} & \dots & \rho_n^{x+1} \\ \rho_1^{x+2} & \rho_2^{x+2} & \dots & \rho_n^{x+2} \\ \cdot & \cdot & \dots & \cdot \\ \rho_1^{x+n} & \rho_2^{x+n} & \dots & \rho_n^{x+n} \end{vmatrix}$$

e know from 12·6, since $p_n = 1$, that $\nu_1, \nu_2, \dots, \nu_n$ are the ofactors of the elements of the last row, each divided by $D(x+1)$. ow we have, as in 13·0,

$$D(x+1) = \rho_1^{x+1} \rho_2^{x+1} \dots \rho_n^{x+1} \prod_{j>i} (\rho_j - \rho_i), \quad (i, j = 1, 2, \dots, n).$$

Consider the cofactor of ρ_n^{x+n}. Clearly this is of the same form s $D(x+1)$, but formed from the elements $\rho_1, \rho_2, \dots, \rho_{n-1}$, and is herefore

$$\rho_1^{x+1} \dots \rho_{n-1}^{x+1} \prod_{j>i} (\rho_j - \rho_i), \quad (i, j = 1, 2, \dots, n-1),$$

nd thus

$$\nu_n = \rho_n^{-x-1} \Big/ \prod_i (\rho_n - \rho_i), \quad (i = 1, 2, \dots, n-1),$$

$$= \rho_n^{-x-1} / f'(\rho_n).$$

The same argument shews that

$$\nu_k = \rho_k^{-x-1} / f'(\rho_k), \quad (k = 1, 2, \dots, n).$$

The required particular solution is therefore

$$\sum_{k=1}^{n} \rho_k^x \mathop{S}_{c}^{x} \left[\rho_k^{-t-1}\phi(t)/f'(\rho_k)\right] \Delta t,$$

and thus the general solution is

$$u(x) = \sum_{k=1}^{n} \left[\varpi_k + \frac{1}{f'(\rho_k)} \mathop{S}_{c}^{x} \rho_k^{-t-1}\phi(t)\,\Delta t\right] \rho_k^x.$$

Example 1. $u(x+2) - u(x+1) - 6u(x) = x.$

Here

$$f(\rho) = \rho^2 - \rho - 6 = (\rho-3)(\rho+2),$$

so that a fundamental system of the homogeneous equation is 3^x, $(-2)^x$. Since $f'(\rho) = 2\rho - 1$, the corresponding multipliers are $3^{-x-1}/5$, $-(-2)^{-x-1}/5$, and the complete solution is

$$u(x) = 3^x\left(\varpi_1 + \mathop{S}_{c}^{x} \frac{3^{-t-1}.t}{5}\Delta t\right) + (-2)^x\left(\varpi_2 - \mathop{S}_{c}^{x} \frac{(-2)^{-t-1}.t}{5}\Delta t\right)$$

Now, from 8·1,

$$\mathop{S}_{0}^{x} t\,a^{-t}\Delta t = -\frac{x\,a^{-x+1}}{a-1} - \frac{a^{-x+1}}{(a-1)^2} + 1.$$

Taking $c = 0$, as is permissible since only a particular solution is required, we have

$$u(x) = \varpi_1 . 3^x + \varpi_2(-2)^x - \tfrac{1}{20}(2x+1-20.3^{x-1})$$
$$- \tfrac{1}{45}(3x-1+9(-2)^{x-1}),$$

which is equivalent to

$$u(x) = \varpi_1 3^x + \varpi_2(-2)^x - \tfrac{1}{6}x - \tfrac{1}{36},$$

where the terms 3^{x-1}, $-\frac{1}{5}(-2)^{x-1}$ have been absorbed into the terms $\varpi_1 3^x$, $\varpi_2(-2)^x$. In fact the constant c contributes nothing to the generality of the solution, so that we can always omit any constant terms in the summation which may arise from the particular value attributed to c.

Example 2. $u(x+2)-5u(x+1)+6u(x) = 5^x.$

$$f(\rho) = (\rho-2)(\rho-3), \quad f'(\rho) = 2\rho-5,$$

$$u(x) = \varpi_1 2^x + \varpi_2 3^x - 2^x \underset{c}{\overset{x}{S}} \frac{5^t}{2^{t+1}} \Delta t + 3^x \underset{c}{\overset{x}{S}} \frac{5^t}{3^{t+1}} \Delta t.$$

Now

$$\underset{c}{\overset{x}{S}} a^t \Delta t = \frac{a^t}{a-1} + \text{constant},$$

whence we obtain

$$u(x) = \varpi_1 2^x + \varpi_2 3^x - \frac{2^x}{2} \cdot \left(\frac{5}{2}\right)^x \div \left(\frac{5}{2}-1\right)$$

$$+ \frac{3^x}{3}\left(\frac{5}{3}\right)^x \div \left(\frac{5}{3}-1\right),$$

$$u(x) = \varpi_1 2^x + \varpi_2 3^x + \tfrac{1}{6} 5^x.$$

In the above discussion we have supposed the roots of the characteristic equation to be distinct. The method is still applicable if the equation present multiple roots, but the solution does not assume the very simple form which we have just found.

We illustrate the method by considering the equation of the third order :

$$u(x+3)-(2a+b)\,u(x+2)+(a^2+2ab)\,u(x+1)-a^2b\,u(x) = \phi(x).$$

The characteristic equation is

$$(\rho-a)^2(\rho-b) = 0.$$

A fundamental system is a^x, xa^x, b^x, and therefore

$$D(x+1) = \begin{vmatrix} a^{x+1} & (x+1)a^{x+1} & b^{x+1} \\ a^{x+2} & (x+2)a^{x+2} & b^{x+2} \\ a^{x+3} & (x+3)a^{x+3} & b^{x+3} \end{vmatrix} = a^{2x+3}\, b^{x+1}(b-a)^2,$$

and the multipliers are therefore

$$\frac{a^{-x-2}\,[(b-a)\,x-2a+b]}{(b-a)^2}, \quad \frac{-a^{-x-2}}{b-a}, \quad \frac{b^{-x-1}}{(b-a)^2},$$

so that

$$u(x) = a^x\left[\varpi_1 + \frac{1}{(b-a)^2}\mathop{S}_{c}^{x} a^{-t-2}[(b-a)t-2a+b]\,\phi(t)\,\Delta t\right]$$

$$+\,x\,a^x\left[\varpi_2 - \frac{1}{b-a}\mathop{S}_{c}^{x} a^{-t-2}\,\phi(t)\,\Delta t\right]$$

$$+\,b^x\left[\varpi_3 + \frac{1}{(b-a)^2}\mathop{S}_{c}^{x} b^{-t-1}\,\phi(t)\,\Delta t\right].$$

Example 3. $u(x+3)-5u(x+2)+8u(x+1)-4u(x) = x\,2^x$.
Here

$$f(\rho) = \rho^3-5\rho^2+8\rho-4 = (\rho-2)^2(\rho-1).$$

A fundamental system is therefore

$$1,\quad 2^x,\quad x\,2^x,$$

and the corresponding multipliers are

$$1,\quad -2^{-x-2}(x+3),\quad 2^{-x-2}.$$

Thus

$$u(x) = \left(\varpi_1 + \mathop{S}_{c}^{x} 2^t\,t\,\Delta t\right) + \left(\varpi_2 - \tfrac{1}{4}\mathop{S}_{c}^{x} t(t+3)\,\Delta t\right)2^x$$

$$+\left(\varpi_3 + \tfrac{1}{4}\mathop{S}_{c}^{x} t\,\Delta t\right)x2^x.$$

The first summation contributes terms of the form 2^x, $x\,2^x$, which already occur in the complementary solution and can be omitted. Taking $c = 0$, we have

$$u(x) = \varpi_1 + [\varpi_2 - \tfrac{1}{4}\{\tfrac{1}{3}B_3(x) + \tfrac{3}{2}B_2(x)\}]2^x + [\varpi_3 + \tfrac{1}{8}B_2(x)]\,x\,2^x.$$

Omitting from the particular solution terms which occur in the complementary solution, we have finally

$$u(x) = \varpi_1 + 2^x(\varpi_2 + x\varpi_3 - \tfrac{3}{8}x^2 + \tfrac{1}{24}x^3).$$

13·2. Boole's Operational Method. The methods hitherto explained have been of a general character and of universal application in so far as the sums exist. The labour of applying the general methods even in simple cases may be very considerable. We now turn to operational methods which considerably shorten the work of finding a particular solution. Boole's method, which we now proceed to explain, is of particularly simple application in three cases, namely, those in which the right-hand side of the complete equation is of one of the following forms :

(I) a polynomial in x;

(II) a^x;

(III) a^x multiplied by a polynomial in x.

The third form, of course, includes I and II.

If $f(\rho)$ be the characteristic function, the equation can be written in the form

$$f(\mathsf{E})\, u(x) = \phi(x),$$

where $\phi(x)$ is a given function of x.

For finding the solution of the homogeneous equation the general method is as simple as Boole's, since both in practice merely involve finding the roots of the characteristic equation $f(\rho) = 0$. We therefore need only consider methods of finding the particular solution. To effect this Boole writes

$$u(x) \doteqdot \frac{1}{f(\mathsf{E})}\phi(x),$$

and proceeds to interpret the meaning to be attached to the operation on the right.

13·21. Case I, $\phi(x) = x^m$, m zero or a positive integer.

Writing $1+\Delta$ for E, the symbolic solution is

$$u(x) \doteqdot \frac{1}{f(1+\Delta)}\, x^m.$$

Now suppose that the characteristic equation does not admit the root unity.

Then

$$f(1+\lambda) = a_0 + a_1\lambda + \ldots + a_{n-1}\lambda^{n-1} + \lambda^n,$$

where $a_0 \neq 0$.

If we expand $\dfrac{1}{f(1+\lambda)}$ in *ascending* powers of λ as far as λ^m, we get

$$\frac{1}{f(1+\lambda)} = b_0 + b_1\lambda + \ldots + b_m\lambda^m + \frac{g(\lambda)\,\lambda^{m+1}}{f(1+\lambda)},$$

where $g(\lambda)$ is a polynomial.

Thus

$$1 \equiv f(1+\lambda)(b_0 + b_1\lambda + \ldots + b_m\lambda^m) + g(\lambda)\,\lambda^{m+1}.$$

Since the expression on the right is a polynomial in λ we can associate with it a definite operation, which is equivalent to unity, by writing Δ for λ.

Thus

$$x^m \equiv f(1+\Delta)(b_0 + b_1\Delta + b_2\overset{2}{\Delta} + \ldots + b_m\overset{m}{\Delta})\,x^m + g(\Delta)\overset{m+1}{\Delta}x^m.$$

Now

$$\overset{m+1}{\Delta}x^m = 0.$$

Hence

$$(b_0 + b_1\Delta + b_2\overset{2}{\Delta} + \ldots + b_m\overset{m}{\Delta})\,x^m$$

satisfies the equation

$$f(1+\Delta)\,u(x) = x^m \quad \text{or} \quad f(\mathsf{E})\,u(x) = x^m,$$

and is therefore a particular solution of the equation. The actual expansion of $\dfrac{1}{f(1+\lambda)}$ can as a rule be most rapidly performed by ordinary long division. An alternative is to express $\dfrac{1}{f(1+\lambda)}$ in partial fractions.

If $\phi(x)$ be a polynomial of degree m the same method obviously applies.

Example 1.

$$u(x+2) + u(x+1) + u(x) = x^2 + x + 1.$$

Here $f(\rho) = \rho^2 + \rho + 1$, and therefore

$$\frac{1}{f(1+\lambda)} = \frac{1}{\lambda^2 + 3\lambda + 3} = \tfrac{1}{3} - \tfrac{1}{3}\lambda + \tfrac{2}{9}\lambda^2 + \ldots\,.$$

A particular solution is therefore

$$u(x) = (\tfrac{1}{3} - \tfrac{1}{3}\Delta + \tfrac{2}{9}\overset{2}{\Delta})(x^2+x+1)$$
$$= \tfrac{1}{3}x^2 - \tfrac{1}{3}x + \tfrac{1}{9}.$$

If the characteristic equation admit the root unity of multiplicity r, our equation becomes

$$f_1(\mathsf{E})(\mathsf{E}-1)^r u(x) = x^m,$$

where $f_1(\rho)$ is a polynomial of degree $n-r$ in ρ.

Putting

$$(\mathsf{E}-1)^r u(x) = \Delta^r u(x) = v(x),$$

the equation for $v(x)$ is

$$f_1(\mathsf{E})\, v(x) = x^m.$$

Now

$$f_1(1+\lambda) = c_0 + c_1\lambda + c_2\lambda^2 + \ldots + c_{n-r}\lambda^{n-r}, \quad c_0 \neq 0,$$

so that we can apply the method already discussed and obtain

$$v(x) = (b_0 + b_1\Delta + b_2\overset{2}{\Delta} + \ldots + b_m\overset{m}{\Delta})\, x^m,$$

which is a polynomial of degree m in x. If we write this in the form (see 2·12),

$$v(x) = d_0\binom{x}{m} + d_1\binom{x}{m-1} + \ldots + d_m\binom{x}{0},$$

a particular solution of the given equation is obtained from

$$\Delta^r u(x) = d_0\binom{x}{m} + d_1\binom{x}{m-1} + \ldots + d_{m-1}\binom{x}{1} + d_m\binom{x}{0}.$$

Since $\Delta\binom{x}{s} = \binom{x}{s-1}$, the required particular solution is

$$u(x) = d_0\binom{x}{m+r} + d_1\binom{x}{m+r-1} + \ldots + d_{m-1}\binom{x}{r+1} + d_m\binom{x}{r}.$$

Example 2.

$$u(x+4) - 5u(x+3) + 9u(x+2) - 7u(x+1) + 2u(x) = x^3 + 1.$$

Here

$$f(\mathsf{E}) = (\mathsf{E}-1)^3(\mathsf{E}-2),$$

and the equation can be written

$$(\Delta - 1)\overset{3}{\Delta} u(x) = x^3 + 1.$$

Putting $\overset{3}{\Delta} u(x) = v(x)$, we have

$$v(x) = \frac{1}{\Delta - 1}(x^3+1) = (-1 - \Delta - \overset{2}{\Delta} - \overset{3}{\Delta})(x^3+1)$$

$$= -(x^3 + 3x^2 + 9x + 14).$$

Thus we have

$$\overset{3}{\Delta} u(x) = -6\binom{x}{3} - 12\binom{x}{2} - 13\binom{x}{1} - 14\binom{x}{0},$$

and a particular solution is

$$-6\binom{x}{6} - 12\binom{x}{5} - 13\binom{x}{4} - 14\binom{x}{3}.$$

The terms 1, x, x^2 belong to the complementary solution, so that we obtain for the general solution, after reduction,

$$u(x) = \varpi_1 2^x + \varpi_2 + \varpi_3 x + \varpi_4 x^2 - \tfrac{17}{24}x^3 - \tfrac{1}{4}x^4 + \tfrac{1}{40}x^5 - \tfrac{1}{120}x^6.$$

13·22. Case II, $\phi(x) = a^x$. Here we have

$$f(\mathsf{E})\, u(x) = a^x,$$

and, symbolically,

$$u(x) \doteqdot \frac{1}{f(\mathsf{E})} a^x.$$

Now, from 2·42, $\phi(\mathsf{E})\, a^x = \phi(a)\, a^x$, so that, if a be not a zero of $f(\mathsf{E})$, we have the particular solution

$$u(x) = \frac{a^x}{f(a)},$$

since

$$f(\mathsf{E})\frac{a^x}{f(a)} = \frac{f(a)}{f(a)} a^x = a^x.$$

If, however, a be a zero of order r of $f(\rho)$, we have

$$f(\rho) = (\rho - a)^r f_1(\rho),$$

where

$$f_1(a) = \frac{f^{(r)}(a)}{r!}.$$

Put $u(x) = a^x v(x)$. Then our equation becomes

$$f_1(\mathsf{E})(\mathsf{E}-a)^r a^x v(x) = a^x.$$

Using the theorem of 2·43, this gives

$$a^x f_1(a\,\mathsf{E})(a\,\mathsf{E}-a)^r v(x) = a^x,$$

whence, since $\Delta \doteqdot \mathsf{E}-1$,

$$a^r \overset{r}{\Delta} v(x) = \frac{1}{f_1(a\,\mathsf{E})}\cdot 1 = \frac{1}{f_1(a+a\,\Delta)}\cdot 1 = \frac{1}{f_1(a)}$$

by our former method in 13·21. Hence

$$\overset{r}{\Delta} v(x) = \frac{a^{-r}\,r!}{f^{(r)}(a)} = \frac{a^{-r}\,r!}{f^{(r)}(a)}\binom{x}{0},$$

so that

$$v(x) = \binom{x}{r}\frac{a^{-r}\,r!}{f^{(r)}(a)},$$

and the required particular solution is

$$u(x) = \frac{a^{x-r}\,x^{(r)}}{f^{(r)}(a)}.$$

Example 1. $u(x+2)+a^2 u(x) = \cos m x$.

We have $\cos m x = R(e^{mix})$ where R denotes the real part. Hence the particular solution is

$$u(x) = \frac{1}{\mathsf{E}^2+a^2}R(e^{mix}) = R\left(\frac{e^{mix}}{a^2+e^{2mi}}\right)$$

$$= \frac{a^2\cos m x+\cos m(x-2)}{a^4+2a^2\cos 2m+1}.$$

Example 2. $u(x+3)-6u(x+2)+12u(x+1)-8u(x) = 2^x$.

Here

$$f(\rho) = (\rho-2)^3, \quad f^{(3)}(2) = 3!,$$

$$u(x) = \frac{x^{(3)}\,2^{x-3}}{3!} = \binom{x}{3}2^{x-3}.$$

13·23. Case III, $\phi(x) = a^x R(x)$, where $R(x)$ is a polynomial of degree m, say.

$$f(\mathsf{E})\, u(x) = a^x R(x).$$

Put $u(x) = a^x v(x)$. Then by 2·43,

$$a^x f(a\,\mathsf{E})\, v(x) = a^x R(x),$$

so that the equation becomes

$$f(a\,\mathsf{E})\, v(x) = R(x),$$

which can be treated as in Case I.

Example.

$$(\mathsf{E}-2)^3(\mathsf{E}-1)\, u(x) = x^2\, 2^x.$$

Write $u(x) = 2^x v(x)$, then

$$8(\mathsf{E}-1)^3(2\mathsf{E}-1)\, v(x) = x^2,$$

$$\overset{3}{\Delta}\, v(x) = \frac{1}{8(2\Delta+1)}\, x^2$$

$$= \tfrac{1}{8}(1 - 2\Delta + 4\overset{2}{\Delta})\, x^2$$

$$= \tfrac{1}{8}(x^2 - 4x + 6)$$

$$= \frac{1}{4}\binom{x}{2} - \frac{3}{8}\binom{x}{1} + \frac{3}{4}\binom{x}{0}.$$

Thus

$$v(x) = \frac{1}{4}\binom{x}{5} - \frac{3}{8}\binom{x}{4} + \frac{3}{4}\binom{x}{3},$$

and the complete solution is

$$u(x) = \varpi_1 + 2^x \left\{\varpi_2 + x\,\varpi_3 + x^2\,\varpi_4 + \frac{1}{4}\binom{x}{5} - \frac{3}{8}\binom{x}{4} + \frac{3}{4}\binom{x}{3}\right\}.$$

13·24. The General Case. When the right-hand member of our equation is not one of the forms already considered we can proceed as follows. For simplicity of writing, we consider the equation of the third order,

$$f(\mathsf{E})\, u(x) \equiv u(x+3) + p_2\, u(x+2) + p_1\, u(x+1) + p_0\, u(x) = \phi(x),$$

$$f(\rho) = \rho^3 + p_2\,\rho^2 + p_1\,\rho + p_0.$$

Suppose $f(\rho)$ to have a repeated root ρ_1 so that

$$f(\rho) = (\rho - \rho_1)^2 (\rho - \rho_3).$$

Then expressing $1/f(\rho)$ in partial fractions, we have

(1) $$\frac{1}{f(\rho)} = \frac{A}{\rho - \rho_1} + \frac{B}{(\rho - \rho_1)^2} + \frac{C}{\rho - \rho_3},$$

and we note for later use that

(2) $$A(\rho - \rho_3)(\rho - \rho_1) + B(\rho - \rho_3) + C(\rho - \rho_1)^2 \equiv 1.$$

The given equation has the symbolic solution

$$u_1(x) = \frac{1}{f(\mathbf{E})} \phi(x).$$

Using (1), we write this in the form

(3) $$u_1(x) = \frac{A}{\mathbf{E} - \rho_1} \phi(x) + \frac{B}{(\mathbf{E} - \rho_1)^2} \phi(x) + \frac{C}{\mathbf{E} - \rho_3} \phi(x),$$

and we proceed to justify this process by shewing that we can interpret the terms of (3) in such a way that the resulting function does in fact satisfy the given equation.

With regard to the interpretation, we first postulate that the relation

(4) $$\psi(x) = \frac{1}{(\mathbf{E} - m)^r} \phi(x)$$

implies that

(5) $$(\mathbf{E} - m)^r \psi(x) = \phi(x).$$

With this law of interpretation, we have

$$\begin{aligned} f(\mathbf{E})\, u_1(x) &= (\mathbf{E} - \rho_1)^2 (\mathbf{E} - \rho_3)\, u_1(x) \\ &= [A(\mathbf{E} - \rho_3)(\mathbf{E} - \rho_1) + B(\mathbf{E} - \rho_3) + C(\mathbf{E} - \rho_1)^2]\, \phi(x) \\ &= \phi(x), \end{aligned}$$

since, by (2), the content of the square bracket is unity.

We have here made use of the commutative property expressed by

$$(\mathbf{E} - \rho_1)^2 (\mathbf{E} - \rho_3)\, v \doteqdot (\mathbf{E} - \rho_3)(\mathbf{E} - \rho_1)^2\, v.$$

Thus we have shewn that (3) does in fact satisfy the given equation if the operations be interpreted according to (4) and (5).

It remains to carry out the operation (4), in other words, we must find a (particular) solution of

$$(\mathsf{E} - m)^r \psi(x) = \phi(x).$$

Using the theorem of 2·43, this becomes

$$m^x (m\,\mathsf{E} - m)^r [m^{-x} \psi(x)] = \phi(x),$$

which gives, since $\Delta \doteqdot \mathsf{E} - 1$,

$$\overset{r}{\Delta}[m^{-x} \psi(x)] = m^{-x-r} \phi(x),$$

whence, from 8·12,

$$\psi(x) = m^x \mathop{\mathrm{S}}_{c}^{x} \binom{x-t-1}{r-1} m^{-t-r} \phi(t)\, \Delta t.$$

Thus to find a particular solution of the equation

$$f(\mathsf{E})\, u(x) = \phi(x),$$

we express $1/f(\rho)$ *in partial fractions ;*

$$\frac{1}{f(\rho)} = \sum_{m,r} \frac{A_{m,r}}{(\rho - m)^r};$$

the particular solution is then

$$\sum_{m,r} A_{m,r}\, m^{x-r} \mathop{\mathrm{S}}_{c}^{x} \binom{x-t-1}{r-1} m^{-t} \phi(t)\, \Delta t,$$

where c *is arbitrary and may be chosen to have any convenient value.*

The case $m = 0$ is an apparent exception.

If, however, $m = 0$, we have

$$f(\rho) = \rho^k f_1(\rho)$$

and the equation becomes

$$f_1(\mathsf{E})\, u(x+k) = \phi(x).$$

Writing $u(x+k) = v(x)$, we have an equation of the type already discussed. This case is really excluded, since we postulated in 13·0 that $p_0 \neq 0$. No generality is gained by the contrary supposition.

Example.

$$u(x+4)-2u(x+3)+2u(x+1)-u(x)=\frac{1}{x}.$$

Here

$$f(\rho)=(\rho-1)^3(\rho+1),$$

$$\frac{1}{f(\rho)}=\frac{1}{2(\rho-1)^3}-\frac{1}{4(\rho-1)^2}+\frac{1}{8(\rho-1)}-\frac{1}{8(\rho+1)},$$

and a particular solution $u_1(x)$ is therefore given by

$$u_1(x)=\tfrac{1}{2}\mathop{S}_1^x\binom{x-t-1}{2}\frac{1}{t}\Delta t-\tfrac{1}{4}\mathop{S}_1^x\binom{x-t-1}{1}\frac{1}{t}\Delta t$$

$$+\tfrac{1}{8}\mathop{S}_1^x\frac{1}{t}\Delta t-\tfrac{1}{8}(-1)^x\mathop{S}_1^x\frac{(-1)^{-t}}{t}\Delta t,$$

$$2\binom{x-t-1}{2}\cdot\frac{1}{t}=\frac{x^2}{t}-x\left(2+\frac{3}{t}\right)+t+3+\frac{2}{t}.$$

Also, we notice that the complementary solution is

$$\varpi(-1)^x+\varpi_1+\varpi_2 x+\varpi_3 x^2,$$

so that terms of this type may be ignored. Hence

$$\begin{aligned}u_1(x)&=\tfrac{1}{4}x^2\,\Psi(x)-\tfrac{3}{4}x\,\Psi(x)+\tfrac{1}{2}\,\Psi(x)\\&\quad-\tfrac{1}{4}x\,\Psi(x)+\tfrac{1}{4}\,\Psi(x)\\&\quad+\tfrac{1}{8}\,\Psi(x)+\tfrac{1}{16}\,g(x),\\u_1(x)&=\Psi(x)\left(\tfrac{1}{4}x^2-x+\tfrac{7}{8}\right)+\tfrac{1}{16}\,g(x);\end{aligned}$$

for $g(x)$ see 11·31.

13·25. Broggi's Method for the Particular Solution.*

Consider the equation

(1) $P[u(x)]=u(x+n)+p_{n-1}u(x+n-1)+\ldots+p_0 u(x)=\phi(x)$,

where $p_0\neq 0$. The characteristic function is

$$f(\rho)=\rho^n+p_{n-1}\rho^{n-1}+\ldots+p_0.$$

Let

$$g(\rho)=\frac{1}{f(\rho)}=\alpha_0+\alpha_1\rho+\alpha_2\rho^2+\ldots.$$

* U. Broggi, *Atti d. r. Acc. d. Lincei* (6), xv (1932), p. 707.

Then

(2) $\alpha_0 p_0 = 1,\ \ \alpha_0 p_1 + \alpha_1 p_0 = 0,\ \ \alpha_0 p_2 + \alpha_1 p_1 + \alpha_2 p_0 = 0,\ \ \ldots,$

$$\alpha_0 p_{n-1} + \alpha_1 p_{n-2} + \ldots + \alpha_{n-1} p_0 = 0,$$

$$\alpha_s + \alpha_{s+1} p_{n-1} + \alpha_{s+2} p_{n-2} + \ldots + \alpha_{s+n} p_0 = 0,\quad (s = 0, 1, 2, \ldots).$$

If then

$$\limsup_{s\to\infty} \sqrt[s]{|\phi(x+s)|}$$

be less than the modulus of the smallest zero of $f(\rho)$, the series

(3) $$F(x) = \alpha_0 \phi(x) + \alpha_1 \phi(x+1) + \alpha_2 \phi(x+2) + \ldots$$

converges and $F(x)$ is a particular solution of (1).

In fact

$$P[F(x)] = \alpha_0 p_0 \phi(x) + (\alpha_0 p_1 + \alpha_1 p_0)\phi(x+1) + \ldots = \phi(x)$$

from the relations (2). Now let

(4) $$\phi(x) = a^x \psi(x).$$

We have, from 2·5 (1),

$$\psi(x+s) = \psi(x) + \binom{s}{1}\Delta\psi(x) + \ldots + \binom{s}{s}\overset{s}{\Delta}\psi(x).$$

If we substitute this in (3), after collecting the coefficients of the differences,

(5) $$F(x) = a^x\left[g(a)\,\psi(x) + \frac{a}{1!}g'(a)\,\Delta\psi(x) + \frac{a^2}{2!}g''(a)\,\overset{2}{\Delta}\psi(x) + \ldots\right],$$

where it is supposed that a is not a zero of $f(\rho)$.

When $\psi(x)$ is a polynomial, the series for $F(x)$ terminates and $F(x)$ is the product of a^x and a polynomial.

But the expression (5) for the particular solution can still be used even when $\psi(x)$ is not a polynomial, provided that the series converges, which will be the case in particular if

$$\limsup_{s\to\infty} \sqrt[s]{\left|\frac{a^s}{s!}g^{(s)}(a)\,\overset{s}{\Delta}\psi(x)\right|} < 1.$$

It will be seen that the method is equivalent to expanding

$$1/f(a+a\Delta)$$

in ascending powers of Δ and contains the justification of this procedure when it is applicable. Broggi proceeds to examine forms which lead to factorial series, but we will not pursue the matter further.

13·26. Solution by Undetermined Coefficients. In cases where the right-hand side of the equation has some particular form it may be possible to guess the form of the particular solution and obtain this by means of undetermined coefficients. This method will succeed in particular if $\phi(x) = a^x \times$ (a polynomial in x). We illustrate the idea with a few examples.

Example 1. $u(x+2) - 6u(x+1) + 4u(x) = 10.$

Try $u_1(x) = c$, a constant,

$$c - 6c + 4c = 10,$$

whence

$$c = -10,$$

$$u(x) = \varpi_1(3+\sqrt{5})^x + \varpi_2(3-\sqrt{5})^x - 10.$$

Example 2. $u(x+2) - 4u(x+1) + 4u(x) = x\,2^x.$

Here 2 is a double zero of the characteristic function. Comparison with 13·23 shews that we should expect

$$u_1(x) = 2^x\left(a + bx + c\binom{x}{2} + d\binom{x}{3}\right).$$

The terms $2^x(a+bx)$ will appear in the complementary solution, so that

$$u_1(x) = 2^x\left(c\binom{x}{2} + d\binom{x}{3}\right).$$

Hence we expect to find c and d, such that

$$4\left(c\frac{(x+2)(x+1)}{2} + d\frac{(x+2)(x+1)x}{6}\right)$$

$$-8\left(c\frac{(x+1)x}{2} + d\frac{(x+1)x(x-1)}{6}\right)$$

$$+4\left(c\frac{x(x-1)}{2} + d\frac{x(x-1)(x-2)}{6}\right) \equiv x$$

Since there is no constant term, $c = 0$, and we see that $d = \frac{3}{4}$ satisfies all the conditions.

Thus

$$u(x) = (\varpi_1 + x\,\varpi_2)\,2^x + x(x-1)(x-2)\,2^{x-3}.$$

Example 3.

$$u(x+3) + 2u(x+2) + 2u(x+1) + u(x) = \frac{3}{x(x+3)} + \frac{3}{(x-1)(x+2)}.$$

The right hand $= \dfrac{1}{x} - \dfrac{1}{x+3} + \dfrac{1}{x-1} - \dfrac{1}{x+2}$.

This suggests putting $u_1(x) = \dfrac{a}{x} + \dfrac{b}{x-1}$, whence

$$\frac{a}{x+3} + \frac{b}{x+2} + \frac{2a}{x+2} + \frac{2b}{x+1} + \frac{2a}{x+1} + \frac{2b}{x} + \frac{a}{x} + \frac{b}{x-1}$$

$$\equiv \frac{1}{x} - \frac{1}{x+3} + \frac{1}{x-1} - \frac{1}{x+2},$$

$$a = -1, \qquad a + 2b = 1,$$

$$2a + b = -1, \qquad b = 1,$$

$$2(a+b) = 0.$$

These equations are consistent and are satisfied by $b = 1$, $a = -1$. Also

$$f(\rho) = (\rho+1)(\rho^2+\rho+1).$$

Hence

$$u(x) = \varpi_1(-1)^x + \varpi_2\,\omega^x + \varpi_2\,\omega^{2x} + \frac{1}{x(x-1)},$$

where ω, ω^2 are the imaginary cube roots of unity. This example is due to Markoff.

13·3. Particular Solution by Contour Integrals. We consider the equation

(1) $$u(x+n) + p_{n-1}\,u(x+n-1) + \dots + p_0\,u(x) = \phi(x),$$

whose characteristic function is

(2) $$f(\rho) = \rho^n + p_{n-1}\,\rho^{n-1} + \dots + p_0.$$

Let $\rho_1, \rho_2, \dots, \rho_k$ be the distinct zeros of $f(\rho)$. About each of these points we describe closed curves, say circles, which are exterior to one another. Denote by C the contour consisting of the aggregate of the contours of these circles. We seek to satisfy (1) by

$$u_1(x) = \frac{1}{2\pi i}\int_C \rho^{x-1}\frac{g(\rho, x)}{f(\rho)}\,d\rho, \tag{3}$$

where $g(\rho, x)$, regarded as a function of ρ, is holomorphic inside and upon each of the circles round the points $\rho_1, \rho_2, \ldots, \rho_k$.

The above expression will satisfy (1) if we have

$$u_1(x+1) = \frac{1}{2\pi i}\int_C \rho^{x}\frac{g(\rho, x)}{f(\rho)}\,d\rho,$$

$$\cdots\cdots\cdots\cdots$$

$$u_1(x+n-1) = \frac{1}{2\pi i}\int_C \rho^{x+n-2}\frac{g(\rho, x)}{f(\rho)}\,d\rho,$$

$$u_1(x+n) = \frac{1}{2\pi i}\int_C \rho^{x+n-1}\frac{g(\rho, x)}{f(\rho)}\,d\rho + \phi(x). \tag{4}$$

For, if this be the case we have, on substituting in the left-hand member of (1),

$$\phi(x) + \frac{1}{2\pi i}\int_C (\rho^n + p_{n-1}\,\rho^{n-1} + \ldots + p_0)\,\rho^{x-1}\frac{g(\rho, x)}{f(\rho)}\,d\rho,$$

which, from (2), is equal to

$$\phi(x) + \frac{1}{2\pi i}\int_C \rho^{x-1}\,g(\rho, x)\,d\rho,$$

and the integral vanishes, since $g(\rho, x)$ is holomorphic by supposition. Thus we have proved that $u_1(x)$ satisfies (1), if (4) be true and if

$$u_1(x+s) = \frac{1}{2\pi i}\int_C \rho^{x+s-1}\frac{g(\rho, x)}{f(\rho)}\,d\rho, \quad s = 0, 1, \ldots, n-1. \tag{5}$$

Change x into $x+1$, then

$$u_1(x+s+1) = \frac{1}{2\pi i}\int_C \rho^{x+s}\frac{g(\rho, x+1)}{f(\rho)}\,d\rho.$$

But, from (5),

$$u_1(x+s+1) = \frac{1}{2\pi i}\int_C \rho^{x+s}\frac{g(\rho, x)}{f(\rho)}\,d\rho, \quad s = 0, 1, \ldots, n-2,$$

and hence, by subtraction,

$$(6) \qquad \frac{1}{2\pi i}\int_C \rho^{x+s}\frac{g(\rho, x+1)-g(\rho, x)}{f(\rho)}\,d\rho = 0, \quad s = 0, 1, \dots, n-2,$$

while

$$(7) \qquad \frac{1}{2\pi i}\int_C \rho^{x+n-1}\,\frac{g(\rho, x+1)-g(\rho, x)}{f(\rho)}\,d\rho = \phi(x).$$

We can fulfil both these conditions if we take for $g(\rho, x)$ a solution of the equation

$$g(\rho, x+1)-g(\rho, x) = \rho^{-x}\,\phi(x),$$

for

$$\frac{1}{2\pi i}\int_C \frac{\rho^s\,\phi(x)}{f(\rho)}\,d\rho = 0, \quad s = 0, 1, \dots, n-2,$$

since $f(\rho)$ is of degree n and the residue at $\rho = \infty$ of $\rho^s / f(\rho)$ is zero.

On the other hand,

$$\frac{1}{2\pi i}\int_C \frac{\rho^{n-1}\,\phi(x)\,d\rho}{f(\rho)} = \phi(x),$$

since the residue is now unity at $\rho = \infty$. Thus we have the theorem, due to Nörlund:

The linear difference equation with constant coefficients

$$f(\mathbf{E})\,u(x) = \phi(x)$$

has the particular solution

$$u_1(x) = \frac{1}{2\pi i}\int_C \rho^{x-1}\,\frac{g(\rho, x)}{f(\rho)}\,d\rho,$$

provided that $g(\rho, x)$ *be a solution of*

$$\Delta_x\, g(\rho, x) = \rho^{-x}\,\phi(x),$$

which is holomorphic inside the contour C, which consists of a set of non-overlapping circles each of which encloses one, and only one, of the distinct zeros of the characteristic function $f(\rho)$.

Example. $u(x+2)-5\,u(x+1)+6\,u(x) = \dfrac{1}{\Gamma(x+1)}$.

Here

$$f(\rho) = (\rho-2)(\rho-3)$$

and the equation for $g(\rho, x)$ is

$$g(\rho, x+1)-g(\rho, x) = \frac{\rho^{-x}}{\Gamma(x+1)},$$

which is seen by direct addition to be satisfied by

$$g(\rho, x) = -\sum_{s=0}^{\infty} \frac{\rho^{-x-s}}{\Gamma(x+s+1)},$$

which is holomorphic in the neighbourhood of $\rho = 2$, $\rho = 3$.

Thus

$$-u_1(x) = \frac{1}{2\pi i}\int_C \left(-\frac{1}{\rho-2}+\frac{1}{\rho-3}\right) \sum_{s=0}^{\infty} \frac{\rho^{-s-1}}{\Gamma(x+s+1)}\, d\rho.$$

Now, the residue of

$$\frac{1}{\rho^{s+1}(\rho-3)}-\frac{1}{\rho^{s+1}(\rho-2)} \quad \text{is} \quad \frac{1}{3^{s+1}}-\frac{1}{2^{s+1}}.$$

Thus

$$-u_1(x) = \frac{1}{3}\left[\frac{1}{\Gamma(x+1)}+\frac{1}{3\,\Gamma(x+2)}+\frac{1}{3^2\,\Gamma(x+3)}+\dots\right]$$

$$-\frac{1}{2}\left[\frac{1}{\Gamma(x+1)}+\frac{1}{2\,\Gamma(x+2)}+\frac{1}{2^2\,\Gamma(x+3)}+\dots\right]$$

$$= \frac{e^{\frac{1}{3}}\, 3^{x-1} P(x\,;\,\frac{1}{3})}{\Gamma(x)} - \frac{e^{\frac{1}{2}}\, 2^{x-1} P(x\,;\,\frac{1}{2})}{\Gamma(x)},$$

in terms of the Incomplete Gamma Function of 11·33.

13·32. Laplace's Integral. If $\phi(x)$ can be expressed by means of Laplace's integral in the form

$$\phi(x) = \int_L \rho^{x-1}\,\psi(\rho)\, d\rho,$$

where the path of integration L passes through none of the zeros of the characteristic function $f(\rho)$, we have the particular solution

$$u_1(x) = \int_L \rho^{x-1}\frac{\psi(\rho)}{f(\rho)}\, d\rho,$$

for in this case

$$f(\mathbf{E})\, u_1(x) = \int_L \rho^{x-1}\frac{\psi(\rho)}{f(\rho)}\, f(\rho)\, d\rho = \phi(x).$$

In particular, this method can be applied whenever $\phi(x)$ can be expanded in a factorial series, for then $\phi(x)$ can be represented by Laplace's integral.

Example. Consider the equation of 13·26, Ex. 3.

We have, if $R(x) > 1$,

$$\frac{3}{x(x+3)}+\frac{3}{(x-1)(x+2)}=\frac{1}{x-1}+\frac{1}{x}-\frac{1}{x+2}-\frac{1}{x+3}$$

$$=\int_0^1 (\rho^{x-2}+\rho^{x-1}-\rho^{x+1}-\rho^{x+2})\,d\rho$$

$$=\int_0^1 \rho^{x-1}\left(\frac{1}{\rho}+1-\rho^2-\rho^3\right)d\rho.$$

Also, $f(\rho)=(\rho+1)(\rho^2+\rho+1)$, so that we avoid the zeros of $f(\rho)$ if we take for L the segment $(0, 1)$ of the real axis. Hence

$$u_1(x)=\int_0^1 \frac{\rho^{x-2}(\rho+1)(1-\rho^3)}{(\rho+1)(\rho^2+\rho+1)}\,d\rho$$

$$=\int_0^1 (\rho^{x-2}-\rho^{x-1})\,d\rho=\frac{1}{x-1}-\frac{1}{x},$$

in agreement with the result obtained by trial in 13·26. The present method, which shews why the trial succeeded, would be applicable even if the coefficients of the given fractions were not equal.

13·4. Equations reducible to Equations with Constant Coefficients. Consider an equation of the type

$$u(x+n)+A_1\psi(x)\,u(x+n-1)+A_2\,\psi(x)\,\psi(x-1)\,u(x+n-2)+\dots$$
$$+A_n\,\psi(x)\,\psi(x-1)\,\psi(x-2)\dots\psi(x-n+1)\,u(x)=\phi(x).$$

Let

$$\mathop{S}_{c}^{x}\log\psi(t-n)\mathop{\Delta}_{-1} t=\chi(x-n)+\text{constant}.$$

Then

$$\chi(x-n+1)=\chi(x-n)+\log\psi(x-n+1),$$

and

$$e^{\chi(x-n+1)}=\psi(x-n+1)\,e^{\chi(x-n)}.$$

If, therefore, we put

$$u(x) = e^{\chi(x-n)}\, v(x),$$

the equation reduces to

$$v(x+n) + A_1\, v(x+n-1) + \ldots + A_n\, v(x) = \phi(x)\, e^{-\chi(x)},$$

and when $A_1, A_2, \ldots, A_n$ are constants, this is an equation with constant coefficients.

In the same way the equation

$$\psi(x)\,.\,\psi(x+1)\ldots\psi(x+n-1)\,u(x+n)$$
$$+A_1\,\psi(x)\,.\,\psi(x+1)\ldots\psi(x+n-2)\,u(x+n-1)+\ldots$$
$$+A_{n-1}\,\psi(x)\,u(x+1)+A_n\,u(x) = \phi(x),$$

reduces to

$$v(x+n) + A_1\, v(x+n-1) + \ldots + A_n\, v(x) = \phi(x)\, e^{\chi(x)},$$

if we put

$$u(x) = v(x)\, e^{-\chi(x)},$$

where

$$\mathop{S}_{c}^{x} \log \psi(t)\,\Delta t = \chi(x) + \text{constant}.$$

Example.

$$u(x+3) + a^x\, u(x+2) + a^{2x}\, u(x+1) + a^{3x}\, u(x) = a^{\frac{1}{2}x^2}.$$

$$a^{2x} = a\,.\,a^x\,.\,a^{x-1}, \quad a^{3x} = a^3\,.\,a^x\,.\,a^{x-1}\,.\,a^{x-2},$$

$$\mathop{S}_{c}^{x} \log a^{t-3} \mathop{\Delta}_{-1} t = \log a \mathop{S}_{c}^{x} (t-3) \mathop{\Delta}_{-1} t$$

$$= (\tfrac{1}{2}\log a)(x-3)(x-2) + \text{constant}.$$

Put

$$u(x) = a^{\frac{1}{2}(x-3)(x-2)}\, v(x).$$

Then

$$v(x+3) + v(x+2) + a\, v(x+1) + a^3\, v(x) = a^{-\frac{1}{2}x},$$

a particular solution of which is seen, by Boole's method, to be

$$v_1(x) = \frac{a^{-\frac{1}{2}x}}{a^{-\frac{3}{2}} + a^{-1} + a^{\frac{1}{2}} + a^3},$$

so that

$$u_1(x) = \frac{a^{\frac{1}{2}(x^2-6x+6)}}{a^{-\frac{3}{2}} + a^{-1} + a^{\frac{1}{2}} + a^3}.$$

13·5. Milne-Thomson's Operational Method.* We now consider an operational method of solution founded upon the operator P^{-1}, which was introduced in 2·6. The method is applicable to those problems in which the variable x proceeds at constant (here taken as unit) intervals from an initial value which can be taken as zero without loss of generality. We then write

$$(1) \qquad \mathsf{P}^{-1} u_x = u_{x-1} + u_{x-2} + \dots + u_1 + u_0,$$

when there is no risk of ambiguity. Otherwise we can use the notation

$$(2) \qquad \mathsf{P}^{-1}_{(x)} u_t = u_{x-1} + u_{x-2} + \dots + u_0.$$

Then

$$\Delta \mathsf{P}^{-1} u_x = u_x,$$

but

$$\mathsf{P}^{-1} \Delta u_x = \Delta u_{x-1} + \Delta u_{x-2} + \dots + \Delta u_0, \text{ and thus}$$

$$(3) \qquad \mathsf{P}^{-1} \Delta u_x = u_x - u_0.$$

Thus $\Delta \mathsf{P}^{-1} u_x = \mathsf{P}^{-1} \Delta u_x$ if, and only if, $u_0 = 0$, in which case no arbitrary elements are introduced and the operators Δ, P^{-1} are completely commutative. It follows that $\Delta^{-1} u_x = \mathsf{P}^{-1} u_x$, if the result of each operation vanish with x.

Let X be a given function of x. Consider the function u_x defined by the three conditions:

(i) $(\Delta - a)^r u_x = X$;

(ii) $u_0 = 0$;

(iii) u_x contains no arbitrary elements.

Operating with P^{-r}, we get from (i),

$$(1 - a\,\mathsf{P}^{-1})^r u_x \doteqdot \mathsf{P}^{-r} X,$$

so that we can write

$$(4) \qquad u_x \doteqdot (\mathsf{P} - a)^{-r} X.$$

Now, from 2·52, we have

$$X = (\Delta - a)^r u_x = (1+a)^{x+r} \overset{r}{\Delta} [(1+a)^{-x} u_x]$$

* Milne-Thomson, *loc. cit.* p. 38.

and therefore comparing with (4)

$$(\mathsf{P}-a)^{-r}X = (1+a)^x\,\mathsf{P}^{-r}[(1+a)^{-x-r}X],$$

and hence, from 2·6 (6), we have *the fundamental theorem of the operator* P, *namely*,

$$(5)\quad (\mathsf{P}-a)^{-r}X(x) = (1+a)^x\,\mathsf{P}^{-1}_{(x-r+1)}\binom{x-t-1}{r-1}(1+a)^{-t-r}X(t),$$

where $X(x)$ *is any function of* x.

13·51. Operations on Unity.

From the definition

$$(1)\qquad \mathsf{P}^{-1}1 = x = \binom{x}{1},$$

and, from 2·71, by repeated applications,

$$(2)\qquad \mathsf{P}^{-r}1 = \binom{x}{r}.$$

Since x is a positive integer,

$$(3)\qquad \mathsf{P}^{-x-1}1 = 0.$$

From 13·5 (5), putting $X = 1$,

$$(\mathsf{P}-a)^{-1}1 = (1+a)^x\,\mathsf{P}^{-1}(1+a)^{-x-1}$$

$$(4)\qquad = [(1+a)^x - 1]\,a^{-1}.$$

Again,

$$(1-a\,\mathsf{P}^{-1})(1+a\,\mathsf{P}^{-1}+a^2\,\mathsf{P}^{-2}+\dots+a^x\,\mathsf{P}^{-x})\,1$$

$$= (1-a^{x+1}\,\mathsf{P}^{-x-1})\,1 = 1,$$

and hence

$$\frac{\mathsf{P}}{\mathsf{P}-a}1 = (1+a\,\mathsf{P}^{-1}+\dots+a^x\,\mathsf{P}^{-x})\,1$$

$$(5)\qquad = (1+a)^x,$$

from (2).

Differentiating $r-1$ times with respect to a, we have

$$(6)\qquad \frac{\mathsf{P}}{(\mathsf{P}-a)^r}1 = \binom{x}{r-1}(1+a)^{x-r+1}.$$

This result can also be proved without difficulty by induction.

Again, from (5),

$$\frac{\mathsf{P}}{\mathsf{P}-ai}1 = (1+ai)^x = (1+a^2)^{\frac{1}{2}x}\exp(ix\tan^{-1}a).$$

Hence

$$(7) \qquad \frac{\mathsf{P}^2}{\mathsf{P}^2+a^2}1 = (1+a^2)^{\frac{1}{2}x}\cos(x\tan^{-1}a),$$

$$(8) \qquad \frac{\mathsf{P}a}{\mathsf{P}^2+a^2}1 = (1+a^2)^{\frac{1}{2}x}\sin(x\tan^{-1}a).$$

The operation $\frac{\phi(\mathsf{P})}{\psi(\mathsf{P})}1$ where ϕ and ψ are polynomials, and the degree of ϕ is not greater than the degree of ψ, can be interpreted by expressing $\frac{\phi(\mathsf{P})}{\mathsf{P}\psi(\mathsf{P})}$ in partial fractions. If $\frac{A}{(\mathsf{P}-a)^r}$ be a typical partial fraction, we have

$$\frac{\phi(\mathsf{P})}{\psi(\mathsf{P})}1 = \sum\frac{A\mathsf{P}}{(\mathsf{P}-a)^r}1 = \sum A\binom{x}{r-1}(1+a)^{x-r+1},$$

from (6). This is the extension to finite differences of Heaviside's Partial Fraction Theorem for the differential * operator p.

13·52. Operations on a given Function X. The interpretation of $\frac{1}{(\mathsf{P}-a)^r}X$ is given by 13·5 (5). Let

$$\frac{\phi(\mathsf{P})}{\psi(\mathsf{P})} = \Sigma\frac{B}{(\mathsf{P}-a)^r}.$$

Then

$$\frac{\phi(\mathsf{P})}{\psi(\mathsf{P})}X = \Sigma\frac{B}{(\mathsf{P}-a)^r}X.$$

To each of the operations on the right 13·5 (5) may be applied. Another method may be used if X be of the form $(1+a)^x f(x)$, where $f(x)$ is a polynomial. We can expand $f(x)$ in factorials so that

$$\begin{aligned} X &= (1+a)^x\,\Sigma A_{r-1}\binom{x}{r-1} \\ &= \Sigma B_r\binom{x}{r-1}(1+a)^{x-r+1} \\ &= \Sigma B_r\frac{\mathsf{P}}{(\mathsf{P}-a)^r}1. \end{aligned}$$

* See H. Jeffreys, *Operational Methods in Mathematical Physics* (1931), for the corresponding theory of the differential operator.

Hence

$$\frac{\phi(\mathsf{P})}{\psi(\mathsf{P})}X = \Sigma B_r \cdot \frac{\phi(\mathsf{P})}{\psi(\mathsf{P})}\frac{\mathsf{P}}{(\mathsf{P}-a)^r}1$$

$$= \Sigma C_r \cdot \frac{\mathsf{P}}{(\mathsf{P}-b)^r}1, \text{ say,}$$

which is interpreted in terms of operations on unity. For example,

$$\frac{9(\mathsf{P}-1)}{\mathsf{P}+2}2^x x^2 = \frac{9(\mathsf{P}-1)}{\mathsf{P}+2}\left(8\cdot\binom{x}{2}2^{x-2}+2x\,.\,2^{x-1}\right)$$

$$= \frac{9(\mathsf{P}-1)}{\mathsf{P}+2}\left(\frac{8\mathsf{P}}{(\mathsf{P}-1)^3}+\frac{2\mathsf{P}}{(\mathsf{P}-1)^2}\right)1$$

$$= \frac{24\mathsf{P}}{(\mathsf{P}-1)^2}1-\frac{2\mathsf{P}}{\mathsf{P}-1}1+\frac{2\mathsf{P}}{\mathsf{P}+2}1$$

$$= 3x\,.\,2^{x+2}-2^{x+1}+2(-1)^x.$$

13·53. Application to Linear Difference Equations with Constant Coefficients. The general equation of order n in one dependent variable is

$$(1) \qquad a_n \overset{n}{\Delta} u_x + a_{n-1}\overset{n-1}{\Delta} u_x + \dots + a_r \overset{r}{\Delta} u_x + \dots + a_0 u_x = X,$$

where the a_r are constant and X is a function of x only. Since

$$\overset{r}{\Delta} u_x = [(1+\Delta)-1]^r u_x = u_{x+r} - \binom{r}{1} u_{x+r-1} + \dots + (-1)^r u_x,$$

(1) can also be exhibited in the form

$$b_n u_{x+n} + b_{n-1} u_{x+n-1} + \dots + b_r u_{x+r} + \dots + b_0 u_x = X.$$

This is the form which generally arises in practice. It may be converted into the form (1) by the formula $u_{x+r} = (1+\Delta)^r u_x$.

Taking the form (1), we obtain the operational solution in terms of the initial conditions

$$\overset{r}{\Delta} u_0 = u_{r,\,0} \quad (r = 0, 1, 2, \dots, n-1)$$

by continually operating with P^{-1} until we arrive at an equation in which the operation Δ does not occur. Each operation with P^{-1} introduces initial values and depresses the order by unity. The final equation in which Δ does not occur is solved for u_x in terms of P. The interpretation of the operations gives the value of u_x in terms of the initial values.

The method, which is quite general and which applies also to simultaneous equations, is best illustrated by examples.

The equation of the first order.

$$\Delta u_x = a\, u_x + X,$$

$$u_x - u_0 = \mathsf{P}^{-1}(a\, u_x + X),$$

$$u_x = \frac{\mathsf{P}}{\mathsf{P}-a} u_0 + \frac{1}{\mathsf{P}-a} X$$

$$= u_0 (1+a)^x + (1+a)^x \mathsf{P}^{-1}[(1+a)^{-x-1} X].$$

The equation of the second order.

$$\overset{2}{\Delta} u_x - (a+b)\,\Delta u_x + ab\, u_x = X.$$

Denote by v_0 the initial value of Δu_x:

$$\Delta u_x - v_0 - (a+b)(u_x - u_0) + \mathsf{P}^{-1} ab\, u_x = \mathsf{P}^{-1} X,$$

$$u_x - u_0 - \mathsf{P}^{-1} v_0 - \mathsf{P}^{-1}(a+b)(u_x - u_0) + \mathsf{P}^{-2} ab\, u_x = \mathsf{P}^{-2} X,$$

$$u_x = \frac{\mathsf{P}^2 u_0 - \mathsf{P}(a+b) u_0 + \mathsf{P} v_0}{(\mathsf{P}-a)(\mathsf{P}-b)} + \frac{1}{(\mathsf{P}-a)(\mathsf{P}-b)} X$$

$$= \frac{v_0 - b u_0}{a-b} \cdot \frac{\mathsf{P}^*}{\mathsf{P}-a} - \frac{v_0 - a u_0}{a-b} \cdot \frac{\mathsf{P}}{\mathsf{P}-b} + \frac{1}{a-b}\left(\frac{1}{\mathsf{P}-a} - \frac{1}{\mathsf{P}-b}\right) X$$

$$= \frac{v_0 - b u_0}{a-b}(1+a)^x - \frac{v_0 - a u_0}{a-b}(1+b)^x$$

$$+ \frac{(1+a)^x}{a-b} \mathsf{P}^{-1}[(1+a)^{-x-1} X]$$

$$- \frac{(1+b)^x}{a-b} \mathsf{P}^{-1}[(1+b)^{-x-1} X].$$

If $a = b$,

$$u_x = \frac{(v_0 - a u_0)\mathsf{P}}{(\mathsf{P}-a)^2} + \frac{\mathsf{P} u_0}{\mathsf{P}-a} + \frac{1}{(\mathsf{P}-a)^2} X$$

$$= (v_0 - a u_0)\, x (1+a)^{x-1} + u_0 (1+a)^x$$

$$+ (1+a)^x \mathsf{P}^{-2}[(1+a)^{-x-2} X].$$

* When no operand is given, unity is to be understood.

13·54. Simultaneous Equations.

$$\Delta u_x + a v_x = X,$$
$$\Delta v_x + b u_x = 0,$$
$$u_x - u_0 + \mathsf{P}^{-1} a v_x = \mathsf{P}^{-1} X,$$
$$v_x - v_0 + \mathsf{P}^{-1} b u_x = 0,$$
$$u_x = \frac{\mathsf{P}^2 u_0 - \mathsf{P} a v_0 + \mathsf{P} X}{\mathsf{P}^2 - ab}, \quad v_x = \frac{\mathsf{P}^2 v_0 - \mathsf{P} b u_0 - bX}{\mathsf{P}^2 - ab},$$

which can be interpreted as before.

13·55. Applications of the Method. *Probability.*

A coin is spun n times. The probability of its shewing head at the first spin is p′; while at any subsequent spin the probability that the coin shews the same face as at the previous spin is p. What is the probability that the coin shews head at the nth spin? *

Let u_{n-1} be the required probability. Then $u_0 = p'$,

$$u_{n-1} = p\, u_{n-2} + (1-p)(1-u_{n-2}),$$
$$\Delta u_{n-2} = (2p-2)\, u_{n-2} + 1 - p,$$
$$u_n - p' = \mathsf{P}^{-1}(2p-2)\, u_n + \mathsf{P}^{-1}(1-p),$$
$$u_n = \frac{\mathsf{P}\, p'}{\mathsf{P}-(2p-2)} + \frac{1}{\mathsf{P}-(2p-2)}(1-p)$$
$$= p'(2p-1)^n + \frac{1-p}{2p-2}[(2p-1)^n - 1],$$
$$u_{n-1} = \tfrac{1}{2} + (2p-1)^{n-1}(p' - \tfrac{1}{2}).$$

If $p' = \frac{1}{2}$, this is $\frac{1}{2}$ for all values of n and p.

Geometry.

A, B, C are three spheres each outside the other two, and a point P is taken inside A. The inverses P′, P″ of P are taken in B and C. The inverses of P′ are taken in C and A, and of P″ in A and B, and this process is continued. Shew that of the 2^n *points which arise from P by n inversions,* $\frac{2}{3}(-1)^n + \frac{1}{3}2^n$ *lie inside A.*†

---

* W. Burnside, *Theory of Probability* (1928), chap. ii.

† This problem is taken from an examination paper set by Professor W. Burnside at the Royal Naval College.

Let u_n, v_n, w_n be the number of points which lie inside A, B, C respectively and which have arisen at the nth stage.

Then
$$u_0 = 1, \quad v_0 = 0, \quad w_0 = 0,$$
$$u_{n+1} = v_n + w_n, \quad v_{n+1} = w_n + u_n, \quad w_{n+1} = u_n + v_n,$$
so that
$$\Delta u_n + u_n - v_n - w_n = 0,$$
$$-u_n + \Delta v_n + v_n - w_n = 0,$$
$$-u_n - v_n - \Delta w_n - w_n = 0,$$
$$(1+\mathsf{P}^{-1})\, u_n - \mathsf{P}^{-1} v_n - \mathsf{P}^{-1} w_n = 1,$$
$$-\mathsf{P}^{-1} u_n + (1+\mathsf{P}^{-1})\, v_n - \mathsf{P}^{-1} w_n = 0,$$
$$-\mathsf{P}^{-1} u_n - \mathsf{P}^{-1} v_n + (1+\mathsf{P}^{-1} w_n) = 0.$$

Solving for u_n,
$$u_n = \frac{\mathsf{P}(\mathsf{P}^2+2\mathsf{P})}{(\mathsf{P}+2)^2(\mathsf{P}-1)}$$
$$= \frac{\mathsf{P}}{3(\mathsf{P}-1)} + \frac{2\mathsf{P}}{3(\mathsf{P}+2)}$$
$$= \tfrac{1}{3}2^n + \tfrac{2}{3}(-1)^n.$$

Dynamics.

Two equal perfectly elastic spheres of masses M, m ($M > m$) lie on a smooth horizontal surface with their line of centres perpendicular to a smooth perfectly elastic wall. The sphere of mass M is projected towards the wall so as to impinge directly with velocity V on the sphere of mass m. Find the velocities of the spheres after the nth impact between them.

Let u_n, v_n be the required velocities of M, m respectively measured positive when towards the wall.

Here $u_0 = V$, $v_0 = 0$ and
$$M(u_{n+1} - u_n) + m(v_{n+1} + v_n) = 0,$$
$$u_{n+1} + u_n - (v_{n+1} - v_n) = 0.$$

That is
$$M\Delta u_n + m(\Delta + 2)\, v_n = 0,$$
$$(\Delta + 2)\, u_n - \Delta v_n = 0,$$
$$M u_n + m(1+2\mathsf{P}^{-1})\, v_n - MV = 0,$$
$$(1+2\mathsf{P}^{-1})\, u_n - v_n - V = 0,$$

so that

$$u_n = \frac{(\mathsf{P}^2+2\mathsf{P})\,mV+\mathsf{P}^2\,MV}{(M+m)\,\mathsf{P}^2+4m\,\mathsf{P}+4m},$$

$$v_n = \frac{(\mathsf{P}^2+2\mathsf{P})\,MV-\mathsf{P}^2\,MV}{(M+m)\,\mathsf{P}^2+4m\,\mathsf{P}+4m}.$$

Now

$$(M+m)\,\mathsf{P}^2+4m\,\mathsf{P}+4m = (M+m)(\mathsf{P}-\alpha)(\mathsf{P}-\beta),$$

where
$$\alpha = \frac{-2m+2i\sqrt{Mm}}{M+m},$$

$$\beta = \frac{-2m-2i\sqrt{Mm}}{M+m},$$

$$u_n = \frac{(M+m)\,\alpha+2m}{(M+m)(\alpha-\beta)}\,\frac{\mathsf{P}\,V}{\mathsf{P}-\alpha} - \frac{(M+m)\,\beta+2m}{(M+m)(\alpha-\beta)}\,\frac{\mathsf{P}\,V}{\mathsf{P}-\beta},$$

$$v_n = \frac{2M}{(M+m)(\alpha-\beta)}\left[\frac{\mathsf{P}\,V}{\mathsf{P}-\alpha}-\frac{\mathsf{P}\,V}{\mathsf{P}-\beta}\right],$$

$$u_n = \tfrac{1}{2}V\,[(1+\alpha)^n+(1+\beta)^n],$$

$$v_n = \frac{1}{2i}\sqrt{\frac{M}{m}}\,[(1+\alpha)^n-(1+\beta)^n].$$

If $\cos\theta = \dfrac{M-m}{M+m}$,

$$1+\alpha = \cos\theta+i\sin\theta,$$

$$1+\beta = \cos\theta-i\sin\theta,$$

so that
$$u_n = V\cos n\theta,$$

$$v_n = \sqrt{\frac{M}{m}}\,V\sin n\theta,$$

and the total energy is $\frac{1}{2}MV^2$, as it should be. It will be noticed that when $n\theta$ first exceeds $\frac{1}{2}\pi$ the more massive sphere is moving away from the wall.

Energy.

A particle starts from a point A_0 with energy E and passes successively through the points A_1, A_2, A_3, ... At the points A_{2r+1} it absorbs a quantity q of energy, while at the points A_{2r} it loses half its energy. Find the energy at the point A_x.

If u_x be the required energy,

$$u_{2r+1} = \tfrac{1}{2} u_{2r-1} + q,$$
$$u_{2r} = \tfrac{1}{2} u_{2r-2} + \tfrac{1}{2} q.$$

Hence
$$u_{x+2} = \tfrac{1}{2} u_x + \frac{q}{4}[3-(-1)^x],$$

or
$$2\Delta^2 u_x + 4\Delta u_x + u_x = q\,\frac{\mathsf{P}+3}{\mathsf{P}+2},$$
$$u_0 = E, \quad \Delta u_0 = q.$$

Operating successively with P^{-1},

$$u_x = \frac{2E\,\mathsf{P}^2 + (4E+2q)\mathsf{P}}{2\mathsf{P}^2+4\mathsf{P}+1} + \frac{\mathsf{P}+3}{(2\mathsf{P}^2+4\mathsf{P}+1)(\mathsf{P}+2)}\,q$$
$$= \frac{2(\alpha+2)E - 2(\alpha+2)q}{2(\alpha-\beta)}\,\frac{\mathsf{P}}{\mathsf{P}-\alpha} - \frac{2(\beta+2)E-2(\beta+2)q}{2(\alpha-\beta)}\,\frac{\mathsf{P}}{\mathsf{P}-\beta}$$
$$-\tfrac{1}{2}q\,\frac{\mathsf{P}}{\mathsf{P}+2} + \tfrac{3}{2}q,$$

where
$$\alpha = \frac{-2+\sqrt{2}}{2}, \quad \beta = \frac{-2-\sqrt{2}}{2}.$$

After reduction,

$$u_x = \tfrac{1}{2}(E-q)\left[\left(\frac{1}{\sqrt{2}}\right)^x \{\sqrt{2}\,[1-(-1)^x] + [1+(-1)^x]\}\right]$$
$$+ \tfrac{1}{2}q\,[3-(-1)^x].$$

Hence for large values of x the energy is alternately q and $2q$, nearly.

The linear oscillator with discontinuous time.

The Hamiltonian of a linear oscillator of mass m, momentum p and displacement q is

$$H = \tfrac{1}{2}\frac{p^2}{m} + \tfrac{1}{2}kq^2,$$

the equations of motion being

$$\frac{\partial H}{\partial p} = \frac{dq}{dt} = \frac{p}{m},$$
$$\frac{\partial H}{\partial q} = -\frac{dp}{dt} = kq.$$

If we suppose a minimum time interval to exist so that time can only increase by integral multiples of this minimum interval σ, we may tentatively generalise the above equations into

$$\Delta_\sigma q = \frac{p}{m},$$

$$\Delta_\sigma p = -kq,$$

where
$$\Delta_\sigma u_t = \frac{u_{t+\sigma} - u_t}{\sigma}.$$

Changing the independent variable to $x = t/\sigma$, these become

$$\Delta q = \frac{p\sigma}{m},$$

$$\Delta p = -\sigma kq.$$

Thus
$$\mathsf{P}^{-1}\frac{p\sigma}{m} - q + q_0 = 0,$$

$$p + \mathsf{P}^{-1}\sigma kq - p_0 = 0.$$

These give

$$p = \frac{\mathsf{P}^2 p_0}{\mathsf{P}^2 + \frac{\sigma^2 k}{m}} - \sigma k q_0 \frac{\mathsf{P}}{\mathsf{P}^2 + \frac{\sigma^2 k}{m}},$$

$$q = \frac{\mathsf{P}^2 q_0}{\mathsf{P}^2 + \frac{\sigma^2 k}{m}} + \frac{\sigma p_0}{m} \frac{\mathsf{P}}{\mathsf{P}^2 + \frac{\sigma^2 k}{m}},$$

$$p = r^{\frac{t}{\sigma}}\left(p_0 \cos\frac{t\theta}{\sigma} - q_0\sqrt{mk}\sin\frac{t\theta}{\sigma}\right),$$

$$q = r^{\frac{t}{\sigma}}\left(q_0 \cos\frac{t\theta}{\sigma} + \frac{p_0}{\sqrt{mk}}\sin\frac{t\theta}{\sigma}\right),$$

where
$$r^2 = 1 + \frac{\sigma^2 k}{m}, \quad \tan\theta = \sigma\sqrt{\frac{k}{m}}.$$

The coefficients of $r^{\frac{t}{\sigma}}$ are in general not periodic, since $\frac{2\pi}{\theta}$ is not in general integral. But we recover the ordinary periodic solution for continuous time when $\sigma \to 0$. If we calculate the Hamiltonian, we get

$$H = \left(\tfrac{1}{2}\frac{p_0^2}{m} + \tfrac{1}{2}kq_0^2\right) r^{\frac{2t}{\sigma}} = H_0 r^{\frac{2t}{\sigma}},$$

which increases with t. It may be observed that the function

$$Hr^{-2t/\sigma}$$

remains constant and might tentatively be called energy. This suggests replacing p and q by

$$p' = pr^{-t/\sigma}, \quad q' = qr^{-t/\sigma}.$$

13·6. Simultaneous Equations. In 13·54, 13·55 we have seen how simultaneous equations can be solved by means of the operator P when the variable is an integer. In general, to solve such equations in, say, two dependent variables, we could proceed to eliminate one of them and then solve the difference equation satisfied by the other. We illustrate the procedure by an example. Consider

$$u_{x+1} + 2v_{x+1} - u_x = 0,$$
$$v_{x+1} - 2u_x - v_x = a^x.$$

We write these in the form

$$(\mathsf{E} - 1)\, u_x + 2\mathsf{E}\, v_x = 0,$$
$$-2u_x + (\mathsf{E} - 1)\, v_x = a^x,$$

whence

$$[(\mathsf{E} - 1)^2 + 4\mathsf{E}]\, u_x = -2\mathsf{E}\, a^x,$$

or

$$(\mathsf{E} + 1)^2\, u_x = -2a^{x+1}.$$

Thus

$$u_x = (\varpi + x\,\varpi_1)\,(-1)^x - \frac{2a^{x+1}}{(a+1)^2}.$$

From the first equation,

$$2v_{x+1} = -\Delta\, u_x,$$

and therefore

$$v_x = (\varpi + \tfrac{1}{2}\varpi_1 + \varpi_1\, x)\,(-1)^x + \frac{a^x(a-1)}{(a+1)^2}.$$

13·7. Sylvester's Non-linear Equations. The solution of two types of non-linear equations has been deduced by Sylvester from the solution of linear equations with constant coefficients.

Consider

(1) $$u_{x+n} + p_{n-1}\, u_{x+n-1} + \dots + p_0\, u_x = 0,$$

where the coefficients are constant. The solution is

(2) $$u_x = \sum_{s=1}^{n} \varpi_s\, \alpha_s^{\,x},$$

where the α_s are the zeros of the characteristic function, so that

$$\alpha_1\alpha_2\ldots\alpha_n=(-1)^n p_0.$$

If we write down (1) for $x+1, x+2, \ldots, x+n$ and eliminate p_0, $p_1, \ldots, p_{n-1}$, we obtain the non-linear difference equation

$$(3)\qquad \begin{vmatrix} u_{x+n} & u_{x+n-1} & \ldots & u_x \\ u_{x+n+1} & u_{x+n} & \ldots & u_{x+1} \\ \ldots & \ldots & \ldots & \ldots \\ u_{x+2n} & u_{x+2n-1} & \ldots & u_{x+n} \end{vmatrix}=0.$$

Since (2) satisfies (1), it also satisfies (3), but since $p_0, p_1, \ldots, p_{n-1}$, on which the values of the α_s depend, do not appear in (3), we may regard the values of α_s as arbitrary. Thus (2) furnishes a solution of (3), the values of α_s being now arbitrary constants. The formal character of the solution given by (2) will not be altered if we replace the α_s by arbitrary periodics. Thus we have a solution which contains $2n$ arbitrary periodics.

The other type of equation is obtained by writing down (1) for the values $x+1, x+2, \ldots, x+n-1$ and then eliminating $p_1, p_2, \ldots, p_{n-1}$. This gives

$$\begin{vmatrix} u_{x+n} & u_{x+n-1} & \ldots & u_{x+1} \\ u_{x+n+1} & u_{x+n} & \ldots & u_{x+2} \\ \ldots & \ldots & \ldots & \ldots \\ u_{x+2n-1} & u_{x+2n-2} & \ldots & u_{x+n} \end{vmatrix}=(-1)^n p_0 \begin{vmatrix} u_{x+n-1} & u_{x+n-2} & \ldots & u_x \\ u_{x+n} & u_{x+n-1} & \ldots & u_{x+1} \\ \ldots & \ldots & \ldots & \ldots \\ u_{x+2n-2} & u_{x+2n-3} & \ldots & u_{x+n-1} \end{vmatrix}.$$

Calling the last determinant $K(x)$, we have

$$K(x+1)=\alpha_1\alpha_2\ldots\alpha_n K(x),$$

whence

$$K(x)=\varpi\,.\,(\alpha_1\alpha_2\ldots\alpha_n)^x.$$

Now, using (2), we have for $K(x)$ the determinantal product

$$\begin{vmatrix} \varpi_1\alpha_1^x & \varpi_2\alpha_2^x & \ldots & \varpi_n\alpha_n^x \\ \varpi_1\alpha_1^{x+1} & \varpi_2\alpha_2^{x+1} & \ldots & \varpi_n\alpha_n^{x+1} \\ \ldots & \ldots & \ldots & \ldots \\ \varpi_1\alpha_1^{x+n-1} & \varpi_2\alpha_2^{x+n-1} & \ldots & \varpi_n\alpha_n^{x+n-1} \end{vmatrix}\times\begin{vmatrix} \alpha_1^{n-1} & \alpha_1^{n-2} & \ldots & \alpha_1 & 1 \\ \alpha_2^{n-1} & \alpha_2^{n-2} & \ldots & \alpha_2 & 1 \\ . & . & \ldots & . & . \\ \alpha_n^{n-1} & \alpha_n^{n-2} & \ldots & \alpha_n & 1 \end{vmatrix}$$

so that

$$K(x) = -\varpi_1 \varpi_2 \dots \varpi_n (\alpha_1 \alpha_2 \dots \alpha_n)^x \prod_{i>j} (\alpha_i - \alpha_j)^2.$$

Comparing the two expressions for $K(x)$, we see that the difference equation

$$\begin{vmatrix} u_{x+n-1} & u_{x+n-2} & \dots & u_x \\ \cdot & \cdot & \cdot & \cdot \\ u_{x+2n-2} & u_{x+2n-3} & \dots & u_{x+n-1} \end{vmatrix} = \varpi m^x,$$

where ϖ is a given periodic, has the solution (2) where $\varpi_1, \varpi_2, \dots, \varpi_n$ are periodics and $\alpha_1, \alpha_2, \dots, \alpha_n$ are constants, which can be arbitrarily chosen subject to the two conditions

$$-\varpi_1 \varpi_2 \dots \varpi_n \prod_{i>j} (\alpha_i - \alpha_j)^2 = \varpi,$$

$$\alpha_1 \alpha_2 \dots \alpha_n = m.$$

Thus $n-1$ of the constants can be replaced by periodics and we have a solution involving $2n-2$ arbitrary periodics.

Example. $$u_{x+2}\, u_x - u_{x+1}^2 = a,$$

where a is a constant or a periodic.

This can be written

$$\begin{vmatrix} u_{x+1} & u_x \\ u_{x+2} & u_{x+1} \end{vmatrix} = -a,$$

and therefore has the solution

$$u_x = \varpi_1 \alpha^x + \varpi_2 \beta^x,$$

where

$$\alpha\beta = 1,$$

$$\varpi_1 \varpi_2 (\alpha - \beta)^2 = a,$$

so that we have

$$u_x = \varpi \alpha^x + \frac{a\, \alpha^{-x+2}}{(\alpha^2 - 1)^2\, \varpi},$$

where ϖ is an arbitrary periodic and α an arbitrary constant. If this be a solution when α is an arbitrary constant, it is likewise a solution when α is an arbitrary periodic. The solution may therefore be regarded as containing two arbitrary periodics.

The equation can be regarded as arising from

$$u_{x+1}+p\,u_x+u_{x-1}=0,$$

whence

$$u_{x+2}+p\,u_{x+1}+u_x=0,$$

so that, eliminating p,

$$u_{x+1}^2-u_x\,u_{x+2}=u_x^2-u_{x-1}\,u_{x+1}=\text{constant}.$$

13·8. Partial Difference Equations with Constant Coefficients. Let u be a function of the two independent variables x, y. Taking the increments of x, y to be unity in each case we have, as in 2·105,

$$\Delta_x u=u(x+1,\,y)-u(x,\,y),\quad \Delta_y u=u(x,\,y+1)-u(x,\,y).$$

It is also convenient to introduce operations E_x, E_y defined by

$$\mathsf{E}_x u=u(x+1,\,y),\quad \mathsf{E}_y u=u(x,\,y+1).$$

Then

$$1+\Delta_x \doteqdot \mathsf{E}_x,\quad 1+\Delta_y \doteqdot \mathsf{E}_y.$$

It is clear that the operators Δ_x, Δ_y are commutative, that is,

$$\Delta_x\,\Delta_y\,u=\Delta_y\,\Delta_x\,u.$$

If then $F(\lambda,\,\mu)$ be a bilinear form in λ, μ whose coefficients are independent of x and y, a difference equation of any of the forms

(1) $$F(\Delta_x,\,\Delta_y)\,u=0,\quad F(\mathsf{E}_x,\,\mathsf{E}_y)\,u=0,$$
$$F(\Delta_x,\,\mathsf{E}_y)\,u=0,\quad F(\mathsf{E}_x,\,\Delta_y)\,u=0,$$

is a partial difference equation with constant coefficients. A more general type of such equations is

$$F(\Delta_x,\,\Delta_y)\,u=f(x,\,y),$$

where $f(x,\,y)$ is a given function.

We can obtain formal symbolic solutions of equations of the forms (1) by the following device. We first replace Δ_y or E_y by a. There results an ordinary difference equation in which a figures as a parameter. Having obtained the solution of this we replace a by the operator which a represents and interpret the solution. The method will be understood by considering some examples.

Example 1. $u(x+1, y)-u(x, y+1)=0.$

This is equivalent to

$$\mathsf{E}_x u-\mathsf{E}_y u=0.$$

Writing a for E_y, we have

$$\mathsf{E}_x u-au=0,$$

a solution of which is

$$u=a^x \phi(y),$$

where $\phi(y)$ is an arbitrary function of y and is written *after* the symbol a^x.

Thus

$$u=(\mathsf{E}_y)^x \phi(y)=\phi(x+y),$$

which clearly satisfies the given equation.

If $\varpi_1(x)$, $\varpi_2(y)$ denote arbitrary periodic functions of x, y of period unity, it is evident that

$$u=\varpi_1(x)\,\varpi_2(y)\,\phi(x+y)$$

is also a solution, which is more general, in that $\varpi_1(x)\,\varpi_2(y)$ is not necessarily a function of $x+y$. We can replace this product by $\varpi(x, y)$, an arbitrary function periodic in both variables.

Arbitrary periodic functions can always be introduced in this way into the solution of an equation of the types (1), but, for simplicity, we shall ignore them.

Example 2. $u(x+1, y+1)-u(x, y+1)-u(x, y)=0.$

This equation can be written

$$\mathsf{E}_y \Delta_x u-u=0.$$

Replacing E_y by a, we have

$$a\,\Delta_x u-u=0,$$

a solution of which is

$$u=(1+a^{-1})^x \phi(y),$$

where $\phi(y)$ is an arbitrary function, again written last. Thus

$$u=(1+\mathsf{E}_y^{-1})^x \phi(y). \tag{2}$$

Developing by the binomial theorem, we have

$$u = \phi(y) + \binom{x}{1}\phi(y-1) + \binom{x}{2}\phi(y-2) + \dots .$$

The series terminates when x is an integer.

If, for example, we are given the initial condition that, when $x = 0$, $u = e^{my}$, we have

$$u = e^{my}\left\{1 + \binom{x}{1}e^{-m} + \binom{x}{2}e^{-2m} + \dots\right\}$$

$$= e^{my}(1+e^{-m})^x.$$

An alternative form of the solution is obtainable as follows. We can write (2) in the form

$$u = (\mathsf{E}_y + 1)^x\, \mathsf{E}_y^{-x}\, \phi(y)$$

$$= (\mathsf{E}_y + 1)^x\, \phi(y-x),$$

whence, developing as before,

$$(3) \qquad u = \phi(y-x) + \binom{x}{1}\phi(y-x+1) + \binom{x}{2}\phi(y-x+2) + \dots .$$

13·81. An Alternative Method. Let us again consider the equation

$$u(x+1,\, y+1) - u(x,\, y+1) - u(x,\, y) = 0.$$

Assume that

$$u = \Sigma\, C\, a^x\, b^y,$$

where the summation extends to an unspecified range of values of a and b. Substituting, we have

$$\Sigma\,(ab - b - 1)\, C\, a^x\, b^y = 0,$$

so that the postulated form is a solution, provided that

$$ab - b - 1 = 0,$$

which gives $a = (1+b)\,b^{-1}$ and we have the solution

$$u = \Sigma\, C\,(1+b)^x\, b^{y-x}.$$

Since C is perfectly arbitrary, we may replace C by $\phi(b)$, where $\phi(b)$ is an arbitrary function, and the summation may be replaced by an integration. Thus we have

$$u = \int_{-\infty}^{+\infty} b^{y-x}(1+b)^x \phi(b)\, db.$$

In this expression $\phi(b)$ being perfectly arbitrary may be taken to vanish outside any specified interval of b, so that we can take for limits of integration any pair of arbitrarily assigned numbers and still obtain a formal solution. If we expand $(1+b)^x$ and then write

$$\psi(z) = \int_{-\infty}^{+\infty} b^z \phi(b)\, db,$$

we obtain

$$u = \psi(y-x) + \binom{x}{1}\psi(y-x+1) + \binom{x}{2}\psi(y-x+2) + \ldots$$

which agrees with 13·8 (3).

13·82. Equations Resolvable into First Order Equations. Consider the equation

$$\overset{2}{\Delta}_x u(x-1, y) = \overset{2}{\Delta}_y u(x, y-1).$$

Replacing $u(x, y)$ by u, we have successively

$$(\overset{2}{\Delta}_x \mathsf{E}_x^{-1} - \overset{2}{\Delta}_y \mathsf{E}_y^{-1})\, u = 0,$$

$$(\overset{2}{\Delta}_x \mathsf{E}_y - \overset{2}{\Delta}_y \mathsf{E}_x)\, u = 0,$$

$$(\mathsf{E}_x^2 \mathsf{E}_y + \mathsf{E}_y - \mathsf{E}_y^2 \mathsf{E}_x - \mathsf{E}_x)\, u = 0,$$

$$(\mathsf{E}_x \mathsf{E}_y - 1)(\mathsf{E}_x - \mathsf{E}_y)\, u = 0.$$

The last equation is resolvable into the two equations

$$(\mathsf{E}_x \mathsf{E}_y - 1)\, u = 0, \quad (\mathsf{E}_x - \mathsf{E}_y)\, u = 0.$$

The first gives

$$\mathsf{E}_x u = \mathsf{E}_y^{-1} u,$$

of which a solution is

$$u = (\mathsf{E}_y^{-1})^x \phi(y) = \phi(y-x)$$

and the second, see 13·8, example 1, gives

$$u = \psi(y+x).$$

Thus the general solution is

$$u = \varpi_1(x, y)\,\phi(y-x) + \varpi_2(x, y)\,\psi(y+x),$$

where ϖ_1, ϖ_2 are arbitrary functions periodic in both x and y with period unity.

13·83. Laplace's Method. Consider the equation

$$A_0 u(x, y) + A_1 u(x-1, y-1) + A_2 u(x-2, y-2) + \ldots = V(x, y),$$

where $A_0, A_1, A_2, \ldots$ are independent of the variables and $V(x, y)$ is a given function. The characteristic property of this equation lies in the fact that the difference of the arguments in any one of the functions $u(x-s, y-s)$ is invariant for $s = 0, 1, 2, \ldots$ and equal to $x-y$. Putting

$$x-y = k, \quad u(x, y) = u(x, x-k) = v_x,$$

the equation becomes

$$A_0 v_x + A_1 v_{x-1} + A_2 v_{x-2} + \ldots = X,$$

which is an ordinary equation with constant coefficients. We solve this and then replace k by $x-y$ and the arbitrary periodics by arbitrary functions of the form

$$\varpi(x, y)\,\phi(x-y),$$

where $\varpi(x, y)$ is periodic in x and y with period unity.

Example. A and B engage in a game, each step of which consists in one of them winning a counter from the other. At the beginning A has x counters and B has y counters, and in each successive step the probability of A's winning a counter from B is p, and therefore of B's winning a counter from A is $1-p$. The game is to terminate when either of the two has n counters. What is the probability of A winning?

Let $u_{x,y}$ be the probability that A will win, any positive integral values being assigned to x and y.

Now A's winning the game may be resolved into two alternatives, namely,

(i) his winning the first step and afterwards winning the game, or

(ii) his losing the first step and afterwards winning the game.

Thus

$$u_{x,\,y} = p\,u_{x+1,\,y-1} + (1-p)\,u_{x-1,\,y+1}.$$

In this equation the sum of the arguments in any particular term is $x+y$. We therefore use Laplace's method and put

$$x+y = k, \quad u_{x,\,y} = v_x,$$

which gives the equation

$$v_x - p\,v_{x+1} - (1-p)\,v_{x-1} = 0,$$

which has the solution

$$v_x = \varpi_1 + \varpi_2 \left(\frac{1-p}{p}\right)^x,$$

and hence

$$u_{x,\,y} = \varpi_1(x,\,y)\,\phi(x+y) + \varpi_2(x,\,y)\left(\frac{1-p}{p}\right)^x \psi(x+y).$$

In the present case the variables are positive integers, so that the arbitrary periodics are constant and can be absorbed into the arbitrary functions ϕ, ψ. Thus

$$u_{x,\,y} = \phi(x+y) + \left(\frac{1-p}{p}\right)^x \psi(x+y),$$

and we have to determine the arbitrary functions.

The number of counters k is invariable throughout the game. Now A's success is certain if he be ever in possession of n counters.

Hence, if $x = n$, $u_{x,\,y} = 1$, and therefore

$$1 = \phi(k) + \left(\frac{1-p}{p}\right)^n \psi(k).$$

Again, A loses the game if ever he have $k-n$ counters, for then B has n. Hence, if $x = k-n$, $u_{x,y} = 0$, and therefore

$$0 = \phi(k) + \left(\frac{1-p}{p}\right)^{k-n} \psi(k).$$

Putting

$$q = \frac{1-p}{p},$$

we obtain

$$\phi(k) = \frac{-q^{k-n}}{q^n - q^{k-n}}, \quad \psi(k) = \frac{1}{q^n - q^{k-n}},$$

whence

$$u_{x,y} = \frac{q^{n-y}-1}{q^{2n-x-y}-1}$$

$$= \frac{\{p^{n-y} - (1-p)^{n-y}\}\, p^{n-x}}{p^{2n-x-y} - (1-p)^{2n-x-y}},$$

which is the probability that A will win.

EXAMPLES XIII

Solve the difference equations :

1. $u_{x+2} - 3u_{x+1} - 4u_x = m^x$.
2. $u_{x+2} + 4u_{x+1} + 4u_x = x$.
3. $u_{x+2} + 2u_{x+1} + u_x = x(x-1)(x-2) + x(-1)^x$
4. $u_{x+2} - 2m\, u_{x+1} + (m^2+n^2)\, u_x = m^x$.
5. $\overset{2}{\Delta} u_x + \Delta u_x = x + \sin x$.
6. $u_{x+4} - 6u_{x+2} + 8u_{x+1} - 3u_x = x^2 + (-3)^x$.
7. $\overset{3}{\Delta} u_x - 5\Delta u_x + 4u_x = 2^x(1+\cos x)$.
8. $\overset{6}{\Delta} u_{x+1} - 2\overset{6}{\Delta} u_x = x + 3^x$.
9. $u_{x+2} \pm n^2 u_x = \cos mx$.
10. $u_{x+4} \pm 2n^2\, u_{x+2} + n^4\, u_x = 0$.
11. $u_{x+n-1} + u_{x+n-2} + \ldots + u_x = 0$.
12. $u_{x+2}\, u_{x+1}^{2n}\, u_x^{n^2} = a$.
13. $v_{x+1} - u_x = (l-m)\, x,$

    $w_{x+1} - v_x = (m-n)\, x,$

    $u_{x+1} - w_x = (n-l)\, x.$

14. $u_{x+1} - v_x = 2m(x+1)$,

$v_{x+1} - u_x = -2m(x+1)$.

15. $u_{x+2} + 2v_{x+1} - 8u_x = a^x$,

$v_{x+2} - u_{x+1} - 2v_x = a^{-x}$.

16. Solve the equation

$$u_x u_{x+1} u_{x+2} = a(u_x + u_{x+1} + u_{x+2})$$

by assuming $u_x = a^{\frac{1}{2}} \tan v_x$.

17. Shew that the general solution of the equation of Ex. 16 is included in that of the equation $u_{x+3} - u_x = 0$, and hence deduce the former.

18. Solve the equation

$$u_{x+1} u_{x+2} + u_{x+2} u_x + u_x u_{x+1} = m^2.$$

19. Solve the equations

$$u_{x+1} = (n - m^2) v_x + u_x,$$

$$v_{x+1} = (2m+1) v_x + u_x,$$

and shew that if m be the integral part of $\sqrt{n}$, u_x / v_x converges as x increases to the decimal part of $\sqrt{n}$.

20. If a_1 be a fourth proportional to a, b, c; b_1 a fourth proportional to b, c, a; and c_1 to c, a, b; and if a_2, b_2, c_2 depend in the same manner on a_1, b_1, c_1, find the linear difference equation on which a_n depends, and hence shew that

$$a_n = a(bc\, a^{-2})^{\frac{1}{3} - \frac{1}{3}(-2)^n}.$$

21. Solve the equation

$$\begin{vmatrix} u_{x+5} & u_{x+4} & u_{x+3} \\ u_{x+4} & u_{x+3} & u_{x+2} \\ u_{x+3} & u_{x+2} & u_{x+1} \end{vmatrix} = C,$$

and consider in particular the case $C = 0$.

22. If $v_0, v_1, v_2, \ldots$ be a sequence, the successive terms of which are connected by the relation

$$v_{m+1} = v_1 v_m - v_{m-1},$$

and if v_0, v_1 be given, prove that

$$v_m = \frac{2\cos\alpha\cos m\alpha - v_0\sin(m-1)\alpha}{\sin\alpha},$$

where $v_1 = 2\cos\alpha$. [Smith's Prize].

23. If n integers be taken at random and multiplied together in the denary scale, shew that the chance that the digit in the units place will be 2 is

$$\tfrac{1}{4}\{(\tfrac{4}{5})^n - (\tfrac{2}{5})^n\}.$$

24. Shew that a solution of

$$u_{x+n}\,u_{x+n-1}\dots u_x = a(u_{x+n} + u_{x+n-1} + \dots + u_x)$$

is included in that of $u_{x+n+1} - u_x = 0$, and is consequently

$$u_x = \varpi_1\,\alpha^x + \varpi_2\,\alpha^{2x} + \dots + \varpi_{n+1}\,\alpha^{(n+1)x},$$

where α is an imaginary $(n+1)$th root of unity, the $n+1$ periodics being subject to an equation of condition.

25. A person finds that his professional income, which for the first year was £a, increases in Arithmetical Progression, the common difference being £b. He saves every year $1/m$ of his income from all sources, laying it out at the end of each year at r per cent. per annum. What will be his income when he has been x years in practice?

26. The seeds of a certain plant when one year old produce ten-fold, and when two years old and upwards produce eighteen-fold. A seed is planted and every seed subsequently produced is planted as soon as it is produced. Prove that the number of grains at the end of the nth year is

$$\frac{1}{a}\left\{\left(\frac{11+a}{2}\right)^n - \left(\frac{11-a}{2}\right)^n\right\},$$

where $a = 3\sqrt{17}$.

27. A series is formed by taking each term as the arithmetic mean of the three terms preceding it. Shew, if u_n be the nth term, that when n is large

$$u_n = \tfrac{1}{6}u_1 + \tfrac{1}{3}u_2 + \tfrac{1}{2}u_3, \text{ nearly.}$$

28. Three vessels contain water. Of the contents of the first, $1/p$ is transferred to the second, $1/q$ of the second is then transferred to the third, and then $1/r$ of the third is transferred to the first. The cycle of operations is repeated many times. Shew that the fraction of the whole volume of water which the first vessel then contains is nearly

$$\frac{p}{p+q+r-2}.$$

29. Two closed vessels A and B each containing gas are connected by a sliding shutter which is opened for t seconds and then closed. This operation is repeated a large number of times. Each time the shutter is open $1/a$ of the molecules in A penetrate into B, while $1/b$ of the molecules in B penetrate into A. Initially there are p molecules in A, and q in B. Find the number of molecules in each vessel after the shutter has been opened n times. Shew that after a long time has elapsed the number of molecules in A and B are in a fixed ratio, nearly. [Royal Naval College.]

30. A circulating library is started with b books. During each year 5 per cent. of the number of books which were in the library at the beginning of the year are added to it. At the end of every third year 10 per cent. of the books are worn out and are destroyed. Shew that at the end of n years the number of books is

$$\tfrac{1}{3} b k^n [1+\omega^n+\omega^{2n}+c(1+\omega^{n+2}+\omega^{2n+1})+c^2(1+\omega^{n+1}+\omega^{2n+2})],$$

where $9c^3 = 10$, $k = 21/(20c)$ and ω is an imaginary cube root of unity. [Royal Naval College.]

31. A large number of equal particles are attached at equal intervals h to a massless inextensible string. The first particle is projected vertically with velocity V and the particles start one by one into vertical motion. Shew that the nth particle will rise from the table if

$$3V^2 > gh\,n(n-1)(2n-1).$$

32. A curve is such that, if a system of n straight lines, originating in a fixed point and terminating on the curve, revolve about that point making always equal angles with each other, their sum

is invariable. Shew that the polar equation of the curve is of the form

$$r = a + \varpi_1 \cos\theta + \varpi_2 \cos 2\theta + \ldots + \varpi_{n-1} \cos (n-1)\theta,$$

the fixed point being the pole. Shew in particular that the curve

$$(x^2 - bx + y^2)^2 = a^2 (x^2 + y^2)$$

satisfies the required condition.

33. Find the curves in which, the abscissae increasing by the constant quantity unity, the subnormals increase in the ratio $1/\alpha$, and shew that

$$y^2 = b\alpha^x + c$$

is such a curve.

34. Find the general equation of curves in which the chord drawn through the origin is of constant length.

35. Find the general equation of the curve in which the product of the two segments of a chord drawn through a fixed point shall be invariable, and shew in particular that

$$r = a\,e^{\sin\theta}$$

is such a curve, a^2 being the invariable product.

36. $u_{x+1,\,y} - u_{x,\,y+1} = x + y.$

37. $u_{x+1,\,y+n} - u_{x,\,y} = a^{x-y}.$

38. $u_{x+2,\,y} - b^2 u_{x,\,y+2} = 0.$

39. $u_{x+3,\,y} - 3u_{x+2,\,y+1} + 3u_{x+1,\,y+2} - u_{x,\,y+3} = x.$

40. $u(x+1, y+1) - a\,u(x+1, y) - b\,u(x, y+1) + ab\,u(x, y) = c^{x+y}.$

41. $u(x+3, y) - 3a^2 u(x+1, y+2) + a^3 u(x, y+3) = xy.$

42. The probability of a coin falling head is p. What is the probability that at some stage in n consecutive spins the number of heads exceeds the number of tails by r? [Burnside.]

CHAPTER XIV

THE LINEAR DIFFERENCE EQUATION WITH RATIONAL COEFFICIENTS. OPERATIONAL METHODS

AFTER equations with constant coefficients the linear equation whose coefficients are rational functions of the independent variable ranks next in order of simplicity. Boole devised a method of symbolic operators for attacking the problem of solution of such equations. By generalising the definitions * of these operators it is possible to apply the method to a well-defined class of such equations and to obtain solutions in Newton's factorial series in much the same manner as power series solutions of differential equations are obtained by the method of Frobenius.

14·0. The Operator ρ. Given a fixed number r and an arbitrary number m, the operator ρ is defined by the relation

$$(1) \qquad \rho^m u(x) = \frac{\Gamma(x-r+1)}{\Gamma(x-r-m+1)} \mathsf{E}^{-m} u(x).$$

This is a generalisation of the definition given by Boole which corresponds to the case $r = 0$, m an integer. In particular, for $m = 1, 0, -1, -\frac{1}{2}$, we have

$$\rho\, u(x) = (x-r)\, u(x-1),$$

$$\rho^0 u(x) = u(x),$$

$$\rho^{-1} u(x) = \frac{1}{x-r+1} u(x+1),$$

$$\rho^{-\frac{1}{2}} u(x) = \frac{\Gamma(x-r+1)}{\Gamma(x-r+\frac{3}{2})} u(x+\tfrac{1}{2}).$$

---

* L. M. Milne-Thomson, On Boole's operational solution of linear finite difference equations, *Proc. Cambridge Phil. Soc.* xxviii (1932), p. 311.

If, for brevity, we write

(2) $$x - r = x',$$

the above definition becomes

$$\rho^m u(x) = \frac{\Gamma(x'+1)}{\Gamma(x'-m+1)} \mathsf{E}^{-m} u(x).$$

The operator ρ^m is clearly distributive. That the index law is obeyed is easily seen, for

$$\rho^m \rho^n u(x) = \frac{\Gamma(x'+1)}{\Gamma(x'-m+1)} \mathsf{E}^{-m} \left\{ \frac{\Gamma(x'+1)}{\Gamma(x'-n+1)} u(x-n) \right\}$$

$$= \frac{\Gamma(x'+1)}{\Gamma(x'-m-n+1)} u(x-m-n) = \rho^{m+n} u(x).$$

If the operand be unity, we shall omit it and write

$$\rho^m = \frac{\Gamma(x'+1)}{\Gamma(x'-m+1)}.$$

Hence, when n is a positive integer, we have

$$\rho^{m+n} = (x'-m)(x'-m-1)\dots(x'-m-n+1)\,\Gamma(x'+1)/\Gamma(x'-m+1),$$

$$\rho^{m-n} = \frac{1}{(x'-m+1)(x'-m+2)\dots(x'-m+n)} \frac{\Gamma(x'+1)}{\Gamma(x'-m+1)}.$$

It follows that a series of the form

$$\frac{a_n}{n!}\rho^{m+n} + \frac{a_{n-1}}{(n-1)!}\rho^{m+n-1} + \dots + a_0\rho^m + b_1\rho^{m-1} + b_2\,2!\,\rho^{m-2} + \dots$$

is equivalent to

$$\frac{\Gamma(x'+1)}{\Gamma(x'-m+1)} \left\{ a_n \binom{x'-m}{n} + a_{n-1}\binom{x'-m}{n-1} + \dots \right.$$

$$\left. + a_0 + \frac{b_0\,1!}{x'-m+1} + \frac{b_2\,2!}{(x'-m+1)(x'-m+2)} + \dots \right\},$$

while a series of the form

$$a_0\rho^m + \frac{a_1}{1!}\rho^{m+1} + \frac{a_2}{2!}\rho^{m+2} + \dots$$

is equivalent to

$$\frac{\Gamma(x'+1)}{\Gamma(x'-m+1)}\left\{a_0+a_1\binom{x'-m}{1}+a_2\binom{x'-m}{2}+a_3\binom{x'-m}{3}+\dots\right\}.$$

In this way we can, apart from the Gamma functions, express factorial series as series of powers of ρ operating on unity. Conversely, a series of powers of ρ can be interpreted by means of the above results.

14·01. The Operator π. The definition of π is

$$\pi\, u(x) = (x-r)\underset{-1}{\Delta}\, u(x) = x'(u(x)-u(x-1)).$$

Boole's definition corresponds to $r=0$. It should be particularly noted that just as a fixed number r is associated with the operator ρ, so we associate the *same* number with the operator π in all cases where π and ρ both occur in the same work.

The operator π is distributive and can be repeated. Thus we can interpret $\pi^2 u(x)$, $\pi^n u(x)$ where n is a positive integer. The index law is clearly obeyed, and π commutes with constants. Thus, if $f(\lambda)$ be a polynomial, the operation $f(\pi)$ has a perfectly determinate meaning. Moreover

$$f(\pi)\, g(\pi)\, u(x) = g(\pi) f(\pi)\, u(x),$$

where $f(\lambda)$ and $g(\lambda)$ are any polynomials.

We can now prove that, if n be a positive integer,

$$\pi^n \rho^m u(x) \doteqdot \rho^m (\pi+m)^n u(x).$$

We have from the definitions

$$\pi\rho^m u(x) = x'\left\{\frac{\Gamma(x'+1)}{\Gamma(x'-m+1)}u(x-m)-\frac{\Gamma(x')}{\Gamma(x'-m)}u(x-m-1)\right\}$$

$$= \frac{\Gamma(x'+1)}{\Gamma(x'-m+1)}\{x'\,u(x-m)-(x'-m)\,u(x-m-1)\}$$

$$= \frac{\Gamma(x'+1)}{\Gamma(x'-m+1)}\,\mathsf{E}^{-m}\{(x'+m)\,u(x)-x'\,u(x-1)\}$$

$$= \rho^m(\pi+m)\,u(x).$$

Repeating the operation,

$$\pi^2 \rho^m u(x) = \pi[\rho^m(\pi+m)u(x)] = \rho^m(\pi+m)[(\pi+m)u(x)]$$
$$= \rho^m(\pi+m)^2 u(x),$$

and continuing thus, the required result is proved for any positive integral index n.

From this we can infer the more general result that, if $f(\lambda)$ be a polynomial,

$$f(\pi)\rho^m u(x) \doteqdot \rho^m f(\pi+m) u(x).$$

14·02. Inverse Operations with π. The equation

$$\pi u(x) = \phi(x)$$

has the symbolic solution $u(x) \doteqdot \pi^{-1}\phi(x)$ and also the particular solution

$$u_1(x) = \mathop{S}_{c}^{x} \frac{1}{t-r}\phi(t) \mathop{\Delta}_{-1} t,$$

so that a possible interpretation of π^{-1} is given by

$$\pi^{-1}\phi(x) = \mathop{S}_{c}^{x} \frac{1}{t-r}\phi(t) \mathop{\Delta}_{-1} t + C,$$

which gives

$$\pi\pi^{-1}\phi(x) = \phi(x).$$

If we use this interpretation, we have, from 8·1 (6),

$$\pi^{-1}\pi\phi(x) = \mathop{S}_{c}^{x} \left[\frac{1}{t-r}(t-r) \mathop{\Delta}_{-1} \phi(t)\right] \mathop{\Delta}_{-1} t + C = \phi(x) + K,$$

where K is a constant whose value depends on the particular value attributed to C. We shall suppose C to be so determined that K is zero. If this be done, π and π^{-1} are commutative operations.

We therefore make the following definition :

(1) $$\pi^{-1}\phi(x) = \mathop{S}_{c}^{x} \frac{1}{t-r}\phi(t) \mathop{\Delta}_{-1} t + C,$$

where the constant C is given a particular value which makes

$$\pi^{-1}\pi\,\phi(x) = \phi(x).$$

In practice it will seldom be necessary to determine C, but the above definition enables us to attach a precise meaning to π^{-1} and thereby gives a wider range of application to this operation.

We can now interpret π^n when n is a positive or negative integer, and we have for all integral values of p and n

$$\pi^p\,\pi^n\phi(x) \doteqdot \pi^{p+n}\,\phi(x).$$

To interpret $(\pi+m)^{-1}\,u(x)$, we have, from 14·01,

$$(\pi+m)\,\rho^{-m}\,[\pi^{-1}\,\rho^m\,u(x)] \doteqdot \rho^{-m}\,\pi\,\pi^{-1}\,\rho^m\,u(x) = u(x).$$

Thus a possible interpretation of $(\pi+m)^{-1}\,u(x)$ is

(2) $$(\pi+m)^{-1}\,u(x) \doteqdot \rho^{-m}\,\pi^{-1}\,\rho^m\,u(x),$$

and if we adopt this we have just proved that

$$(\pi+m)\,(\pi+m)^{-1}\,u(x) = u(x).$$

Moreover, (2) gives

$$(\pi+m)^{-1}(\pi+m)\,u(x) \doteqdot \rho^{-m}\,\pi^{-1}\,\rho^m\,[\,(\pi+m)\,u(x)\,]$$
$$\doteqdot \rho^{-m}\,\pi^{-1}\,\pi\,\rho^m\,u(x) = u(x).$$

Thus, with the interpretation (2), we have

$$(\pi+m)^{-1}(\pi+m)\,u(x) \doteqdot (\pi+m)\,(\pi+m)^{-1}\,u(x) = u(x),$$

so that the interpretation (2) makes the operators $\pi+m$, $(\pi+m)^{-1}$ commute, and this interpretation is therefore suitable inasmuch as it preserves the commutative property of π and π^{-1} when $m = 0$.

It follows at once that, when p and n are integers,

$$(\pi+m)^p\,(\pi+m)^n\,u = (\pi+m)^{p+n}\,u.$$

From the commutative property of the direct and inverse operations we have the important result that if $f(\lambda)$, $g(\lambda)$ be two rational functions of λ, then

$$f(\pi)\,g(\pi)\,u = g(\pi)\,f(\pi)\,u,$$

and further that, to interpret $f(\pi)\,u(x)$, we may express $f(\lambda)$ as the sum of terms of the form $A\,\lambda^n$, $B(\lambda-b)^m$ (that is, we may use the method of partial fractions). Thus we see that $f(\pi)\,u(x)$ is the sum of terms like $A\,\pi^n\,u(x)$, $B\,(\pi-b)^m\,u(x)$.

14·03. The Operators π_1 and ρ_1. These are defined by the relations

$$\pi_1 u(x) = x' \Delta u(x) = x' \{u(x+1) - u(x)\},$$

$$\rho_1^m u(x) = \frac{\Gamma(x'+m)}{\Gamma(x')} \mathsf{E}^m u(x), \; x' = x - r.$$

With the necessary modifications in the definitions the results which we have already obtained for the operators π and ρ apply to the operators π_1 and ρ_1, and it will be unnecessary to repeat the arguments.

Further generalisation can be made by substituting $\underset{\omega}{\Delta}$ for Δ in the definition of π, and a corresponding change in the definition of ρ. The cases which we consider are those in which $\omega = 1$ or $\omega = -1$.

We shall now proceed to prove some general theorems for the four operators π, ρ, π_1, ρ_1. The theorems will be stated for both sets of operators, but will be proved only for π and ρ. The reader will have no difficulty in supplying the proofs for π_1 and ρ_1.

14·1. Theorem I. *If $f(\lambda)$ be a rational function, then*

$$f(\pi)\, \rho^m u \doteqdot \rho^m f(\pi+m)\, u,$$

$$f(\pi_1)\, \rho_1^m u \doteqdot \rho_1^m f(\pi_1+m)\, u.$$

The theorem has already been proved for the case of a polynomial (see 14·01).

Suppose $f(\lambda)$ expressed in partial fractions, say,

$$f(\lambda) = P(\lambda) + \sum \frac{A}{(\lambda-\alpha)^n},$$

where $P(\lambda)$ is a polynomial. From 14·01,

$$(\pi-a)^n \rho^m [(\pi-a+m)^{-n} u] = \rho^m (\pi-a+m)^n [(\pi-a+m)^{-n} u] = \rho^m u.$$

Operating with $(\pi-a)^{-n}$, we have

$$(\pi-a)^{-n} \rho^m u = \rho^m (\pi-a+m)^{-n} u.$$

The theorem is therefore true for $f(\lambda) = (\lambda-a)^{-n}$ and is therefore true for any rational function.

14·11. Theorem II.

$$\pi(\pi-1)(\pi-2)\dots(\pi-n+1)u \doteqdot x'(x'-1)(x'-2)\dots(x'-n+1)\overset{n}{\underset{-1}{\Delta}} u$$

$$\pi_1(\pi_1-1)(\pi_1-2)\dots(\pi_1-n+1)u \doteqdot x'(x'+1)(x'+2)\dots(x'+n-1)\overset{n}{\Delta} u.$$

From Theorem I, we have

$$(\pi-k)\,u \doteqdot (\pi-k)\,\rho^k\,\rho^{-k}\,u \doteqdot \rho^k\,\pi\,\rho^{-k}\,u,$$

so that

$$\begin{aligned}(\pi-n+1)(\pi-n+2)\dots(\pi-1)\,\pi\,u \\ &\doteqdot \rho^{n-1}\,\pi\,\rho^{-n+1}\,\rho^{n-2}\,\pi\,\rho^{-n+2}\dots\rho^{-2}\,\rho\,\pi\,\rho^{-1}\,\pi\,u \\ &\doteqdot \rho^n(\rho^{-1}\,\pi)^n\,u.\end{aligned}$$

Now

$$\pi\,u(x) = x'\,[\,u(x)-u(x-1)\,],$$

and therefore

$$\begin{aligned}\rho^{-1}\,\pi\,u(x) &\doteqdot (x'+1)\,[u(x+1)-u(x)\,] \div (x'+1) \\ &\doteqdot \underset{-1}{\Delta}\,u(x+1) \doteqdot \mathsf{E}\,\underset{-1}{\Delta}\,u(x).\end{aligned}$$

Hence

$$(\rho^{-1}\,\pi)^n\,u(x) \doteqdot \mathsf{E}^n\,\overset{n}{\underset{-1}{\Delta}}\,u(x),$$

$$\rho^n(\rho^{-1}\,\pi)^n\,u(x) \doteqdot x'(x'-1)\dots(x'-n+1)\,\mathsf{E}^{-n}\,\mathsf{E}^n\,\overset{n}{\underset{-1}{\Delta}}\,u(x),$$

so that

$$(\pi-n+1)(\pi-n+2)\dots(\pi-1)\,\pi u \doteqdot x'(x'-1)\dots(x'-n+1)\,\overset{n}{\underset{-1}{\Delta}}\,u,$$

which is the required result.

14·12. Theorem III. *If $F(\lambda)$ be a polynomial,*

$$F(\pi+\rho)\,u \doteqdot \left[F(\pi)+F_1(\pi)\,\rho+\frac{1}{2!}F_2(\pi)\,\rho^2+\frac{1}{3!}F_3(\pi)\,\rho^3+\dots\right]u,$$

$$F(\pi_1-\rho_1)\,u \doteqdot \left[F(\pi_1)-F_1(\pi_1)\,\rho_1+\frac{1}{2!}F_2(\pi_1)\,\rho_1^2-\frac{1}{3!}F_3(\pi_1)\,\rho_1^3+\dots\right]u,$$

where

$$F_n(\lambda) = \overset{n}{\underset{-1}{\Delta}}\,F(\lambda), \quad n = 1, 2, 3, \dots.$$

The theorem is clearly true for

(1) $$F(\lambda) = \binom{\lambda}{1}.$$

Suppose it to be true for

(2) $$F(\lambda) = \binom{\lambda}{n},$$

that is to say,

$$\binom{\pi+\rho}{n} u \doteqdot \left\{\binom{\pi}{n} + \sum_{s=1}^{n} \binom{\pi-s}{n-s} \frac{\rho^s}{s!}\right\} u,$$

since

$$\overset{s}{\underset{-1}{\Delta}} \binom{\lambda}{n} = \binom{\lambda-s}{n-s}.$$

Operating with $(\pi+\rho-n)/(n+1)$, we obtain

$$\binom{\pi+\rho}{n+1} u \doteqdot \left\{\binom{\pi}{n+1} + \frac{1}{n+1} \sum_{s=1}^{n} \left[(\pi-n)\binom{\pi-s}{n-s}\frac{\rho^s}{s!} + \rho\binom{\pi-s+1}{n-s+1}\frac{\rho^{s-1}}{(s-1)!}\right] + \frac{\rho^{n+1}}{(n+1)!}\right\} u.$$

From Theorem I, the second term in the square brackets is seen to be

$$\binom{\pi-s}{n-s+1}\frac{\rho^s}{(s-1)!},$$

so that we at once obtain

$$\binom{\pi+\rho}{n+1} u \doteqdot \left\{\binom{\pi}{n+1} + \sum_{s=1}^{n+1} \binom{\pi-s}{n+1-s}\frac{\rho^s}{s!}\right\} u.$$

The theorem thus follows by induction, from (1), when $F(\lambda)$ is of the form (2). Since any polynomial can be expressed as the sum of terms of the form (2), the theorem is proved.

The application of this theorem is as follows:

We have, from the definitions,

$$\pi u_x = (x-r)(u_x - u_{x-1}), \quad \rho u_x = (x-r)\, u_{x-1},$$

whence, by addition,

$$(\pi+\rho)\, u_x = (x-r)\, u_x.$$

Thus multiplication by x' or $x-r$ is equivalent to operation with $\pi+\rho$. Symbolically,

$$x' = x - r \doteqdot \pi + \rho,$$

We can now express any polynomial as an operator for, if $f(x)$ be a polynomial,

$$f(x)\, u \doteq f(\pi+\rho+r)\, u,$$

and we can apply Theorem III to developing the right-hand member. Thus, for example,

$$x^3 u \doteq (\pi+\rho+r)^3 u.$$

Here

$$\begin{aligned} F(\lambda) &= (\lambda+r)^3 \\ &= (\lambda+r)(\lambda+r-1)(\lambda+r-2)+3(\lambda+r)(\lambda+r-1)+(\lambda+r), \end{aligned}$$

$$F_1(\lambda) = 3(\lambda+r-1)(\lambda+r-2)+6(\lambda+r-1)+1,$$

$$F_2(\lambda) = 6(\lambda+r-2)+6, \quad F_3(\lambda) = 6.$$

Thus

$$x^3 u \doteq \{ (\pi+r)^3+[3(\pi+r)^2-3(\pi+r)+1]\rho+3(\pi+r-1)\rho^2+\rho^3 \} u.$$

14·13. Theorem IV. *If $f(\lambda)$ be a rational function, then*

$$f(\pi)\,\rho^m . 1 = f(m)\,\rho^m 1,$$

$$f(\pi_1)\,\rho_1^m . 1 = f(m)\,\rho_1^m 1.$$

By Theorem I,

$$f(\pi)\,\rho^m 1 = \rho^m f(\pi+m)\, 1.$$

By Taylor's theorem, we have

$$f(\lambda+m) = f(m)+f'(m)\,\lambda+f''(m)\frac{\lambda^2}{2!}+\dots,$$

and therefore

$$f(\pi+m)\,1 = f(m)\,1+f'(m)\,\pi . 1+\dots .$$

But $\pi . 1 = 0$, $\pi^2 . 1 = 0$, and so on, so that the theorem is true for a polynomial.

To prove the theorem for any rational function, since we may express the function in partial fractions, it is only necessary to consider the case $f(\lambda) = (\lambda+a)^{-n}$. By the first part,

$$(\pi+a)^n \rho^m 1 = (m+a)^n \rho^m 1.$$

Operate with $(m+a)^{-n}(\pi+a)^{-n}$, and we have

$$(m+a)^{-n} \rho^m 1 = (\pi+a)^{-n} \rho^m 1.$$

Thus the theorem is true for any rational function.

14·14. Theorem V. *Every linear difference equation whose coefficients are rational functions of x can be expressed in either of the forms*

$$[f_0(\pi)+f_1(\pi)\,\rho+f_2(\pi)\,\rho^2+\dots+f_m(\pi)\,\rho^m]\,u(x)=f(x),$$

$$[g_0(\pi_1)+g_1(\pi_1)\,\rho_1+g_2(\pi_1)\,\rho_1^2+\dots+g_m(\pi_1)\,\rho_1^m]\,u(x)=g(x),$$

where $f_s(\lambda)$, $g_s(\lambda)$, $(s=0,\,1,\,2,\dots,\,m)$ are polynomials and $f(x)$, $g(x)$ are known functions of x.

Suppose the equation to be given in the form

(1) $$X_0\,u(x)+X_1\,u(x-1)+X_2\,u(x-2)+\dots+X_n\,u(x-n)=X,$$

where the coefficients are rational functions of x, which may, without loss of generality, be supposed polynomials, since multiplication of the equation by a suitable polynomial will produce this case.

Multiply the equation by $x'(x'-1)(x'-2)\dots(x'-n+1)$ and observe that $x'u(x-1)=\rho\,u(x)$, $x'(x'-1)\,u(x-2)=\rho^2\,u(x)$, and so on. The equation then assumes the form

$$\phi_0(x)\,u(x)+\phi_1(x)\,\rho\,u(x)+\dots+\phi_n(x)\,\rho^n\,u(x)=f(x),$$

where the coefficients are polynomials in x.

Now we have seen that multiplication by x' is the equivalent of operation with $\pi+\rho$, and therefore that multiplication by x is equivalent to the operation $\pi+\rho+r$. If then we replace x in the coefficients by $\pi+\rho+r$ and expand these coefficients by using Theorem III, we obtain the form stated in the enunciation.

If the equation be given in the form

(2) $$X_0\,u(x)+X_1\,u(x+1)+\dots+X_n\,u(x+n)=X,$$

we can multiply by $x'(x'+1)\dots(x'+n-1)$ and put

$$x'\,u(x+1)=\rho_1\,u(x),\quad x'(x'+1)\,u(x+2)=\rho_1^2\,u(x),$$

and so on. If we then replace x in the coefficients by $-\pi_1+\rho_1+r$ and again use Theorem III, we have the second of the forms stated.

Since equation (1) can be transformed into the form (2) and vice versa, each of these equations can be expressed in either of the forms given in the enunciation.

We shall call the forms given in the enunciation the *first and second canonical forms* respectively.

The above theorem is fundamental in Boole's method and gives rise to the following remarks:

If the equation be given in the form

$$X_0 \overset{n}{\underset{-1}{\Delta}} u(x) + X_1 \overset{n-1}{\underset{-1}{\Delta}} u(x) + \dots + X_n u(x) = X,$$

the simplest procedure is often, not to reduce it to one of the forms used in the proof of Theorem V, but to multiply by

$$x'(x'-1)(x'-2)\dots(x'-n+1).$$

Then, by Theorem II, the equation assumes the form

$$\phi_0(x)\,\pi(\pi-1)\dots(\pi-n+1)\,u(x) \\ +\phi_1(x)\,\pi(\pi-1)\dots(\pi-n+2)\,u(x)+\dots = f(x).$$

If we then replace x in the coefficients by $\pi+\rho+r$ and effect the proper reductions by use of Theorem I, we arrive at the first canonical form of Theorem V.

It might also be noticed that another way of reducing the equation

$$X_0 u(x) + X_1 u(x-1) + \dots + X_n u(x-n) = X$$

is to make the change of variable

$$u(x) = v(x) / \Gamma(x'+1),$$

which gives

$$u(x-1) = \frac{1}{\Gamma(x'+1)} \rho\, v(x),$$

$$u(x-2) = \frac{1}{\Gamma(x'+1)} \rho^2 v(x),$$

and so on, so that we obtain

$$X_0 v(x) + X_1 \rho\, v(x) + \dots + X_n \rho^n v(x) = X\,\Gamma(x'+1),$$

which can be reduced to the first canonical form by the method already explained.

In the same way the equation

$$X_0 u(x) + X_1 u(x+1) + \dots + X_n u(x+n) = X$$

becomes by the substitution $u(x) = v(x)\,\Gamma(x')$,

$$X_0 v(x) + X_1 \rho_1 v(x) + \dots + X_n \rho_1^n v(x) = X / \Gamma(x').$$

It must, however, be clearly understood that a change of the dependent variable of the kind just described may so affect the solutions of the transformed equation as to render the method of solution in series which will presently be described inoperative. On the other hand, should an equation when reduced by Theorem V prove intractable, the change of variable may lead to an equation to which our method will apply.

14·2. Formal Solution in Series. Consider the homogeneous equation

(1) $$X_0 u(x)+X_1 u(x-1)+\dots+X_n u(x-n)=0,$$

where the coefficients are polynomials. We first make the change of variable $u(x)=\mu^x v(x)$. The equation then becomes

$$\mu^n X_0 v(x)+\mu^{n-1} X_1 v(x-1)+\dots$$
$$+\mu X_{n-1} v(x-n+1)+X_n v(x-n)=0.$$

If this equation be reduced to the first canonical form, we have

(2) $$[f_0(\pi)+f_1(\pi)\rho+f_2(\pi)\rho^2+\dots+f_m(\pi)\rho^m]\,v(x)=0,$$

where $f_0(\pi), f_1(\pi), \dots, f_m(\pi)$ involve the parameter μ rationally. For the moment we shall leave μ undetermined, and we seek to satisfy the equation for $v(x)$ by a series of the form

(3) $$v(x)=a_0\rho^k+a_1\rho^{k-1}+a_2\rho^{k-2}+\dots+a_s\rho^{k-s}+\dots,$$

where the operand unity is understood. Substituting this series in (2), we shall have a formal solution of the equation if the coefficients of the several powers of ρ vanish. Using Theorem IV, we thus obtain

(4) $$a_0 f_m(m+k)=0,$$

$$a_1 f_m(m+k-1)+a_0 f_{m-1}(m+k-1)=0,$$
$$a_2 f_m(m+k-2)+a_1 f_{m-1}(m+k-2)+a_0 f_{m-2}(m+k-2)=0,$$
$$\dots\dots\dots\dots\dots\dots\dots\dots$$

(5) $$a_s f_m(m+k-s)+a_{s-1} f_{m-1}(m+k-s)+\dots$$
$$+a_{s-m} f_0(m+k-s)=0 \quad (s\geqslant m).$$

If we suppose $a_0\neq 0$, equation (4) yields a certain number of values of k, say, $k_1, k_2, \dots, k_\nu$, which for the present we shall suppose to be all different, and such that no two of them differ by an integer. The equation

$$(6) \qquad f_m(m+k) = 0$$

will be called the *indicial equation.*

To each root of the indicial equation there corresponds a series of the form (3), whose coefficients are determined successively by the above recurrence relations, which can be successively evaluated, since, by hypothesis, no two roots of (6) differ by an integer, and therefore, if k be a root of (6), $f_m(m+k-s) \neq 0$, $s = 1, 2, 3, \ldots$. Each series obtained in this way is a formal solution of (2).

Denote the solutions corresponding to $k_1, k_2, \ldots, k_\nu$ by

$$v_1(x),\ v_2(x),\ \ldots,\ v_\nu(x).$$

We have then the formal solutions

$$\mu^x v_1(x),\ \mu^x v_2(x),\ \ldots,\ \mu^x v_\nu(x)$$

of (1). Whether these solutions converge can of course be examined in any particular case. Whether they are linearly independent is as yet undecided.

If $\nu = n$ we have obtained n solutions, but if $\nu < n$ the equation has other solutions which we have yet to determine. Leaving these questions for the present, it may happen that the indicial equation does not contain $m+k$, in other words, that $f_m(\pi)$ is independent of π. If $f_m(\pi)$ be also independent of μ the method fails completely, but if $f_m(\pi)$, while independent of π, be not independent of μ we choose, if possible, a non-zero value of μ such that $f_m(\pi)$ vanishes. Let $\mu_1, \mu_2, \ldots, \mu_\lambda$ be the *distinct* non-zero values of μ which cause $f_m(\pi)$ to vanish.

To each such value of μ we have an equation of the form

$$[f_0(\pi)+f_1(\pi)\,\rho+\ldots+f_{m-1}(\pi)\,\rho^{m-1}]\,v(x) = 0,$$

and we attempt to satisfy this equation by a series of the form (3). If corresponding to $\mu = \mu_1$ this equation yields formal solutions $v_1(x), \ldots, v_\sigma(x)$, we have as solutions of (1)

$$\mu_1^x v_1(x),\ \ldots,\ \mu_1^x v_\sigma(x).$$

Similarly for $\mu_2, \mu_3, \ldots, \mu_\lambda$ we may obtain corresponding sets of solutions.

Thus we see that if equation (1) have a particular solution of the form

$$\mu^x \{a_0 \rho^k + a_1 \rho^{k-1} + a_2 \rho^{k-2} + \dots\},$$

this solution will in general be detected by the above method. Since

$$\rho^m = \frac{\Gamma(x'+1)}{\Gamma(x'-m+1)} = \frac{\Gamma(x-r+1)}{\Gamma(x-r-m+1)},$$

we shall expect our method to determine any solution of the form

$$\frac{\mu^x \Gamma(x-r+1)}{\Gamma(x-k-r+1)}\left\{a_0 + \frac{a_1}{(x-r-k+1)} + \frac{a_2}{(x-r-k+1)(x-r-k+2)} + \dots\right\}.$$

Example. $(x-2)\,u(x) - (2x-3)\,u(x-1) - 3(x-1)\,u(x-2) = 0.$

Putting $u(x) = \mu^x v(x)$, we have

$$\mu^2(x-2)\,v(x) - \mu(2x-3)\,v(x-1) - 3(x-1)\,v(x-2) = 0.$$

If we take $r = 0$, so that

$$x\,v(x-1) = \rho\, v(x), \quad x(x-1)\,v(x-2) = \rho^2 v(x),$$

the equation becomes, on multiplication by x,

$$[\mu^2(x-2)\,x - \mu(2x-3)\,\rho - 3\rho^2]\,v(x) = 0.$$

Writing $\pi + \rho$ for x, we get, by Theorem III,

$$[\mu^2\{\pi^2 - 2\pi + (2\pi-3)\,\rho + \rho^2\} - \mu(2\pi - 3 + 2\rho)\rho - 3\rho^2]\,v(x) = 0,$$

$$[\mu^2(\pi^2 - 2\pi) + (\mu^2 - \mu)(2\pi - 3)\,\rho + (\mu^2 - 2\mu - 3)\,\rho^2]\,v(x) = 0.$$

Since $f_2(\pi) = \mu^2 - 2\mu - 3$ is independent of π, we choose μ so that $\mu^2 - 2\mu - 3 = 0$. This gives $\mu = 3$ or -1. With either of these values for μ the equation becomes

$$[\mu(\pi^2 - 2\pi) + (\mu - 1)(2\pi - 3)\,\rho]\,v(x) = 0.$$

Assume

$$v(x) = a_0\rho^k + a_1\rho^{k-1} + a_2\rho^{k-2} + \dots.$$

The indicial equation is

$$2(k+1) - 3 = 0, \text{ whence } k = \tfrac{1}{2}.$$

The recurrence relation for the coefficients is

$$(\mu - 1)(2k + 2 - 2s - 3)\,a_s + \mu(k + 1 - s)(k - 1 - s)\,a_{s-1} = 0,$$

which gives, since $k=\frac{1}{2}$,

$$a_s = p\frac{(2s-3)(2s+1)}{s}a_{s-1},\quad p=\frac{\mu}{8(\mu-1)},$$

$$a_1=-3\,pa_0,\quad a_2=-p^2\frac{3\,.\,5}{2}a_0,\quad a_3=-p^3\frac{3\,.\,3\,.\,5\,.\,7}{2\,.\,3}a_0,$$

$$a_s=-p^s a_0[(2s-3)(2s-5)\ldots 5\,.\,3(2s+1)(2s-1)\ldots 3]/s!.$$

When $\mu=3$, $p=\frac{3}{16}$, and when $\mu=-1$, $p=\frac{1}{16}$.

Hence we have the formal solutions

$$u_1(x)=\frac{3^x\Gamma(x+1)}{\Gamma(x+\frac{1}{2})}\left\{1-\frac{3\,.\,3}{16(x+\frac{1}{2})}-\frac{3^2}{16^2}\frac{3\,.\,5}{(x+\frac{1}{2})(x+\frac{3}{2})2}-\ldots\right\},$$

$$u_2(x)=\frac{(-1)^x\Gamma(x+1)}{\Gamma(x+\frac{1}{2})}\left\{1-\frac{3}{16(x+\frac{1}{2})}-\frac{3\,.\,5}{16^2(x+\frac{1}{2})(x+\frac{3}{2})2}-\ldots\right\},$$

where the successive values of the coefficients are determined by the formula above for a_s.

If t_{s-1}, t_s denote successive terms of either series,

$$\frac{t_s}{t_{s-1}}=\frac{p(2s-3)(2s+1)}{s(x-\frac{1}{2}+s)}=\frac{4p(1-\frac{3}{2}s^{-1})(1+\frac{1}{2}s^{-1})}{1+(x-\frac{1}{2})s^{-1}}.$$

Thus, for $u_1(x)$, $\left|\frac{t_s}{t_{s-1}}\right|\to\frac{3}{4}$, and for $u_2(x)$, $\left|\frac{t_s}{t_{s-1}}\right|\to\frac{1}{4}$.

Thus both series are absolutely convergent.

14·21. Solution in Newton's Series. The method of operational solution can also be applied to finding a solution in the form

$$u(x)=\mu^x\frac{\Gamma(x'+1)}{\Gamma(x'-k+1)}\sum_{s=0}^{\infty}a_s(x'-k)(x'-k-1)\ldots(x'-k-s+1).$$

The equation having been reduced, after the substitution

$$u(x)=\mu^x v(x),$$

to the form

$$[f_0(\pi)+f_1(\pi)\rho+\ldots+f_m(\pi)\rho^m]v(x)=0,$$

and μ chosen, if possible, so as to make the term $f_m(\pi)$ vanish, we substitute

$$v(x)=a_0\rho^k+a_1\rho^{k+1}+\ldots+a_s\rho^{k+s}+\ldots.$$

Equating to zero the several powers of ρ, we obtain the indicial equation

$$f_0(k) = 0,$$

together with the recurrence relations

$$a_s f_0(k+s) + a_{s-1} f_1(k+s) + a_{s-2} f_2(k+s) + \dots = 0,$$

by means of which the coefficients can be successively determined when the value of k has been found from the indicial equation.

If the series obtained in this way be convergent, we have a solution of the equation in the required form. The following example illustrates the method:

Example.

$$(x-\alpha)(x-\beta)\,u(x) - [2x(x\quad 1) - \delta(x-1) + \alpha\beta]\,u(x-1)$$
$$+ (x-2)(x-\gamma-1)\,u(x-2) = 0,$$

where

$$\delta = \alpha + \beta + \gamma + 1.$$

Take $x' = x - 1$. Putting $u(x) = \mu^x v(x)$ and multiplying by $x-1$, we get

$$\mu^2(\pi+\rho)(\pi+1-\alpha+\rho)(\pi+1-\beta+\rho)\,v(x)$$
$$-\mu[2(\pi+\rho)(\pi+1+\rho) - \delta(\pi+\rho) + \alpha\beta]\,\rho\, v(x)$$
$$+(\pi+\rho-\gamma)\,\rho^2\, v(x) = 0.$$

The coefficient of ρ^3 is $(\mu-1)^2$. We therefore take $\mu = 1$, so that $u(x) = v(x)$, and the equation reduces to

$$[\pi(\pi-\alpha+1)(\pi-\beta+1) + \pi(\pi-\alpha-\beta+\gamma)\,\rho]\,u(x) = 0.$$

Put

$$u(x) = a_0\,\rho^k + a_1\,\rho^{k+1} + \dots + a_s\,\rho^{k+s} + \dots .$$

The indicial equation is then

$$k(k-\alpha+1)(k-\beta+1) = 0,$$

whence

$$k = 0, \quad \alpha - 1, \quad \beta - 1.$$

The recurrence relation for the coefficients is

$$a_s(k+s)(k+s-\alpha+1)(k+s-\beta+1) + a_{s-1}(k+s)(k+s-\alpha-\beta+\gamma) = 0,$$

so that we have for a_s the expression

$$\frac{(-1)^s(k+1-\alpha-\beta+\gamma)(k+2-\alpha-\beta+\gamma)\dots(k+s-\alpha-\beta+\gamma)\,a_0}{(k+2-\alpha)(k+3-\alpha)\dots(k+s+1-\alpha)(k+2-\beta)(k+3-\beta)\dots(k+s+1-\beta)}.$$

Putting in turn $k=0$, $k=\alpha-1$, $k=\beta-1$, we have the three solutions

$$u_1(x)=1+\sum_{s=1}^{\infty}\frac{(-1)^s(1-\alpha-\beta+\gamma)\dots(s-\alpha-\beta+\gamma)\,s!}{(2-\alpha)\dots(s+1-\alpha)(2-\beta)\dots(s+1-\beta)}\binom{x-1}{s},$$

$$u_2(x)=\frac{\Gamma(x)}{\Gamma(x-\alpha+1)}\left[1+\sum_{s=1}^{\infty}\frac{(-1)^s(\gamma-\beta)\dots(\gamma-\beta+s-1)}{(\alpha-\beta+1)\dots(\alpha-\beta+s)}\binom{x-\alpha}{s}\right],$$

$$u_3(x)=\frac{\Gamma(x)}{\Gamma(x-\beta+1)}\left[1+\sum_{s=1}^{\infty}\frac{(-1)^s(\gamma-\alpha)\dots(\gamma-\alpha+s-1)}{(\beta-\alpha+1)\dots(\beta-\alpha+s)}\binom{x-\beta}{s}\right].$$

The ratio of the sth term to the preceding term is

$$\frac{(k+s-\alpha-\beta+\gamma)(s-x+k)}{(k+s-\alpha+1)(k+s-\beta+1)}=1-\frac{x-\gamma+2}{s}+\dots.$$

All three series are therefore absolutely convergent if

$$R(x)>R(\gamma-1).$$

In the case of $u_1(x)$, neither α nor β may be a positive integer greater than 1.

For $u_2(x)$, $\alpha-\beta$ must not be a negative integer, and in the case of $u_3(x)$, $\beta-\alpha$ must not be a negative integer.

These three solutions cannot be linearly independent.

If $\alpha=\beta=1$, the indicial equation has a multiple root and the three solutions coincide. The method of dealing with multiple roots of the indicial equation is discussed in section 14·22.

This equation can also be satisfied by factorial series of the first kind, for, putting

$$u(x)=b_0\,\rho^k+b_1\,\rho^{k-1}+\dots+b_s\,\rho^{k-s}+\dots,$$

we have the indicial equation

$$(k+1)(k+1-\alpha-\beta+\gamma)=0,$$

whence $\quad k=-1 \quad\text{or}\quad \alpha+\beta-\gamma-1.$

The recurrence relation is

$$b_s(k-s+1-\alpha-\beta+\gamma)+b_{s-1}(k-s+2-\alpha)(k-s+2-\beta)=0,$$

which gives for b_s the expression

$$\frac{(s-2-k+\alpha)\dots(-1-k+\alpha)(s-2-k+\beta)\dots(-1-k+\beta)\,b_0}{(s-k-1+\alpha+\beta-\gamma)(s-k-2+\alpha+\beta-\gamma)\dots(-k+\alpha+\beta-\gamma)}.$$

Writing, for brevity, $c=\alpha+\beta-\gamma+1$, we have the solutions

$$u_4(x)=\frac{1}{x}+\frac{\alpha\beta}{cx(x+1)}+\frac{\alpha(\alpha+1)\beta(\beta+1)}{c(c+1)x(x+1)(x+2)}$$
$$+\frac{\alpha(\alpha+1)(\alpha+2)\beta(\beta+1)(\beta+2)}{c(c+1)(c+2)x(x+1)(x+2)(x+3)}+\dots,$$

$$u_5(x)=\frac{\Gamma(x)}{\Gamma(x-c+2)}\left[1+\frac{(\gamma-\alpha)(\gamma-\beta)}{1!\,(x-c+2)}\right.$$
$$\left.+\frac{(\gamma-\alpha)(\gamma-\alpha+1)(\gamma-\beta)(\gamma-\beta+1)}{2!\,(x-c+2)(x-c+3)}+\dots\right],$$

so that in terms of the hypergeometric function

$$u_5(x)=\frac{\Gamma(x)}{\Gamma(x-c+2)}F(\gamma-\alpha,\,\gamma-\beta\,;\,x-c+2\,;\,1).$$

Thus, using 9·82, we have

$$u_5(x)=\frac{\Gamma(x)\,\Gamma(x-\gamma+1)}{\Gamma(x-\beta+1)\,\Gamma(x-\alpha+1)}.$$

The series for $u_4(x)$, $u_5(x)$ converge for $R(x)>R(\gamma-1)$. When $|x|\to\infty$ in the half-plane of convergence we have the asymptotic relations

$$u_4(x)\sim x^{-1},\quad u_5(x)\sim x^{c-2},$$

the latter result following from 10·43.

It follows, from 12·16, that $u_4(x)$, $u_5(x)$ form a fundamental system of solutions.

14·22. Exceptional Cases. In the preceding discussion we excepted the cases in which the indicial equation has multiple roots or roots which differ by an integer. In the case of a multiple root the method only gives one series corresponding to that root, while in the case where two roots differ by an integer, the equations 14·2 (5) may lead to infinite coefficients, owing to the possible vanishing of $f_m(m+k-s)$ for certain values of s. To discuss these cases we shall suppose that the given equation

$$X_0\,u(x)+X_1\,u(x-1)+\dots+X_n\,u(x-n)=0$$

has been transformed by the substitution $u(x) = \mu^x v(x)$ and that the value of μ has been assigned in the manner previously described, so that for the value of μ in question the equation assumes the first canonical form

(1) $$[f_0(\pi) + f_1(\pi)\,\rho + f_2(\pi)\,\rho^2 + \dots + f_m(\pi)\,\rho^m]\,v(x) = 0.$$

The indicial equation is

$$f_m(m+k) = 0.$$

If the indicial equation have roots which differ by zero or an integer, we begin by arranging all the roots in groups such that any pair of roots of the same group differ by zero or an integer. The roots of such a group will be called congruent. Let p be the greatest positive integer by which a pair of roots of the indicial equation differ.

Consider the non-homogeneous equation

(2) $$[f_0(\pi) + f_1(\pi)\,\rho + \dots + f_m(\pi)\,\rho^m]\,v\,(x) = a(k)\,f_m(m+k)\,\rho^{k+m},$$

where

$$a(k) = b_0 f_m(m+k-1)\,f_m(m+k-2)\dots f_m(m+k-p).$$

If round each of the roots of the indicial equation we describe circles of radius y, we can make y so small that when k varies in the domain K formed by these circles the function $f_m(m+k-s)$, $s > p$, does not vanish at all. Under these conditions we can find a formal solution of (2) by putting

$$v(x) = a(k)\,\rho^k + b_1\,\rho^{k-1} + b_2\,\rho^{k-2} + \dots .$$

For if we substitute this series in (2) we see that the coefficients of ρ^{k+m} are equal, while the coefficients $b_1, b_2, \dots, b_s, \dots$ are found from the recurrence relations

$$b_1\,f_m(m+k-1) + a(k)\,f_{m-1}(m+k-1) = 0,$$

$$b_2\,f_m(m+k-2) + b_1\,f_{m-1}(m+k-2) + a(k)\,f_{m-2}(m+k-2) = 0,$$

. . . .

$$b_p\,f_m(m+k-p) + b_{p-1}\,f_{m-1}(m+k-p) + \dots = 0,$$

. . . .

$$b_s\,f_m(m+k-s) + b_{s-1}\,f_{m-1}(m+k-s) + \dots = 0,$$

and these equations lead to determinate values of the coefficients, for should any of the coefficients $f_m(m+k-s)$, $s = 1, 2, \dots, p$ vanish, we can first remove the vanishing coefficient which also appears in $a(k)$ and therefore in $b_1, b_2, \dots$.

Moreover, $f_m(m+k-s)$, $s > p$, cannot vanish for any value of k in K. We thus obtain a formal solution of (2) in the form

$$v_k(x) = \left[a(k) + \frac{b_1}{x'-k+1} + \frac{b_2}{(x'-k+1)(x'-k+2)} + \dots\right] \frac{\Gamma(x'+1)}{\Gamma(x'-k+1)}.$$

If the factorial series

$$\frac{b_1}{z+1} + \frac{b_2}{(z+1)(z+2)} + \frac{b_3}{(z+1)(z+2)(z+3)} + \dots$$

converge uniformly with respect to z for $R(z) > \lambda$, the series for $v_k(x)$ will converge uniformly with respect to k for $R(x) > \lambda'$, where $\lambda' > \lambda$ depends on the exact disposition of the region K. Consequently, for $R(x) > \lambda'$ and k in K we can differentiate the factorial series term by term, and we thus obtain the result that $\partial^s v_k(x) / \partial k^s$ exists as an analytic function and satisfies the difference equation

$$\text{(3)} \qquad [f_0(\pi) + \dots + f_m(\pi)\rho^m]\, v(x) = \frac{\partial^s}{\partial k^s}\left\{a(k) f_m(m+k)\, \rho^{m+k}\right\}.$$

Now consider

$$a(k) f_m(m+k).$$

Let $\alpha_0, \alpha_1, \alpha_2, \dots, \alpha_{l-1}$ be the congruent roots which constitute the first group of the roots of the indicial equation and suppose them arranged in non-descending order of their real parts, so that

$$R(\alpha_0) \leqslant R(\alpha_1) \leqslant R(\alpha_2) \leqslant \dots \leqslant R(\alpha_{l-1}).$$

Let $\alpha_0, \alpha_\lambda, \alpha_\mu, \dots, \alpha_\nu$ denote those roots which are distinct. Then

$$\alpha_0 = \alpha_1 = \alpha_2 = \dots = \alpha_{\lambda-1},$$

so that α_0 is of multiplicity λ.

Again,

$$\alpha_\lambda = \alpha_{\lambda+1} = \dots = \alpha_{\mu-1},$$

so that α_λ is of multiplicity $\mu - \lambda$, and so on. Thus

$$a(k) = b_0 (k-\alpha_\lambda)^\lambda (k-\alpha_\mu)^\mu \dots (k-\alpha_\nu)^\nu f(k),$$

where $f(k)$ does not vanish for any root of this group.

Now

$$f_0(m+k) = (k-\alpha_0)^\lambda (k-\alpha_\lambda)^{\mu-\lambda} \dots (k-\alpha_\nu)^{l-\nu} g(k).$$

Thus

$$a(k) f_0(m+k) = (k-\alpha_0)^\lambda (k-\alpha_\lambda)^{\mu} \dots (k-\alpha_\nu)^{l} \phi(k),$$

where $\phi(k)$ does not vanish for any root of the group.

It follows that

$$\frac{\partial^s}{\partial k^s}[a(k) f_m(m+k)\, \rho^{m+k}]$$

vanishes when

$$k=\alpha_0, \quad s = 0, 1, 2, \dots, \lambda-1,$$
$$k=\alpha_\lambda, \quad s = \lambda, \lambda+1, \dots, \mu-1,$$
$$\cdot \quad \cdot \quad \cdot \quad \cdot \quad \cdot \quad \cdot \quad \cdot \quad \cdot \quad \cdot \quad \cdot \quad \cdot$$
$$k=\alpha_\nu, \quad s = \nu, \nu+1, \dots, l-1,$$

and in these cases the equation (3) coincides with (1) and therefore we have l solutions of (1), namely, $\frac{\partial^s}{\partial k^s}[v_k(x)]$ corresponding to the above set of values of k and s.

That these solutions are linearly distinct will be proved later from a consideration of their asymptotic values. The corresponding solutions of the equation in $u(x)$ are obtained by multiplying the values of $\frac{\partial^s}{\partial k^s}[v_k(x)]$ by μ^x.

Example 1.

$$(x^3+1)\,u(x) - (2x-1)(x-1)(x-a)\,u(x-1) + (x-2)(x-a)(x-a-1)\,u(x-2) = 0.$$

Writing $u(x) = v(x)\,\mu^x$ and taking $x' = x-a$, we have

$$\mu^2[(\pi+a+\rho)^3+1]\,v(x) - \mu[2(\pi+a+\rho)^2 - 3(\pi+a+\rho)+1]\,\rho\, v(x) + (\pi+a-2+\rho)\,\rho^2\, v(x) = 0.$$

The coefficient of ρ^3 is $\mu^2-2\mu+1$. We therefore take $\mu = 1$, and the equation reduces to

$$[(\pi+a)^3+1+(\pi+a)^2\,\rho]\,u(x) = 0.$$

Putting

$$u(x) = a_0\,\rho^k + a_1\,\rho^{k-1} + \dots$$

we have the indicial equation

$$(k+a+1)^2 = 0.$$

We therefore consider the equation

$$[(\pi+a)^3+1+(\pi+a)^2 \rho]\, u(x) = a_0(k+a+1)^2 \rho^{k+1},$$

which gives

$$(k+a)^2 a_1 + a_0(1+(k+a)^3) = 0,$$

$$(k+a-s+1)^2 a_s + a_{s-1}(1+(k+a-s+1)^3) = 0.$$

Writing $l = k+a+1$,

$$a_s = \frac{[(s-l)^3-1][(s-l-1)^3-1][(s-l-2)^3-1]\dots[(1-l)^3-1]}{(s-l)^2(s-l-1)^2(s-l-2)^2\dots(1-l)^2}\, a_0.$$

Putting $k = -a-1$, that is, $l = 0$, we see that $a_1 = 0$ and therefore $a_s = 0$, $s = 2, 3, 4, \dots$. One solution is therefore

$$u_1(x) = \rho^{-a-1} = \Gamma(x-a+1) \,/\, \Gamma(x+2).$$

A second solution is the value when $l = 0$ of

$$a_0 \frac{\partial}{\partial l} \rho^k + a_1 \frac{\partial}{\partial l} \rho^{k-1} + \dots + \rho^k \frac{\partial a_1}{\partial l} + \rho^k \frac{\partial a_2}{\partial l} + \dots,$$

and from the form of a_s we see that when $l = 0$,

$$\frac{\partial a_s}{\partial l} = \frac{(s^3-1)\dots(2^3-1)(-3)}{s^2(s-1)^2\dots 2^2}\, a_0.$$

Thus a second solution is

$$u_2(x) = \frac{\Gamma(x-a+1)\,\Psi(x+2)}{\Gamma(x+2)} - 3\sum_{s=1}^{\infty} \frac{(s^3-1)\dots(2^3-1)}{s^2(s-1)^2\dots 2^2}\,\frac{\Gamma(x-a+1)}{\Gamma(x+s+2)}.$$

The series converges if $R(x) > 0$.

The following example illustrates the application of the method to solutions in factorial series of the second kind.

Example 2.

$$(x-1)\,u(x) - (2x-1)\,u(x-1) + (x-1)\,u(x-2) = 0.$$

Multiply by x and take $x' = x$. The equation becomes

$$[x(x-1) - (2x-1)\,\rho + \rho^2]\, u(x) = 0,$$

which reduces at once to

$$[\pi(\pi-1) - \rho]\, u(x) = 0.$$

Clearly this has no solutions by factorial series of the first kind. We therefore put

$$u(x) = a_0\, \rho^k + a_1\, \rho^{k+1} + a_2\, \rho^{k+2} + \dots .$$

The indicial equation has the roots 0 and 1 which differ by an integer.

We therefore consider the non-homogeneous equation

$$[\pi(\pi-1)-\rho]\, u(x) = k(k-1)\, a_0(k)\, \rho^k,$$

where

$$a_0(k) = f_0(k+1)\, b_0 = k(k+1)\, b_0.$$

Putting

$$u(x) = a_0(k)\, \rho^k + b_1\, \rho^{k+1} + b_2\, \rho^{k+2} + \dots ,$$

we obtain the recurrence relations

$$(k+1)\, k\, b_1 = a_0(k) = b_0\, k(k+1),$$

$$(k+2)(k+1)\, b_2 = b_1,$$

$$\cdots \quad \cdots \quad \cdots$$

$$(k+s)(k+s-1)\, b_s = b_{s-1},$$

whence

$$b_1 = b_0,$$

$$b_s = \frac{b_0}{(k+s)(k+s-1)\dots(k+2)(k+s-1)\dots(k+1)}.$$

Thus

$$u(x) = \frac{\Gamma(x+1)}{\Gamma(x-k+1)} \left\{ k(k+1) + \sum_{s=1}^{\infty} \frac{s!}{(k+s)\dots(k+2)\,.\,(k+s-1)\dots(k+1)} \binom{x-k}{s} \right\}.$$

The series in the bracket converges in the whole plane so that $u(x)$ is a meromorphic function with poles at the poles of $\Gamma(x+1)$.

We get one solution by putting $k = 0$, whence

$$u_1(x) = \sum_{s=1}^{\infty} \frac{1}{(s-1)!} \binom{x}{s}.$$

To obtain a second solution we differentiate $u(x)$ with respect to k and then put $k=0$. Now

$$u(x) = \frac{k(k+1)\,\Gamma(x+1)}{\Gamma(x-k+1)} + \sum_{s=1}^{\infty} \frac{\Gamma(k+2)\,\Gamma(k+1)\,\Gamma(x+1)}{\Gamma(k+s+1)\,\Gamma(k+s)\,\Gamma(x-k-s+1)}.$$

Writing t_s for the term under the summation sign and taking the logarithmic differential coefficient with respect to k, we have

$$\frac{1}{t_s}\frac{\partial t_s}{\partial k} = \Psi(k+2)+\Psi(k+1)-\Psi(k+s+1) \\ -\Psi(k+s)+\Psi(x-k-s+1).$$

Putting $k=0$, we obtain the solution

$$u_2(x) = 1+\sum_{s=1}^{\infty}\frac{1}{(s-1)!}\binom{x}{s} \\ \times\{\Psi(x-s+1)-\Psi(s)-\Psi(s+1)+\Psi(2)+\Psi(1)\}.$$

14·3. Asymptotic Forms of the Solutions. We have found that when the indicial equation presents roots which differ by zero or an integer, the solutions are obtained by differentiating partially with respect to k the expression

$$v_k(x) = w_k(x)\frac{\Gamma(x-r+1)}{\Gamma(x-r-k+1)},$$

where

$$w_k(x) = a(k)+\frac{b_1}{x-r-k+1}+\frac{b_2}{(x-r-k+1)(x-r-k+2)}+\dots,$$

$$a(k) = b_0(k-\alpha_\lambda)^\lambda(k-\alpha_\mu)^\mu\dots(k-\alpha_\nu)^\nu f(k).$$

Now, by Leibniz' theorem, we have

$$\frac{\partial^s v_k(x)}{\partial k^s} = \sum_{t=0}^{s}\binom{s}{t}\frac{\partial^t}{\partial k^t}\frac{\Gamma(x-r+1)}{\Gamma(x-r-k+1)}\frac{\partial^{s-t}w_k(x)}{\partial k^s},$$

and by 10·43,

$$(x-r-1)^{-k}\frac{\partial^t}{\partial k^t}\frac{\Gamma(x-r+1)}{\Gamma(x-r-k+1)} = \Omega_0(x-r+1) \\ +\Omega_1(x-r+1)\log\frac{1}{x-r+1}+\dots+(1+\Omega_t(x))\left(\log\frac{1}{x-r+1}\right)^t,$$

where $\Omega_0, \Omega_1, \dots, \Omega_t$ are inverse factorial series without a constant term.

It follows that for large values of $|x|$ we can replace the right-hand member by its largest term, namely, $[\log\{1/(x-r+1)\}]^t$.

Thus we have

$$\frac{\partial^s v_k(x)}{\partial k^s} \sim (x-r-1)^k\sum_{t=0}^{s}\binom{s}{t}\frac{d^{s-t}a(k)}{dk^{s-t}}\left(\log\frac{1}{x-r+1}\right)^t.$$

For the λ roots equal to α_0 we have therefore, if we retain only the largest term on the right,

$$\left(\frac{\partial^s v_k(x)}{\partial k^s}\right)_{k=\alpha_0} \sim (x-r+1)^{\alpha_0}\left(\log\frac{1}{x-r+1}\right)^s a(\alpha_0)$$

$$\sim x^{\alpha_0}\left(\log\frac{1}{x}\right)^s a(\alpha_0), \quad s = 0, 1, 2, \ldots, \lambda-1.$$

For the roots equal to a_λ, we observe that a_λ is a root of $\iota(k) = 0$, of multiplicity λ, so that $a^{(t)}(\alpha_\lambda) = 0$, $t = 0, 1, 2, \ldots, \lambda-1$. Thus for these roots,

$$\left(\frac{\partial^s v_k(x)}{\partial k^s}\right)_{k=a_\lambda} \sim x^{a_\lambda}\left(\log\frac{1}{x}\right)^{s-\lambda}\binom{s}{\lambda} a^{(\lambda)}(\alpha_\lambda), \; s = \lambda, \lambda+1, \ldots, \mu-1.$$

Proceeding in this way we have finally for the roots equal to α_ν,

$$\left(\frac{\partial^s v_k(x)}{\partial k^s}\right)_{k=a_\nu} \sim x^{a_\nu}\left(\log\frac{1}{x}\right)^{s-\nu}\binom{s}{\mu} a^{(\nu)}(\alpha_\nu), \; s = \nu, \nu+1, \ldots, l-1.$$

We have thus obtained asymptotic expressions for the solutions belonging to the same group of roots of the indicial equation.

Since the roots $\alpha_0, \alpha_\lambda, \ldots, \alpha_\nu$ were arranged according to non-descending order of their real parts, if $V_s(x)$, $V_{s+1}(x)$ denote successive solutions belonging to the same group of roots, it follows that

$$\lim_{|x|\to\infty} \frac{V_s(x)}{V_{s+1}(x)} = 0,$$

provided that $x \to \infty$ by a path inside the half-plane of convergence. More generally when $V_s(x)$, $V_t(x)$ are two solutions belonging to the same group, then

$$\lim_{|x|\to\infty} \frac{V_s(x)}{V_t(x)} = 0,$$

provided that $s < t$.

If we consider all the solutions to which the indicial equation gives rise, it follows that we can, in general, so number them, in the order $v_1(x), v_2(x), \ldots, v_n(x)$, say, that

$$\lim_{|x|\to\infty} \frac{v_s(x)}{v_{s+1}(x)} = 0, \quad s = 1, 2, \ldots, n-1.$$

The linear independence of these solutions then follows from the theorem of 12·16. We can therefore make the following statements:

(I) The solutions corresponding to a congruent set of roots of the indicial equation are linearly independent.

(II) When n solutions of a linear difference equation of order n satisfy the conditions of 12·16, they form a fundamental set.

(III) If the indicial equation of a linear difference equation of order n be of degree n, the corresponding set of solutions in general forms a fundamental system of solutions. For, in general, they can be so numbered as to satisfy the conditions of 12·16.

14·31. Series Solution Convergent in a Half Plane on the Left. The solutions in series obtained by the use of the operators π and ρ, if they do not converge everywhere or nowhere, converge in a half plane on the right, that is to say, in a half plane which contains the point $x = +\infty$. Any difference equation with rational coefficients can also be prepared by means of the operators π_1 and ρ_1 for reduction to the second canonical form of Theorem V. The series obtained from the equation so reduced will converge everywhere or nowhere or in a half plane on the left, that is to say, in a half plane which contains the point $x = -\infty$. The types of solution obtainable in this way are

$$\frac{\mu^x \Gamma(x'+k)}{\Gamma(x')}\left\{a_0 + \frac{a_1}{x'+k-1} + \frac{a_2}{(x'+k-1)(x'+k-2)} + \frac{a_3}{(x'+k-1)(x'+k-2)(x'+k-3)} + \dots\right\}$$

$$\frac{\mu^x \Gamma(x'+k)}{\Gamma(x')}\left\{b_0 + b_1(x'+k) + b_2(x'+k)(x'+k+1) + b_3(x'+k)(x'+k+1)(x'+k+2) + \dots\right\},$$

where $x' = x - r$.

Example.

$$4x(x+1)\,u(x+2) - 4(x^2+x+1)\,u(x+1) + x(x+1)\,u(x) = 0.$$

Put $u(x) = \mu^x v(x)$, $x' = x$ and multiply by x, then

$$4\mu^2 x\, \rho_1^2\, v(x) - 4\,\mu(x^2+x+1)\,\rho_1\, v(x) + x^2(x+1)\,v(x) = 0.$$

With $-\pi_1+\rho_1$ for x, we have, from Theorem III,

$$x^2+x+1 = (\pi_1-\rho_1)^2-(\pi_1-\rho_1)+1 = \pi_1^2-\pi_1+1-(2\pi_1-2)\rho_1+\rho_1^2,$$

$$-x^2(x+1) = (\pi_1-\rho_1)^3-(\pi_1-\rho_1)^2$$
$$= \pi_1^3-\pi_1^2-(\pi_1^2-5\pi_1+2)\rho_1+(3\pi_1-4)\rho_1^2-\rho_1^3.$$

The coefficient of ρ_1^3 is $4\mu^2-4\mu+1$. We therefore take $\mu = \frac{1}{2}$ and the equation reduces to

$$[\pi_1^3-\pi_1^2+(\pi_1^2+3\pi_1)\rho_1]\,v(x) = 0.$$

For factorial series of the first kind, put

$$v(x) = a_0\rho_1^k+a_1\rho_1^{k-1}+a_2\rho_1^{k-2}+\dots .$$

The indicial equation is

$$(k+1)(k+4) = 0,$$

whence $k = -1$ or -4.

Series of factorials of the second kind can also be obtained by putting

$$v(x) = b_0\rho_1^k+b_1\rho_1^{k+1}+b_2\rho_1^{k+2}+\dots .$$

14·4. The Complete Equation. Take the complete equation

(1) $$X_0\,u(x)+X_1\,u(x-1)+\dots+X_n\,u(x-n) = X,$$

where $X_0, X_1, \dots, X_n, X$ are all functions of x.

To obtain solutions we can of course consider the corresponding homogeneous equation and, by the use of Lagrange's method, 12·7 deduce a special solution of the complete equation from the general solution of the homogeneous equation. Another method which is more direct, when it is applicable, is the following :

Make the substitution $u(x) = \mu^x v(x)$ and reduce the equation by means of the operators π and ρ to the form

(2) $$[f_0(\pi)+f_1(\pi)\rho+f_2(\pi)\rho^2+\dots+f_m(\pi)\rho^m]\,v(x) = \mu^{-x}X,$$

the parameter μ being at our choice.

If possible, we expand the right-hand side in one or other of the forms

(3) $$\mu^{-x}X = c_0\rho^k+c_1\rho^{k-1}+c_2\rho^{k-2}+\dots,$$

(4) $$\mu^{-x}X = d_0\rho^k+d_1\rho^{k+1}+d_2\rho^{k+2}+\dots,$$

where the index k and the coefficients are of course known numbers.

When $\mu^{-x} X$ has an expansion of the form (3), we assume that

$$v(x) = a_0 \rho^{k-m} + a_1 \rho^{k-m-1} + a_2 \rho^{k-m-2} + \dots .$$

Equating coefficients of like powers of ρ we obtain

$$f_m(k)\, a_0 = c_0,$$
$$a_1 f_m(k-1) + a_0 f_{m-1}(k-1) = c_1,$$
$$a_2 f_m(k-2) + a_1 f_{m-1}(k-2) + a_0 f_{m-2}(k-2) = c_2,$$
$$\dots\dots\dots\dots\dots\dots$$

whence the coefficients can be determined successively.

If the resulting series converge we have a special solution of the complete equation. To this we add the general solution of the homogeneous equation. The given equation is then completely solved.

When $\mu^{-x} X$ has an expansion of the form (4) we put

$$v(x) = b_0 \rho^k + b_1 \rho^{k+1} + b_2 \rho^{k+2} + \dots ,$$

and equate coefficients as before.

If $\mu^{-x} X$ have expansions of the above types convergent in a half-plane on the lèft we use the operators π_1, ρ_1.

14·5. Monomial Difference Equations. A difference equation which after reduction by Theorem V assumes the form

$$(1) \qquad f(\pi)\, u_x = X$$

is said to be monomial.

It is evidently sufficient to assume that $f(\lambda)$ is a polynomial, for the case in which $f(\lambda)$ is a rational function can evidently be reduced to this.

Let $f(\pi) = a_n \pi(\pi-1)\dots(\pi-n+1)$
$$+ a_{n-1}\pi(\pi-1)\dots(\pi-n+2) + \dots + a_0.$$

It follows at once, from Theorem II, that (1) can be exhibited in the form

$$a_n (x-a)\dots(x-a-n+1) \overset{n}{\underset{-1}{\Delta}} u$$
$$+ a_{n-1}(x-a)\dots(x-a-n+2) \overset{n-1}{\underset{-1}{\Delta}} u + \dots + a_0 u = X,$$

which is therefore the general type of monomial equation.

The monomial equation can be completely solved as follows. Consider first the homogeneous equation

$$(2) \qquad f(\pi)\, u_x = 0.$$

This is satisfied by $u_x = \rho^k$, provided that k be a root of the equation $f(k) = 0$. If the roots of this equation be denoted by $\alpha_1, \alpha_2, \dots, \alpha_n$ when these are all distinct, we have for the complementary function

$$\varpi_1 \rho^{\alpha_1} + \dots + \varpi_n \rho^{\alpha_n} = \varpi_1 \frac{\Gamma(x'+1)}{\Gamma(x'-\alpha_1+1)} + \dots + \varpi_n \frac{\Gamma(x'+1)}{\Gamma(x'-\alpha_n+1)}.$$

If the equation $f(k) = 0$ present a multiple root, we have

$$f(k) = (k-\alpha)^s \phi(k),$$

where α is a root of multiplicity s. We then consider the equation

$$f(\pi)\, u_x = f(k)\, \rho^k,$$

which gives on partial differentiation

$$f(\pi) \frac{\partial^t u_x}{\partial k^t} = \sum_{\nu=0}^{t} \binom{t}{\nu} \frac{\partial^{t-\nu} f(k)}{\partial k^{t-\nu}} \frac{\partial^\nu \rho^k}{\partial k^\nu}.$$

Since $\partial^{t-\nu} f(k) / \partial k^{t-\nu}$ vanishes when

$$k = \alpha, \quad t - \nu = 0, 1, 2, \dots, s-1,$$

we see that, corresponding to $k = \alpha$, (2) has as solutions the values of ρ^k, $\dfrac{\partial}{\partial k}\rho^k, \dots, \dfrac{\partial^{s-1} \rho^k}{\partial k^{s-1}}$ when $k = \alpha$, that is to say, the solutions

$$\frac{\Gamma(x'+1)}{\Gamma(x'-\alpha+1)}, \quad \frac{\partial}{\partial \alpha} \frac{\Gamma(x'+1)}{\Gamma(x'-\alpha+1)}, \dots, \quad \frac{\partial^{s-1}}{\partial \alpha^{s-1}} \frac{\Gamma(x'+1)}{\Gamma(x'-\alpha+1)}.$$

We can thus find the complementary function in all cases.

To find a particular solution of (1) we have, symbolically,

$$u_x \doteqdot \frac{1}{f(\pi)} X.$$

Let us express $1 / f(\lambda)$ in partial fractions, so that

$$\frac{1}{f(\lambda)} = \sum \frac{A_s}{(\lambda - a)^s}.$$

Then

$$u_x \doteqdot \sum \frac{A_s}{(\pi - a)^s} X \doteqdot \sum \rho^a A^s \pi^{-s} (\rho^{-a} X),$$

by Theorem I.

To interpret the expression on the right, we have

$$\rho^{-a} X(x) = \frac{\Gamma(x'+1)}{\Gamma(x'+a+1)} X(x+a) = \phi(x),$$

say. Then we can take

$$\pi^{-1}\phi(x) = \mathop{S}_{c}^{x} \frac{1}{t}\phi(t) \mathop{\Delta}_{-1} t,$$

$$\pi^{-2}\phi(x) = \mathop{S}_{c}^{x} \frac{1}{t_1} \mathop{S}_{c}^{t_1} \frac{1}{t_2} \phi(t_2) \mathop{\Delta}_{-1} t_2 \mathop{\Delta}_{-1} t_1,$$

and so on, so that $\pi^{-s}\phi(x) = \psi(x)$, say.

Hence, finally,

$$\rho^a \psi(x) = \frac{\Gamma(x'+1)}{\Gamma(x'-a+1)} \psi(x-a).$$

The process simplifies if X can be expanded in the form

$$X = c_0 \rho^\alpha + c_1 \rho^{\alpha-1} + \dots .$$

We have then

$$u(x) = \frac{1}{f(\pi)} X = \frac{c_0}{f(\alpha)} \rho^\alpha + \frac{c_1}{f(\alpha-1)} \rho^{\alpha-1} + \dots,$$

by Theorem IV, provided that $f(\alpha) \neq 0$.

If, however, α be a zero of order s of $f(k)$, we have

$$f(k) = (k-\alpha)^s \phi(k),$$

so that

$$\frac{1}{f(\pi)} \rho^\alpha \doteqdot \frac{1}{(\pi-\alpha)^s \phi(\pi)} \rho^\alpha \doteqdot \frac{1}{(\pi-\alpha)^s} \frac{\rho^\alpha}{\phi(\alpha)}$$

$$\doteqdot \frac{\rho^\alpha}{\phi(\alpha)} \frac{1}{\pi^s} 1,$$

where the operation π^{-s} is now interpreted as explained above.

Example.

$$2x(x-1)(x-2)\mathop{\Delta}_{-1}^{3} u(x)+x(x-1)\mathop{\Delta}_{-1}^{2} u(x)+x\mathop{\Delta}_{-1} u(x)-u(x)=x^3.$$

Taking $x'=x$, this becomes

$$[2\pi(\pi-1)(\pi-2)+\pi(\pi-1)+\pi-1]\,u(x)$$
$$=x(x-1)(x-2)+3x(x-1)+x,$$

$$(\pi-1)^2(2\pi-1)\,u(x)=\rho+3\rho^2+\rho^3.$$

For the complementary solution, we consider

$$(\pi-1)^2(2\pi-1)\,u(x)=(k-1)^2(2k-1)\,\rho^k,$$

which is satisfied by

$$u(x)=\frac{\Gamma(x+1)}{\Gamma(x-k+1)}.$$

Putting $k=1$, $k=\frac{1}{2}$, we have

$$\frac{\Gamma(x+1)}{\Gamma(x)},\quad \frac{\Gamma(x+1)}{\Gamma(x+\frac{1}{2})}.$$

Also

$$\frac{\partial}{\partial k}\frac{\Gamma(x+1)}{\Gamma(x-k+1)}=\frac{\Gamma(x+1)}{\Gamma(x-k+1)}\Psi(x-k+1).$$

Putting $k=1$, we get $x\Psi(x)$.

The complementary solution is therefore

$$x(\varpi_1+\varpi_2\Psi(x))+\varpi_3\Gamma(x+1)/\Gamma(x+\tfrac{1}{2}).$$

For the particular solution, we have

$$u(x)=(\pi-1)^{-2}(2\pi-1)^{-1}(\rho^3+3\rho^2+\rho)$$
$$=\tfrac{1}{20}\rho^3+\rho^2+(\pi-1)^{-2}\rho.$$

To interpret this we have

$$(\pi-1)^{-2}\rho=\rho\,\pi^{-2}.1,$$

$$\pi^{-1}1=\Psi(x\,|-1),$$

$$\pi^{-2}1=\mathop{S}_{1}^{x}\frac{1}{t}\Psi(t\,|-1)\mathop{\Delta}_{-1}t,$$

$$\rho\,\pi^{-2}1=x\mathop{S}_{1}^{x-1}\frac{1}{t}\Psi(t\,|-1)\mathop{\Delta}_{-1}t.$$

Hence the complete solution is

$$u(x) = x(\varpi_1 + \varpi_2 \Psi(x)) + \varpi_3 \frac{\Gamma(x+1)}{\Gamma(x+\frac{1}{2})}$$

$$+ \frac{1}{20} x(x-1)(x-2) + x(x-1) + x \mathop{\mathrm{S}}_{1}^{x-1} \frac{1}{t} \Psi(t\,|-1) \mathop{\Delta}_{-1} t.$$

14·6. Binomial Equations. An equation which can be reduced to the form

$$[f_0(\pi) + f_m(\pi)\, \rho^m]\, u = 0$$

is called a binomial equation.

Putting $u = a_0 \rho^k + a_1 \rho^{k-1} + \dots,$

we have $a_1 = a_2 = \dots = a_{m-1} = 0.$

Thus we can assume that

$$u = b_0 \rho^k + b_1 \rho^{k-m} + b_2 \rho^{k-2m} + \dots$$

and we obtain the indicial equation

$$f_m(k+m) = 0,$$

and the recurrence relation

$$b_s f_m(k-(s-1)m) + b_{s-1} f_0(k-(s-1)m) = 0,$$

which gives

$$\frac{b_s}{b_0} = \frac{(-1)^s f_0\{k-(s-1)m\} f_0\{k-(s-2)m\} \dots f_0(k)}{f_m\{k-(s-1)m\} f_m\{k-(s-2)m\} \dots f_m(k)}.$$

If one of the factors in the numerator vanish, the solution is given by a finite series.

Thus we can always obtain an explicit expression for the coefficients of the series which satisfy a binomial equation.

The particular binomial equation

$$u + \frac{1}{a\pi + b} \rho u = X,$$

being at once reducible to an equation of the first order, can always be solved in compact form.*

* We say that the solution is in compact form when expressed by a finite number of operations of the form S.

Again, the binomial equation

$$[1-a^n\,\phi(\pi)\,\rho^n]\,u = X,$$

where

$$\phi(\pi) = \{(\pi-b)(\pi-b-1)\dots(\pi-b-n+1)\}^{-1},$$

can be written (see below) in the form

$$\left[1-\frac{a\,\varepsilon_1}{\pi-b}\rho\right]\left[1-\frac{a\,\varepsilon_2}{\pi-b}\rho\right]\dots\left[1-\frac{a\,\varepsilon_n}{\pi-b}\rho\right]u = X,$$

where $\varepsilon_1, \varepsilon_2, \dots, \varepsilon_n$ are the nth roots of unity.

If we put

$$\left[1-\frac{a\,\varepsilon_s}{\pi-b}\rho\right]\left[1-\frac{a\,\varepsilon_{s+1}}{\pi-b}\rho\right]\dots\left[1-\frac{a\,\varepsilon_n}{\pi-b}\rho\right]u = u_{s-1}(x),$$

the given equation is equivalent to the n linear equations of the first order:

$$\left[1-\frac{a\,\varepsilon_1}{\pi-b}\rho\right]u_1(x) = X,$$

$$\left[1-\frac{a\,\varepsilon_2}{\pi-b}\rho\right]u_2(x) = u_1(x),$$

$$\dots\dots\dots\dots$$

$$\left[1-\frac{a\,\varepsilon_n}{\pi-b}\rho\right]u(x) = u_{n-1}(x).$$

This is a particular application of the more general theorem that the equation

$$[1+a_1\,\phi(\pi)\,\rho+a_2\,\phi(\pi)\,\phi(\pi-1)\,\rho^2+\dots$$
$$+a_n\,\phi(\pi)\,\phi(\pi-1)\dots\phi(\pi-n+1)\,\rho^n]\,u(x) = X$$

can be resolved into n linear equations of the type

$$[1-q_r\,\phi(\pi)\,\rho]\,u_r(x) = u_{r-1}(x), \quad r = 1, 2, \dots, n,$$

where $u_0(x) = X$, $u_n(x) = u(x)$, and $q_1, q_2, \dots, q_n$ are the roots of the equation

$$q^n+a_1\,q^{n-1}+a_2\,q^{n-2}+\dots+a_n = 0.$$

We have in fact

$$[1-a\,\phi(\pi)\,\rho]\,[1-b\,\phi(\pi)\,\rho]\,u$$
$$= [1-(a+b)\,\phi(\pi)\,\rho+ab\,\phi(\pi)\,\rho\,\phi(\pi)\,\rho]\,u$$
$$= [1-(a+b)\,\phi(\pi)\,\rho+ab\,\phi(\pi)\,\phi(\pi-1)\,\rho^2]\,u,$$

and so on, whence the theorem follows by a simple induction.

14·7. Transformation of Equations. The following problem has been investigated by Boole. Given rational functions $\varphi(\lambda)$, $\psi(\lambda)$, $F(\lambda)$ to determine, if possible, $\chi(\lambda)$, such that

$$F\{\varphi(\pi)\rho^n\}\chi(\pi)X = \chi(\pi)F\{\psi(\pi)\rho^n\}X.$$

For the special case $F(\lambda) = \lambda$, the above relation becomes

$$\varphi(\pi)\rho^n\chi(\pi)X = \chi(\pi)\psi(\pi)\rho^n X,$$

or, by Theorem I,

$$\varphi(\pi)\chi(\pi-n)\rho^n X = \chi(\pi)\psi(\pi)\rho^n X.$$

This will be satisfied if

$$\varphi(\lambda)\chi(\lambda-n) = \chi(\lambda)\psi(\lambda),$$

which gives

$$\chi(\lambda) = \frac{\varphi(\lambda)\varphi(\lambda-n)\varphi(\lambda-2n)\dots}{\psi(\lambda)\psi(\lambda-n)\psi(\lambda-2n)\dots} = \Pi_n\frac{\varphi(\lambda)}{\psi(\lambda)}.$$

Since Theorem I has only been established for rational functions, we shall assume $\varphi(\lambda)$ and $\psi(\lambda)$ to be so related that $\chi(\lambda)$ is a rational function.

With this value of $\chi(\lambda)$ we have then, denoting $1/\chi(\lambda)$ by $\chi^{-1}(\lambda)$,

$$\begin{aligned}\varphi(\pi)\rho^n X &= \varphi(\pi)\rho^n\chi(\pi)\chi^{-1}(\pi)X\\ &= \varphi(\pi)\chi(\pi-n)\rho^n\chi^{-1}(\pi)X\\ &= \chi(\pi)\psi(\pi)\rho^n\chi^{-1}(\pi)X.\end{aligned}$$

Repeating the operation

$$\begin{aligned}[\varphi(\pi)\rho^n]^2 X &= \chi(\pi)\psi(\pi)\rho^n\chi^{-1}(\pi)\chi(\pi)\psi(\pi)\rho^n\chi^{-1}(\pi)X\\ &= \chi(\pi)\{\psi(\pi)\rho^n\}^2\chi^{-1}(\pi)X.\end{aligned}$$

Continuing in this way we see that

$$[\varphi(\pi)\rho^n]^m X = \chi(\pi)\{\psi(\pi)\rho^n\}^m\chi^{-1}(\pi)X.$$

The problem has thus been solved for $F(\lambda) = \lambda^m$ and hence for any rational function $F(\lambda)$. Thus we have proved the following:

Theorem VI. *If $\varphi(\lambda)$, $\psi(\lambda)$, $F(\lambda)$ be rational functions, and if*

$$\chi(\lambda) = \frac{\varphi(\lambda)\varphi(\lambda-n)\varphi(\lambda-2n)\dots}{\psi(\lambda)\psi(\lambda-n)\psi(\lambda-2n)\dots} = \Pi_n\frac{\varphi(\lambda)}{\psi(\lambda)},$$

then, provided that $\chi(\lambda)$ be rational,

$$F[\varphi(\pi)\rho^n]X \doteq \chi(\pi)F[\psi(\pi)\rho^n]\chi^{-1}(\pi)X.$$

A more general form of this theorem is obtained by assuming $F(\mu, \lambda)$ to be a rational function of two variables μ, λ.

In this case we have

$$F[\mu, \varphi(\pi)\rho^n]\chi(\pi)X = \chi(\pi)F[\mu, \psi(\pi)\rho^n]\chi^{-1}(\pi)X.$$

If we now replace μ by π, we have

Theorem VII. *If* $\varphi(\lambda)$, $\psi(\lambda)$, $F(\mu, \lambda)$ *be rational functions, and if*

$$\chi(\lambda) = \frac{\varphi(\lambda)\varphi(\lambda-n)\varphi(\lambda-2n)\ldots}{\psi(\lambda)\psi(\lambda-n)\psi(\lambda-2n)\ldots},$$

then, provided that $\chi(\lambda)$ *be rational,*

$$F[\pi, \varphi(\pi)\rho^n]X \doteqdot \chi(\pi)F[\pi, \psi(\pi)\rho^n]\chi^{-1}(\pi)X.$$

The reader will have no difficulty in proving the following:

Theorem VIII. *If* $F(\lambda)$, $\varphi(\lambda)$ *be rational functions, then*

$$F[\varphi(\pi)\rho^n]X \doteqdot \rho^m F[\varphi(\pi+m)\rho^n]\rho^{-m}X.$$

We now apply these considerations to the transformation of equations.

The equation

$$(1) \qquad u + \varphi(\pi)\rho^n u = X,$$

can be transformed into the equation

$$(2) \qquad v + \psi(\pi)\rho^n v = \Pi_n[\psi(\pi)/\varphi(\pi)]X$$

by the substitution

$$(A) \qquad u = \Pi_n[\varphi(\pi)/\psi(\pi)]v = \chi(\pi)v.$$

For making this substitution the equation becomes

$$\chi(\pi)v + \varphi(\pi)\rho^n\chi(\pi)v = X.$$

Operate with $\chi^{-1}(\pi)$, then

$$v + \chi^{-1}(\pi)\varphi(\pi)\rho^n\chi(\pi)v = \chi^{-1}(\pi)X,$$

which by Theorem VI is equivalent to (2).

Similarly, by means of Theorem VII, we can shew that the substitution

$$u = \Pi_1[\varphi(\pi)/\psi(\pi)]v$$

will reduce the equation

$$[f_0(\pi) + f_1(\pi)\varphi(\pi)\rho + f_2(\pi)\varphi(\pi)\varphi(\pi-1)\rho^2]u = X$$

to the form

$$[f_0(\pi)+f_1(\pi)\,\psi(\pi)\,\rho+f_2(\pi)\,\psi(\pi)\,\psi(\pi-1)\,\rho^2]\,v = \Pi_1\,[\psi(\pi)\,/\,\varphi(\pi)]\,X.$$

Again, the substitution

(B) $$u = \rho^m\,v$$

will reduce the equation

$$u+\varphi(\pi)\,\rho^n\,u = X$$

to the form

$$v+\varphi(\pi+m)\,\rho^n\,v = \rho^{-m}\,X.$$

This follows at once from Theorem VIII or can be proved independently by means of Theorem I.

Boole has applied the foregoing considerations to the discovery of conditions for compact solution, that is to say, solution by means of a finite number of operations of summation, of certain equations of the second order. We reproduce these discussions in full, as they throw an interesting light on the structure of certain classes of difference equations.

14·71. The Equation with Linear Coefficients. Let the equation be

(1) $$(ax+b)\,u(x)+(cx+e)\,u(x-1)+(fx+g)\,u(x-2) = X.$$

If $f \neq 0$, the linear change of variable $fx+g = f(x'-1)$ brings the equation into the form

$$(ax'+b')\,u'(x')+(cx'+e')\,u'(x'-1)+f(x'-1)\,u'(x'-2) = X',$$

where $$b' = b-a(g+f)\,/\,f,\ e' = e-c(g+f)\,/\,f.$$

Suppressing the primes we may therefore consider the equation

(2) $$(ax+b)\,u(x)+(cx+e)\,u(x-1)+f(x-1)\,u(x-2) = X.$$

Putting $u(x) = \mu^x\,v(x)$, $\rho\,u(x) = x\,u(x-1)$, we obtain

(3) $$\mu^2(a\pi^2+b\pi)\,v(x)+\mu\,[(2a\mu+c)\,\pi+(b-a)\,\mu+e]\,\rho\,v(x) + (a\mu^2+c\mu+f)\,\rho^2\,v(x) = x\,\mu^{-x+2}\,X.$$

If we determine μ so that

(4) $$a\mu^2+c\mu+f = 0,$$

the equation assumes the binomial form

(5) $$v(x)+\frac{A\,(\pi+m)}{\pi\,(\pi+n)}\,\rho\,v(x) = V,$$

where

$$A = 2 + c\,a^{-1}\,\mu^{-1}, \quad m = [(b-a)\,\mu + e]\,[2a\mu + c]^{-1}, \quad n = b\,a^{-1},$$
$$V = [(a\mu)\,\pi(\pi+n)]^{-1}(Xx\,\mu^{-x+1}),$$

and where we have assumed $a \neq 0$, $2a\mu + c \neq 0$.

We have here two cases of compact solution.

(I) Let m be an integer.

In this case the equation can be reduced by the substitution (A)

$$(6) \qquad v(x) = \Pi_1\,[(\pi+m)\,\pi^{-1}]\,w(x)$$

to the form

$$w(x) + A\,(\pi+n)^{-1}\,\rho\,w(x) = \Pi_1\,[\pi(\pi+m)^{-1}]\,V$$

or

$$(x+n)\,w(x) - (1-A)\,x\,w(x-1) = (\pi+n)\,\Pi_1\,[\pi(\pi+m)^{-1}]\,V = W,$$

which is an equation of the first order whose complementary solution is

$$\varpi_1(1-A)^x\,\Gamma(x+1)\,/\,\Gamma(x+n+1).$$

To this we must add a particular solution. From (6), we then determine $v(x)$ and finally $u(x) = \mu_1^x\,v(x)$ or $\mu_2^x\,v(x)$, where μ_1 and μ_2 are the roots of (4).

(II) Let $m-n$ be an integer.

In this case we again use substitution (A) in the form

$$v(x) = \Pi_1\,[(\pi+m)\,(\pi+n)^{-1}]\,w(x),$$

which yields

$$w(x) + A\,\pi^{-1}\,\rho\,w(x) = \Pi_1\,[(\pi+n)\,(\pi+m)^{-1}]\,V,$$

or

$$w(x) - (1-A)\,w(x-1) = x^{-1}\,\pi\,\Pi_1\,[(\pi+n)\,(\pi+m)^{-1}]\,V$$

with the complementary solution $(1-A)^x$.

(III) Returning to (3), let us, if possible, so choose μ that the coefficient of $\rho\,v(x)$ vanishes.

This is only possible if $2a\mu + c = 0$, $(b-a)\mu + e = 0$, which imposes the condition

$$2ae - (b-a)c = 0.$$

Supposing this to be satisfied, we obtain, with $\mu = -c\,/\,(2a)$,

$$v(x) - h^2\,\pi^{-1}\,(\pi+n)^{-1}\,\rho^2\,v(x) = V,$$

where

$$h^2 = (c^2 - 4af)/c^2, \quad V = a^{-1}\pi^{-1}(\pi+n)^{-1} x\,\mu^{-x} X.$$

This equation has compact solutions if n be an odd integer positive or negative, for with the substitution (A) in the form

$$v(x) = \Pi_2[(\pi+n)^{-1}(\pi-1)]\,w(x)$$
$$= \frac{(\pi-1)(\pi-3)\ldots}{(\pi+n)(\pi+n-2)\ldots}\,w(x),$$

the operator is rational if n be odd.

The equation then reduces to

$$w(x) - h^2\pi^{-1}(\pi-1)^{-1}\rho^2 w(x) = \Pi_2[(\pi-1)^{-1}(\pi+n)]\,V = W.$$

Now

$$[1 - h^2\pi^{-1}(\pi-1)^{-1}\rho^2]\,w(x) = [1 - (h\pi^{-1}\rho)(h\pi^{-1}\rho)]\,w(x)$$
$$= [1 + h\pi^{-1}\rho][1 - h\pi^{-1}\rho]\,w(x).$$

The further substitution

$$t(x) = [1 - h\pi^{-1}\rho]\,w(x)$$

gives

$$[1 + h\pi^{-1}\rho]\,t(x) = W,$$

so that the solution is made to depend on two equations of the first order.

This case is an illustration of the method explained in 14·6.

Example.

$$(x+2)\,u(x) - (x+2)\,u(x-1) - 2(x-1)\,u(x-2) = 0.$$

Putting $u(x) = \mu^x v(x)$, we have $\mu^2 - \mu - 2 = 0$, whence $\mu = -1$ or 2.

Taking $\mu = -1$, $m = 1$, $A = 3$, $n = 2$, we get

$$v(x) + \frac{3(\pi+1)}{\pi(\pi+2)}\rho\,v(x) = 0.$$

Substitute $v(x) = \Pi_1[(\pi+1)\pi^{-1}]\,w(x) = (\pi+1)\,w(x)$, then

$$w(x) + 3(\pi+2)^{-1}\rho\,w(x) = 0,$$

$$(x+2)\,w(x) + 2x\,w(x-1) = 0,$$

$$w(x) = (-2)^x\,\Gamma(x+1)/\Gamma(x+3) = (-2)^x(x+2)^{-1}(x+1)^{-1},$$

$$v(x) = (\pi+1)\,w(x) = -(-2)^{x-1}(3x+4)(x+1)^{-1}(x+2)^{-1}.$$

Therefore

$$u(x) = \tfrac{1}{2}\, 2^x (3x+4)(x+1)^{-1}(x+2)^{-1}.$$

Taking $\mu = 2,\ m = 0,\ A = \tfrac{3}{2},\ n = 2,$ we have

$$v(x) + \tfrac{3}{2}(\pi+2)^{-1}\rho\, v(x) = 0,$$

$$v(x) = (-2)^{-x}(x+2)^{-1}(x+1)^{-1},$$

$$u(x) = (-1)^x (x+2)^{-1}(x+1)^{-1}.$$

The general solution is therefore

$$u(x) = \frac{\varpi_1 2^x (3x+4)}{(x+1)(x+2)} + \frac{\varpi_2(-1)^x}{(x+1)(x+2)}.$$

14·73. Discussion of the Equation

$$(ax^2+bx+c)\,u(x) + (ex+f)\,u(x-1) + g\,u(x-2) = 0.$$

Write $u(x) = \mu^x v(x)/\Gamma(x+1)$, $\rho = x\,\mathsf{E}^{-1}$; then the equation becomes

$$\mu^2(ax^2+bx+c)\,v(x) + \mu(ex+f)\,\rho\, v(x) + g\,\rho^2 v(x) = 0,$$

whence, writing $\pi+\rho$ for x, we obtain

$$\{\mu^2(a\pi^2+b\pi+c) + \mu\,[\,(2a\,\mu+e)\,\pi + (b+a)\,\mu + f\,]\,\rho$$
$$+ (\mu^2 a + \mu\, e + g)\,\rho^2\}\, v(x) = 0.$$

(I) Choose μ so that

$$a\mu^2 + e\mu + g = 0.$$

The equation then assumes the form

$$[a\pi^2 + b\pi + c + (A\pi + B)\,\rho]\,v(x) = 0,$$

where

$$A\mu = 2a\mu + e, \quad B\mu = (b+a)\,\mu + f.$$

This equation is formally satisfied by one factorial series of the first kind and two of the second kind, all of which can easily be obtained by our general methods.

If we put $ak^2+bk+c = a(k-\alpha)(k-\beta)$, the equation can be written

$$\left[1 + C\frac{\pi + c}{(\pi-\alpha)(\pi-\beta)}\,\rho\,\right] v(x) = 0,$$

where

$$C = Aa^{-1}. \qquad = BA^{-1}.$$

If either $c-\alpha$ or $c-\beta$ be an integer, a compact solution exists. If, for example, $c-\beta=n$, an integer, the substitution

$$v(x) = \Pi_1[(\pi+c)(\pi-\beta)^{-1}]\,w(x)$$

leads to the equation

$$w(x) = C(\pi-\alpha)^{-1}\rho\,w(x),$$

which is of the first order.

(II) When the coefficients are related by the equation

$$2af+(a-b)e = 0,$$

we can choose μ so that

$$2a\mu+e=0, \quad (b-a)\mu+f=0.$$

Thus putting $\mu=-e/(2a)$, $h^2=(e^2-4ag)/e^2$, the equation becomes

$$v(x)-h^2(\pi-\alpha)^{-1}(\pi-\beta)^{-1}\rho^2 v(x) = 0.$$

If $\beta-\alpha$ be an odd integer (positive or negative), the substitution (A) in the form

$$v(x) = \Pi_2[(\pi-\beta)^{-1}(\pi-\alpha-1)]\,w(x)$$

leads to the equation

$$w(x)-h^2(\pi-\alpha)^{-1}(\pi-\alpha-1)^{-1}\rho^2 w(x) = 0,$$

which can be resolved into two equations of the first order as in 14·6.

Example. $(x^2+x-2)\,u(x)+5x\,u(x-1)+4u(x)=0.$

Putting $u(x)=\mu^x v(x)/\Gamma(x+1)$, the equation becomes

$$[\mu^2(\pi^2+\pi-2)+\mu(2\mu+5)\pi\rho+(\mu^2+5\mu+4)\rho^2]\,v(x) = 0.$$

If $\mu=-\frac{5}{2}$, this gives

$$[1-\tfrac{9}{25}(\pi-1)^{-1}(\pi+2)^{-1}\rho^2]\,v(x) = 0.$$

Put

$$v(x) = \Pi_2[(\pi+1)(\pi-1)^{-1}]\,w(x) = (\pi+1)\,w(x).$$

Then

$$[1-\tfrac{9}{25}(\pi+2)^{-1}(\pi+1)^{-1}\rho^2]\,w(x) = 0,$$

which gives the pair of equations

$$[1-\tfrac{3}{5}(\pi+2)^{-1}\rho]\,t(x)=0,$$

$$[1+\tfrac{3}{5}(\pi+2)^{-1}\rho]\,w(x)=t(x).$$

The first of these gives

$$t(x)=\varpi_1\left(\frac{8}{5}\right)^x\frac{\Gamma(x+1)}{\Gamma(x+3)}=\left(\frac{8}{5}\right)^x\frac{\varpi_1}{(x+1)(x+2)}.$$

The second then becomes

$$(x+2)\,w(x)-\tfrac{2}{5}x\,w(x-1)=\left(\frac{8}{5}\right)^{x-1}\frac{3\varpi_1}{5(x+1)},$$

which can be solved by summation. We then have

$$u(x)=(-\tfrac{5}{2})^x(\pi+1)\,w(x).$$

14·75. Discussion of the Equation

$$(ax^2+bx+c)\overset{2}{\Delta}u(x)+(ex+f)\,\Delta u(x)+g\,u(x)=0.$$

This equation can be written in the form

$$a(x-\alpha)(x-\beta)\overset{2}{\Delta}u(x)+e(x-\gamma)\,\Delta u(x)+g\,u(x)=0.$$

Here it is convenient to use the operators π_1 and ρ_1.

Taking $x'=x-\alpha-1$ and multiplying by x', we obtain

$$a(x'+\alpha-\beta+1)\,\pi_1(\pi_1-1)\,u(x)$$
$$+e(x'+\alpha-\gamma+1)\,\pi_1 u(x)+x'g\,u(x)=0.$$

Write $-\pi_1+\rho_1$ for x', we then obtain

$$[a(-\pi_1+\alpha-\beta+1+\rho_1)\,\pi_1(\pi_1-1)+e(-\pi_1+\alpha-\gamma+1+\rho_1)\,\pi_1$$
$$+g(-\pi_1+\rho_1)]\,u(x)=0,$$

which, using Theorem I, becomes

$$\pi_1[a(\pi_1-\alpha+\beta-1)(\pi_1-1)+e(\pi_1-\alpha+\gamma-1)+g]\,u(x)$$
$$-[a(\pi_1-1)(\pi_1-2)+e(\pi_1-1)+g]\,\rho_1 u(x)=0,$$

which is a binomial equation formally satisfied by three series in ascending powers of ρ_1 and by two series in descending powers of ρ_1, all of which can be found by the usual method.

14·8. Bronwin's Method. Certain forms of linear equation can be solved by performing Δ upon them one or more times.

Consider the equation

$$(a+bx)\overset{2}{\Delta}u+(c+dx)\Delta u+eu=0.$$

Operate with $\overset{n}{\Delta}$. Then by the analogue of Leibniz' theorem, 2·51, we obtain

$$[a+b(x+n)]\overset{n+2}{\Delta}u+nb\overset{n+1}{\Delta}u$$
$$+[c+d(x+n)]\overset{n+1}{\Delta}u+nd\overset{n}{\Delta}u+e\overset{n}{\Delta}u=0.$$

If we take $n=-e/d$, supposing that to be a positive integer, we have a linear equation of the first order for $\overset{n+1}{\Delta}u$.

Example. $x\overset{2}{\Delta}u+(x-2)\Delta u-u=0.$

Performing Δ, we have

$$(x+1)\overset{3}{\Delta}u+x\overset{2}{\Delta}u=0,$$

whence

$$\overset{2}{\Delta}u=\frac{\varpi}{\Gamma(x+1)},$$

$$\Delta u=\mathop{S}_{c}^{x}\frac{\varpi}{\Gamma(t+1)}\Delta t+\varpi_1.$$

Substituting in the given equation, we have

$$u=\frac{x\,\varpi}{\Gamma(x+1)}+(x-2)\,\varpi_1+(x-2)\mathop{S}_{c}^{x}\frac{\varpi}{\Gamma(t+1)}\Delta t.$$

14·9. Linear Partial Difference Equations. The principles of solution enunciated in 13·8 are applicable to partial equations of the following forms, namely,

$$F(x,\Delta_x,\Delta_y)\,u=0,\quad F(y,\Delta_x,\Delta_y)\,u=0,$$
$$F(x,y,\Delta_x)\,u=0,\qquad F(x,y,\Delta_y)\,u=0.$$

In each of these equations one of the independent variables or one of the partial operators is absent. If y or Δ_y be absent, we treat y as constant and the equation as an ordinary equation in x and thereafter interpret the solution.

Example. $u_{x,\,y} - x\,u_{x-1,\,y-1} = 0.$

This equation can be expressed in the form

$$u - x\,\mathsf{E}_x^{-1}\,\mathsf{E}_y^{-1}\,u = 0.$$

Replacing E_y^{-1} by a, we have

$$u - ax\,\mathsf{E}_x^{-1}\,u = 0,$$

which is equivalent to

$$v_x - a\,x\,v_{x-1} = 0,$$

where $v_x = u_{x,\,y}$. We thus obtain

$$v_x = a^x\,\Gamma(x+1)\,\phi(y),$$

and therefore

$$u_{x,\,y} = \mathsf{E}_y^{-x}\,\Gamma(x+1)\,\phi(y) = \Gamma(x+1)\,\phi(y-x),$$

where ϕ is an arbitrary function.

14·91. Laplace's Method. The method of 13·83 is applicable to equations of the form

$$A_0\,u(x,\,y) + A_1\,u(x-1,\,y-1) + A_2\,u(x-2,\,y-2) + \ldots = V(x,\,y),$$

in which the difference of the arguments in $u(x-s,\,y-s)$ is invariant for $s = 0, 1, 2, \ldots$.

Putting $x - y = k$, we obtain

$$B_0\,v(x) + B_1\,v(x-1) + \ldots = V(x,\,x-k),$$

in which the coefficients are functions of x and of the parameter k. Thus in the equation

$$u_{x,\,y} - x\,u_{x-1,\,y-1} = 0,$$

we have

$$v_x - x\,v_{x-1} = 0,$$

whence $$v_x = c\,\Gamma(x+1).$$

Replacing c by an arbitrary function of k, we get

$$u_{x,\,y} = \Gamma(x+1)\,\phi(x-y)$$

as before.

EXAMPLES XIV

Investigate the solution of the following difference equations:

1. $(x+2)\,u(x+2)-x\,u(x+1)-u(x)=0.$

2. $(x-a)\,u_x-(2x-a-1)\,u_{x-1}+(1-q^2)(x-1)\,u_{x-2}=0.$

3. $(x+3)\,u_{x+2}-(x+3)\,u_{x+1}-2x\,u_x=0.$

4. $x(x+1)\overset{2}{\Delta}u-2x\,\Delta u+2u=x(x+1)(x+2).$

5. $x(x+1)\,u_{x+2}-2(x+2)\,x\,u_{x+1}+(x+1)(x-2)\,u_x=0.$

6. $(x^2-1)(x+1)\,u_{x+2}-(x^2+x+1)\,(x^2+x-1)\,u_{x+1}+x^2(x+2)\,u_x$
$=0.$

7. $x(x+1)\overset{2}{\Delta}u+x\,\Delta u-n^2\,u=0.$

8. $(x+2)(2x+1)\,u_{x+2}-4(x+1)^2\,u_{x+1}+x(2x+3)\,u_x=0.$

9. $u(x+2)-x^2\,u(x+1)-c(c-x^2)\,u(x)=0.$

10. $u_{x+2}-u_{x+1}-x^2\,u_x=0.$

11. $(x^2+ax)\overset{2}{\Delta}u-(2x+a-1)\,\Delta u+2u=bx+cx^2.$

12. $u_x=x(u_{x-1}+u_{x-2}).$

13. $u_{x+1}=x(u_x+u_{x-1}).$

14. $(x+3)^2\,u_{x+2}-\dfrac{2(x+2)^3}{x+1}\,u_{x+1}+\dfrac{(x+1)^2(x+2)}{x}\,u_x=0.$

15. Shew that the equation

$$u_{x+1}\,u_x+a_x\,u_{x+1}+b_x\,u_x=c_x$$

can be reduced to a linear equation of the second order by the substitution

$$u_x\,v_x=v_{x+1}-a_x\,v_x,$$

and shew that the two periodics which appear in the value of v_x effectively produce only one periodic in the value of u_x.

16. $u_{x+2}-2(x-1)\,u_{x+1}+(x-1)(x-2)\,u_x=\Gamma(x+1).$

17. $x(x+1)\overset{2}{\Delta}u+k(1-x)\,\Delta u+ku=0.$

18. $u_{x+1,\,y+1}-(a-x-2y-2)\,u_{x,\,y+1}+(x+y)\,u_{x,\,y}=0.$

CHAPTER XV

THE LINEAR DIFFERENCE EQUATION WITH RATIONAL COEFFICIENTS. LAPLACE'S TRANSFORMATION

IN this chapter we discuss the application of Laplace's transformation to the linear equation and the solution by means of contour integrals.

15·0. Laplace's Transformation. Another method of solving difference equations with rational coefficients is founded upon the substitution

$$(1) \qquad u(x) = \int_l t^{x-1}\, v(t)\, dt,$$

where l is a line of integration suitably determined and where the function $v(t)$ is found from a certain differential equation. As all the essential points of the method are illustrated by the equation of the second order we shall consider the equation

$$(2) \qquad p_2(x)\, u(x+2) + p_1(x)\, u(x+1) + p_0(x)\, u(x) = 0,$$

where $p_2(x)$, $p_1(x)$, $p_0(x)$ are polynomials.

An equation of this type will be called "normal" if the following conditions be satisfied.

(i) The extreme coefficients have the same degree p while that of the remaining coefficients does not exceed p.

(ii) The differential equation satisfied by $v(t)$ is of Fuchsian type, that is to say, all the singular points of the differential equation are regular.*

* The somewhat unfortunate term "regular" is here used in the sense in which the term is applied in the theory of linear differential equations. See *e.g.* É. Goursat, *Cours d'Analyse*, t. ii (2nd edition), chap. xx. The term regular must not be confused with holomorphic.

We shall suppose equation (2) to be normal.

We then write the coefficients in the following form:

$$p_2(x) = A_p(x+2)(x+3)\dots(x+p+1)+\dots$$
$$+A_2(x+2)(x+3)+A_1(x+2)+A_0,$$
$$p_1(x) = B_p(x+1)(x+2)\dots(x+p)+\dots$$
$$+B_2(x+1)(x+2)+B_1(x+1)+B_0,$$
$$p_0(x) = C_p\,x(x+1)(x+2)\dots(x+p-1)+\dots$$
$$+C_2\,x(x+1)+C_1\,x+C_0,$$

where $A_p \neq 0$, $C_p \neq 0$.

Putting

$$\phi_p(t) = A_p t^2 + B_p t + C_p,$$

(3) $$\phi_i(t) = A_i t^2 + B_i t + C_i, \quad i = 0, 1, 2, \dots, p-1,$$

the equation

$$\phi_p(t) = 0$$

is called the *characteristic equation*. By our hypothesis the roots of the characteristic equation are both different from zero. We shall denote these roots by a_1, a_2.

With the value (1) for $u(x)$, we have by successive partial integrations

$$x(x+1)\dots(x+s-1)\,u(x) = (-1)^s \int_l t^{x+s-1}\, v^{(s)}(t)\, dt$$
$$+[(x+s-1)\dots(x+1)\,t^x\, v(t) - (x+s-1)\dots(x+2)\,t^{x+1}\, v'(t)+\dots$$
$$+(-1)^{s-1}\, t^{x+s-1}\, v^{(s-1)}(t)]_l.$$

Substituting for $u(x)$ in (2), we obtain for the left-hand member the expression

$$\int_l t^{x-1} \sum_{s=0}^{p} (-t)^s\, \phi_s(t)\, v^{(s)}(t)\, dt + [I(x,t)]_l,$$

where

(4) $$I(x,t) = v(t) \sum_{k=0}^{p-1} \frac{d^k}{dt^k}[t^{x+k}\phi_{k+1}(t)] - v'(t) \sum_{k=0}^{p-2} \frac{d^k}{dt^k}[t^{x+k+1}\phi_{k+2}(t)] + \dots$$
$$+(-1)^{p-1}\, v^{(p-1)}(t)\, [t^{x+p-1}\phi_p(t)].$$

It follows that (1) provides a solution of the difference equation (2) if $v(t)$ be a solution of the differential equation

(5) $$t^p \phi_p(t) \frac{d^p v}{dt^p} - t^{p-1}\phi_{p-1}(t) \frac{d^{p-1} v}{dt^{p-1}} + \dots + (-1)^p \phi_0(t)\, v = 0,$$

and if the line of integration l be chosen so that $I(x, t)$ has the same value at each extremity of the line, when the line is open. If the line be closed, $I(x, t)$ must return to the same value after t has described the line.

The singular points of the differential equation are $t = 0$, $t = \infty$ and the zeros of $\phi_p(t)$, that is to say, the points $t = a_1, t = a_2$.

To find the solutions of (5) in the neighbourhood of the origin, we substitute

$$v(t) = c_0 t^m + c_1 t^{m+1} + c_2 t^{m+2} + \dots,$$

and equate to zero the coefficient of t^m. This gives, as indicial equation for m,

$$c_0 [C_p m(m-1) \dots (m-p+1) - C_{p-1} m(m-1) \dots (m-p+2) + \dots \\ + (-1)^{p-1} C_1 m + (-1)^p C_0] = 0,$$

which, by the definition of $p_0(x)$, is equivalent to

$$p_0(-m) = 0.$$

Thus if, as in 12·0, we denote the zeros of $p_0(x)$ by $\alpha_1, \alpha_2, \dots, \alpha_p$, we have as values of m, $-\alpha_1, -\alpha_2, \dots, -\alpha_p$. We shall suppose these values arranged so that

$$R(\alpha_1) \leqslant R(\alpha_2) \leqslant R(\alpha_3) \leqslant \dots \leqslant R(\alpha_p).$$

The differential equation has then p solutions in the neighbourhood of the origin of the form

$$(6) \qquad v_s(t) = t^{-\alpha_s} [f_0(t) + f_1(t) \log t + \dots + f_r(t) (\log t)^r], \\ s = 1, 2, \dots, p, \; r \leqslant p-1,$$

where the functions $f_0(t), f_1(t), \dots, f_r(t)$ are holomorphic at $t = 0$. If no two of the numbers $\alpha_1, \alpha_2, \dots, \alpha_p$ be congruent, no logarithmic terms occur. In the extreme case where all the α_s are congruent, $r = p-1$, when $s = p$.

Again, the product $t^x v_s(t)$ vanishes when $t = 0$, provided that $R(x - \alpha_s) > 0$. This condition is satisfied for every s, provided that $R(x - \alpha_p) > 0$.

Now, the functions $v_s(t)$, $(s = 1, 2, \dots, p)$ form a fundamental system of integrals of (5). It follows that any integral $v(t)$ is of the form

$$(7) \qquad v(t) = b_1 v_1(t) + b_2 v_2(t) + \dots + b_p v_p(t),$$

where $b_1, b_2, \dots, b_p$ are constants.

Thus $t^x v(t)$ vanishes when $t=0$, provided that $R(x-\alpha_p)>0$. It follows, from (4), that $I(x, t)$ vanishes when $t=0$, provided that $R(x-\alpha_p)>0$.

To examine the point $t=\infty$, we put

$$v(t) = c_0 t^m + c_1 t^{m-1} + c_2 t^{m-2} + \dots .$$

This yields the indicial equation

$$A_p m(m-1)\dots(m-p+1) - A_{p-1} m(m-1)\dots(m-p+2) + \dots \\ + (-1)^{p-1} A_1 m + (-1)^p A_0 = 0,$$

which is equivalent to

$$p_2(-m-2) = 0.$$

If we denote the zeros of $p_2(x-2)$ by $\gamma_1, \gamma_2, \dots, \gamma_p$, arranged so that $R(\gamma_1) \geqslant R(\gamma_2) \geqslant \dots \geqslant R(\gamma_p)$, we have for m the values $-\gamma_1, -\gamma_2, \dots, -\gamma_p$ and a fundamental set of solutions of the form

$$V_s(t) = t^{-\gamma_s}[g_0(t) + g_1(t)\log t + \dots + g_r(t)(\log t)^r], \\ s = 1, 2, \dots, p, \quad r \leqslant p-1,$$

where $g_0(t), \dots, g_r(t)$ are holomorphic at infinity.

It is clear then that $t^x V_s(t)$ vanishes at $t=\infty$, provided that

$$R(x+2-\gamma_p) < 0, \quad s = 1, 2, \dots, p,$$

and, if this be so, we conclude in the same way as before that $I(x, t)$ vanishes at $t=\infty$.

It remains to discuss the singular points $t=a_1$, $t=a_2$.

Two cases can arise ;

$$\text{(i) } a_1 \neq a_2; \quad \text{(ii) } a_1 = a_2.$$

In the second case the differential equation is of Fuchsian type if, and only if, a_1 be a zero of $\phi_{p-1}(t)$. We shall suppose this to be the case, so that the difference equation is normal in accordance with the definition.

In the differential equation, substitute

$$v(t) = c_0(t-a_1)^m + c_1(t-a_1)^{m+1} + c_2(t-a_1)^{m+2} + \dots .$$

In case (i), the lowest power of $(t-a_1)$ is $(t-a_1)^{m-p+1}$. Equating to zero the coefficient of this, we have the indicial equation

$$(8) \quad -a_1 \phi_p'(a_1)\, m(m-1)\dots(m-p+1)\, c_0 \\ + \phi_{p-1}(a_1)\, m(m-1)\dots(m-p+2)\, c_0 = 0,$$

which gives for m the $p-1$ integral values $0, 1, 2, \dots, p-2$ and one other value which we denote by β_1. The solutions corresponding to the integral values of m are holomorphic at $t = a_1$. With these solutions we are not concerned. On the other hand, β_1 is not, in general, an integer and the corresponding solution is

$$(9) \qquad v_1^*(t) = (t-a_1)^{\beta_1} f_1(t),$$

where $f_1(t)$ is holomorphic at $t = a_1$.

Similarly, at $t = a_2$, we have $p-1$ holomorphic solutions and another solution

$$(10) \qquad v_2^*(t) = (t-a_2)^{\beta_2} f_2(t),$$

where β_2 is not, in general, an integer and $f_2(t)$ is holomorphic at $t = a_2$.

In case (ii), the indicial equation for m is

$$c_0 a_1^2 m(m-1)\dots(m-p+1)\,\phi_p''(a_1)/2! \\ -c_0 a_1 m(m-1)\dots(m-p+2)\,\phi_{p-1}'(a_1) \\ +c_0 m(m-1)\dots(m-p+3)\,\phi_{p-2}(a_1) = 0,$$

which gives for m the $p-2$ integral values $0, 1, \dots, p-3$ and two other values not, in general, integral which we denote by β_1 and β_2 with $R(\beta_1) \geqslant R(\beta_2)$.

The corresponding solutions are of the forms

$$(11) \qquad \begin{aligned} v_1^*(t) &= (t-a_1)^{\beta_1} f_1(t), \\ v_2^*(t) &= (t-a_1)^{\beta_2}[f_2(t) + f_3(t)\log(t-a_1)], \end{aligned}$$

where $f_1(t), f_2(t), f_3(t)$ are holomorphic at $t = a_1$. The logarithmic term will only occur when β_1, β_2 are congruent.†

15·1. The Canonical Systems of Solutions. The integrals $v_1^*(t)$, $v_2^*(t)$ of the differential equation 15·0 (5) are many-valued functions.

---

† For the method Frobenius applied to the case of congruent indices, see Forsyth, *Theory of Differential Equations*, vol. iv (1902), pp. 243-258. The solutions can be written

$$v_k^*(t) = \frac{\partial^{k-1}}{\partial m^{k-1}}[t^{-m} f(m, t)],$$

where $k=1$, $m=\beta_1$, $k=2$, $m=\beta_2$.

Two ways in which $t^{x-1}v_1^*(t)$, $t^{x-1}v_2^*(t)$ may be made one-valued are shewn in Figs. 15 and 16. In Fig. 15 we have cut the t plane

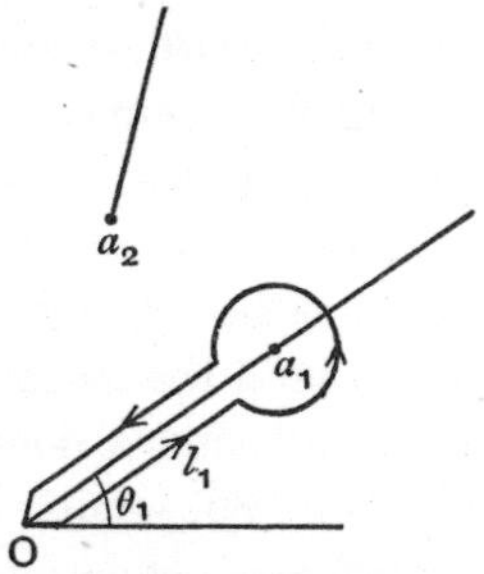

FIG. 15.

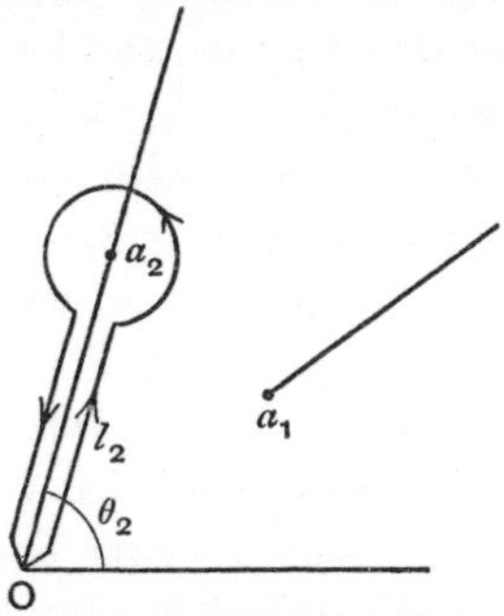

FIG. 16.

from O through a_1 to infinity and from a_2 to infinity along the line Oa_2. In the cut plane both the above functions are single-valued. Fig. 16 is explained in the same way. In the figures l_1 and l_2 are loops from the origin round a_1 and a_2 respectively.

If $R(x-\alpha_p) > 0$, we have seen that the function $I(x, t)$ given by 15·0 (4) vanishes at the origin, so that

$$(1) \qquad u_1(x) = \frac{1}{2\pi i}\int_{l_1} t^{x-1} v_1^*(t)\, dt,$$

$$(2) \qquad u_2(x) = \frac{1}{2\pi i}\int_{l_2} t^{x-1} v_2^*(t)\, dt$$

are solutions of the difference equation 15·0 (2). These solutions have been called by Nörlund the first canonical system. That these solutions are linearly independent and therefore form a fundamental set will be proved later.

If $a_1 = r_1 e^{i\theta_1}$, $a_2 = r_2 e^{i\theta_2}$, $0 \leqslant \theta_1 \leqslant \theta_2 < 2\pi$, we shall suppose that as t describes l_1 in the positive sense starting from O, $\arg(t-a_1)$ increases from $\theta_1 - \pi$ to $\theta_1 + \pi$, and that as t describes l_2, $\arg(t-a_2)$ increases from $\theta_2 - \pi$ to $\theta_2 + \pi$, while $\arg t = \theta_1$ or θ_2 along the straight parts.

If $a_1 = a_2$, only one cut, namely, $Oa_1a_2\infty$, is necessary, and only one loop circuit is needed for both solutions. If $r_1 < r_2$, $\theta_1 = \theta_2$, both a_1 and a_2 lie on the cut, and we must deform the loop l_2 so that the point a_1 is not enclosed by l_2. In every case each loop must be drawn so as to enclose only one point which represents a root of the characteristic equation.

Consistent with this, the loops may be of any shape, the most convenient shape for l_1, say, generally being two straight lines ultimately coincident with Oa_1 and a vanishing circle round a_1. We note also that, if $R(\beta_1) > -1$, the integral taken round the circular part tends to zero when the radius of the circle tends to zero. In any case we shall suppose that neither β_1 nor β_2 is an integer, for in this case the integrals taken round the loops vanish.

It may be noted here that integrals taken round a double loop contour (such as used for the Beta function in 9·89) joining any two of O, a_1, a_2 will furnish a solution of the difference equation.†

The second canonical system of solutions is furnished by cutting the plane as already described and taking infinite loops L_1 and L_2 round a_1 and a_2 as illustrated in Fig. 17 for the point a_1.

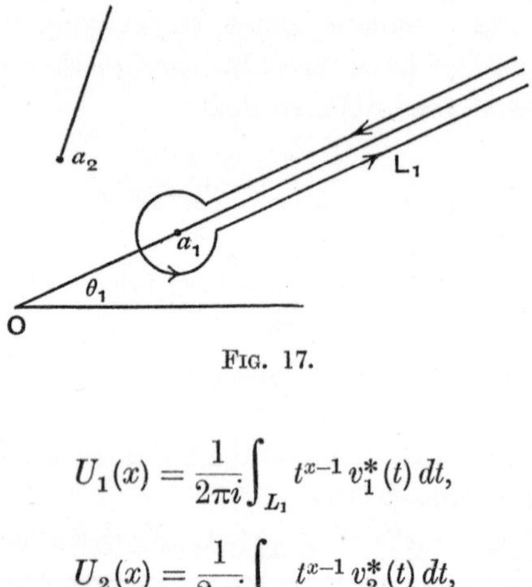

FIG. 17.

This gives

$$(3)\qquad U_1(x) = \frac{1}{2\pi i}\int_{L_1} t^{x-1}\, v_1^*(t)\, dt,$$

$$(4)\qquad U_2(x) = \frac{1}{2\pi i}\int_{L_2} t^{x-1}\, v_2^*(t)\, dt,$$

where along L_1 we take $\arg(t-a_1)$ to vary from θ_1 along the upper side of the loop to $2\pi+\theta_1$ along the lower side, $\arg t$ being θ_1 along the straight parts. Here again the shape of the loops is immaterial,

† See E. W. Barnes, *Messenger of Mathematics*, 34 (1905).

provided each encloses only one point representing a root of the characteristic equation.

The second canonical system of solutions also forms a fundamental set.

15·2. Factorial Series for the Canonical Solutions.

We consider for simplicity the case in which the roots of the characteristic equation are incongruent.

We have by 15·0 (9),

$$u_1(x) = \frac{1}{2\pi i}\int_{l_1} t^{x-1}(t-a_1)^{\beta_1} f(t)\, dt,$$

where $f(t)$ is holomorphic at $t = a_1$.

The only singular points of $v_1^*(t)$ inside and upon l_1 are $t = a_1$, $t = 0$. Thus $f(t)$ is holomorphic inside and upon l_1 except at $t = 0$.

Make the change of variable

$$t = a_1 z^{1/\omega}, \quad \omega > 1.$$

Then

$$u_1(x) = \frac{1}{2\pi i}\int_C \frac{a_1^{x+\beta_1}}{\omega} z^{x/\omega-1}(z^{1/\omega}-1)^{\beta_1} f(a_1 z^{1/\omega})\, dz,$$

where C is a loop from the origin round $z = 1$, Fig. 18.

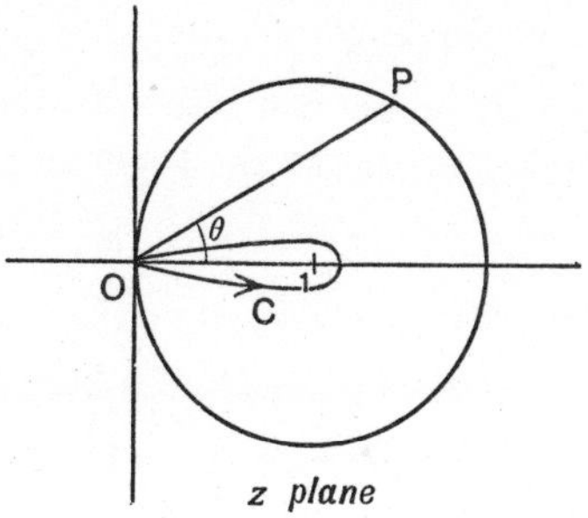

z plane
FIG. 18.

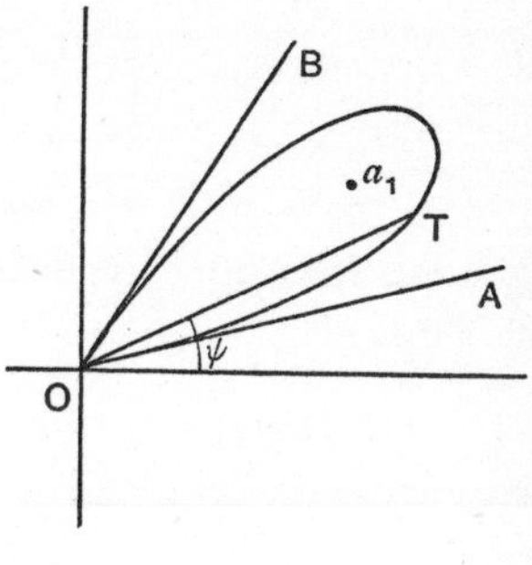

t plane
FIG. 19.

Now the circle $|z-1| = 1$ in the z plane transforms into a loop in the t plane, round $t = a_1$, enclosed by two rays OA, OB inclined at angle π/ω.

For, if

$$z = r\, e^{i\theta}, \quad t = \tau\, e^{i\psi}, \quad a_1 = r_1\, e^{i\theta_1},$$

we have

$$\tau^\omega e^{i\psi\omega} = r_1^\omega\, r\, e^{i\theta+i\theta_1\omega},$$

so that

$$\tau^{\omega} = r_1^{\omega} r, \quad \omega\psi = \theta + \theta_1 \omega.$$

When P describes the circle, θ varies from $-\frac{\pi}{2}$ to $+\frac{\pi}{2}$ and r varies from 0 through 2 to 0, so that $\psi - \theta_1$ varies from $-\frac{\pi}{2\omega}$ to $+\frac{\pi}{2\omega}$, while τ varies from 0 through $r_1 2^{1/\omega}$ to 0, so that T describes a loop of the kind stated.

By taking ω large enough, that is, by making the angle AOB small enough, we can ensure that 0, a_1 are the only singular points of $v_1^*(t)$ on or inside this loop, and consequently that $f(t)$ is holomorphic in and on the loop except at $t = 0$. It follows that $f(a_1 z^{1/\omega})$ is holomorphic inside and on the circle $|z-1| = 1$, except at $z = 0$.

We can therefore find an expansion

$$\frac{a_1^{\beta_1}}{2\pi i \omega}\left(\frac{z^{1/\omega}-1}{z-1}\right)^{\beta_1} f(a_1 z^{1/\omega}) = \sum_{\nu=0}^{\infty} C_\nu (1-z)^\nu,$$

which is convergent inside the circle $|z-1| = 1$, so that

$$u_1(x) = \int_C a_1^x z^{x/\omega - 1}(z-1)^{\beta_1} \sum_{\nu=0}^{\infty} C_\nu (1-z)^\nu dz.$$

Since the loop C is interior to the circle, we can integrate term by term. Since by hypothesis $\arg(z-1) = -\pi$ at the beginning of the loop,

$$u_1(x) = e^{-\pi i \beta_1} a_1^x \sum_{\nu=0}^{\infty} C_\nu \int_C z^{x/\omega - 1}(1-z)^{\beta_1+\nu} dz$$

$$= e^{-\pi i \beta_1} a_1^x (1 - e^{2\pi i \beta_1}) \sum_{\nu=0}^{\infty} C_\nu \mathrm{B}\left(\frac{x}{\omega}, \beta_1 + \nu + 1\right),$$

in terms of the Beta function from 9·88.

Since

$$\mathrm{B}(x/\omega, \beta_1+\nu+1) = \Gamma(x/\omega)\Gamma(\beta_1+\nu+1)/\Gamma(x/\omega+\beta_1+\nu+1),$$

we can write

$$u_1(x) = a_1^x \Gamma(x/\omega)\,\Omega(x, \beta_1)/\Gamma(x/\omega+\beta_1+1),$$

where $\Omega(x, \beta_1)$ is a factorial series of the form

$$\Omega(x, \beta_1) = D_0 + \sum_{\nu=1}^{\infty} D_\nu \frac{(\beta_1+1)\ldots(\beta_1+\nu)}{(x+\omega\,\beta_1+\omega)\ldots(x+\omega\,\beta_1+\nu\,\omega)},$$

where $D_0 \neq 0$ and where the series is convergent for $R(x-\alpha_p) > 0$.

In the same way by means of the change of variable

$$t = a_1(1-z)^{-1/\omega},$$

we can shew for the second canonical system that

$$U_1(x) = a_1^x \sum_{\nu=0}^{\infty} F_\nu \,\mathrm{B}\left(-\frac{x}{\omega}-\beta_1,\ \beta_1+\nu+1\right).$$

15·3. Asymptotic Properties. If $x \to \infty$ in the region of convergence, since

$$\frac{\Gamma(x/\omega)}{\Gamma(x/\omega+\beta_1+1)} \sim \left(\frac{x}{\omega}\right)^{-\beta_1-1},$$

we have

$$u_1(x) \sim a_1^x (x/\omega)^{-\beta_1-1} D_0.$$

Similarly,

$$u_2(x) \sim a_2^x (x/\omega)^{-\beta_2-1} D_0'.$$

Hence, if

$$|a_1| > |a_2|,$$

$$\lim_{x\to\infty} \frac{u_2(x)}{u_1(x)} = 0,$$

so that, by the theorem of 12·16, the first system of canonical solutions forms a fundamental system.

The same can be proved for the second system of canonical solutions.

As we have thus found two fundamental systems, it follows that the members of one must be linearly related to those of the other. General methods of finding the periodic coefficients of these relations have been developed by Nörlund. They are too long to introduce here but they will be illustrated by an example later.

15·31. Casorati's Determinant. By Heymann's Theorem, 12·12, the determinant

$$D(x) = \begin{vmatrix} u_1(x) & u_2(x) \\ u_1(x+1) & u_2(x+1) \end{vmatrix}$$

satisfies the difference equation

$$\frac{D(x+1)}{D(x)} = \frac{p_0(x)}{p_2(x)} = \frac{C_p(x-\alpha_1)\dots(x-\alpha_p)}{A_p(x-\gamma_1+2)\dots(x-\gamma_p+2)},$$

$$C_p / A_p = a_1 a_2 = b, \text{ say.}$$

Hence we have

$$D(x) = b^x \frac{\Gamma(x-\alpha_1)\Gamma(x-\alpha_2)\dots\Gamma(x-\alpha_p)}{\Gamma(x-\gamma_1+2)\dots\Gamma(x-\gamma_p+2)} \varpi(x),$$

where $\varpi(x)$ is a periodic whose value will now be determined.

By the asymptotic formulae for $u_1(x)$, $u_2(x)$, we have

$$u_1(x) = a_1^x x^{-\beta_1-1} D_0(1+\eta_1(x)),$$
$$u_2(x) = a_1^x x^{-\beta_2-1} D_0'(1+\eta_2(x)),$$

where $\eta_1(x)$, $\eta_2(x) \to 0$ when $x \to \infty$ in the region of convergence.

Now $$u_1(x+1) = a_1^{x+1}(x+1)^{-\beta_1-1} D_0(1+\eta_1(x+1))$$
$$= a_1^{x+1} x^{-\beta_1-1} D_0(1+\eta_3(x)),$$

where $\eta_3(x) \to 0$ when $x \to \infty$. Thus

$$D(x) = b^x x^{-\beta_1-\beta_2-2} D_0 D_0'(a_2-a_1)(1+\eta(x)),$$

where $\eta(x) \to 0$ when $x \to \infty$, so that

$$D(x) \sim b^x x^{-\beta_1-\beta_2-2} D_0 D_0'(a_2-a_1).$$

But

$$\frac{\Gamma(x-\alpha_1)}{\Gamma(x-\gamma_1+2)} \sim x^{\gamma_1-\alpha_1-2},$$

so that, from the value of $D(x)$ in terms of the Gamma functions, we have

$$D(x) \sim b^x x^{k-2p} \varpi(x),$$

where

$$k = \sum_{s=1}^{p} (\gamma_s - \alpha_s).$$

Comparing the two asymptotic values, we have

$$\varpi(x) \sim x^{2p-2-\beta_1-\beta_2-k} D_0 D_0'(a_2-a_1).$$

We shall now show that the index of x is zero. From the expressions for $p_0(x)$, $p_2(x)$, we have

$$-\sum_{s=1}^{p} \alpha_s = (C_{p-1} + \tfrac{1}{2}p(p-1)C_p)/C_p,$$

$$-\sum_{s=1}^{p} \gamma_s = (A_{p-1} + \tfrac{1}{2}p(p-1)A_p)/A_p.$$

Thus

$$k = \frac{C_{p-1}}{C_p} - \frac{A_{p-1}}{A_p}.$$

Again, from 15·0 (8),

$$\beta_1 - p + 1 = \frac{\phi_{p-1}(a_1)}{a_1 \phi_p'(a_1)},$$

so that

$$\beta_1 + \beta_2 - 2p + 2 = \frac{\phi_{p-1}(a_1)}{a_1 \phi_p'(a_1)} + \frac{\phi_{p-1}(a_2)}{a_2 \phi_p'(a_2)}.$$

If we express $\phi_{p-1}(x)/\phi_p(x)$ in partial fractions, we get

$$\frac{\phi_{p-1}(x)}{\phi_p(x)} = \frac{A_{p-1}}{A_p} + \frac{\phi_{p-1}(a_1)}{(x-a_1)\phi_p'(a_1)} + \frac{\phi_{p-1}(a_2)}{(x-a_2)\phi_p'(a_2)}.$$

Putting $x = 0$, we obtain

$$\beta_1 + \beta_2 - 2p + 2 = \frac{A_{p-1}}{A_p} - \frac{C_{p-1}}{C_p},$$

and therefore

$$2p - 2 - \beta_1 - \beta_2 - k = 0.$$

Thus

$$\varpi(x) \sim D_0 D_0'(a_2 - a_1).$$

It follows that the periodic $\varpi(x)$ is a constant whose value is $D_0 D_0'(a_2 - a_1)$.

Thus we have the value of Casorati's determinant, namely,

$$D(x) = \frac{\Gamma(x-\alpha_1)\ldots\Gamma(x-\alpha_p)}{\Gamma(x-\gamma_1+2)\ldots\Gamma(x-\gamma_p+2)} b^x D_0 D_0'(a_2 - a_1).$$

The above result, which is due to Nörlund, has been obtained on the assumption $a_1 \neq a_2$, but even if $a_1 = a_2$ Nörlund † has shewn that $\varpi(x)$ still reduces to a constant.

† N. E. Nörlund, *Équations linéaires aux différences finies* (1929), chap. iii.

15·4. Partial Fraction Series. The canonical solutions, as is evident from their developments in factorial series, are analytic except at poles in the region of convergence. By means of the difference equation itself these solutions can be prolonged over the whole plane. It thus appears that these solutions are meromorphic functions and must therefore, in accordance with a theorem of Mittag-Leffler, have a representation by a series of partial fractions.

To obtain the development we make use of the solutions of 15·0 (5) in the neighbourhood of the origin.

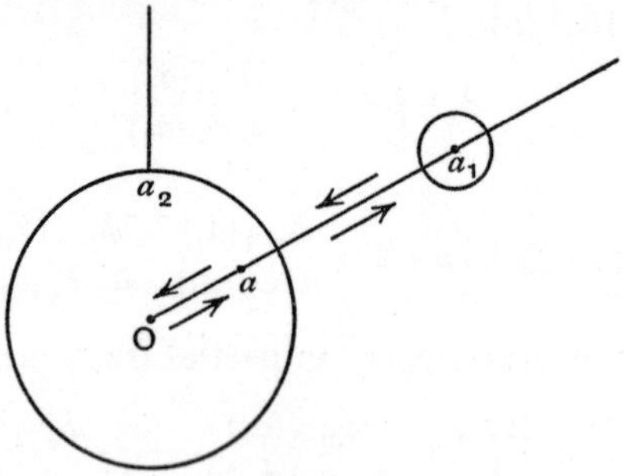

FIG. 20.

On the line Oa_1, take a point a which is nearer to O than a_2 is. Denote by C the path of integration $OaaO$ and by C' the loop from a round a_1 and back to a, Fig. 20.

Then

$$2\pi i\, u_1(x) = \int_C t^{x-1} v_1^*(t)\, dt + \int_{C'} t^{x-1} v_1^*(t)\, dt.$$

The second term on the right is an integral function which we can denote by $2\pi i\, E(x)$.

In the first integral, using 15·0 (7), we have, on the path Oa,

$$v_1^*(t) = b_1 v_1(t) + b_2 v_2(t) + \dots + b_p v_p(t),$$

while on the return path aO we have

$$v_1^*(t) = c_1 v_1(t) + c_2 v_2(t) + \dots + c_p v_p(t),$$

where b_s, c_s $(s = 1, 2, \dots, p)$ denote two sets of constants corresponding to the two determinations of $v_1^*(t)$ on opposite sides of the cut in the t plane.

Thus

$$\int_C t^{x-1} v_1^*(t)\, dt = \sum_{s=1}^{p} (b_s - c_s) \int_0^a t^{x-1} v_s(t)\, dt.$$

Now, by 15·0 (6),

$$v_s(t) = t^{-\alpha_s} [f_0(t) + f_1(t) \log t + \ldots + f_r(t) (\log t)^r],$$

where $f_0(t), f_1(t), \ldots$, are holomorphic in the neighbourhood of O, and consequently along the path Oa, since

$$|a| < |a_1| \quad \text{and} \quad |a| < |a_2|.$$

Making the change of variable $t = az$ and expanding the holomorphic functions in powers of z, we have

$$\frac{1}{2\pi i} \int_C t^{x-1} v_1^*(t)\, dt = a^x \sum_{s=0}^{\infty} \sum_{\mu=1}^{p} \sum_{\nu=0}^{r} A_{s\mu\nu} \int_0^1 z^{x+s-\alpha_\mu-1} (\log z)^\nu\, dz,$$

where the $A_{s\mu\nu}$ are numerical coefficients.

Now

$$\int_0^1 z^{x+s-\alpha_\mu-1} (\log z)^\nu\, dz = \frac{(-1)^\nu \nu!}{(x+s-\alpha_\mu)^{\nu+1}}.$$

Thus, with $B_{s\mu\nu} = (-1)^\nu \nu! A_{s\mu\nu}$, we have

$$u_1(x) = E(x) + a^x \sum_{s=0}^{\infty} \sum_{\mu=1}^{p} \sum_{\nu=0}^{r} \frac{B_{s\mu\nu}}{(x+s-\alpha_\mu)^{\nu+1}},$$

which is the required development of $u_1(x)$ in a series of partial fractions. The series converges over the whole plane except at the points $\alpha_s, \alpha_s - 1, \alpha_s - 2, \ldots, (s = 1, 2, \ldots, p)$ which are poles. If no two of the α_s be congruent no logarithmic terms can appear in the functions $v_s(t)$ and we have in this case the simpler development

$$u_1(x) = E(x) + a^x \sum_{s=0}^{\infty} \sum_{\mu=1}^{p} \frac{B_{s\mu}}{(x+s-\alpha_\mu)}.$$

15·5. Laplace's Difference Equation. This name is given to the equation whose coefficients are linear functions of x. The general form of the homogeneous equation is

$$[A_1(x+n) + A_2]\, u(x+n) + [B_1(x+n-1) + B_2]\, u(x+n-1) + \ldots + [K_1 x + K_2]\, u(x) = 0.$$

If $A_1 = B_1 = \dots = K_1 = 0$, we have an equation with constant coefficients. Some cases of the application of Laplace's transformation have already been discussed in 13·3. For simplicity we shall again consider the equation of the second order

$$[A_1(x+2)+A_0]\,u(x+2)+[B_1(x+1)+B_0]\,u(x+1)$$
$$+[C_1 x+C_0]\,u(x)=0.$$

If $A_1 \neq 0$, $C_1 \neq 0$, this equation is of the normal type.

Making the substitution

$$u(x)=\frac{1}{2\pi i}\int_l t^{x-1}\,v(t)\,dt,$$

we have for $v(t)$ the differential equation

$$(A_1 t^2+B_1 t+C_1)\,t\,v'(t)-(A_0 t^2+B_0 t+C_0)\,v(t)=0.$$

When the roots a_1, a_2 of the characteristic equation

$$\phi_1(t)=A_1 t^2+B_1 t+C_1=0$$

are unequal, we have, using partial fractions,

$$\frac{v'(t)}{v(t)}=\frac{-\alpha}{t}+\frac{\beta_1}{t-a_1}+\frac{\beta_2}{t-a_2},$$

$$v^*(t)=t^{-\alpha}(t-a_1)^{\beta_1}(t-a_2)^{\beta_2},$$

where

$$C_1\alpha+C_0=0.$$

Again, from 15·0 (4),

$$I(x,t)=t^{x-\alpha}(t-a_1)^{\beta_1+1}(t-a_2)^{\beta_2+1}.$$

The canonical solutions are

$$u_1(x)=\frac{1}{2\pi i}\int_{l_1} t^{x-1}\,v^*(t)\,dt,\qquad u_2(x)=\frac{1}{2\pi i}\int_{l_2} t^{x-1}\,v^*(t)\,dt;$$

$$U_1(x)=\frac{1}{2\pi i}\int_{L_1} t^{x-1}\,v^*(t)\,dt,\qquad U_2(x)=\frac{1}{2\pi i}\int_{L_2} t^{x-1}\,v^*(t)\,dt.$$

The expressions for $u_1(x)$, $u_2(x)$ are valid in the half plane $R(x-\alpha)>0$; those for $U_1(x)$, $U_2(x)$ in the half plane

$$R(x-\alpha+\beta_1+\beta_2)<0.$$

15·51. Reducible Cases. Since $v^*(t)$ is multiplied by $e^{2\pi i\beta_1}$ on passing round $t=a_1$, we have

$$u_1(x)=\frac{1-e^{2\pi i\beta_1}}{2\pi i}\int_0^{a_1}t^{x-\alpha-1}(t-a_1)^{\beta_1}(t-a_2)^{\beta_2}\,dt.$$

If β_1 be a positive integer or zero, we see that $I(x,t)$ vanishes when $t=a_1$, so that we can replace $u_1(x)$, which vanishes, by

$$u_{1,1}(x)=\int_0^{a_1}t^{x-\alpha-1}(t-a_1)^{\beta_1}(t-a_2)^{\beta_2}\,dt.$$

In this case if we make the change of variable $t=a_2 z$ and for brevity write $\xi=x-\alpha$, we have

$$u_2(x)=\frac{1}{2\pi i}\,a_2^{\xi+\beta_1+\beta_2}\int_l z^{\xi-1}(z-1)^{\beta_2}\left(z-1+1-\frac{a_1}{a_2}\right)^{\beta_1}dz,$$

where l denotes a loop from the origin round $z=1$.

Expanding the last term of the integrand by the binomial theorem in powers of $z-1$, we have

$$u_2(x)=\frac{1}{2\pi i}\,a_2^{\xi+\beta_1+\beta_2}\sum_{s=0}^{\beta_1}\left(1-\frac{a_1}{a_2}\right)^{\beta_1-s}\binom{\beta_1}{s}\int_l z^{\xi-1}(z-1)^{\beta_2+s}\,dz.$$

Thus, from 9·88, we have

$$u_2(x)=a_2^{\xi+\beta_1+\beta_2}\sum_{s=0}^{\beta_1}\left(1-\frac{a_1}{a_2}\right)^{\beta_1-s}\binom{\beta_1}{s}\frac{\Gamma(\xi)}{\Gamma(\xi+\beta_2+s+1)\,\Gamma(-\beta_2-s)}$$

$$=a_2^{\xi+\beta_1+\beta_2}\sum_{s=0}^{\beta_1}\left(1-\frac{a_1}{a_2}\right)^{\beta_1-s}\binom{\beta_1}{s}\frac{\Gamma(\xi)(\xi+\beta_2+s+1)\dots(\xi+\beta_2+\beta_1)}{\Gamma(\xi+\beta_1+\beta_2+1)\,\Gamma(-\beta_2-s)}.$$

Hence, when β_1 is a positive integer, we have (omitting a constant factor),

$$u_2(x)=a_2^x\,\frac{\Gamma(x-\alpha)}{\Gamma(x-\alpha+\beta_1+\beta_2+1)}\,P(x),$$

where

$$P(x)=(x-k_1)(x-k_2)\dots(x-k_{\beta_1})$$

is a polynomial of degree β_1.

It follows that

$$u_2(x)=a_2^x\,\frac{\Gamma(x-\alpha)\,\Gamma(x-k_1+1)\dots\Gamma(x-k_{\beta_1}+1)}{\Gamma(x-\alpha+\beta_1+\beta_2+1)\,\Gamma(x-k_1)\dots\Gamma(x-k_{\beta_1})}.$$

Thus $u_2(x)$ satisfies an equation of the form

$$u(x+1) = r(x)\, u(x),$$

where

$$r(x) = \frac{a_2(x-\alpha)(x-k_1+1)\ldots(x-k_{\beta_1}+1)}{(x-\alpha+\beta_1+\beta_2+1)(x-k_1)\ldots(x-k_{\beta_1})},$$

and the given difference equation is reducible (see 12·24).

Again, if $\beta_1 = -n$, a negative integer, we have

$$u_1(x) = \frac{1}{2\pi i}\int_{l_1} \frac{t^{\xi-1}(t-a_2)^{\beta_2}}{(t-a_1)^n}\, dt.$$

The residue of the integrand at the only pole $t = a_1$ is the coefficient of y^{n-1} in $(y+a_1)^{\xi-1}(y+k)^{\beta_2}$, where $k = a_1 - a_2$. This is

$$a_1^{\xi-1} k^{\beta_2} \sum_{s=0}^{n-1} \binom{\beta_2}{n-1-s}\binom{\xi-1}{s} a_1^{-s} k^{-n+s+1},$$

so that

$$u_1(x) = a_1^x P(x),$$

where $P(x)$ is a polynomial and the equation is again reducible. Thus Laplace's equation is reducible when either β_1 or β_2 is an integer.

15·52. Hypergeometric Solutions. We suppose that neither β_1 nor β_2 is an integer and that $|a_1| < |a_2|$. We have then a solution of the form

$$u_1(x) = \int_{l_1} t^{\xi-1}(a_1-t)^{\beta_1}(a_2-t)^{\beta_2}\, dt,$$

where $\xi = x - \alpha$. Putting $t = a_1 z$, $a_1 = k a_2$, this becomes

$$u_1(x) = a_1^{\xi+\beta_1} a_2^{\beta_2} \int_l z^{\xi-1}(1-z)^{\beta_1}(1-kz)^{\beta_2}\, dt,$$

where l is a loop from the origin round $z = 1$.

Since the integrand is multiplied by $e^{2\pi i\beta_1}$ on passing round $z = 1$, we have

$$u_1(x) = a_1^{\xi+\beta_1} a_2^{\beta_2}(1-e^{2\pi i\beta_1}) \int_0^1 z^{\xi-1}(1-z)^{\beta_1}(1-kz)^{\beta_2}\, dt$$

$$= a_1^{\xi+\beta_1} a_2^{\beta_2}(1-e^{2\pi i\beta_1}) \frac{\Gamma(\xi)\,\Gamma(\beta_1+1)}{\Gamma(\xi+\beta_1+1)} F(\xi, -\beta_2; \xi+\beta_1+1; k),$$

from 9·86. This is valid, provided that

$$R(\xi) > 0, \quad R(\beta_1+1) > 0.$$

These restrictions can be removed if we replace l by a double loop of the form used in 9·89. By various changes of variable we can get altogether 16 solutions of the above type. Eight more can be obtained by taking a loop from a_1 round a_2 and a loop from a_2 round a_1.

On account of the existence of these solutions, Laplace's difference equation of the second order is also known as the hypergeometric difference equation.

15·53. Partial Fraction Series. Taking $|a|$ less than $|a_1|$ and $|a_2|$, we have, as in 15·4,

$$u_1(x) = \int_{l_1} t^{\xi-1}(a_1-t)^{\beta_1}(a_2-t)^{\beta_2}\,dt$$

$$= (1-e^{2\pi i\beta_1})\int_0^a t^{\xi-1}(a_1-t)^{\beta_1}(a_2-t)^{\beta_2}\,dt + E(x),$$

where $E(x)$ denotes an integral function.

Now, by the binomial theorem,

$$\left(1-\frac{t}{a_1}\right)^{\beta_1}\left(1-\frac{t}{a_2}\right)^{\beta_2} = 1-\left(\frac{\beta_1}{a_1}+\frac{\beta_2}{a_2}\right)t+\dots .$$

Thus

$$a_1^{-\beta_1}a_2^{-\beta_2}\int_0^a t^{\xi-1}(a_1-t)^{\beta_1}(a_2-t)^{\beta_2}\,dt$$

$$= a^{\xi}\int_0^1\left[t^{\xi-1}-\left(\frac{\beta_1}{a_1}+\frac{\beta_2}{a_2}\right)at^{\xi}+\dots\right]dt$$

$$= a^{\xi}\left[\frac{1}{\xi}-\left(\frac{\beta_1}{a_1}+\frac{\beta_2}{a_2}\right)\frac{a}{\xi+1}+\dots\right].$$

We can put $|a|$ equal to the smaller of $|a_1|, |a_2|$.

If $|a_1| < |a_2|$, $R(\beta_1) > -1$, the integral round a_1 vanishes, and we have

$$u_1(x) = a_1^{\xi+\beta_1}a_2^{\beta_2}(1-e^{2\pi i\beta_1})\left[\frac{1}{\xi}-\left(\frac{\beta_1}{a_1}+\frac{\beta_2}{a_2}\right)\frac{a}{\xi+1}+\dots\right].$$

The partial fraction series are valid in the whole plane and put in evidence the poles at $x = \alpha - s$, $s = 0, 1, 2, \dots$.

15·54. The Relations between the Canonical Systems.

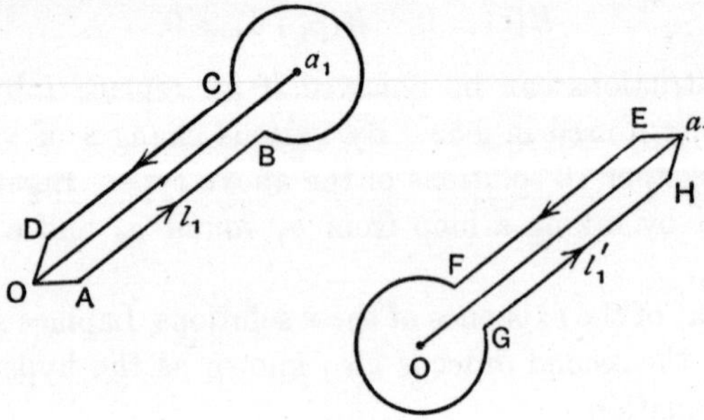

FIG. 21.

Let $a_1 = r_1 e^{i\theta_1}$, $a_2 = r_2 e^{i\theta_2}$, $0 \leqslant \theta_1 < \theta_2 < 2\pi$.

Consider the loops l_1, l_1' shewn in Fig. 21, where the straight parts coincide with Oa_1 and the radii of the circles tend to zero.

We first suppose that

$$R(\xi) > 0, \quad R(\beta_1) > -1,$$

and put

$$\chi(t) = t^{\xi-1}(t-a_1)^{\beta_1}(t-a_2)^{\beta_2}.$$

On AB let $\arg t = \theta_1$, $\arg(t-a_1) = \theta_1 - \pi$, then

$$2\pi i\, u_1(x) = (1-e^{2\pi i\beta_1})\int_0^{a_1} \chi(t)\, dt,$$

since the integral round the circle tends to zero with the radius.

On EF $\quad \arg(t-a_1) = \theta_1 + \pi, \quad \arg t = \theta_1,$

while on GH $\quad \arg t = \theta_1 + 2\pi, \quad \arg(t-a_1) = \theta_1 + \pi.$

Hence

$$\int_{l_1'} \chi(t)\, dt = \int_{a_1}^{0} e^{2\pi i\beta_1}\chi(t)\, dt + \int_0^{a_1} e^{2\pi i(\xi+\beta_1)}\chi(t)\, dt.$$

Thus, comparing these results, we have

$$(1) \qquad 2\pi i\, u_1(x) = \frac{e^{-2\pi i\beta_1}-1}{e^{2\pi i\xi}-1}\int_{l_1'} t^{x-1} v^*(t)\, dt.$$

This integral has a meaning even when $R(\xi) < 0$, so that we have obtained the analytic continuation of $u_1(x)$ over the whole x plane, except of course at the singular points. We can therefore now suppose that $R(\xi+\beta_1+\beta_2) < 0$. Without crossing any of the cuts in the t plane (see Fig. 15), we can enlarge the loop l_1' into a large indented circle whose centre is the origin as shewn in Fig. 22, and when the radius $\to \infty$ since $R(\xi+\beta_1+\beta_2)<0$, the integral along the circular arcs will be zero.

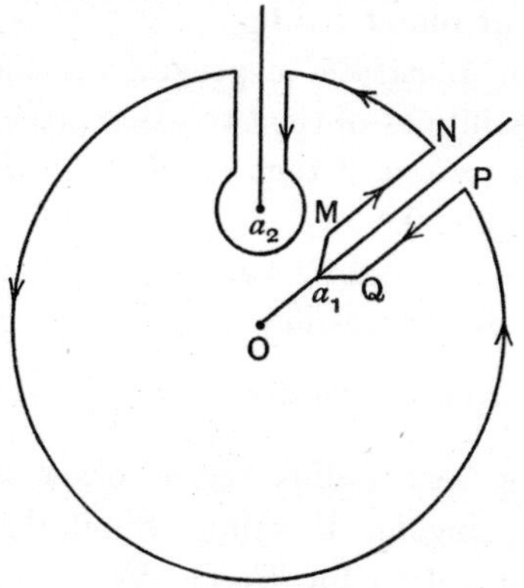

FIG. 22.

Let M, Q be supposed to coincide with a_1 and N, P to be at infinity along Oa_1. We then have on MN, $\arg(t-a_1)=\theta_1$, $\arg t=\theta_1$, and on PQ, $\arg(t-a_1)=\theta_1+2\pi$, $\arg t_1=\theta_1+2\pi$. Thus, if λ denote the limit of the contour PQa_1MN when the radius $\to\infty$, we have

$$\int_\lambda t^{x-1}v^*(t)\,dt=\int_\infty^{a_1}e^{3\pi i\beta_1+2\pi i\xi}\chi(t)\,dt+\int_{a_1}^\infty e^{\pi i\beta_1}\chi(t)\,dt.$$

Dealing with the canonical solution $U_1(x)$ in the same way as with $u_1(x)$, we obtain

$$2\pi i\,U_1(x)=\int_\infty^{a_1}e^{\pi i\beta_1}\chi(t)\,dt+\int_{a_1}^\infty e^{3\pi i\beta_1}\chi(t)\,dt.$$

Thus we have

$$\frac{1}{2\pi i}\int_\lambda t^{x-1}v^*(t)\,dt=\frac{1-e^{2\pi i(\xi+\beta_1)}}{e^{2\pi i\beta_1}-1}U_1(x).$$

Also the loop round a_2 is equivalent to $-L_2$.

We have now the complete value of the integral round l_1' and, substituting in (1), we obtain

$$u_1(x)=\frac{e^{-2\pi i\beta_1}-1}{e^{2\pi i\xi}-1}\left\{\frac{1-e^{2\pi i(\xi+\beta_1)}}{e^{2\pi i\beta_1}-1}U_1(x)-U_2(x)\right\}$$

This is an identity between analytic functions and we can therefore remove the restrictions originally placed on ξ, β_1, β_2. The expression of $u_2(x)$ in terms of $U_1(x)$, $U_2(x)$ is obtained from the above by interchanging the suffixes 1 and 2 and then writing $e^{2\pi i\xi}\, U_1(x)$ for $U_1(x)$, the factor being introduced on account of the additional circuit round $t=0$.

This investigation illustrates a general method of finding relations between the solutions of the two canonical systems.

If $x = re^{i\theta}$ and $r \to \infty$, then $e^{2\pi i\xi} \to 0$, if $0 < \theta < \pi$, and $e^{2\pi i\xi} \to \infty$, if $-\pi < \theta < 0$.

Using the general asymptotic values of 15·3, it is easily proved by means of the above expressions that

$$u_1(x) \sim \text{constant} \times a_1^x \left(\frac{1}{x}\right)^{\beta_1+1},$$

when $x \to \infty$ along any radius vector other than the negative real axis which is a singular direction. Similarly, the positive real axis is a singular direction for $U_1(x)$. These are particular cases of a more general theorem that the asymptotic properties of the solutions of a normal equation hold when $x \to \infty$ in any direction which is not singular.

15·55. The Case $a_1 = a_2$. When the roots of the characteristic equation are equal, the difference equation is of normal form only if a_1 be a zero of $\phi_0(t)$. In this case, writing $a_1 = a_2 = a$ the differential equation of 15·5 becomes

$$\frac{v'(t)}{v(t)} = \frac{A_0(t-b)}{t(t-a)} = -\frac{\alpha}{t} + \frac{\beta}{t-a},$$

whence $v^*(t) = t^{-\alpha}(t-a)^\beta$ and therefore

$$u_1(x) = \frac{1}{2\pi i}\int_{l_1} t^{x-\alpha-1}(t-a)^\beta\, dt.$$

Put $t = az$, we have, using 9·88,

$$u_1(x) = a^{x-\alpha+\beta}\frac{1}{2\pi i}\int^{(1+)} z^{x-\alpha-1}(z-1)^\beta\, dz$$

$$= \frac{a^{x-\alpha+\beta}\,\Gamma(x-\alpha)}{\Gamma(x-\alpha+\beta+1)\,\Gamma(-\beta)}.$$

In this case the equation is reducible, and in fact we see that a second solution is a^x since, by hypothesis,

$$A_1a^2 + B_1a + C_1 = 0,\quad 2A_1a + B_1 = 0,\quad A_0a^2 + B_0a + C_0 = 0.$$

Thus we have found two solutions which are obviously linearly independent.

When a is not a zero of $\phi_0(t)$ the equation is no longer of normal form, and if we make Laplace's substitution, we obtain

$$\frac{v'(t)}{v(t)} = -\frac{\alpha}{t} + \frac{\beta}{t-a} - \frac{\gamma}{(t-a)^2},$$

whence $$v(t) = t^{-\alpha}\ (t-a)^{\beta}\, e^{\gamma/(t-a)}.$$

This yields a solution

$$u_1(x) = \frac{1}{2\pi i}\int_{l_1} t^{x-\alpha-1}(t-a)^{\beta}\, e^{\gamma/(t-a)}\, dt$$

valid if $R(x-\alpha) > 0$.

To obtain a second solution, we observe that if

$$\gamma = \lambda e^{i\phi}, \quad t-a = r e^{i\theta},$$

then $$\frac{\gamma}{t-a} = \frac{\lambda}{r} e^{i(\phi-\theta)}.$$

Hence when $t \to a$, $e^{\gamma/(t-a)} \to 0$ if $|\phi-\theta| > \frac{1}{2}\pi$ and $\to \infty$ if $|\phi-\theta| < \frac{1}{2}\pi$.

Through a draw a line AB perpendicular to the line joining a to $a+\gamma$, Fig. 23.

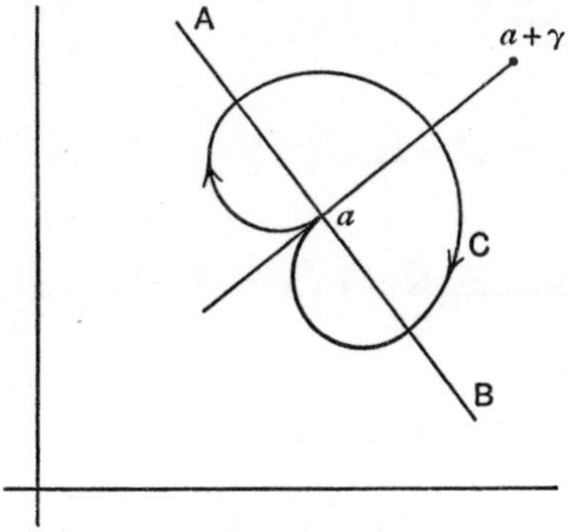

FIG. 23.

Then $e^{\gamma/(t-a)} \to 0$ when $t \to a$, provided that t be on the side of AB remote from $a+\gamma$. Draw the contour C as shewn in Fig. 23, which departs from a on the side remote from $a+\gamma$

with $\arg(t-a) = \pi+\phi$ and returns on the same side with $\arg(t-a) = -\pi+\phi$. Then

$$u_2(x) = \int_C t^{x-\alpha-1}(t-a)^\beta e^{\frac{\gamma}{t-a}}\,dt$$

is a second solution of the difference equation, for by the way in which we have chosen C the integrated part corresponding to $I(x, t)$ of 15·0 (4) vanishes.

Making the change of variable,

$$t-a = \frac{-\gamma}{z},$$

and suppressing a constant factor, we have

$$u_2(x) = a^x \int_L \left(\frac{1}{z}\right)^{\beta+2}\left(1-\frac{\gamma}{az}\right)^{x-\alpha-1} e^{-z}\,dz,$$

where L is the contour of Fig. 10, 9·72.

Since the contour C can be made on as small a scale as we please, we can arrange that

$$|\gamma/(az)| < 1.$$

Expanding the integrand by the binomial theorem, we obtain in terms of the complementary gamma function, 9·72,

$$u_2(x) = a^x \sum_{s=0}^{\infty} (-1)^{s+1}\left(\frac{\gamma}{a}\right)^s \binom{x-\alpha-1}{s} \Gamma_1(-\beta-s-1).$$

Since

$$\Gamma_1(-\beta) = (-\beta-1)\ldots(-\beta-s-1)\,\Gamma_1(-\beta-s-1),$$

we have

$$u_2(x) = a^x\,\Gamma_1(-\beta) \sum_{s=0}^{\infty} \left(\frac{\gamma}{a}\right)^s \binom{x-\alpha-1}{s} \frac{1}{(\beta+1)\ldots(\beta+s+1)}$$

the series being a Newton's Series. This case is interesting in that we have found solutions of an equation which is not of normal form.

15·6. Equations not of Normal Form. Equations whose coefficients are polynomials and which are not of normal form may sometimes be reduced to normal form by a suitable change of variable. Consider

$$p_n(x)\,u_{x+n} + p_{n-1}(x)\,u_{x+n-1} + \ldots + p_0(x)\,u_x = 0,$$

and suppose that the degree of $p_n(x)$ is p, that the degree of $p_0(x)$ is $p+nk$, and that the degree of $p_{n-s}(x)$ does not exceed $p+sk$, $s=1, 2, \dots, n-1$, where k is a fixed integer positive or negative. The equation will be reduced to the normal form by the substitution

$$u_x = [\Gamma(x)]^k v_x.$$

For, if k be positive, the term $p_{n-s}(x)\, u_{x+n-s}$ becomes, after division by $[\Gamma(x)]^k$,

$$[(x+n-s-1)\dots(x+1)\,x]^k\, p_{n-s}(x)\, v_{x+n-s},$$

whose coefficient is of degree not exceeding

$$(n-s)\,k+p+sk = p+nk,$$

while the extreme coefficients are of degree $p+nk$. If k be negative, we multiply the equation by

$$[(x+n-1)(x+n-2)\dots x]^{-k}$$

and obtain coefficients of degree not exceeding p.

Example.

$$(a_1 x^2+a_2 x+a_3)\, u_{x+2}+(b_1 x+b_2)\, u_{x+1}+c_1 u_x = 0.$$

Here $p=2$, $k=-1$. Writing $u_x = v_x [\Gamma(x)]^{-1}$, we get

$$(a_1 x^2+a_2 x+a_3)\, v_{x+2}+(x+1)(b_1 x+b_2)\, v_x+c_1 x(x+1)\, v_x = 0,$$

which is of normal form.

EXAMPLES XV

Discuss the solution of the following difference equations:

1. $(x+2)\, u_{x+2}-(7x+3)\, u_{x+1}+12x\, u_x = 0.$

2. $(x-3)\, u_{x+2}-(4x-3)\, u_{x+1}+(4x+2)\, u_x = 0.$

3. $(4x+5)\, u_{x+2}+(12x+10)\, u_{x+1}+(9x+7)\, u_x = 0.$

4. Use the method of 12·72 to shew that the solution of the complete equation

$$\sum_{s=0}^{n} (a_s x+b_s)\, u(x+s) = f(x),$$

where $f(x)$ is a polynomial, can, in general, be made to depend upon the case in which $f(x)$ is replaced by a constant.

5. With the notation of 15·5, shew that the complete equation

$$[A_1(x+2)+A_0]\,u_{x+2}+[B_1(x+1)+B_0]\,u_{x+1}+(C_1\,x+C_0)\,u_x = c,$$

where c is a constant, can be satisfied by taking

$$u_x = \lambda \int_{a_1}^{1} t^{x-a-1}(t-a_1)^{\beta_1}(t-a_2)^{\beta_2}\,dt,$$

where λ is so chosen that

$$A_1\,\lambda(1-a_1)^{\beta_1+1}(1-a_2)^{\beta_2+1} = c.$$

6. If $\phi(\lambda)$, $\psi(\lambda)$ be polynomials, shew that in terms of the operator E Laplace's equation can be written in the form

$$[\phi(\mathsf{E})+x\,\psi(\mathsf{E})]\,u(x) = f(x).$$

If $f(x)$ can be expressed in the form

$$f(x) = \int_{a}^{\beta} t^{x-1}\,F(t)\,dt,$$

discuss the conditions under which the difference equation will have a particular solution of the form

$$u(x) = \int_{a}^{\beta} t^{x-1}\,v(t)\,dt.$$

In particular, shew that $v(t)$ must satisfy the differential equation

$$t\,\frac{d\,[\psi(t)\,v(t)]}{dt} - \phi(t)\,v(t)+F(t) = 0.$$

7. Shew that the equation

$$(x+a)(x+b)\,u_{x+2}+(a_1\,x+b_1)\,u_{x+1}+b_2\,u_x = f(x)$$

can be reduced to the normal form by the substitution

$$v_x = u_x\,\Gamma(x+a-1).$$

Shew how the method of Ex. 6 may be applied to this equation in the case where $f(x) = px+q$.

8. Apply Laplace's substitution to the equation

$$(x-\alpha)(x-\beta)\,u_x - [2x(x-1) - \delta(x-1) + \alpha\beta]\,u_{x-1} + (x-2)(x-\gamma-1)\,u_{x-2} = 0,$$

where $\delta = \alpha + \beta + \gamma + 1$.

CHAPTER XVI

EQUATIONS WHOSE COEFFICIENTS ARE EXPRESSIBLE BY FACTORIAL SERIES

AFTER equations with rational coefficients the next type in order of simplicity appears to be formed by those equations whose coefficients can be represented by inverse factorial series. Such equations have been considered in detail by Nörlund who has shewn how to form series which satisfy certain classes of these equations and has proved the convergence of the solutions. Nörlund's method consists in the direct substitution of a series, followed by transformations. It seems, however, simpler to use an operational method which leads ultimately to the same series but avoids the transformation of the terms which is inherent in the method of direct substitution. We shall begin by establishing the necessary theorems of operation.*

16·0. With definitions of Chapter XIV, we have

$$x' = x - r, \quad \pi\, u(x) = x' \underset{-1}{\Delta}\, u(x),$$

$$\rho^m\, u(x) = \frac{\Gamma(x'+1)}{\Gamma(x'-m+1)}\, \mathsf{E}^{-m}\, u(x).$$

We shall now prove

Theorem IX.

$$(\pi+\rho+a)^{-1} \doteqdot \rho^{-1} - (\pi+a+1)\,\rho^{-2} + (\pi+a+1)(\pi+a+2)\,\rho^{-3} - \dots$$

$$\doteqdot \rho^{-1} + \sum_{s=1}^{\infty} (-1)^s\, \phi(\pi+a+1, s)\, \rho^{-1-s},$$

where the operand is any function of x, *and*

$$\phi(\lambda+a+1, s) = (\lambda+a+1)(\lambda+a+2) \dots (\lambda+a+s).$$

---

* L. M. Milne-Thomson, "On the operational solution of linear difference equations whose coefficients are expressible by factorial series," *Proc. Cambridge Phil. Soc.*, 28 (1932).

Proof. Assume that

$$(\pi+\rho+a)^{-1} \doteqdot f_0(\pi)\,\rho^{-1}+f_1(\pi)\,\rho^{-2}+f_2(\pi)\,\rho^{-3}+\dots .$$

Operating with $\pi+\rho+a$, we have

$$1 \doteqdot \rho f_0(\pi)\,\rho^{-1}+[\rho f_1(\pi)\,\rho^{-2}+(\pi+a)\,f_0(\pi)\,\rho^{-1}]+\dots$$
$$+[\rho f_s(\pi)\,\rho^{-s-1}+(\pi+a)\,f_{s-1}(\pi)\,\rho^{-s}]+\dots .$$

Using Theorem I, 14·1, this gives

$$1 \doteqdot f_0(\pi-1)+[f_1(\pi-1)+(\pi+a)\,f_0(\pi)\,]\,\rho^{-1}+\dots$$
$$+[\,f_s(\pi-1)+(\pi+a)\,f_{s-1}(\pi)]\,\rho^{-s}+\dots .$$

Thus we must have

$$f_0(\lambda-1) = 1,$$
$$f_1(\lambda-1)+(\lambda+a)\,f_0(\lambda) = 0,$$
$$\dots\dots\dots\dots$$
$$f_s(\lambda-1)+(\lambda+a)\,f_s(\lambda) = 0,$$
$$\dots\dots\dots\dots$$

whence

$$f_0(\lambda) = 1,\quad f_1(\lambda) = -(\lambda+a+1),\quad f_2(\lambda) = (\lambda+a+1)(\lambda+a+2),$$

and generally

$$f_s(\lambda) = (-1)^s(\lambda+a+1)\dots(\lambda+a+s),$$

which proves the theorem.

16·01. Theorem X.

$$[\,(\pi+\rho+a+n-1)(\pi+\rho+a+n-2)\dots(\pi+\rho+a)\,]^{-1}$$
$$\doteqdot \rho^{-n}-\binom{n}{1}(\pi+a+n)\,\rho^{-n-1}$$
$$+\binom{n+1}{2}(\pi+a+n)(\pi+a+n+1)\,\rho^{-n-2}+\dots$$
$$\doteqdot \rho^{-n}+\sum_{s=1}^{\infty}(-1)^s\binom{n+s-1}{s}\,\phi(\pi+a+n,\,s)\,\rho^{-n-s},$$

where

$$\phi(\lambda+a+n,\,s) = (\lambda+a+n)\dots(\lambda+a+n+s-1),$$

and the operand is any function of x.

Proof. The theorem is true when $n = 1$ for it is then the same as Theorem IX. We therefore proceed by induction. Assume Theorem X to be true for a positive integer n, that is to say

$$(1)\qquad [(\pi+\rho+a+n-1)\dots(\pi+\rho+a)]^{-1}$$
$$\doteqdot \rho^{-n}+\sum_{s=1}^{\infty}(-1)^s\binom{n+s-1}{s}\phi(\pi+a+n,s)\,\rho^{-n-s}.$$

By Theorem IX, with $a+n$ for a, we have

$$[\pi+\rho+a+n]^{-1}\doteqdot\rho^{-1}+\sum_{s=1}^{\infty}(-1)^s\phi(\pi+a+n+1,s)\,\rho^{-1-s}.$$

Operating with this on (1), we get

$$(2)\qquad [(\pi+\rho+a+n)(\pi+\rho+a+n-1)\dots(\pi+\rho+a)]^{-1}$$
$$\doteqdot\rho^{-n-1}+\sum_{s=1}^{\infty}\sum_{\nu=0}^{s}(-1)^s\binom{n+s-\nu-1}{s-\nu}$$
$$\times\,\phi(\pi+a+n+1,\nu)\,\rho^{-1-\nu}\,\phi(\pi+a+n,s-\nu)\,\rho^{-n-s+\nu}$$

Now, by Theorem I,

$$\phi(\pi+a+n+1,\nu)\,\rho^{-1-\nu}\,\phi(\pi+a+n,s-\nu)\,\rho^{-n-s+\nu}$$
$$\doteqdot\phi(\pi+a+n+1,\nu)\,\phi(\pi+a+n+1+\nu,s-\nu)\,\rho^{-n-1-s}$$
$$\doteqdot\phi(\pi+a+n+1,s)\,\rho^{-n-1-s}.$$

Also

$$\sum_{\nu=0}^{s}\binom{n+s-\nu-1}{s-\nu}=\sum_{\nu=0}^{s}\binom{n+s-\nu-1}{n-1}$$
$$=\binom{n+1+s-1}{n}=\binom{n+1+s-1}{s},$$

so that the right-hand side of (2) is

$$\rho^{-n-1}+\sum_{s=1}^{\infty}(-1)^s\binom{n+1+s-1}{s}\phi(\pi+a+n+1,s)\,\rho^{-n-1-s},$$

whence the theorem follows by induction from the case $n = 1$.

In proving Theorem X we have written in a certain order the factors in the left-hand member of the statement in the enunciation. That the order is immaterial depends on the fact that the same expansion is obtained for $[(\pi+\rho+a)(\pi+\rho+b)]^{-1}$ as for $[(\pi+\rho+b)(\pi+\rho+a)]^{-1}$. This is quite simply proved by assuming an expansion for each as in Theorem IX and then operating on the first with $(\pi+\rho+a)(\pi+\rho+b)$ and on the second with $(\pi+\rho+b)(\pi+\rho+a)$. These last two operators are equivalent and we are led to the same functional equations for the coefficients in each case.

The application of Theorem X to the theory of difference equations reposes on the equivalence of $\pi+\rho$ and $x-r=x'$ regarded as an operator.

Thus with any operand

$$\frac{1}{x'}=\frac{1}{\pi+\rho}\doteqdot\rho^{-1}-(\pi+1)\,\rho^{-2}+(\pi+1)(\pi+2)\,\rho^{-3}-\dots,$$

$$\frac{1}{x'(x'+1)}=\frac{1}{(\pi+\rho)(\pi+\rho+1)}\doteqdot\rho^{-2}-\binom{2}{1}(\pi+2)\,\rho^{-3}+\binom{3}{2}(\pi+2)(\pi+3)\,\rho^{-4}-\dots,$$

and so on.

It follows at once that a factorial series of the first kind can be replaced by an equivalent operator.

Thus with $r=1$, $x'=x-1$,

$$(3)\quad a_0+\frac{a_1}{x}+\frac{a_2}{x(x+1)}+\dots+\frac{a_{s+1}}{x(x+1)\dots(x+s)}+\dots$$
$$\doteqdot a_0+a_1\,\rho^{-1}+[a_2-a_1(\pi+2)]\,\rho^{-2}+\left[a_3-\binom{2}{1}a_2(\pi+3)+a_1(\pi+2)(\pi+3)\right]\rho^{-3}+\dots,$$

the general term being

$$\left(a_s-\binom{s-1}{1}a_{s-1}(\pi+s)+\binom{s-1}{2}a_{s-2}(\pi+s)(\pi+s-1)-\dots\right)\rho^{-s}.$$

$$(4)\quad =\sum_{\nu=0}^{s-1}a_{s-\nu}(-1)^{\nu}\binom{s-1}{\nu}(\pi+s)(\pi+s-1)\dots(\pi+s-\nu+1)\,\rho^{-s},$$

the product $(\pi+s)(\pi+s-2)\dots(\pi+s-\nu+1)$ being interpreted as unity when $\nu=0$.*

* We shall make the corresponding convention throughout the chapter as the formulae are more readily expressed when it is adopted.

16·1. First Normal Form. Consider the difference equation

(1) $p_n(x)\,u(x-n)+p_{n-1}(x)\,u(x-n+1)+\ldots+p_0(x)\,u(x)=0.$

Since

$$u(x-r)=\mathsf{E}^{-r}u(x)=\Big(1-\underset{-1}{\Delta}\Big)^r u(x),$$

we can reduce the equation to the form

(2) $$q_n(x)\overset{n}{\underset{-1}{\Delta}}u(x)+q_{n-1}(x)\overset{n-1}{\underset{-1}{\Delta}}u(x)+\ldots+q_0(x)\,u(x)=0.$$

If $q_s(x)=a_s(x-1)(x-2)\ldots(x-s+1),$

$(s=1,2,\ldots,n),$ and $q_0(x)=a_0,$

the equation is of the form which we have called monomial (see 14·5) and has solutions of the type $\dfrac{\partial^\nu}{\partial k^\nu}\dfrac{\Gamma(x)}{\Gamma(x-k)}$. An obvious generalisation of the monomial type is obtained by supposing in the definition of $q_s(x)$ that a_s is replaced by

(3) $$t_s(x)=a_s+\frac{b_{1,s}}{x}+\frac{b_{2,s}}{x(x+1)}+\frac{b_{3,s}}{x(x+1)(x+2)}+\ldots.$$

When $x\to\infty$ the modified coefficient $\to a_s$, and we should expect such an equation to have solutions which behave asymptotically in the same way as the solutions of the corresponding monomial equation.

We shall therefore consider an equation of the form

(4) $$t_n(x)(x-1)(x-2)\ldots(x-n+1)\overset{n}{\underset{-1}{\Delta}}u$$
$$+t_{n-1}(x)(x-1)(x-2)\ldots(x-n+2)\overset{n-1}{\underset{-1}{\Delta}}u+\ldots+t_0(x)\,u=0,$$

where $t_s(x)$, $s=0,1,2,\ldots,n$, is of the form (3) and where $a_n\neq 0$. An equation of this type will be called the first normal form.

Since $a_n\neq 0$, we can divide (4) by $t_n(x)$ and thus obtain an equation of the same type in which $t_n(x)=1$. We shall therefore suppose this to have been done.

16·2. Operational Solution of an Equation of the First Normal Form. For simplicity we consider an equation of the second order, which we write in the form

$$(1)\quad (x-1)(x-2)\underset{-1}{\overset{2}{\Delta}} u-(a+p(x))(x-1)\underset{-1}{\Delta} u+(b+q(x))\,u = c_0\,\alpha(k)\,f_0(k)\,\rho^{-k}\,1.$$

Here a and b are constants and $p(x)$, $q(x)$ are factorial series,

$$(2)\qquad p(x)=\frac{a_1}{x}+\frac{a_2}{x(x+1)}+\frac{a_3}{x(x+1)(x+2)}+\dots,$$

$$(3)\qquad q(x)=\frac{b_1}{x}+\frac{b_2}{x(x+1)}+\frac{b_3}{x(x+1)(x+2)}+\dots,$$

while the *indicial equation* is

$$(4)\qquad f_0(k)\equiv k(k+1)+ak+b=0.$$

When the roots k_1, k_2 of this equation are congruent, say

$$k_2=k_1+p$$

where p is a positive integer or zero, we take

$$\alpha(k)=f_0(k+1)\,f_0(k+2)\dots f_0(k+p).$$

The right-hand member of (1) is introduced, as in 14·22, to allow for this case. Taking $x'=x-1$, we have $\rho^{-k}\,1=\Gamma(x)/\Gamma(x+k)$, and we note that the right-hand member of (1) vanishes when $k=k_1$, and its partial derivate with respect to k vanishes when $k=k_1$. As in 14·22, we suppose the variation of k to be restricted to a small region K in the neighbourhood of k_1, k_2.

Using 16·01 (3), we have

$$p(x)\doteqdot\sum_{s=1}^{\infty}\phi_s(\pi)\,\rho^{-s},\quad q(x)\doteqdot\sum_{s=1}^{\infty}\psi_s(\pi)\,\rho^{-s},$$

where

$$\phi_s(\pi)=\sum_{\nu=0}^{s-1}a_{s-\nu}(-1)^{\nu}\binom{s-1}{\nu}(\pi+s)\dots(\pi+s-\nu+1),$$

and a similar expression for $\psi_s(\pi)$ obtained by writing $b_{s-\nu}$ for $a_{s-\nu}$. Thus, using Theorem II, our equation assumes the operational form

$$\pi(\pi-1)\,u-(a+\phi_1(\pi)\,\rho^{-1}+\phi_2(\pi)\,\rho^{-2}+\dots)\,\pi u$$
$$+(b+\psi_1(\pi)\,\rho^{-1}+\psi_2(\pi)\,\rho^{-2}+\dots)\,u=c_0\,\alpha(k)\,f_0(k)\,\rho^{-k}\,1,$$

which can be written

$$(5)\quad [f_0(-\pi)+f_1(-\pi)\,\rho^{-1}+f_2(-\pi)\,\rho^{-2}+\dots]\,u = c_0\,\alpha(k)\,f_0(k)\,\rho^{-k}\,1,$$

where, using Theorem I,

$$(6)\quad \begin{aligned} f_0(-\pi) &= \pi(\pi-1)-a\pi+b,\\ f_1(-\pi) &= -\phi_1(\pi)(\pi+1)+\psi_1(\pi),\\ f_2(-\pi) &= -\phi_2(\pi)(\pi+2)+\psi_2(\pi), \end{aligned}$$

and so on.

We can at once obtain a formal solution of this equation by assuming that

$$(7)\quad u = u(x,k) = c_0\,\alpha(k)\,\rho^{-k}+c_1\,\rho^{-k-1}+c_2\,\rho^{-k-2}+\dots,$$

where the operand unity is understood.

Equating coefficients, we thus obtain

$$\begin{aligned} &f_0(k)\,c_0\,\alpha(k) = f_0(k)\,c_0\,\alpha(k), \text{ an identity;}\\ &c_1 f_0(k+1)+c_0\,\alpha(k)\,f_1(k+1) = 0,\\ &c_2 f_0(k+2)+c_1 f_1(k+2)+c_0\,\alpha(k)\,f_2(k+2) = 0,\\ &\quad\dots\dots\dots\dots\dots\dots\dots\dots\end{aligned}$$

$$(8)\quad c_s f_0(k+s)+c_{s-1} f_1(k+s)+c_{s-2} f_2(k+s)+\dots +c_0\,\alpha(k)\,f_s(k+s) = 0.$$

$$\dots\dots\dots\dots\dots\dots\dots\dots$$

As already explained in 14·22, these equations yield determinate values of $c_1, c_2, \dots$ in terms of c_0, provided the domain of variation of k be sufficiently restricted. We have thus found a formal solution of the non-homogeneous equation (1). Calling this solution $u(x,k)$, the homogeneous equation

$$(9)\quad (x-1)(x-2)\underset{-1}{\overset{2}{\Delta}}u-(a+p(x))(x-1)\underset{-1}{\Delta}u+(b+q(x))\,u = 0$$

has the solutions $u(x,k_1)$, $u(x,k_2)$ when k_1, k_2 are incongruent and the solutions

$$(10)\quad u(x,k_1),\quad \frac{\partial u(x,k_1)}{\partial k_1}$$

when k_1, k_2 are congruent.

16·3. Convergence of the Formal Solution. We have found the formal solution of 16·2 (1) in the form

$$(1)\quad u(x, k) = c_0 \alpha(k) \frac{\Gamma(x)}{\Gamma(x+k)} + c_1 \frac{\Gamma(x)}{\Gamma(x+k+1)} + c_2 \frac{\Gamma(x)}{\Gamma(x+k+2)} + \cdots,$$

which may be written in the form

$$u(x, k) = \frac{\Gamma(x)}{\Gamma(x+k)} v,$$

where

$$(2)\qquad v = c_0 \alpha(k) + \frac{c_1}{(x+k)} + \frac{c_2}{(x+k)(x+k+1)} + \cdots.$$

Using 2·51, we have

$$\underset{-1}{\Delta} u = -\frac{\Gamma(x-1)}{\Gamma(x+k)} \left[kv - (x+k-1) \underset{-1}{\Delta} v \right],$$

$$\underset{-1}{\overset{2}{\Delta}} u = \frac{\Gamma(x-2)}{\Gamma(x+k)} \Big[k(k+1) v - 2k(x+k-1) \underset{-1}{\Delta} v + (x+k-1)(x+k-2) \underset{-1}{\overset{2}{\Delta}} v \Big].$$

Substituting in 16·2 (1), we obtain the equation satisfied by v, namely,

$$(3)\quad (x+k-1)(x+k-2) \underset{-1}{\overset{2}{\Delta}} v - [(2k+a) + p(x)](x+k-1) \underset{-1}{\Delta} v + [f_0(k) + kp(x) + q(x)] v = c_0 \alpha(k) f_0(k).$$

If in the definitions of π and ρ we now take $x' = x+k-1$, then (3) assumes the form

$$[\pi(\pi-1) - (2k+a)\pi + f_0(k)] v - p(x) \pi v + [kp(x) + q(x)] v = c_0 \alpha(k) f_0(k).$$

Since

$$\pi(\pi-1) - (2k+a)\pi + k(k+1) + ak + b = f_0(-\pi+k),$$

we have finally

$$(4)\qquad f_0(-\pi+k) v = c_0 \alpha(k) f_0(k) + [p(x)(\pi-k) - q(x)] v,$$

which is the original equation with $\pi - k$ written for π.

Now, let the factorial series for $p(x)$, $q(x)$ be supposed transformed so that

$$(5) \qquad p(x) = \sum_{s=0}^{\infty} \frac{-\alpha_s\, s!}{x'(x'+1)\dots(x'+s)},$$

$$(6) \qquad k\,p(x)+q(x) = \sum_{s=0}^{\infty} \frac{-\beta_s\, s!}{x'(x'+1)\dots(x'+s)}.$$

Then (4) becomes

$$f_0(-\pi+k)\,v = c_0\,\alpha(k)\,f_0(k) + \sum_{s=0}^{\infty} \frac{s!}{x'\dots(x'+s)}[-\alpha_s\,\pi+\beta_s].$$

Now, since $x' \doteqdot \pi+\rho$,

$$\sum_{s=0}^{\infty} \frac{s!}{x'\dots(x'+s)}[-\alpha_s\,\pi+\beta_s] \doteqdot \sum_{s=0}^{\infty} \frac{s!}{(\pi+\rho)\dots(\pi+\rho+s)}[-\alpha_s\,\pi+\beta_s]$$

$$\doteqdot \sum_{s=0}^{\infty}\sum_{h=0}^{s} (-1)^{s-h}\,h!\binom{s}{s-h}(\pi+h+1)\dots(\pi+s)\,\rho^{-1-s}[-\alpha_h\,\pi+\beta_h],$$

using Theorem X. Thus (4) becomes

$$(7) \qquad f_0(-\pi+k)\,v = c_0\,\alpha(k)\,f_0(k) + \sum_{s=0}^{\infty} F_s(-\pi)\,\rho^{-1-s}\,v,$$

where

(8) $F_s(-\pi)$

$$= \sum_{h=0}^{s} (-1)^{s-h}\,h!\binom{s}{h}(\pi+h+1)\dots(\pi+s)[-(\pi+s+1)\,\alpha_h+\beta_h].$$

Now we know that (7) has the formal solution (2), which can be written in the form

$$v = c_0\,\alpha(k) + c_1\,\rho^{-1} + c_2\,\rho^{-2} + c_3\,\rho^{-3} + \dots.$$

Substituting this in (7), we get

$$f_0(-\pi+k)\,[c_0\,\alpha(k)+c_1\,\rho^{-1}+\dots] = c_0\,\alpha(k)\,f_0(k)$$
$$+[F_0(-\pi)\,\rho^{-1}+F_1(-\pi)\,\rho^{-2}+\dots][c_0\,\alpha(k)+c_1\,\rho^{-1}+\dots].$$

Equating the coefficients of the powers of ρ, we have

$$c_1 f_0(1+k) = F_0(1)\,d_0, \quad d_0 = c_0\,\alpha(k),$$
$$c_2 f_0(2+k) = F_1(2)\,d_0 + F_0(2)\,c_1,$$
$$c_3 f_0(3+k) = F_2(3)\,d_0 + F_1(3)\,c_1 + F_0(3)\,c_2,$$
$$\dots\dots\dots\dots\dots$$

$$(9) \qquad c_s f_0(s+k) = c_{s-1}\,F_0(s) + c_{s-2}\,F_1(s) + \dots + d_0\,F_{s-1}(s).$$

Now, from (8), we have

$$F_s(\nu) = \sum_{h=0}^{s} h! \binom{s}{h} (\nu - h - 1) \dots (\nu - s) [(\nu - s - 1)\alpha_h + \beta_h]$$

$$= s! \sum_{h=0}^{s} \binom{\nu - h - 1}{\nu - s - 1} [(\nu - s - 1)\alpha_h + \beta_h].$$

Put

$$A_h = \alpha_0 + \alpha_1 + \dots + \alpha_h, \quad B_h = \beta_0 + \beta_1 + \dots + \beta_h.$$

Then by Abel's Identity, 10·07, we have

$$(10) \qquad F_s(\nu) = s! \sum_{h=0}^{s} \binom{\nu - h - 2}{\nu - s - 2} [(\nu - s - 1) A_h + B_h].$$

Thus if $\nu > s$, a condition always fulfilled by (9), we see that $F_s(\nu)$ is a linear form in A_h, B_h with positive coefficients. Hence, if in the difference equation (3) we replace the factorial series (5) and (6) for $p(x)$ and $kp(x) + q(x)$ by majorant factorial series (see 10·091) the numbers corresponding to the $F_s(\nu)$ in the formal solution will be replaced by numbers which are larger in absolute value than the numbers $F_s(\nu)$ in (9). We have supposed k to be restricted to a small region K in the neighbourhood of k_1, k_2. We can therefore find a number $\mu \geqslant 0$, independent of k, such that the factorial series (5), (6) certainly converge if $R(x') > \mu$. We then take as majorant series (see 10·091) both for $p(x)$ and $kp(x) + q$ the function

$$\frac{M}{x' - \mu - \varepsilon} = \sum_{s=0}^{\infty} \frac{M(\mu + \varepsilon)(\mu + \varepsilon + 1) \dots (\mu + \varepsilon + s - 1)}{x'(x' + 1) \dots (x' + s)},$$

where $\varepsilon > 0$ and M is a fixed positive number chosen sufficiently large for the majorant property to hold for all values of k in K.

Now consider the difference equation

$$(11) \quad cx'(x' - 1) \mathop{\Delta}_{-1}^{2} v + cx' \mathop{\Delta}_{-1} v + v = \frac{M}{x' - \mu - \varepsilon} \left[-x' \mathop{\Delta}_{-1} v + v \right] + \gamma_0,$$

where $0 < c < 1$ and γ_0 is a constant whose value will be determined later. This equation being analogous to (3) has a formal solution (which we shall presently determine) of the form (2), namely,

$$(12) \qquad w = \sum_{s=0}^{\infty} \frac{\gamma_s}{(x' + 1)(x' + 2) \dots (x' + s)}.$$

The coefficients γ_s are given by equations of the same form as (9), namely,

$$\gamma_s(c s^2+1) = \gamma_{s-1}\chi_0(s)+\gamma_{s-2}\chi_1(s)+\dots+\gamma_0\chi_{s-1}(s), \tag{13}$$

but the numbers $\chi_s(\nu)$, which correspond to $F_s(\nu)$, are now all positive, as is easily seen from the form analogous to (10). Moreover, we have shewn that

$$\chi_s(\nu) > |F_s(\nu)|, \quad \nu > s. \tag{14}$$

Now, since $0 < c < 1$, we can find a positive integer n, such that

$$c s^2+1 < |f_0(k+s)|, \quad s \geqslant n, \tag{15}$$

for all values of k in K. Also, by successive applications of the recurrence relations (13), we have $\gamma_s = m_s\gamma_0$ where m_s is a positive number, while in a similar way from (9) we obtain

$$c_s = \psi_s(k),$$

where $\psi_s(k)$ is a rational function of k. It follows that if m be the smallest of the numbers $1, m_1, m_2, \dots, m_n$, and if

$$\psi > \max\,[|c_0\alpha(k)|, |\psi_1(k)|, \dots, |\psi_n(k)|],$$

we shall have

$$\gamma_s > |c_s|, \quad s = 1, 2, \dots, n, \quad \gamma_0 > |c_0\alpha(k)|, \tag{16}$$

provided that γ_0 be so chosen that $m\gamma_0 > \psi$. If this condition be satisfied, it follows from (13), (14), (15), (16) that, interpreting c_{n-n} as d_0,

$$\gamma_{n+1} > \sum_{h=0}^{n} |F_h(n+1)\,c_{n-h}| \div |f_0(k+n+1)| > |c_{n+1}|,$$

from (9). We prove in the same way that $\gamma_{n+2} > |c_{n+2}|$ and so on, and thus we have $\gamma_\nu > |c_\nu|$ for $\nu = 1, 2, \dots, n, n+1, \dots$. It follows from this inequality that, when the series (12) converges, the series (2) also converges. To establish the convergence of (12) we substitute this series in (11), which gives in operational form

$$(c\pi^2+1)\sum_{s=0}^{\infty}\gamma_s\rho^{-s} = \frac{M}{\pi+\rho-\mu-\varepsilon}(-\pi+1)\sum_{s=0}^{\infty}\gamma_s\rho^{-s}+\gamma_0,$$

whence, using Theorem IV, we obtain

$$(\pi+\rho-\mu-\varepsilon)\sum_{s=0}^{\infty}(cs^2+1)\gamma_s\rho^{-s}$$
$$=M\sum_{s=0}^{\infty}(s+1)\gamma_s\rho^{-s}+(\pi+\rho-\mu-\varepsilon)\gamma_0.$$

Using Theorem IV again, we obtain

$$\sum_{s=1}^{\infty}[-(s+\mu+\varepsilon)(cs^2+1)\gamma_s\rho^{-s}+(cs^2+1)\gamma_s\rho^{-s+1}]$$
$$=M\sum_{s=0}^{\infty}(s+1)\gamma_s\rho^{-s}.$$

Equating the coefficients, we obtain

$$(c+1)\gamma_1=M\gamma_0,$$
$$\gamma_{s+1}[c(s+1)^2+1]-(s+\mu+\varepsilon)(cs^2+1)\gamma_s=M(s+1)\gamma_s.$$

Thus

$$\frac{\gamma_{s+1}}{\gamma_s}=\frac{(s+\mu+\varepsilon)(cs^2+1)+M(s+1)}{c(s+1)^2+1}=\frac{(s-l_1)(s-l_2)(s-l_3)}{(s-m_1)(s-m_2)}$$

say, where

(17) $$l_1+l_2+l_3=-\mu-\varepsilon,\quad m_1+m_2=-2.$$

Thus if T_s, T_{s+1} be consecutive terms of (12), we have

$$\frac{T_{s+1}}{T_s}=\frac{(s-l_1)(s-l_2)(s-l_3)}{(s-m_1)(s-m_2)(x'+s+1)}$$
$$=1-\frac{x'+l_1+l_2+l_3-m_1-m_2+1}{s}+O\left(\frac{1}{s^2}\right),$$

and therefore by Weierstrass' criterion (see 9·8), the series (12) is absolutely convergent if

$$R(x'+l_1+l_2+l_3-m_1-m_2+1)>1,$$

which gives, using (17),

$$R(x')>\mu+\varepsilon-2.$$

Since $x'=x+k-l_1$, we see that (12) converges in the half plane determined by

(18) $$R(x+k)>\mu-1.$$

We have therefore proved the convergence of (12) and therefore of (2) and consequently of (1) in the above half plane. Since the convergence of a factorial series is uniform in a half plane interior to the half plane of convergence we have established the existence as analytic functions of the solutions $u(x, k_1)$, $u(x, k_2)$ of the difference equation 16·2 (9), at least in half planes defined by (18).

Moreover, since μ is independent of k, the convergence is uniform with respect to k, so that we have established the existence of the solutions 16·2 (10) when the indicial equation presents congruent roots. The linear independence of these solutions follows at once, as in 14·3, from their asymptotic behaviour when $x \to \infty$ in the half plane of convergence.

16·4. Example of Solution. Consider the equation

$$(1) \quad \left(a_2+\frac{b_2}{x}\right)(x-1)(x-2)\underset{-1}{\overset{2}{\Delta}} u-\left(a_1+\frac{b_1}{x}\right)(x-1)\underset{-1}{\Delta} u+\left(a_0+\frac{b_0}{x}\right) u=0.$$

This equation has rational coefficients. We shall, however, here regard it as an equation with factorial (in this case finite) series for coefficients. The equation is of the first normal form, if $a_2 \neq 0$.

The indicial equation is

$$f_0(k) = a_2 k(k+1)+a_1 k+a_0 = a_2(k-k_1)(k-k_2).$$

Take $x'=x-1$, then the operational form of the equation is

$$\left(a_2+\frac{b_2}{\pi+\rho+1}\right)\pi(\pi-1)u-\left(a_1+\frac{b_1}{\pi+\rho+1}\right)\pi u+\left(a_0+\frac{b_0}{\pi+\rho+1}\right)u$$
$$= d_0 f_0(k)\rho^{-k}.$$

When the roots of the indicial equation are congruent, say $k_2 = k_1+p$, $p \geqslant 0$, we take

$$d_0 = c_0 f_0(k+1) f_0(k+2) \ldots f_0(k+p).$$

When the roots are incongruent, we take $d_0 = c_0$.

Expanding by Theorem IX, we have

$$\left\{f_0(-\pi)+\sum_{s=1}^{\infty}(-1)^{s-1}(\pi+2)\ldots(\pi+s)\rho^{-s}[b_2\pi(\pi-1)-b_1\pi+b_0]\right\}u$$
$$= d_0 f_0(k)\rho^{-k},$$

whence, using Theorem I,

$$\Big\{f_0(-\pi)+\sum_{s=1}^{\infty}(-1)^{s-1}(\pi+2)\dots(\pi+s)$$
$$[b_2(\pi+s)(\pi+s-1)-b_1(\pi+s)+b_0]\,\rho^{-s}\Big\}\,u=d_0\,f_0(k)\,\rho^{-k},$$

which becomes

$$(2)\quad [f_0(-\pi)+f_1(-\pi)\,\rho^{-1}+f_2(-\pi)\,\rho^{-2}+\dots]\,u=d_0\,f_0(k)\,\rho^{-k},$$

where

$$f_1(-\pi)=b_2(\pi+1)\,\pi-b_1(\pi+1)+b_0,$$
$$f_\nu(-\pi)=(-1)^{\nu-1}(\pi+2)\dots(\pi+\nu)f_1(-\pi-\nu+1),$$
$$(3)\quad f_{\nu+1}(k+s+1)=(k+s-1)\dots(k+s-\nu+1)f_1(k+s-\nu+1)$$
$$=(k+s-1)f_\nu(k+s).$$

Now substitute

$$u=d_0\,\rho^{-k}+c_1\,\rho^{-k-1}+c_2\,\rho^{-k-2}+\dots$$

in (2). Equating the coefficients we get

$$c_1\,f_0(k+1)+d_0\,f_1(k+1)=0,$$
$$(4)\qquad c_s\,f_0(k+s)+c_{s-1}\,f_1(k+s)+\dots+d_0\,f_s(k+s)=0,$$
$$(5)\quad c_{s+1}\,f_0(k+s+1)+c_s\,f_1(k+s+1)+c_{s-1}\,f_2(k+s+1)+\dots$$
$$+d_0\,f_{s+1}(k+s+1)=0.$$

Using (3), we get

$$c_{s+1}\,f_0(k+s+1)+c_s\,f_1(k+s+1)$$
$$+(k+s-1)[c_{s-1}\,f_1(k+s)+\dots+d_0\,f_0(k+s)]=0,$$

whence, using (4),

$$c_{s+1}\,f_0(k+s+1)+c_s\,[f_1(k+s+1)-(k+s-1)f_0(k+s)]=0.$$

Put

$$kf_0(k+1)-f_1(k+1)=a_2(k-l_1)(k-l_2)(k-l_3),$$
$$f_1(k)=b_2(k-m_1-1)(k-m_2-1).$$

Then

$$\frac{c_{s+1}}{c_s}=\frac{a_2(k-l_1+s-1)(k-l_2+s-1)(k-l_3+s-1)}{a_2(k-k_1+s+1)(k-k_2+s+1)},$$

and

$$\frac{c_1}{d_0}=\frac{-b_2(k-m_1)(k-m_2)}{a_2(k+1-k_1)(k+1-k_2)}.$$

Thus using the factorial notation

$$-c_{s+1} = \frac{(k-l_1+s-1)^{(s)}(k-l_2+s-1)^{(s)}(k-l_3+s-1)^{(s)}(k-m_1)(k-m_2)\,b_2\,d_0}{a_2(k-k_1+s+1)^{(s+1)}(k-k_2+s+1)^{(s+1)}}.$$

Thus (2) has the solution

$$u(x, k) = d_0\,\rho^{-k}+c_1\,\rho^{-k-1}+c_2\,\rho^{-k-2}+\dots$$

$$= \frac{\Gamma(x)}{\Gamma(x+k)}\left\{d_0+\frac{c_1}{x+k}+\frac{c_2}{(x+k)(x+k+1)}+\dots\right\}$$

$$= \frac{\Gamma(x)}{\Gamma(x+k)}\,d_0\left\{1-\frac{b_2}{a_2}(k-m_1)(k-m_2)\,\phi(x, k)\right\},$$

where

$$\phi(x, k) = \sum_{s=0}^{\infty}\frac{(k-l_1+s-1)^{(s)}(k-l_2+s-1)^{(s)}(k-l_3+s-1)^{(s)}}{(k-k_1+s+1)^{(s+1)}(k-k_2+s+1)^{(s+1)}(x+k)\dots(x+k+s)}$$

and the solutions of (1) are $u(x, k_1)$, $u(x, k_2)$ when k_1, k_2 are incongruent and $u(x, k_1)$, $\partial u(x, k_1)\,/\,\partial k_1$ when k_1, k_2 are congruent.

16·5. The Second Normal Form. An equation which can be expressed in the form

$$T_n(x)\,x(x+1)\dots(x+n-1)\overset{n}{\Delta}u$$
$$+T_{n-1}(x)\,x(x+1)\dots(x+n-2)\overset{n-1}{\Delta}u+\dots+T_0(x)\,u = 0,$$

where

$$T_s(x) = a_s+\frac{a_{s,1}}{x-1}+\frac{a_{s,2}}{(x-1)(x-2)}+\frac{a_{s,3}}{(x-1)(x-2)(x-3)}+\dots,$$
$$s = 0, 1, 2, \dots, n,$$

and where $a_n \neq 0$, is said to be of the second normal form.

The operational method of solving such an equation is exactly the same as that already explained except that the operators π, ρ are replaced by π_1, ρ_1. The basic theorem for these operators is

Theorem XI.

$$(-\pi_1-a+\rho_1)^{-1} \doteqdot \rho_1^{-1}+(\pi_1+a+1)\,\rho_1^{-2}$$
$$+(\pi_1+a+1)(\pi_1+a+2)\,\rho_1^{-3}+\dots,$$

where the operand is any function of x.

The proof of this theorem, which is analogous to Theorem IX, offers no difficulty and is left to the reader.

An equation of the second normal form has solutions of the form

$$U(x, k) = \frac{\Gamma(1-x)}{\Gamma(1-x+k)} \sum_{s=0}^{\infty} \frac{c_s}{(x-k-1)\dots(x-k-s)},$$

and partial derivates of this with respect to k, when the indicial equation presents multiple or congruent roots.

The region of convergence is $R(x) < \max(\lambda+n,\ n+1,\ R(1+k))$, where λ is the smallest abscissa of convergence of the coefficients of the given equation and k is the root of the indicial equation whose real part is smallest.

The proof of these statements follows exactly the same lines as that for the first normal form.

The solutions have the same asymptotic forms as those of an equation of the first normal type and form a fundamental system.

16·6. Note on the Normal Forms. Consider the equation

(1) $$p_2(x) \underset{-1}{\overset{2}{\Delta}} u + p_1(x) \underset{-1}{\Delta} u + p_0(x) u = 0.$$

If $p_2(x)$, $p_1(x)$, $p_0(x)$ be polynomials of descending degree, the equation can be reduced to the first normal type, for we can write the equation in the form

$$(x-1)(x-2) \underset{-1}{\overset{2}{\Delta}} u + \frac{p_1(x)(x-2)}{p_2(x)} (x-1) \underset{-1}{\Delta} u + \frac{p_0(x)(x-1)(x-2)}{p_2(x)} u = 0,$$

and since the degree of the numerators of

$$\frac{p_1(x)(x-2)}{p_2(x)}, \quad \frac{p_0(x)(x-1)(x-2)}{p_2(x)}$$

does not exceed the degree of the corresponding denominators these rational functions can be expressed in factorial series of the type necessary for the equation to be normal. Now, with $v(x+2) = u(x)$, (1) can be written in the form

$$[p_2(x)+p_1(x)+p_0(x)] \overset{2}{\Delta} v + [p_1(x)+2p_0(x)] \Delta v + p_0(x) v = 0,$$

and the coefficients are again of descending degree, so that this equation can be reduced to the second normal form.

Thus we see that an equation like (1) in which the coefficients are polynomials of descending degree can be expressed in both normal forms. We can thus get two fundamental sets of solutions according to the type to which we reduce the equation. These correspond to the two canonical sets of solutions discussed in Chapter XV.

More generally an equation of the first normal form

$$t_2(x)(x-1)(x-2)\overset{2}{\underset{-1}{\Delta}} u + t_1(x)(x-1)\underset{-1}{\Delta} u + t_0(x)\, u = 0$$

can be reduced also to the second normal form, provided that the factorial series which represent $t_0(x)$, $t_1(x)$, $t_2(x)$ be holomorphic in the whole domain of the point infinity.

If a given equation cannot be reduced to either normal form it may still be possible to obtain a certain number of solutions by the operational method. These will not of course form a fundamental set, for the normal forms constitute the only type in which the solutions are all represented by the class of factorial series already obtained.

Example.

$$\left(2-\frac{1}{x+1}\right)x(x+1)\overset{2}{\Delta} u - \left(1-\frac{1}{x}\right)x\,\Delta u + u = 0.$$

The equation is expressed in the second normal form.

The indicial equation is, taking $x' = x$,

$$f_0(k) = 2k(k+1)+k+1 = (2k+1)(k+1) = 0,$$

whence $k_1 = -\frac{1}{2}$, $k_2 = -1$.

These are incongruent, so we write

$$\left[\left(2-\frac{1}{-\pi_1+1+\rho_1}\right)\pi_1(\pi_1-1) - \left(1-\frac{1}{-\pi_1+\rho_1}\right)\pi_1 + 1\right]u = 0.$$

Expanding by Theorem XI, we get

$$\Big[f_0(-\pi_1) - \sum_{s=1}^{\infty}\Big(\pi_1(\pi_1+1)\dots(\pi_1+s-2)\,\rho_1^{-s}\,\pi_1(\pi_1-1)$$

$$-(\pi_1+1)\dots(\pi_1+s-1)\,\rho_1^{-s}\,\pi_1\Big)\Big]u = 0,$$

$$\left[f_0(-\pi_1) - \sum_{s=1}^{\infty}(\pi_1-1)(\pi_1+1)(\pi_1+2)\dots(\pi_1+s)\,\rho_1^{-s}\right]u = 0.$$

Put

$$u = c_0 \rho_1^{-k} + c_1 \rho_1^{-k-1} + c_2 \rho_1^{-k-2} + \dots,$$

then

$$c_0 f_0(k) = 0, \quad c_1 f_0(k+1) - c_0(k+2)k = 0,$$

$$\begin{aligned} c_s f_0(k+s) - c_{s-1}(k+s+1)(k+s-1) \\ + c_{s-2}(k+s+1)(k+s-1)(k+s-2) - \dots \\ + (-1)^s c_0 (k+s+1)(k+s-1)(k+s-2)\dots k = 0, \end{aligned}$$

$$\begin{aligned} c_{s+1} f_0(k+s+1) - c_s(k+s+2)(k+s) \\ + c_{s-1}(k+s+2)(k+s)(k+s-1) - \dots \\ + (-1)^{s+1} c_0 (k+s+2)(k+s)(k+s-1)\dots k = 0. \end{aligned}$$

The last two equations give

$$\frac{c_s f_0(k+s)}{k+s+1} + \frac{c_{s+1} f_0(k+s+1)}{(k+s+2)(k+s)} - c_s = 0,$$

whence we obtain

$$\frac{c_{s+1}}{c_s} = -\frac{(k+s)(k+s)}{k+s+\frac{3}{2}},$$

$$c_{s+1} = \frac{(-1)^s (k+s)(k+s-1)\dots(k+1)(k+s)(k+s-1)\dots(k+1)}{(k+s+\frac{3}{2})(k+s+\frac{1}{2})\dots(k+\frac{5}{2})} \times \frac{k}{2k+3} c_0.$$

Thus we have

$$u(x;\, -\tfrac{1}{2}) = \frac{\Gamma(x+\frac{1}{2})}{\Gamma(x)}\left[1 - \frac{1}{4(x-\frac{1}{2})} + \frac{1}{2^5(x-\frac{1}{2})(x-\frac{3}{2})} - \dots\right],$$

$$u(x;\, -1) = \frac{\Gamma(x+1)}{\Gamma(x)} - 1 = x - 1.$$

EXAMPLES XVI

Solve the following difference equations:

1. $(x-1)(x-2) \underset{-1}{\overset{2}{\Delta}} u - \left(a_1 + \frac{b_1}{x}\right)(x-1) \underset{-1}{\Delta} u + \left(a_0 + \frac{b_0}{x}\right) u = 0.$

2. $(x-1)(x-2) \underset{-1}{\overset{2}{\Delta}} u - \left(2 + \frac{1}{x}\right)(x-1) \underset{-1}{\Delta} u + \left(2 + \frac{1}{x}\right) u = 0.$

3. $(x-1)(x-2)\left(1+\dfrac{2}{x-2}\right)\overset{2}{\underset{-1}{\Delta}}u-\left(6+\dfrac{1}{x-1}\right)(x-1)\underset{-1}{\Delta}u+12u=0.$

4. $(x-1)(x-2)\left(4+\dfrac{3}{x-2}\right)\overset{2}{\underset{-1}{\Delta}}u$

$$-\left(8+\frac{2}{x-1}\right)(x-1)\underset{-1}{\Delta}u+\left(9+\frac{3}{x}\right)u=0.$$

5. $(x+1)(x+2)\left(1-\dfrac{3}{x-1}\right)\overset{2}{\Delta}u$

$$-\left(1-\frac{3}{x-1}\right)(x+1)\Delta u+\left(1-\frac{2}{x-1}\right)u=0.$$

6. $x(x+1)\left(4-\dfrac{1}{x-2}\right)\overset{2}{\Delta}u-\left(8-\dfrac{1}{x-2}\right)x\Delta u+9u=0.$

7. $x(x+1)\left(1-\dfrac{3}{x+1}\right)\overset{2}{\Delta}u-\left(5-\dfrac{2}{x}\right)x\Delta u+\left(8-\dfrac{2}{x-1}\right)u=0.$

8. $x(x+1)\left(4-\dfrac{3}{x+1}\right)\overset{2}{\Delta}u-\left(8+\dfrac{2}{x}\right)x\Delta u+9u=0.$

9. Establish for the operators π_1, ρ_1 the theorem corresponding to Theorem X.

CHAPTER XVII

THE THEOREMS OF POINCARÉ AND PERRON

IN this chapter we discuss certain theorems on the asymptotic behaviour of solutions of linear difference equations. The theorem of Poincaré * marks the beginning of modern methods of research in the theory of linear difference equations. The failure of the theorem in certain cases leads us to discuss the theorem of Perron. The proof here given is Perron's and is based on the properties of sum equations.†

It has been considered advisable to reproduce here the whole of Perron's paper both on account of the elegance of the method employed and also to give an insight into the theory of sum equations which have an interest of their own apart from the particular application in view.

17·0. The Linear Equation with Constant Coefficients. Consider the equation

$$(1)\quad u(x+3)-(\alpha+\beta+\gamma)\,u(x+2) \\ +(\alpha\beta+\beta\gamma+\gamma\alpha)\,u(x+1)-\alpha\beta\gamma\,u(x)=0,$$

where α, β, γ are constants. The roots of the characteristic equation are α, β, γ. If we put

$$(2)\qquad \alpha=r_1 e^{i\theta},\quad \beta=r_2 e^{i\phi},\quad \gamma=r_3 e^{i\psi},$$

we have

$$|\alpha|=r_1,\quad |\beta|=r_2,\quad |\gamma|=r_3.$$

* H. Poincaré, *American Journal of Math.*, 7 (1885), p. 213.

† O. Perron, "Über Summengleichungen und Poincarésche Differenzengleichungen," *Math. Annalen*, 84 (1921), p. 1.

We propose to investigate the value of

$$(3)\qquad \lim_{n\to\infty} \frac{u(x+n+1)}{u(x+n)},$$

where n is a positive integer.

Case I. $\qquad |\alpha| > |\beta| > |\gamma|.$

The general solution of (1) is

$$u(x) = \varpi_1(x)\,\alpha^x + \varpi_2(x)\,\beta^x + \varpi_3(x)\,\gamma^x,$$

where $\varpi_1(x)$, $\varpi_2(x)$, $\varpi_3(x)$ are arbitrary periodics. We dismiss once for all the trivial solution $u(x) = 0$, which corresponds to the case in which these arbitrary periodics are all identically zero Let us choose an initial value of x, say x_0, for which $\varpi_1(x_0) \neq 0$. Then

$$\frac{u(x_0+n+1)}{u(x_0+n)} = \frac{\varpi_1(x_0)\,\alpha^{x_0+n+1} + \varpi_2(x_0)\,\beta^{x_0+n+1} + \varpi_3(x_0)\,\gamma^{x_0+n+1}}{\varpi_1(x_0)\,\alpha^{x_0+n} + \varpi_2(x_0)\,\beta^{x_0+n} + \varpi_3(x_0)\,\gamma^{x_0+n}}$$

$$= \alpha\,\frac{\varpi_1(x_0) + \varpi_2(x_0)\left(\dfrac{\beta}{\alpha}\right)^{x_0+n+1} + \varpi_3(x_0)\left(\dfrac{\gamma}{\alpha}\right)^{x_0+n+1}}{\varpi_1(x_0) + \varpi_2(x_0)\left(\dfrac{\beta}{\alpha}\right)^{x_0+n} + \varpi_3(x_0)\left(\dfrac{\gamma}{\alpha}\right)^{x_0+n}}.$$

Since $\left|\dfrac{\beta}{\alpha}\right|$, $\left|\dfrac{\gamma}{\alpha}\right|$, are less than unity, we have

$$(4)\qquad \lim_{n\to\infty} \frac{u(x_0+n+1)}{u(x_0+n)} = \alpha.$$

Similarly, if $\varpi_1(x_0) = 0$ while $\varpi_2(x_0) \neq 0$, we have

$$\frac{u(x_0+n+1)}{u(x_0+n)} = \frac{\varpi_2(x_0)\,\beta^{x_0+n+1} + \varpi_3(x_0)\,\gamma^{x_0+n+1}}{\varpi_2(x_0)\,\beta^{x_0+n+1} + \varpi_3(x_0)\,\gamma^{x_0+n+1}},$$

so that

$$(5)\qquad \lim_{n\to\infty} \frac{u(x_0+n+1)}{u(x_0+n)} = \beta.$$

Finally, if $\varpi_3(x_0) \neq 0$ while $\varpi_1(x_0) = 0$, $\varpi_2(x_0) = 0$, we have

$$(6)\qquad \lim_{n\to\infty} \frac{u(x_0+n+1)}{u(x_0+n)} = \gamma.$$

Thus, if $u(x)$ be any solution of (1), which is not zero, we have proved that

$$\lim_{n\to\infty} \frac{u(x+n+1)}{u(x+n)}$$

is equal to one of the roots of the characteristic equation.

Case II. $\alpha = \beta$, $|\alpha| > |\gamma|$.
In this case

$$u(x) = \varpi_1(x)\,\alpha^x + \varpi_2(x)\,x\,\alpha^x + \varpi_3(x)\,\gamma^x.$$

Suppose that when $x = x_0$, $\varpi_2(x_0) \neq 0$. Then

$$\frac{u(x_0+n+1)}{u(x_0+n)} = \frac{\alpha(x_0+n+1)\left[\dfrac{\varpi_1(x_0)}{x_0+n+1} + \varpi_2(x_0) + \dfrac{\varpi_3(x_0)}{x_0+n+1}\left(\dfrac{\gamma}{\alpha}\right)^{x_0+n+1}\right]}{(x_0+n)\left[\dfrac{\varpi_1(x_0)}{x_0+n} + \varpi_2(x_0) + \dfrac{\varpi_3(x_0)}{x_0+n}\left(\dfrac{\gamma}{\alpha}\right)^{x_0+n}\right]}$$

so that

$$\lim_{n\to\infty} \frac{u(x_0+n+1)}{u(x_0+n)} = \alpha.$$

Similarly, if $\varpi_2(x_0) = 0$, $\varpi_1(x_0) \neq 0$, the value of the limit is again α, and if $\varpi_1(x_0) = 0$, $\varpi_2(x_0) = 0$, $\varpi_3(x_0) \neq 0$, the limit exists and is equal to γ. If $|\alpha| > |\beta|$, $\beta = \gamma$, a similar conclusion is ched.

Case III. $\alpha = \beta = \gamma$.
In this case

$$u(x) = \varpi_1(x)\,\alpha^x + \varpi_2(x)\,x\,\alpha^x + \varpi_3(x)\,x^2\,\alpha^x,$$

and we can easily prove as in Case II, that the limit (3) exists and is equal to α.

Case IV. $|\alpha| = |\beta|$, $\theta \neq \phi$, $|\alpha| > |\gamma|$.
In this case

$$u(x) = \varpi_1(x)\,r_1^x\,e^{ix\theta} + \varpi_2(x)\,r_1^x\,e^{ix\phi} + \varpi_3(x)\,\gamma^x.$$

If $\varpi_1(x_0) \neq 0$, $\varpi_2(x_0) \neq 0$, we have

$$\lim_{n\to\infty} \frac{u(x_0+n+1)}{u(x_0+n)} = r_1 \lim_{n\to\infty} \frac{\varpi_1(x_0)\,e^{i(x_0+n+1)\theta} + \varpi_2(x_0)\,e^{i(x_0+n+1)\phi}}{\varpi_1(x_0)\,e^{i(x_0+n)\theta} + \varpi_2(x_0)\,e^{i(x_0+n)\phi}}.$$

Since $e^{in\theta}$, $e^{in\phi}$ do not tend to definite limits when $n \to \infty$, we see that the limit (3) does not exist. For particular solutions the limit may exist; for example, if $\varpi_2(x_0) = 0$, $\varpi_1(x_0) \neq 0$, the limit is α, while for $\varpi_1(x_0) = 0$, $\varpi_2(x_0) \neq 0$ the limit is β, and for $\varpi_1(x_0) = 0$, $\varpi_2(x_0) = 0$ the limit is γ.

Thus in this case we can state that the limit (3) does not always exist.

The cases $|\alpha| > |\beta|$, $|\beta| = |\gamma|$, $\phi \neq \psi$ and $|\alpha| = |\beta| = |\gamma|$, $\theta \neq \phi \neq \psi$ are similar to the last and do not require separate discussion.

The method of reasoning evidently applies to a homogeneous equation with constant coefficients of any order, and we can state the following general theorem.

Theorem. *Given a homogeneous linear difference equation with constant coefficients, let $u(x)$ be any solution such that $u(x_0) \neq 0$. Then, if n be a positive integer,*

$$\lim_{n\to\infty} \frac{u(x_0+n+1)}{u(x_0+n)}$$

exists and is equal to a root of the characteristic equation, whether these roots be distinct or not, provided that those roots which are distinct have distinct moduli.

If the characteristic equation have two or more distinct roots with the same modulus, the above limit does not in general exist, but particular solutions can always be found for which the limit exists and is equal to a given root of the characteristic equation.

17·1. Poincaré's Theorem. Poincaré has generalised this theorem for equations whose coefficients tend to constant values for large values of the variable. For simplicity we consider an equation of the third order. The particular initial value x_0 which figures in the above theorem may by a displacement of the origin be taken as unity. We therefore consider the equation

$$(1)\quad u(n+3)+[a+x(n)]\,u(n+2) + [b+y(n)]\,u(n+1)+[c+z(n)]\,u(n) = 0,$$

where n is a positive integral variable and a, b, c are constants. If when $n \to \infty$,

$$\lim x(n) = 0, \quad \lim y(n) = 0, \quad \lim z(n) = 0, \tag{2}$$

we shall call an equation of the form (1) a difference equation of Poincaré's type.

When n is large, the difference equation (1) approximates to the form

$$u(n+3)+a\,u(n+2)+b\,u(n+1)+c\,u(n) = 0, \tag{3}$$

which we may call the associated equation with constant coefficients.

With these definitions we may state the following theorem:

Poincaré's Theorem. *If $u(n)$ be any solution of a homogeneous linear difference equation whose coefficients tend to constant values, when $n \to +\infty$, then*

$$\lim_{n\to\infty} \frac{u(n+1)}{u(n)}$$

exists, and is equal to one of the zeros of the characteristic function of the associated difference equation with constant coefficients, provided that the moduli of the zeros of the characteristic function be distinct.

We prove the theorem for equation (1), which is of the third order. The characteristic function of the associated equation (3) is

$$f(t) = t^3+at^2+bt+c = (t-\alpha_1)(t-\alpha_2)(t-\alpha_3), \tag{4}$$

and we can suppose that

$$|\alpha_1| > |\alpha_2| > |\alpha_3| \tag{5}$$

since, by hypothesis, the moduli are distinct. It also follows that $f'(\alpha_1)$, $f'(\alpha_2)$, $f'(\alpha_3)$ are all different from zero. Now put

$$\begin{aligned} u(n) &= p_1(n)+p_2(n)+p_3(n), \\ u(n+1) &= \alpha_1 p_1(n)+\alpha_2 p_2(n)+\alpha_3 p_3(n), \\ u(n+2) &= \alpha_1^2 p_1(n)+\alpha_2^2 p_2(n)+\alpha_3^2 p_3(n). \end{aligned} \tag{6}$$

These equations are compatible since

$$\begin{vmatrix} 1 & 1 & 1 \\ \alpha_1 & \alpha_2 & \alpha_3 \\ \alpha_1^2 & \alpha_2^2 & \alpha_3^2 \end{vmatrix} = (\alpha_1-\alpha_2)(\alpha_2-\alpha_3)(\alpha_3-\alpha_1) \neq 0.$$

Multiply equations, (6), by $\alpha_2\alpha_3$, $-(\alpha_2+\alpha_3)$, 1 respectively and add. We then obtain

$$\alpha_2\alpha_3 u(n)-(\alpha_2+\alpha_3)u(n+1)+u(n+2)$$
$$=[\alpha_1^2-\alpha_1(\alpha_2+\alpha_3)+\alpha_2\alpha_3]p_1(n)=f'(\alpha_1)p_1(n).$$

Writing $(n+1)$ for n, we get

$$(7)\quad \alpha_2\alpha_3 u(n+1)-(\alpha_2+\alpha_3)u(n+2)+u(n+3)=f'(\alpha_1)p_1(n+1).$$

Substitute the value of $u(n+3)$ from (1) and observe that

$$\alpha_1+\alpha_2+\alpha_3=-a,\quad \alpha_1\alpha_2+\alpha_2\alpha_3+\alpha_3\alpha_1=b,\quad \alpha_1\alpha_2\alpha_3=-c.$$

We then have

$$f'(\alpha_1)p_1(n+1)=\alpha_1[u(n+2)-(\alpha_2+\alpha_3)u(n+1)+\alpha_2\alpha_3 u(n)]$$
$$-x(n)u(n+2)-y(n)u(n+1)-z(n)u(n),$$

whence, using (6) and (7),

$$f'(\alpha_1)p_1(n+1)$$
$$=\alpha_1 f'(\alpha_1)p_1(n)-X_1(n)p_1(n)-X_2(n)p_2(n)-X_3(n)p_3(n),$$

where

$$X_s(n)=\alpha_s{}^2x(n)+\alpha_s y(n)+z(n),\quad s=1,2,3,$$

so that, from (2), $X_s(n)\to 0$ when $n\to\infty$.

Thus we have the three equations

$$(8)\quad p_1(n+1)=\alpha_1 p_1(n)-\xi_1(n)p_1(n)-\eta_1(n)p_2(n)-\zeta_1(n)p_3(n),$$
$$p_2(n+1)=\alpha_2 p_2(n)-\xi_2(n)p_1(n)-\eta_2(n)p_2(n)-\zeta_2(n)p_3(n),$$
$$p_3(n+1)=\alpha_3 p_3(n)-\xi_3(n)p_1(n)-\eta_3(n)p_2(n)-\zeta_3(n)p_3(n),$$

where $\xi_1(n)=X_1(n)\div f'(\alpha_1),\ldots,$ so that the coefficients $\xi_s(n)$, $\eta_s(n)$, $\zeta_s(n)\to 0$ when $n\to\infty$.

Since $|\alpha_1|>|\alpha_2|>|\alpha_3|$, we can choose a positive number β such that

$$(9)\qquad \frac{|\alpha_3|+\beta}{|\alpha_1|-\beta}<1,\quad \frac{|\alpha_3|+\beta}{|\alpha_2|-\beta}<1,\quad \frac{|\alpha_2|+\beta}{|\alpha_1|-\beta}<1,$$

it being sufficient to take 2β less than the smaller of

$$|\alpha_1|-|\alpha_2|,\quad |\alpha_2|-|\alpha_3|.$$

Since the coefficients $\xi_s(n)$, $\eta_s(n)$, $\zeta_s(n)$ in (8) tend to zero, we can find a positive integer n_0 such that the absolute value of each of these coefficients is less than $\frac{1}{3}\beta$, provided that $n \geqslant n_0$.

We exclude the trivial case $u(n) \equiv 0$, from and after some fixed value of n. It then follows, from (6), that $p_1(n)$, $p_2(n)$, $p_3(n)$ do not vanish identically. Now take a fixed integer $N \geqslant n_0$ and consider the sequence of functions

$$|p_1(N)|, \quad |p_2(N)|, \quad |p_3(N)|.$$

As we proceed from left to right in this sequence we must, at a definite stage, first come to a function whose value is at least as great as the value of any of its successors in the sequence.

Let $|p_i(N)|$ be the function defined in this way.

If we change N into $N+1$ we shall shew that the suffix i cannot increase. It will then follow that i will tend to a limiting value when $N \to \infty$; for i cannot increase and has one of the values 1, 2, 3.

The possible distinct types of inequality between the functions of the sequence are

(A) $\quad |p_1(N)| \geqslant |p_2(N)|, \quad |p_1(N)| \geqslant |p_3(N)|, \quad i=1;$

(B) $\quad |p_2(N)| > |p_1(N)|, \quad |p_2(N)| \geqslant |p_3(N)|, \quad i=2;$

(C) $\quad |p_3(N)| > |p_1(N)|, \quad |p_3(N)| > |p_2(N)|, \quad i=3.$

Since $|a+b| \leqslant |a|+|b|$, $|a-b| \geqslant |a|-|b|$, we have in case (A), from (8),

$$\begin{aligned}|p_1(N+1)| &\geqslant |\alpha_1|\,|p_1(N)| \\ &\quad -\tfrac{1}{3}\beta\{|p_1(N)|+|p_2(N)|+|p_3(N)|\} \geqslant [|\alpha_1|-\beta]\,|p_1(N)|,\\ |p_2(N+1)| &\leqslant |\alpha_2|\,|p_2(N)| \\ &\quad +\tfrac{1}{3}\beta\{|p_1(N)|+|p_2(N)|+|p_3(N)|\} \leqslant [|\alpha_2|+\beta]\,|p_1(N)|,\\ |p_3(N+1)| &\leqslant |\alpha_3|\,|p_3(N)| \\ &\quad +\tfrac{1}{3}\beta\{|p_1(N)|+|p_2(N)|+|p_3(N)|\} \leqslant [|\alpha_3|+\beta]\,|p_1(N)|.\end{aligned}$$

Thus, by division, since $p_1(N) \neq 0$, we have, using (9),

$$\left|\frac{p_2(N+1)}{p_1(N+1)}\right| \leqslant \frac{|a_2|+\beta}{|\alpha_1|-\beta} < 1, \quad \left|\frac{p_3(N+1)}{p_1(N+1)}\right| \leqslant \frac{|\alpha_3|+\beta}{|\alpha_1|-\beta} < 1,$$

which shews that case (A) when once established for sufficiently large values of n will persist for all greater values of n.

In case (B) we have from (8), in the same way as above,

$$|p_2(N+1)| \geqslant [|\alpha_2| - \beta] |p_2(N)|,$$
$$|p_3(N+1)| \leqslant [|\alpha_3| + \beta] |p_2(N)|,$$

and thus, using (9),

$$\left| \frac{p_3(N+1)}{p_2(N+1)} \right| \leqslant \frac{|\alpha_3| + \beta}{|\alpha_2| - \beta} < 1,$$

so that $|p_2(N+1)| > |p_3(N+1)|$, and therefore

if $|p_2(N+1)| > |p_1(N+1)|$, (B) has persisted, while

if $|p_2(N+1)| \leqslant |p_1(N+1)|$, (B) has become a case of (A).

Evidently (C) either persists or becomes (B) or (A).

Thus we have proved that the suffix i cannot increase, so that for sufficiently large n, i remains constant.

Suppose, for example, $i = 2$. We now prove that

$$\text{(10)} \qquad \lim_{n\to\infty} \frac{p_1(n)}{p_2(n)} = 0, \quad \lim_{n\to\infty} \frac{p_3(n)}{p_2(n)} = 0.$$

For suppose, if possible, that

$$\limsup_{n\to\infty} \left| \frac{p_1(n)}{p_2(n)} \right| = l,$$

where $l > 0$. Then, given $\varepsilon > 0$, we have, for sufficiently large values of n,

$$\left| \frac{p_1(n)}{p_2(n)} \right| < l + \varepsilon.$$

Suppose that N be chosen large enough for this to be the case. then, from (8) and (B), we have

$$|p_1(N+1)| \geqslant |\alpha_1| |p_1(N)| - \beta |p_2(N)|,$$
$$|p_2(N+1)| \leqslant |\alpha_2| |p_2(N)| + \beta |p_2(N)|,$$

and thus, by division,

$$\frac{|\alpha_1| |p_1(N)| - \beta |p_2(N)|}{\{|\alpha_2| + \beta\} |p_2(N)|} \leqslant \left| \frac{p_1(N+1)}{p_2(N+1)} \right| < l + \varepsilon,$$

and thus

$$\left| \frac{p_1(N)}{p_2(N)} \right| < \frac{(l+\varepsilon)\{|\alpha_2| + \beta\} + \beta}{|\alpha_1|}.$$

Now, from the property of the upper limit (10·08), we have

$$\left| \frac{p_1(N)}{p_2(N)} \right| > l - \varepsilon$$

for infinitely many values of N. Thus we have

$$|\alpha_1|(l-\varepsilon) < (l+\varepsilon)\{|\alpha_2|+\beta\}+\beta,$$

which gives

$$\varepsilon > \frac{l\{|\alpha_1|-|\alpha_2|-\beta\}-\beta}{|\alpha_1|+|\alpha_2|+\beta},$$

which is impossible, since ε and β are arbitrarily small, and

$$|\alpha_1|-|\alpha_2|>0.$$

Thus we must have $l=0$, which proves the first part of (10).

The second part is proved in the same way. Then, from (6), we have

$$\lim_{n\to\infty} \frac{u(n)}{p_2(n)} = 1, \quad \lim_{n\to\infty} \frac{u(n+1)}{p_2(n)} = \alpha_2,$$

and thus

$$\lim_{n\to\infty} \frac{u(n+1)}{u(n)} = \alpha_2,$$

which proves Poincaré's theorem in the case $i=2$. The cases $i=1$, $i=3$ present no new features. Thus Poincaré's theorem is proved for the third order equation.

The method of proof for the equation of general order follows exactly the same lines, the essential point being the proof that the suffix i cannot increase.

Poincaré's theorem shews that

$$\lim_{n\to\infty} \frac{u(x+n+1)}{u(x+n)}$$

is equal to one of the roots of the characteristic equation. A more general theorem has been proved by Perron,* namely :

If the coefficient of $u(x)$ *in the difference equation of order* n *be not zero, for* $x = 0, 1, 2, \ldots$, *and the other hypotheses be fulfilled, then*

* O. Perron, *Journal f. rein. u. angew. Math.* 136 (1909), 17-37.

the equation possesses n fundamental solutions $u_1(x), \ldots, u_n(x)$, *such that*

$$\lim_{x\to\infty} \frac{u_i(x+1)}{u_i(x)} = \alpha_i, \quad i = 1, 2, \ldots, n,$$

where α_i *is a root of the characteristic equation, and* $x \to \infty$ *by positive integral increments.*

When the conditions of the enunciation of Poincaré's theorem are not all fulfilled, that is, when the characteristic equation presents two or more roots of the same modulus, the matter becomes very complicated, and it may be shewn by examples that the theorem may even fail completely. We shall discuss another theorem due to Perron which frees us of these complications.

17·2. Continued Fraction Solution of the Second Order Equation. We first establish a certain identity due to Thiele. Let

(1) $$z_s = \frac{x_s - x_{s+1}}{x_s - x_{s+2}} \div \frac{x_{s+1} - x_{s+3}}{x_{s+2} - x_{s+3}}, \quad s = 1, 2, \ldots, n-3,$$

(2) $$v_s = \frac{x_n - x_s}{x_n - x_{s+1}} \div \frac{x_s - x_{s+2}}{x_{s+1} - x_{s+2}}, \quad v_{n-2} = 1.$$

Then

$$\frac{z_s}{v_{s+1}} = \frac{x_s - x_{s+1}}{x_s - x_{s+2}} \times \frac{x_n - x_{s+2}}{x_n - x_{s+1}},$$

and thus we obtain

$$1 - \frac{z_s}{v_{s+1}} = v_s, \quad s = 1, 2, 3, \ldots, n-3,$$

and hence

$$v_1 = 1 - \frac{z_1}{v_2} = 1 - \cfrac{z_1}{1 - \cfrac{z_2}{v_3}}.$$

Proceeding in this way we obtain the identity

(3) $$v_1 = 1 - \cfrac{z_1}{1 - \cfrac{z_2}{1 - \cdots - \cfrac{z_{n-4}}{1 - z_{n-3}}}}.$$

Now consider the Poincaré difference equation

$$u(x+2)+p(x)\,u(x+1)+q(x)\,u(x)=0,$$

where

$$\lim_{x\to\infty} p(x)=a_1, \quad \lim_{x\to\infty} q(x)=a_2,$$

where $x\to\infty$ by positive integral increments.

The characteristic equation is

$$t^2+a_1 t+a_2=0.$$

We shall suppose the roots α, β of this equation to be of unequal modulus and that $|\alpha|>|\beta|$.

Now let $u_1(x)$, $u_2(x)$ be a fundamental system of solutions. We then obtain from the difference equation

$$p(x)=\frac{u_1(x+2)\,u_2(x)-u_2(x+2)\,u_1(x)}{u_1(x)\,u_2(x+1)-u_2(x)\,u_1(x+1)},$$

$$q(x)=\frac{u_1(x+1)\,u_2(x+2)-u_2(x+1)\,u_1(x+2)}{u_1(x)\,u_2(x+1)-u_2(x)\,u_1(x+1)}.$$

If in (1) we take

$$x_s=\frac{u_1(x+s-2)}{u_2(x+s-2)},$$

we have

(4) $$z_s=\frac{q(x+s-1)}{p(x+s-2)\,p(x+s-1)}.$$

Writing $n+2$ for n, we have, after reduction,

$$v_1-1=\frac{u_1(x+n)\,u_2(x+1)-u_2(x+n)\,u_1(x+1)}{u_1(x+n)\,u_2(x)-u_2(x+n)\,u_1(x)}\,\frac{1}{p(x-1)}.$$

Substituting in (3), we have, by means of (4), the identity

(5) $$\frac{u_1(x+n)\,u_2(x+1)-u_2(x+n)\,u_1(x+1)}{u_1(x+n)\,u_2(x)-u_2(x+n)\,u_1(x)}$$

$$\equiv\cfrac{-q(x)}{p(x)-\cfrac{q(x+1)}{p(x+1)-\cdots-\cfrac{q(x+n-2)}{p(x+n-2)}}}.$$

The right-hand member of this identity depends only on the coefficients of the difference equation and is therefore independent of the particular fundamental system chosen. Let us choose our fundamental solutions so that

$$\lim_{n\to\infty} \frac{u_1(x+n+1)}{u_1(x+n)} = \alpha, \quad \lim_{n\to\infty} \frac{u_2(x+n+1)}{u_2(x+n)} = \beta,$$

which is possible by Perron's theorem, given at the end of 17·1.

Then

$$\lim_{n\to\infty} \left| \frac{u_2(x+n+1)}{u_1(x+n+1)} \div \frac{u_2(x+n)}{u_1(x+n)} \right| = \left| \frac{\beta}{\alpha} \right| < 1,$$

from which it follows that

$$\lim_{n\to\infty} \frac{u_2(x+n)}{u_1(x+n)} = 0.$$

Hence, dividing the numerator and denominator of (5) by $u_1(x+n)$ and then letting $n\to\infty$, we obtain

$$\frac{u_2(x+1)}{u_2(x)} = \cfrac{-q(x)}{p(x) - \cfrac{q(x+1)}{p(x+1) - \cfrac{q(x+2)}{p(x+2) - \cdots}}}$$

and $u_2(x)$ is obtained as a solution of an equation of the first order.

In a similar manner, by writing $-t-2$ for x in the difference equation, we can prove that a second solution is given by

$$\frac{u_3(x)}{u_3(x+1)} = \cfrac{-1}{p(x-1) - \cfrac{q(x-1)}{p(x-2) - \cfrac{q(x-2)}{p(x-3) - \cdots}}}$$

17·3. Sum Equations. By the name sum equations we understand a system of infinitely many equations in infinitely many unknowns, such that in the $(\mu+1)$th equation the first μ unknowns are absent.*

Thus we can write such a system in the form

$$\begin{aligned} a_{0,0}\,x_0+a_{0,1}\,x_1+a_{0,2}\,x_2+a_{0,3}\,x_3+\ldots &= c_0,\\ a_{1,0}\,x_1+a_{1,1}\,x_2+a_{1,2}\,x_3+\ldots &= c_1,\\ a_{2,0}\,x_2+a_{2,1}\,x_3+\ldots &= c_2,\\ \cdots\cdots\cdots\cdots \end{aligned}$$

or, more briefly,

(1) $$\sum_{\nu=0}^{\infty} a_{\mu,\nu}\,x_{\mu+\nu} = c_\mu, \quad \mu = 0, 1, 2, \ldots.$$

We assume that

(2) $$|a_{\mu,\nu}| < K\vartheta^\nu, \quad K > 0, \quad 0 < \vartheta < 1,$$

(3) $$\limsup_{\mu\to\infty} \sqrt[\mu]{|c_\mu|} \leqslant 1.$$

We then seek solutions for which

(4) $$\limsup_{\nu\to\infty} \sqrt[\nu]{|x_\nu|} \leqslant 1.$$

For such solutions the series (1) are absolutely convergent. Now let

$$f(z) = \sum_{\nu=0}^{\infty} \gamma_\nu z^\nu$$

be an arbitrary power series, which for $|z| \leqslant 1$ is holomorphic and different from zero, so that the reciprocal

$$\frac{1}{f(z)} = \sum_{\nu=0}^{\infty} \gamma'_\nu z^\nu$$

is likewise holomorphic for $|z| \leqslant 1$ and different from zero. It follows that the radii of convergence are both greater than unity, so that †

(5) $$\limsup_{\nu\to\infty} \sqrt[\nu]{|\gamma_\nu|} < 1, \quad \limsup_{\nu\to\infty} \sqrt[\nu]{|\gamma'_\nu|} < 1.$$

---

* I have translated the German "Summengleichungen" by "sum equations". The equations form a semi-reduced or semi-normal linear system. The idea of these equations is due to J. Horn, *Journal f. rein. u. angew. Math.* 140, (1911).

† K. Knopp, *Infinite Series*, p. 155.

Moreover, from the definition of the coefficients,

(6) $$\sum_{\kappa=0}^{\lambda} \gamma_{\lambda-\kappa}\gamma'_{\kappa} = \sum_{\kappa=0}^{\lambda} \gamma'_{\lambda-\kappa}\gamma_{\kappa} = \begin{cases} 1 \text{ for } \lambda = 0, \\ 0 \text{ for } \lambda > 0. \end{cases}$$

If then we put

(7) $$\sum_{\lambda=0}^{\nu} a_{\mu+\lambda,\,\nu-\lambda}\,\gamma_{\lambda} = a'_{\mu,\,\nu},$$

(8) $$\sum_{\lambda=0}^{\infty} c_{\mu+\lambda}\,\gamma_{\lambda} = c'_{\mu},$$

we obtain without difficulty

(9) $$|a'_{\mu,\,\nu}| < K'\vartheta'^{\nu}, \quad K' > 0, \quad 0 < \vartheta' < 1.$$

(10) $$\limsup_{\mu\to\infty} \sqrt[\mu]{|c'_{\mu}|} \leqslant 1.$$

From (7), we have

$$\sum_{\kappa=0}^{\nu} a'_{\mu+\kappa,\,\nu-\kappa}\,\gamma'_{\kappa} = \sum_{\kappa=0}^{\nu}\sum_{\lambda=0}^{\nu-\kappa} a_{\mu+\kappa+\lambda,\,\nu-\kappa-\lambda}\,\gamma_{\lambda}\gamma'_{\kappa}$$

$$= \sum_{\lambda=0}^{\nu}\sum_{\kappa=0}^{\lambda} a_{\mu+\lambda,\,\nu-\lambda}\,\gamma_{\lambda-\kappa}\gamma'_{\kappa} = a_{\mu,\,\nu},$$

from (6). Again, from (8), since by (3) and (5) the double series is absolutely and therefore unconditionally convergent, we have

$$\sum_{\kappa=0}^{\infty} c'_{\mu+\kappa}\,\gamma'_{\kappa} = \sum_{\kappa=0}^{\infty}\sum_{\lambda=0}^{\infty} c_{\mu+\kappa+\lambda}\,\gamma_{\lambda}\gamma'_{\kappa}$$

$$= \sum_{\lambda=0}^{\infty}\sum_{\kappa=0}^{\lambda} c_{\mu+\lambda}\,\gamma_{\lambda-\kappa}\gamma'_{\kappa} = c$$

from (6). Hence we have proved that

(11) $$\sum_{\kappa=0}^{\nu} a'_{\mu+\kappa,\,\nu-\kappa}\,\gamma'_{\kappa} = a_{\mu,\,\nu},$$

(12) $$\sum_{\kappa=0}^{\infty} c'_{\mu+\kappa}\,\gamma'_{\kappa} = c_{\mu}.$$

If now we form the sum equations

(13) $$\sum_{\nu=0}^{\infty} a'_{\mu,\,\nu}\,x_{\mu+\nu} = c'_{\mu}, \quad \mu = 0, 1, 2, \ldots,$$

these are equivalent to (1) in so far as every solution of (1) (which satisfies (4)) is also a solution of (13) and conversely. To see this, it is sufficient to shew that (13) follows from (1).

The converse is then obtained by interchanging the letters with primes and those without. In (1) put $\mu+\lambda$ for μ, multiply by γ_λ, and sum with respect to λ. Then

$$\sum_{\lambda=0}^{\infty}\sum_{\nu=0}^{\infty} a_{\mu+\lambda,\,\nu}\, x_{\lambda+\mu+\nu}\,\gamma_\lambda = \sum_{\lambda=0}^{\infty} c_{\mu+\lambda}\,\gamma_\lambda = c'_\mu,$$

and since by (2), (4), (5) the double series converges absolutely, by interchanging the members, we have

$$c'_\mu = \sum_{\nu=0}^{\infty}\sum_{\lambda=0}^{\nu} a_{\mu+\lambda,\,\nu-\lambda}\,\gamma_\lambda\, x_{\mu+\nu} = \sum_{\nu=0}^{\infty} a'_{\mu,\,\nu}\, x_{\mu+\nu}$$

from (7), so that (13) follows from (1).

17·4. Homogeneous Sum Equations with Constant Coefficients.

Theorem I. *Let the coefficients of the homogeneous sum equations*

$$\sum_{\nu=0}^{\infty} a_\nu\, x_{\mu+\nu} = 0, \quad \mu = 0, 1, 2, \ldots$$

be such that $a_0 \neq 0$ *and such that the function*

$$F(z) = \sum_{\nu=0}^{\infty} a_\nu z^\nu$$

is holomorphic and has $n(\geqslant 0)$ *zeros (multiple zeros being counted according to their multiplicity) in the region* $|z| \leqslant q$. *Then the sum equations have exactly* n *linearly independent solutions for which*

$$\limsup_{\nu\to\infty} \sqrt[\nu]{|x_\nu|} \leqslant q.$$

These solutions are

$$x_\nu = \rho_\lambda{}^\nu, \quad \nu\,\rho_\lambda{}^\nu, \ldots, \quad \nu^{m_\lambda-1}\rho_\lambda{}^\nu,$$

where ρ_λ *is a zero of* $F(z)$ *of order* m_λ.

That the above values are solutions is easily verified, for the statement amounts to proving that

$$\left(z\frac{d}{dz}\right)^s [z^\mu F(z)] = 0, \quad s = 0, 1, 2, \ldots, m_\lambda - 1,$$

when $z = \rho_\lambda$.

Clearly we can take $q = 1$, since the substitution

$$a_\nu = b_\nu q^{-\nu}, \quad x_\nu = q^\nu y_\nu$$

brings us to this case.

Since the series is now convergent for $|z| \leqslant 1$, we have

$$|a_\nu| < K\vartheta^\nu, \quad K > 0, \quad 0 < \vartheta < 1,$$

so that condition 17·3(2) is fulfilled ($a_{\mu,\nu} = a_\nu$). Let

$$P(z) = z^n + g_1 z^{n-1} + \ldots + g_n = \sum_{\nu=0}^{n} g_{n-\nu} z^\nu$$

have the same zeros as $F(z)$ for $|z| \leqslant 1$. Then the function

$$\frac{P(z)}{F(z)} = f(z) = \sum_{\nu=0}^{\infty} \gamma_\nu z^\nu$$

is holomorphic and has no zeros if $|z| \leqslant 1$ and therefore fulfils the hypothesis of 17·3. The sum equations can therefore be transformed and, by 17·3(7),

$$a'_{\mu,\nu} = \sum_{\lambda=0}^{\nu} a_{\nu-\lambda} \gamma_\lambda.$$

But multiplying the former equation by $F(z)$, we have

$$\sum_{\nu=0}^{n} g_{n-\nu} z^\nu = \sum_{\nu=0}^{\infty} a_\nu z^\nu \sum_{\nu=0}^{\infty} \gamma_\nu z^\nu,$$

so that

$$a'_{\mu,\nu} = g_{n-\nu}, \quad \nu = 0, 1, 2, \ldots, n,$$

$$a'_{\mu,\nu} = 0, \quad \nu > n.$$

The transformed sum equations are therefore

$$\sum_{\nu=0}^{n} g_{n-\nu} x_{\mu+\nu} = 0,$$

or

$$x_{\mu+n} + g_1 x_{\mu+n-1} + \ldots + g_n x_\mu = 0, \quad \mu = 0, 1, 2, \ldots,$$

which are linear difference equations with constant coefficients whose solutions are just those given in the theorem. The point of the theorem lies not so much in the fact that the given values are solutions as that there are no further independent solutions.

17·5. A Second Transformation. Returning to the hypotheses of 17·3, let us put

(1) $$a_{\mu,\nu} = a_\nu + b_{\mu,\nu}, \quad \mu = 0, 1, 2, \dots,$$

thus obtaining the equations

$$\sum_{s=0}^{\infty} (a_\nu + b_{\mu,\nu})\, x_{\mu+\nu} = c_\mu,$$

and assume that for *all* μ

(2) $$a_0 + b_{\mu,0} \neq 0,$$

so that in the $(\mu+1)$th equation the unknown x_μ actually occurs. Moreover, let

(3) $$|b_{\mu,\nu}| < k_\mu \vartheta^\nu, \quad 0 < \vartheta < 1,$$

(4) $$\lim_{\mu \to \infty} k_\mu = 0.$$

Finally, let the function

(5) $$F(z) = \sum_{\nu=0}^{\infty} a_\nu z^\nu$$

be holomorphic for $|z| \leqslant 1$, so that, if necessary replacing ϑ by a greater number which is still less than unity, in addition to (3), we have also

(6) $$|a_\nu| < b\vartheta^\nu, \quad b > 0.$$

Then the hypotheses of 17·3 are fulfilled. If $n \geqslant 0$ be the number of zeros of $F(z)$ in $|z| \leqslant 1$ (counted according to multiplicity), we let

(7) $$P(z) = z^n + g_1 z^{n-1} + \dots + g_n = \sum_{\nu=0}^{n} g_{n-\nu} z^\nu$$

be the polynomial with just those zeros. Put

(8) $$\frac{P(z)}{F(z)} = f(z) = \sum_{\nu=0}^{\infty} \gamma_\nu z^\nu.$$

Then $f(z)$ is holomorphic for $|z| \leqslant 1$ and has no zeros in this region. We can therefore use the transformation of 17·3, whereby (1) becomes

$$\sum_{\nu=0}^{\infty} (a'_\nu + b'_{\mu,\nu})\, x_{\mu+\nu} = c'_\mu, \quad \mu = 0, 1, 2, \ldots, \tag{9}$$

where, analogously to 17·3 (7), (8), we have

$$a'_\nu = \sum_{\lambda=0}^{\nu} a_{\nu-\lambda}\, \gamma_\lambda, \tag{10}$$

$$b'_{\mu,\nu} = \sum_{\lambda=0}^{\nu} b_{\mu+\lambda,\nu-\lambda}\, \gamma_\lambda, \tag{11}$$

$$c'_\mu = \sum_{\lambda=0}^{\infty} c_{\mu+\lambda}\, \gamma_\lambda, \tag{12}$$

and in particular from (2),

$$a'_0 + b'_{\mu,0} = (a_0 + b_{\mu,0})\, \gamma_0 \neq 0. \tag{13}$$

Multiplying (8) by $F(z)$, we get

$$\sum_{\nu=0}^{n} g_{n-\nu}\, z^\nu = \sum_{\nu=0}^{\infty} a_\nu\, z^\nu \sum_{\nu=0}^{\infty} \gamma_\nu\, z^\nu,$$

so that

$$a'_\nu = \sum_{\lambda=0}^{\nu} a_{\nu-\lambda}\, \gamma_\lambda = g_{n-\nu}, \quad \nu = 0, 1, 2, \ldots, n,$$

and $a'_\nu = 0$, for $\nu > n$. The transformed sum equations therefore take the form

$$x_{\mu+n} + g_1\, x_{\mu+n-1} + \ldots + g_n\, x_\mu + \sum_{\nu=0}^{\infty} b'_{\mu,\nu}\, x_{\mu+\nu} = c'_\mu, \quad \mu = 0, 1, 2, \ldots, \tag{14}$$

and, by (13),

$$g_n + b'_{\mu,0} \neq 0. \tag{15}$$

For $b'_{\mu,\nu}$, from (3), (4) and 17·3 (5), we have

$$|b'_{\mu,\nu}| < k'_\mu\, \vartheta'^\nu, \quad 0 < \vartheta' < 1, \tag{16}$$

$$\lim_{\mu \to \infty} k'_\mu = 0. \tag{17}$$

We also obtain

$$\limsup_{\mu \to \infty} \sqrt[\mu]{|c'_\mu|} \leqslant 1. \tag{18}$$

In solving the system, (14), it is clearly sufficient to satisfy these equations for $\mu \geqslant M$, where M can be as large as we like. When we have done this the missing unknowns $x_{M-1}, x_{M-2}, \dots, x_0$ can, on account of (15), be found from the equations (14) by putting successively $\mu = M-1, M-2, \dots, 0$.

We shall now transform (14) when $\mu \geqslant M$, leaving the precise determination of M till later. Put then

$$\frac{z^n}{P(z)} = \sum_{\nu=0}^{\infty} \frac{\delta_\nu}{z^\nu}. \tag{19}$$

A majorant function for this series is clearly

$$\frac{z^n}{(z-1)^n} = \sum_{\nu=0}^{\infty} \binom{n+\nu-1}{\nu} \frac{1}{z^\nu},$$

so that we have

$$|\delta_\nu| \leqslant \binom{n+\nu-1}{\nu}. \tag{20}$$

Also, from (19), multiplying by $P(z)$, we get

$$1 = \sum_{\nu=0}^{n} \frac{g_\nu}{z^\nu} \sum_{\nu=0}^{\infty} \frac{\delta_\nu}{z^\nu}, \tag{21}$$

and hence $\delta_0 = 1$. Now, in (14), put successively

$$\mu = M, M+1, M+2, \dots, \mu$$

and we have

$$x_{M+n} + g_1 x_{M+n-1} + \dots + g_n x_M = c'_M - \sum_{\nu=0}^{\infty} b'_{M,\nu} x_{M+\nu},$$

$$x_{M+n+1} + g_1 x_{M+n} + \dots + g_n x_{M+1} = c'_{M+1} - \sum_{\nu=0}^{\infty} b'_{M+1,\nu} x_{M+1+\nu},$$

. . . .

$$x_{\mu+n} + g_1 x_{\mu+n-1} + \dots + g_n x_\mu = c'_\mu - \sum_{\nu=0}^{\infty} b'_{\mu,\nu} x_{\mu+\nu}.$$

Multiply these equations in order by $\delta_{\mu-M}, \delta_{\mu-M-1}, \dots, \delta_0$ and add the results. Then, from the identity (21), the numbers

$$x_{M+n}, x_{M+n+1}, \dots, x_{\mu+n-1}$$

disappear and, since $\delta_0 = 1$, we obtain

$$(22)\qquad x_{\mu+n} + \sum_{\nu=0}^{n-1} \sum_{\lambda=0}^{\nu} g_{n-\nu+\lambda}\, \delta_{\mu-M-\lambda}\, x_{M+\nu}$$

$$= \sum_{\lambda=0}^{\mu-M} c'_{\mu-\lambda}\, \delta_\lambda - \sum_{\nu=0}^{\infty} \sum_{\lambda=0}^{\mu-M} b'_{\mu-\lambda,\nu}\, \delta_\lambda\, x_{\mu+\nu-\lambda},$$

where the δ with negative suffixes which may appear on the left are to be replaced by zero.

The system (22) for $\mu = M, M+1, M+2, \ldots$, is clearly the full equivalent of the system (14) for the same values of μ. The condition 17·3 (4) is here unnecessary, and we shall therefore allow solutions of (14) and (22), for which this condition is not fulfilled.

17·6. General Solution of Sum Equations. Let ζ be any number in the interval

$$(1)\qquad 1 < \zeta < 1/\vartheta'.$$

Then from 17·5 (17), if M be sufficiently large, we have

$$(2)\qquad k'_\nu < \tfrac{1}{2}(1-\vartheta'\zeta)(\zeta-1)^n, \quad \nu \geqslant M,$$

an inequality which still holds if ζ be replaced by another number sufficiently near to ζ. We can therefore determine two numbers ζ_1, ζ_2, such that, in the interval

$$1 < \zeta_1 < \zeta < \zeta_2 < 1/\vartheta',$$

we have

$$(2a)\qquad k'_\nu < \tfrac{1}{2}(1-\vartheta'\zeta_1)(\zeta_1-1)^n, \quad \nu \geqslant M,$$

$$(2b)\qquad k'_\nu < \tfrac{1}{2}(1-\vartheta'\zeta_2)(\zeta_2-1)^n, \quad \nu \geqslant M.$$

We now prove that, if the number ζ and the index M be chosen to satisfy (1) and (2), then the sum equations 17·5 (14), when

$$x_M,\, x_{M+1},\, \ldots,\, x_{M+n-1}$$

are arbitrarily assigned, have *exactly* one solution such that

$$\limsup_{\nu\to\infty} \sqrt[\nu]{|x_\nu|} \leqslant \zeta.$$

From 17·5, we see that it is sufficient to consider the system 17·5 (22).

In the first place it is easy to shew that there is *at most* one such solution.

For, if possible, let x_ν, y_ν be two such solutions. Then their difference $x_\nu - y_\nu = z_\nu$ satisfies the homogeneous sum equations:

$$(3) \qquad z_{\mu+n} = -\sum_{\nu=0}^{\infty} \sum_{\lambda=0}^{\mu-M} b'_{\mu-\lambda,\,\nu}\, \delta_\lambda\, z_{\mu+\nu-\lambda}, \quad \mu \geqslant M,$$

and

$$(4) \qquad z_M = z_{M+1} = \dots = z_{M+n-1} = 0.$$

Also, since

$$\limsup_{\nu\to\infty} \sqrt[\nu]{|x_\nu|} \leqslant \zeta < \zeta_2, \quad \limsup_{\nu\to\infty} \sqrt[\nu]{|y_\nu|} \leqslant \zeta < \zeta_2,$$

we can find a number C such that

$$(5) \qquad |z_\mu| = |x_\mu - y_\mu| \leqslant C\,\zeta_2^\mu.$$

We here take C to be the smallest number for which this holds, which is possible since the aggregate of all such numbers clearly includes their lower limit. Then, from (3), using 17·5 (16) (20), the relation (5) gives

$$\begin{aligned} |z_{\mu+n}| &\leqslant \sum_{\nu=0}^{\infty} \sum_{\lambda=0}^{\mu-M} k'_{\mu-\lambda}\, \vartheta'^{\nu} \binom{n+\lambda-1}{\lambda} C\,\zeta_2^{\mu+\nu-\lambda} \\ &\leqslant \frac{C\,\zeta_2^\mu}{1-\vartheta'\zeta_2} \sum_{\lambda=0}^{\mu-M} k'_{\mu-\lambda} \binom{n+\lambda-1}{\lambda} \zeta_2^{-\lambda} \\ &\leqslant \tfrac{1}{2} C\,\zeta_2^\mu (\zeta_2-1)^n \sum_{\lambda=0}^{\infty} \binom{n+\lambda-1}{\lambda} \zeta_2^{-\lambda} \\ &\leqslant \tfrac{1}{2} C\,\zeta_2^{\mu+n}, \end{aligned}$$

where, in the last line but one, we have used (2*b*).

Taken in conjunction with (4), this states that

$$|z_\mu| \leqslant \tfrac{1}{2} C\,\zeta_2^\mu, \quad \text{for } \mu \geqslant M:$$

in other words, that in (5) we can replace C by $\frac{1}{2}C$. Since C was already chosen as small as possible, we must have $C = 0$ and therefore $x_\mu = y_\mu$ for $\mu \geqslant M$. Thus we have proved that there is at most one solution of the prescribed kind.

To prove that there is actually one solution, denote the prescribed initial values by

$$x_M = \xi_M, \dots, x_{M+n-1} = \xi_{M+n-1},$$

and let us seek to solve the system 17·5 (22) by successive approximation, putting

(6) $$x_\mu^{(0)} = 0, \quad \mu \geqslant M+n,$$

(7) $$x_\mu^{(s)} = \xi_\mu, \quad M \leqslant \mu \leqslant M+n-1,$$

(8) $$x_{\mu+n}^{(s+1)} = \sum_{\lambda=0}^{\mu-M} c'_{\mu-\lambda}\,\delta_\lambda - \sum_{\nu=0}^{\infty}\sum_{\lambda=0}^{\mu-M} b'_{\mu-\lambda,\nu}\,\delta_\lambda\, x_{\mu+\nu-\lambda}^{(s)}$$
$$- \sum_{\nu=0}^{n-1}\sum_{\lambda=0}^{\nu} g_{n-\nu+\lambda}\,\delta_{\mu-M-\lambda}\,\xi_{M+\nu}, \quad \mu \geqslant M.$$

We first shew that the successively formed series converge in that

(9) $$|\, x_\mu^{(s)} \,| < C\,\zeta_1^\mu, \quad \mu \geqslant M,$$

where C is independent of μ and s.

From 17·5 (18), (20), we see that

$$|\, c'_\mu \,| < K_1 \zeta_1^\mu,$$

$$\left| \sum_{\nu=0}^{n-1}\sum_{\lambda=0}^{\nu} g_{n-\nu+\lambda}\,\delta_{\mu-M-\lambda}\,\xi_{M+\nu} \right| < K_2 \zeta_1^\mu,$$

where K_1, K_2 are independent of μ. Now, on account of (7), no proof of (9) is needed for $M \leqslant \mu \leqslant M+n-1$. Also for $s=0$ no proof is necessary. If then (9) be true for a certain value of s, we have from (8),

$$\left| x_{\mu+n}^{(s+1)} \right| < \sum_{\lambda=0}^{\mu-M} K_1 \zeta_1^{\mu-\lambda} \binom{n+\lambda-1}{\lambda}$$
$$+ \sum_{\nu=0}^{\infty}\sum_{\lambda=0}^{\mu-M} k'_{\mu-\lambda}\,\vartheta''^{\nu} \binom{n+\lambda-1}{\lambda} C\,\zeta_1^{\mu+\nu-\lambda} + K_2 \zeta_1^\mu,$$

and if we approximate by the same method as that just used in discussing (5), but using (2a) instead of (2b), we get

$$\left| x_{\mu+n}^{(s+1)} \right| < \frac{K_1}{(\zeta_1-1)^n}\zeta_1^{\mu+n} + \tfrac{1}{2} C\,\zeta_1^{\mu+n} + K_2\,\zeta_1^{\mu+n}.$$

If then we take

$$C > 2\left(\frac{K_1}{(\zeta-1)^n} + K_2\right),$$

we have proved (9) by induction.

From (8), it follows that

$$(10) \qquad x_{\mu+n}^{(s+1)} - x_{\mu+n}^{(s)} = -\sum_{\nu=0}^{\infty}\sum_{\lambda=0}^{\mu-M} b'_{\mu-\lambda,\nu}\,\delta_\lambda\left[x_{\mu+\nu-\lambda}^{(s)} - x_{\mu+\nu-\lambda}^{(s-1)}\right].$$

We now prove that

$$(11) \qquad \left| x_\mu^{(s)} - x_\mu^{(s-1)} \right| < \frac{2C\,\zeta_1^\mu}{2^{s-1}}, \quad \mu \geqslant M.$$

By (7) no proof is needed, for $M \leqslant \mu \leqslant M+n-1$. Also (11) is true for $s = 1$, by (9). If (11) be true for a certain value of s, we have, from (10),

$$\left| x_{\mu+n}^{(s+1)} - x_{\mu+n}^{(s)} \right| < \sum_{\nu=0}^{\infty}\sum_{\lambda=0}^{\mu-M} k'_{\mu-\lambda}\,\vartheta'^{\nu}\binom{n+\lambda-1}{\lambda}\frac{2C\,\zeta_1^{\mu+\nu-\lambda}}{2^{s-1}}$$
$$\leqslant \frac{2C\,\zeta_1^{\mu+n}}{2^s},$$

again using the method employed in treating (5). Hence (11) follows by induction.

From (11) we infer the existence of the limit

$$(12) \qquad \lim_{s\to\infty} x_\mu^{(s)} = x_\mu,$$

and in fact

$$(13) \qquad \left| x_\mu^{(s)} - x_\mu \right| < \frac{2C\,\zeta_1^\mu}{2^{s-1}}.$$

From this we get

$$\left| \sum_{\nu=0}^{\infty}\sum_{\lambda=0}^{\mu-M} b'_{\mu-\lambda,\nu}\,\delta_\lambda\left(x_{\mu+\nu-\lambda}^{(s)} - x_{\mu+\nu-\lambda}\right) \right|$$
$$\leqslant \sum_{\nu=0}^{\infty}\sum_{\lambda=0}^{\mu-M} k'_{\mu-\lambda}\,\vartheta'^{\nu}\binom{n+\lambda-1}{\lambda}\frac{2C\,\zeta_1^{\mu+\nu-\lambda}}{2^{s-1}}$$
$$\leqslant \frac{C}{2^{s-1}}\zeta_1^{\mu+n},$$

once more using the method of approximation adopted for (5).

Hence

$$\lim_{s\to\infty}\sum_{\nu=0}^{\infty}\sum_{\lambda=0}^{\mu-M} b'_{\mu-\lambda,\nu}\,\delta_\lambda\, x_{\mu+\nu-\lambda}^{(s)} = \sum_{\nu=0}^{\infty}\sum_{\lambda=0}^{\mu-M} b'_{\mu-\lambda,\nu}\,\delta_\lambda\, x_{\mu+\nu-\lambda},$$

and hence, when $s \to \infty$, equation (8) become equation 17·5 (22). The solutions obtained by the successive approximations therefore all satisfy 17·5 (22) and therefore 17·5 (14). They also satisfy the postulated condition, for from (13) and (9),

$$(14) \qquad \limsup_{\mu \to \infty} \sqrt[\mu]{|x_\mu|} \leqslant \zeta_1 < \zeta,$$

so that the proposition is proved. But from this proposition, in conjunction with (14), we can draw a further conclusion, namely, that *if a solution of* 17·5 (14) *satisfy the condition*

$$\limsup_{\mu \to \infty} \sqrt[\mu]{|x_\mu|} \leqslant \zeta,$$

then the sign of equality never occurs.

Now ζ is *any* number in the interval (1) and hence ζ can be taken to differ from unity by an arbitrarily small quantity, so that we can replace (14) by the sharper inequality

$$\limsup_{\mu \to \infty} |\sqrt[\mu]{x_\mu}| \leqslant 1.$$

For solutions which satisfy this condition the sum equations 17·5 (14) are equivalent to the sum equations given at the beginning of 17·5, namely,

$$\sum_{\nu=0}^{\infty} (a_\nu + b_{\mu,\nu})\, x_{\mu+\nu} = c_\mu,$$

so that we have solved these also.

If these equations be homogeneous so that all the c_μ and therefore all the c'_μ are zero, then there are n linearly independent solutions,

$$x_{\nu,1}, \quad x_{\nu,2}, \quad x_{\nu,3}, \ldots, \quad x_{\nu,n},$$

which can be fixed with, say, the initial values

$$\begin{bmatrix} x_{M,1} & x_{M+1,1} & \cdots & x_{M+n-1,1} \\ x_{M,2} & x_{M+1,2} & \cdots & x_{M+n-1,2} \\ \cdot & \cdot & \cdot & \cdot \\ x_{M,n} & x_{M+1,n} & \cdots & x_{M+n-1,n} \end{bmatrix} = \begin{bmatrix} 1 & 0 & \cdots & 0 \\ 0 & 1 & \cdots & 0 \\ \cdot & \cdot & \cdot & \cdot \\ 0 & 0 & \cdots & 1 \end{bmatrix}$$

The general solution has then the form

$$x_\nu = \sum_{\lambda=1}^{n} C_\lambda\, x_{\nu,\lambda},$$

where the C_λ are arbitrary constants. In the non-homogeneous equation the difference of two solutions is clearly a solution of the homogeneous equation. If then $x_\nu = x_{\nu,0}$ be a particular solution of the non-homogeneous equation, the general solution is

$$x_\nu = x_{\nu,0} + \sum_{\lambda=1}^{n} C_\lambda x_{\nu,\lambda}.$$

We may sum up all these results in the following theorem.

Theorem II. *Let the coefficients of the sum equations*

$$\sum_{\nu=0}^{\infty} (a_\nu + b_{\mu,\nu}) x_{\mu+\nu} = c_\mu, \quad \mu = 0, 1, 2, \ldots$$

satisfy the conditions ; $a_0 + b_{\mu,0} \neq 0, \quad \mu = 0, 1, 2, \ldots,$

$$|b_{\mu,\nu}| \leqslant k_\mu \vartheta^\nu, \quad 0 < \vartheta < 1,$$

$$\lim_{\mu\to\infty} k_\mu = 0, \quad \limsup_{\mu\to\infty} \sqrt[\mu]{|c_\mu|} \leqslant 1.$$

Let the function

$$F(z) = \sum_{\nu=0}^{\infty} a_\nu z^\nu$$

be holomorphic for $|z| \leqslant 1$. *If* $n (\geqslant 0)$ *be the number of zeros of* $F(z)$ *in this region, counted according to their multiplicity, then the general solution of the sum equations which satisfy the condition*

$$\lim_{\mu\to\infty} \sqrt[\mu]{|x_\mu|} \leqslant 1$$

contains exactly n *arbitrary constants* C_λ, *and has the form*

$$x_\nu = x_{\nu,0} + \sum_{\lambda=1}^{n} C_\lambda x_{\nu,\lambda}.$$

If M *be a large enough index, there is one, and only one, such solution for which the* n *unknowns*

$$x_M, x_{M+1}, \ldots, x_{M+n-1}$$

have prescribed values. For $n = 0$ *there is exactly one solution and no arbitrary constants.*

17·7. Difference Equations of Poincaré's Type. Consider the following difference equation of the rth order,

$$(1)\quad u(\mu+r)+\alpha_{\mu,r-1}\,u(\mu+r-1)+\dots+\alpha_{\mu,1}\,u(\mu+1)+\alpha_{\mu,0}\,u(\mu)=0,$$

where the independent variable μ takes the values 0, 1, 2, 3, ... This equation is of Poincaré's type (see 17·1) if the limits

$$\lim_{\mu\to\infty}\alpha_{\mu,\nu}=\alpha_\nu,\qquad \nu=0,1,2,\dots,r-1,$$

all exist. We now prove

Perron's Theorem. *Let $q_1, q_2, q_3, \dots, q_\sigma$ be the distinct moduli of the roots of the characteristic equation*

$$t^r+\alpha_{r-1}t^{r-1}+\alpha_{r-2}t^{r-2}+\dots+\alpha_1 t+\alpha_0=0,$$

and let l_λ be the number of roots whose modulus is q_λ, multiple roots being counted according to their multiplicity, so that

$$l_1+l_2+\dots+l_\sigma=r.$$

Then, provided that $a_{\mu,0}$ be different from zero for all values of μ, the difference equation (1) has a fundamental system of solutions, which fall into σ classes, such that, for the solutions of the λth class and their linear combinations,

$$\limsup_{\mu\to\infty}\sqrt[\mu]{|u(\mu)|}=q_\lambda.$$

The number of solutions of the λth class is l_λ.

Let the numbers q_λ be arranged in ascending order of magnitude

$$0\leqslant q_1<q_2<q_3<\dots<q_\sigma.$$

Let p be an arbitrary positive number and let

$$\alpha_\nu=\frac{a_\nu}{p^\nu},\quad \alpha_{\mu,\nu}-\alpha_\nu=\frac{b_{\mu,\nu}}{p^\nu},\quad \nu=0,1,2,\dots,r-1,$$

$$(2)\qquad \alpha_r=1=\frac{a_r}{p^r},\quad 0=\frac{b_{\mu,r}}{p^r},$$

$$(3)\qquad u(\mu)=p^\mu x_\mu,\quad \mu=0,1,2,\dots.$$

Then the difference equation (1) is equivalent to

$$\sum_{\nu=0}^{r}(a_\nu+b_{\mu,\nu})\,x_{\mu+\nu}=0.$$

Let us regard this new equation as a system of sum equations whose coefficients clearly satisfy the conditions of Theorem II, since they vanish for $\nu > r$. The number of zeros of the function

$$F(z) = \sum_{\nu=0}^{r} a_\nu z^\nu = \sum_{\nu=0}^{r} \alpha_\nu p^\nu z^\nu,$$

for $|z| \leqslant 1$ depends on the choice of the positive number p. If we choose p smaller than q_1 (provided $q_1 \neq 0$), there are no zeros in $|z| \leqslant 1$ and hence no solution, other than zero, for which

$$\limsup_{\mu \to \infty} \sqrt[\mu]{|x_\mu|} \leqslant 1,$$

that is to say, for which

$$\limsup_{\mu \to \infty} \sqrt[\mu]{|u(\mu)|} \leqslant p < q_1.$$

If we choose for p a number between q_1 and q_2, there are l_1 zeros and therefore l_1 solutions, such that

$$\limsup_{\mu \to \infty} \sqrt[\mu]{|x_\mu|} \leqslant 1,$$

that is to say, for which

$$\limsup_{\mu \to \infty} \sqrt[\mu]{|u(\mu)|} \leqslant p < q_2.$$

Since p can be taken arbitrarily near to q_1, we have for these l_1 solutions

$$\limsup_{\mu \to \infty} \sqrt[\mu]{|u(\mu)|} = q_1.$$

If now we choose p between q_2 and q_3, there are $l_1 + l_2$ zeros and hence $l_1 + l_2$ solutions for which

$$\limsup_{\mu \to \infty} \sqrt[\mu]{|u(\mu)|} \leqslant p < q_3.$$

The l_1 solutions already found are of course included among these; for the l_2 others, since p can be taken arbitrarily near to q_2, we have

$$\limsup_{\mu \to \infty} \sqrt[\mu]{|u(\mu)|} = q_2.$$

Proceeding in this way the theorem is proved.

EXAMPLES XVII

1. In the case of the equation

$$u(n+2)-\left(1+\frac{(-1)^n}{n+1}\right)u(n)=0,$$

shew that

$$\lim_{n\to 0}\frac{u(n+1)}{u(n)}$$

does not exist for any solution at all. [Perron.]

2. In the equation

$$u(n+2)-[2+p_1(n)]\,u(n+1)+[1+p_0(n)]\,u(n)=0,$$

where

$$p_0(n),\ p_1(n)\to 0 \text{ when } n\to\infty,$$

and for sufficiently large n, $p_1(n)\geqslant 0$, $p_1(n)-p_0(n)\geqslant 0$, shew that

$$\lim_{n\to\infty}\frac{u(n+1)}{u(n)}=1,$$

for every solution which is not constantly zero for large values of n. [Perron.]

3. In the equation

$$u(n+2)+p_1(n)\,u(n+1)+p_0(n)\,u(n)=0,$$

where $p_0(n)$, $p_1(n)\to 0$ when $n\to\infty$, and where

$$\lim_{n\to\infty}\frac{p_0(n)}{p_1(n-1)\,p_1(n)}=a,$$

where a is not a real number $\geqslant \frac{1}{4}$, prove that for every solution which does not constantly vanish for large n,

$$\lim_{n\to\infty}\frac{u(n+1)}{u(n)}=0. \qquad \text{[Perron.]}$$

4. Shew that the limit given in Poincaré's theorem does not exist in the case of the equation

$$u(n+2)-\frac{(n+2)+2(-1)^n}{(n+2)^2(n+3)}\,u(n)=0.$$

5. Let a be a number whose modulus is greater than that of every root of the characteristic equation of a difference equation of Poincaré's type. Prove that

$$\lim_{n\to\infty} \frac{u(n)}{a^n} = 0,$$

where $u(n)$ is any solution of the equation. [Poincaré.]

*6. Let $u(n)$ be any solution of a homogeneous linear difference equation of order r, with constant coefficients, and let

$$D(m, n) = \begin{vmatrix} u(n) & u(n+1) & \dots & u(n+m-1) \\ u(n+1) & u(n+2) & \dots & u(n+m) \\ \cdot & \cdot & \dots & \cdot \\ u(n+m-1) & u(n+m) & \dots & u(n+2m-2) \end{vmatrix}$$

where $m \leqslant r$ and n is a positive integer.

Then if $D(m, n) \neq 0$, prove that

$$\lim_{n\to\infty} D(m, n+1) / D(m, n)$$

exists, and is equal to the continued product of m zeros of the characteristic function, provided that those zeros which are distinct have distinct moduli. [Aitken.]

*7. If the difference equation of Ex. 6 be replaced by an equation of Poincaré's type, shew that the corresponding result (which is a generalisation of Poincaré's theorem) still holds, provided that no two zeros of the characteristic function of the associated difference equation with constant coefficients have the same modulus. [Aitken.]

*I have to thank Dr. A. C. Aitken for communicating these elegant generalisations.

INDEX

The references are to pages.